SAFETY SYMBOLS

SAFETY SYMBOLS	HAZARD	PRECAUTION	REMEDY
Disposal	Special disposal required	Dispose of wastes as directed by your teacher.	Ask your teacher how to dispose of laboratory materials.
Biological	Organisms that can harm humans	Avoid breathing in or skin contact with organisms. Wear dust mask or gloves. Wash hands thoroughly.	Notify your teacher if you suspect contact.
Extreme Temperature	Objects that can burn skin by being too cold or too hot	Use proper protection when handling.	Go to your teacher for first aid.
Sharp Object	Use of tools or glassware that can easily puncture or slice skin	Practice common sense behavior and follow guidelines for use of the tool.	Go to your teacher for first aid.
Fumes	Potential danger from smelling fumes	Must have good ventilation and never smell fumes directly.	Leave foul area and notify your teacher immediately.
Electrical	Possible danger from electrical shock or burn	Double-check setup with instructor. Check condition of wires and apparatus.	Do not attempt to fix electrical problems. Notify your teacher immediately.
Irritant	Substances that can irritate your skin or mucous membranes	Wear dust mask or gloves. Practice extra care when handling these materials.	Go to your teacher for first aid.
Chemical	Substances (acids and bases) that can react with and destroy tissue and other materials	Wear goggles and an apron.	Immediately flush with water and notify your teacher.
Toxic	Poisonous substance	Follow your teacher's instructions. Always wash hands thoroughly after use.	Go to your teacher for first aid.
Fire	Flammable and combustible materials may burn if exposed to an open flame or spark	Avoid flames and heat sources. Be aware of locations of fire safety equipment.	Notify your teacher immediately. Use fire safety equipment if necessary.

Eye Safety
This symbol appears when a danger to eyes exists.

Clothing Protection
This symbol appears when substances could stain or burn clothing.

Animal Safety
This symbol appears whenever live animals are studied and the safety of the animals and students must be ensured.

GLENCOE
SCIENCE VOYAGES

Exploring the Life, Earth, and Physical Sciences

NATIONAL
GEOGRAPHIC
SOCIETY

Glencoe
McGraw-Hill

New York, New York   Columbus, Ohio   Woodland Hills, California   Peoria, Illinois

A Glencoe Program

Glencoe Science Voyages

Student Edition
Teacher Wraparound Edition
Assessment
    Chapter Review
    Standardized Test Practice
    Performance Assessment
    Assessment—Chapter and Unit Tests
    ExamView Test Bank Software
    Performance Assessment in the Science
        Classroom
    Alternate Assessment in the Science Classroom
Study Guide for Content Mastery, SE and TE
Chapter Overview Study Guide, SE and TE
Reinforcement
Enrichment
Critical Thinking/Problem Solving
Multicultural Connections
Activity Worksheets

Laboratory Manual, SE and TE
Science Inquiry Activities, SE and TE
Home Involvement
Teaching Transparencies
Section Focus Transparencies
Science Integration Transparencies
Spanish Resources
Lesson Plans
Lab and Safety Skills in the Science Classroom
Cooperative Learning in the Science Classroom
Exploring Environmental Issues
MindJogger Videoquizzes and Teacher Guide
English/Spanish Audiocassettes
Electronic Teacher Classroom Resources/Interactive
    Lesson Planner CD-ROM
Interactive CD-ROM
Internet Site
Using the Internet in the Science Classroom

THE PRINCETON REVIEW

The "Test-Taking Tip" and "Test Practice" features in this book were written by The Princeton Review, the nation's leader in test preparation. Through its association with McGraw-Hill, The Princeton Review offers the best way to help students excel on standardized assessments.

The Princeton Review is not affiliated with Princeton University or Educational Testing Service.

Glencoe/McGraw-Hill
A Division of The McGraw-Hill Companies

Send all inquiries to:
Glencoe/McGraw-Hill
8787 Orion Place
Columbus, OH 43240

ISBN 0-02-828669-3
Printed in the United States of America.
4 5 6 7 8 9 10 071/043 06 05 04 03 02 01 00

Series Authors

Patricia Horton
Math and Science Teacher
Summit Intermediate School
Etiwanda, California

Eric Werwa, Ph.D.
Department of Physics and Astronomy
Otterbein College
Westerville, Ohio

Cathy Ezrailson
Science Department Head
Oak Ridge High School
Conroe, Texas

Thomas McCarthy, Ph.D.
Science Department Chair
St. Edwards School
Vero Beach, Florida

Ralph Feather, Jr., Ph.D.
Science Department Chair
Derry Area School District
Derry, Pennsylvania

John Eric Burns
Science Teacher
Ramona Jr. High School
Chino, California

Susan Leach Snyder
Science Department Chair
Jones Middle School
Upper Arlington, Ohio

Lucy Daniel, Ph.D.
Teacher, Consultant
Rutherford County Schools
Rutherfordton, North Carolina

Ed Ortleb
Science Consultant
St. Louis Public Schools
St. Louis, Missouri

Alton Biggs
Biology Instructor
Allen High School
Allen, Texas

National Geographic Society
Educational Division
Washington D.C.

Contributing Authors

Al Janulaw
Science Teacher
Creekside Middle School
Rohnert Park, California

Penny Parsekian
Science Writer
New London, Connecticut

Gerry Madrazo, Ph.D.
Mathematics and Science Education
  Network
University of North Carolina, Chapel Hill
Chapel Hill, North Carolina

Series Consultants

Chemistry

Douglas Martin, Ph.D.
Chemistry Department
Sonoma State University
Rohnert Park, California

Cheryl Wistrom, Ph.D.
Associate Professor of
    Chemistry
Saint Joseph's College
Rensselaer, Indiana

Earth Science

Tomasz K. Baumiller, Ph.D.
Museum of Paleontology
University of Michigan
Ann Arbor, Michigan

Maureen Allen
Science Resource Specialist
Irvine Unified School District
Laguna Hills, California

Connie Sutton, Ph.D.
Department of Geoscience
Indiana University
Indiana, Pennsylvania

Physics

Thomas Barrett, Ph.D.
Department of Physics
The Ohio State University
Columbus, Ohio

David Haase, Ph.D.
Professor of Physics
North Carolina State
    University
North Carolina

Life Science

William Ausich, Ph.D.
Department of Geological
    Sciences
The Ohio State University
Columbus, Ohio

Dennis Stockdale
Asheville High School
Asheville, North Carolina

Daniel Zeigler, Ph.D.
Director
Bacillus Genetic Stock Center
The Ohio State University
Columbus, Ohio

Reading

Nancy Farnan, Ph.D.
School of Teacher Education
San Diego State University
San Diego, California

Gary Kroesch
Mount Carmel High School
San Diego, California

Safety

Mark Vinciguerra
Lab Safety Instructor
Department of Physics
The Ohio State University
Columbus, Ohio

Curriculum

Tom Custer, Ph.D.
Maryland State Department of
    Education
Challenge/Reconstructed
    Schools
Baltimore, Maryland

Series Reviewers

Jhina Alvarado
Potrero Hill Middle School
    for the Arts
San Francisco, California

Richard Cheeseman
Bert Lynn Middle School
Torrance, California

Linda Cook
Rider High School
Wichita Falls, Texas

John B. Davis
Niagara-Wheatfield
    Central School
Sanborn, New York

Shirley Ann DeFilippo
Timothy Edwards
    Middle School
South Windsor, Connecticut

Janet Doughty
H J McDonald Middle School
New Bern, North Carolina

Jason Druten
Jefferson Middle School
Torrance, California

Lin Harp
Magellan Middle School
Raleigh, North Carolina

Doris Holland
West Cary Middle School
Raleigh, North Carolina

Deborah Huffine
Noblesville Intermediate
    School
Noblesville, Indiana

Paul Osborne
DeValls Bluff High School
DeValls Bluff, Arkansas

Erik Resnick
Robert E. Peary Middle School
Gardena, California

Robert Sirbu
Lowell Junior High School
Oakland, California

Michael Tally
Wake County
    Public Schools
Raleigh, North Carolina

Cindy Williamson
Whiteville City Schools
Whiteville, North Carolina

Maurice Yaggi
Middlebrook School
Wilton, Connecticut

Donna York
Anchorage School District
Anchorage, Alaska

Activity Testers

Clayton Millage
Science Teacher
Lynden Middle School
Lynden, Washington

Science Kit and Boreal Laboratories
Tonawanda, New York

Contents in Brief

Contents

Contents

Contents

Contents

Contents

HO—C=O
CH₂
CH₂
CH₂
CH₂
CH₂
CH₂
CH₂
CH₂
CH₂
CH₂
CH₂
CH₂
CH₂
CH₂
CH₂
CH₂
CH₃

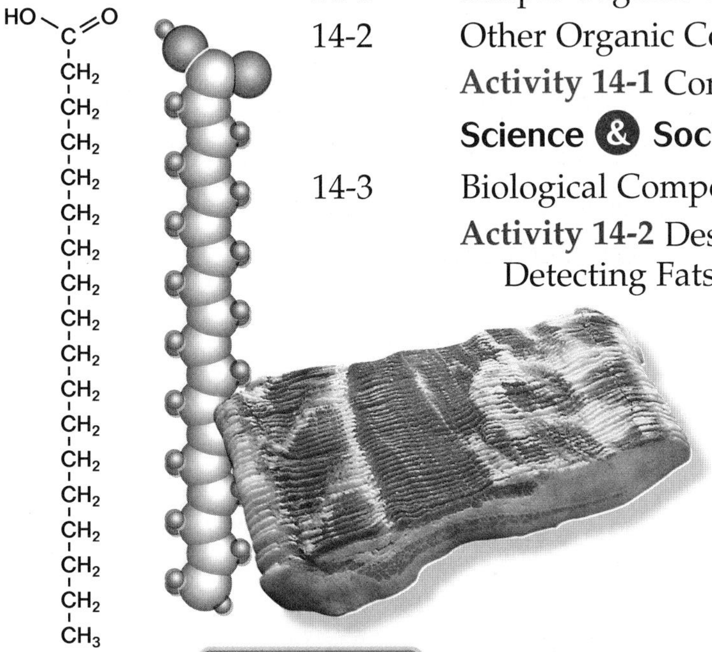

Contents

Contents

Contents

Contents

NATIONAL GEOGRAPHIC

Science Connections

History of Science

How it Works

Reading & Writing in Science

Activities

Activities

Mini Lab

Try at Home
Mini Lab

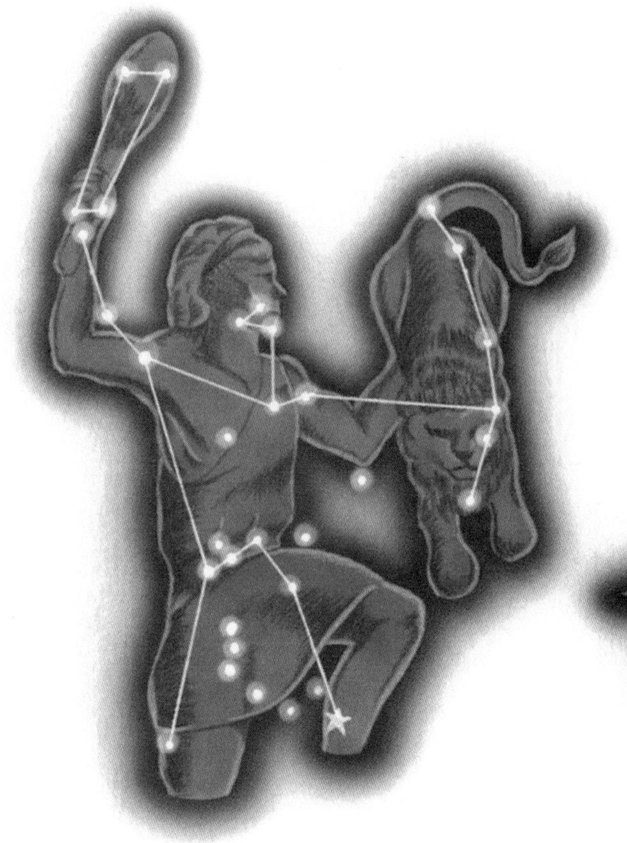

Explore Activities

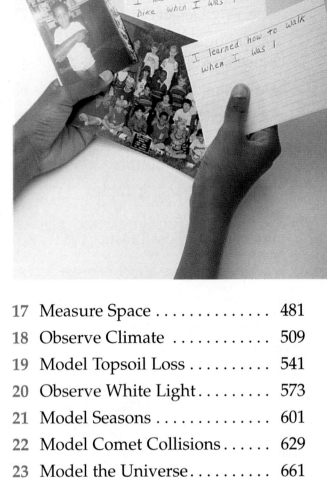

Problem Solving

Skill Builders

Skill Activities

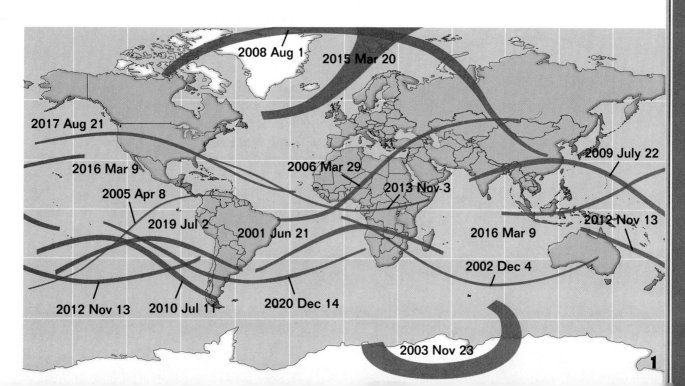

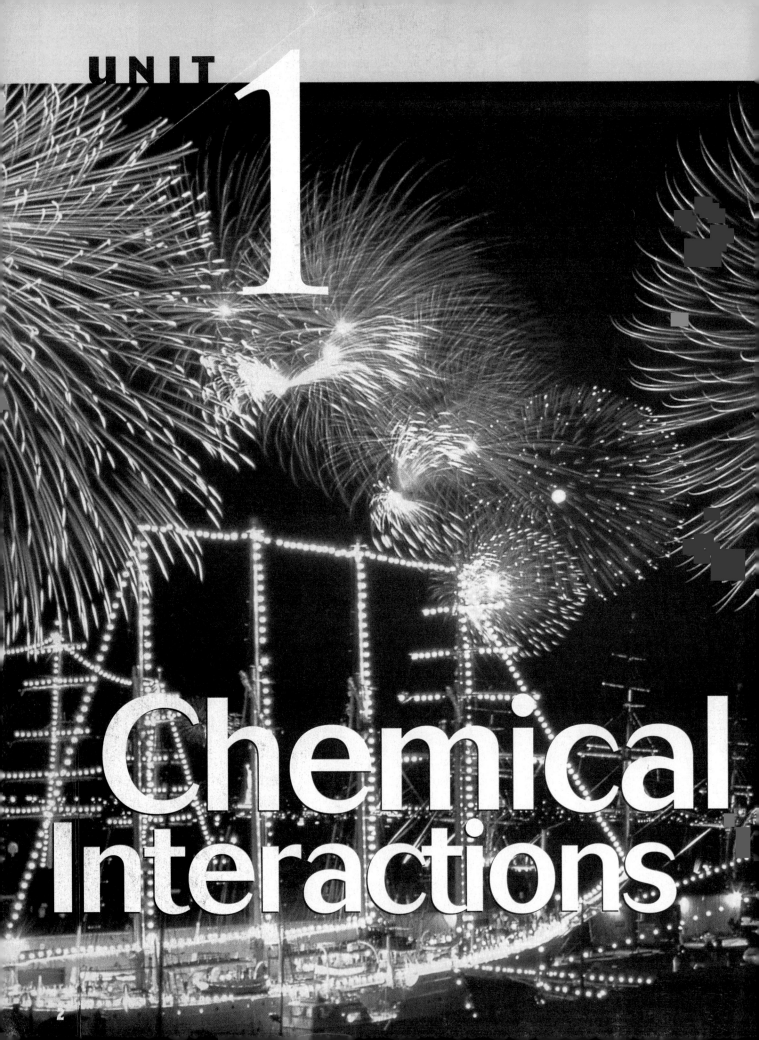

UNIT 1

Chemical Interactions

What's Happening Here?

Have you ever seen a firecracker before it exploded? It doesn't look anything like this spectacle of glowing colors illuminating the night sky over New York City's East River (left). How does the firecracker change from a cardboard tube to this magical fireworks display? By a chemical reaction. The chemical bonds that hold atoms together break, and new combinations of atoms are formed, releasing energy in the form of light and heat. But, fireworks displays are only one example of the wonders of chemistry. The salt water you find in the ocean (below) is another. Though you can taste the salt, you cannot see it, even with the aid of a microscope. Why? Where is the salt hiding? In this unit, you will learn how the interplay of atoms explains some of these seeming mysteries.

*inter*NET CONNECTION

Explore the Glencoe Science Web Site at **www.glencoe.com/sec/ science** to find out more about topics found in this unit.

CHAPTER

1 The Nature of Science

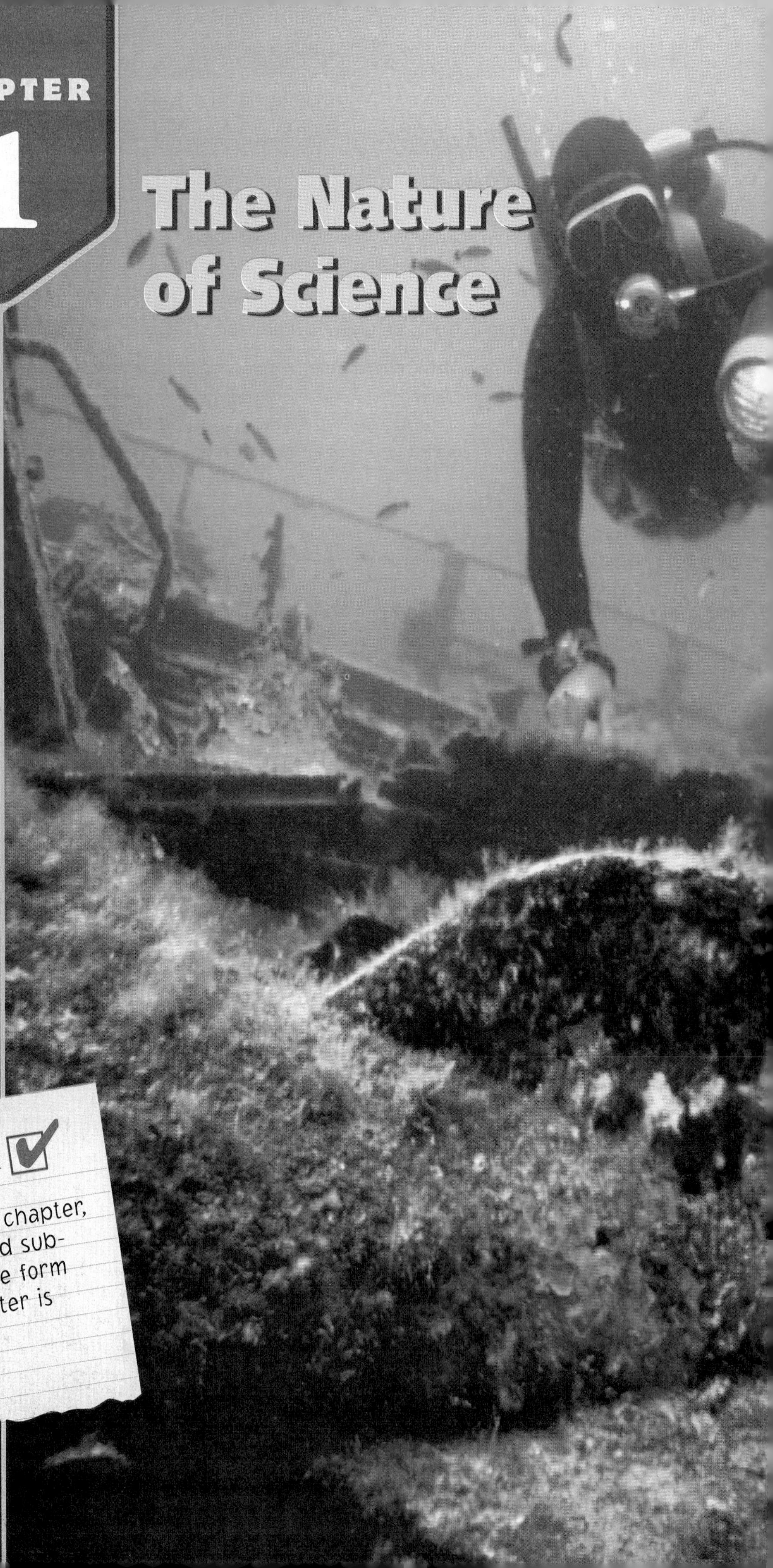

Chapter Preview

Section 1-1
Scientific Problem Solving

Section 1-2
Using Science to Explore

Skills Preview

Skill Builders
- Sequence
- Interpret Data

Activities
- Design an Experiment
- Use Scientific Methods

MiniLabs
- Measure
- Infer

Reading Check ✓

Before you begin this chapter, write its headings and subheadings in an outline form to see how the chapter is organized.

Explore Activity

How can a ship that weighs several thousand tons float on water while a coin would sink right next to the ship? Why will the ship sink if the hull of a ship is damaged and water pours in? Around the world, there are many ships at the bottom of the ocean. How can they be floating one minute and sinking the next?

Observe Water Displacement

1. Fill a small bucket with two liters of water.

2. Use a balance to find the mass of an empty soda-pop can and a quarter.

3. Record the mass of each object.

4. Predict which object will float. Place the can on its side in the water. Observe what happens.

5. Place the quarter in the water. Observe what happens.

Science Journal

In your Science Journal, record whether your prediction was correct. Compare and contrast the empty can and the quarter to try to explain what you observed.

1·1 Scientific Problem Solving

What You'll Learn

▶ What science is
▶ How to use a scientific method in problem solving

Vocabulary
science
scientific method
hypothesis
theory
law
control
independent variable
dependent variable
constant
graph

Why It's Important

▶ You can use scientific methods to search for new knowledge and to solve everyday problems.

What Science Is

It was Current Events Day in Mr. Hayes's science class. Every other Wednesday, each student presented an article from a newspaper or magazine on a topic that related to science. Mr. Hayes wanted his students to be aware of the latest scientific advances. He also wanted them to understand that science wasn't a subject that disappeared when they closed their science books. "Science affects you every day," he often reminded them.

Several students presented their articles. Then, Deon stood to present. "This article describes how scientists found a shipwreck that was sunk in more than 2400 meters of water. They were able to find hundreds of articles used by the passengers, such as dishes and clothing. They even—"

Brianna waved her hand impatiently. "Excuse me," she interrupted, "but this is science class, not social studies or a movie review. Check your schedule, Dee!"

Several students laughed.

Mr. Hayes spoke. "Why do you think this article doesn't apply to science, Brianna?"

Figure 1-1 What are some ways science affects you and your classmates every day?

Brianna replied, "Because people who look at shipwrecks aren't scientists, they're explorers. They're just looking for something, not inventing something or testing some theory. They're not using scientific methods. They should be discussed in history class."

Mr. Hayes looked at Deon. "Deon, can you respond to what Brianna said? How is your article related to science?"

Deon looked embarrassed. "Well, I'm not sure either. This article says scientists looked for the shipwreck. And, the article was interesting, so I cut it out of the newspaper."

"Why don't you finish your report, Deon," said Mr. Hayes. "Then, we'll continue to debate whether or not it relates to science."

Deon described more of the objects from the ship that were found. He told the class that sonar was used to help find the wreck. Sonar stands for **SO**und **NA**vigation **R**anging. Sound waves are sent through the water and bounce back when they hit something, such as the ocean floor or part of a ship. Scientists can calculate how deep that spot is by the amount of time it takes the sound waves to reach the object and bounce back. A remotely operated vehicle, or ROV, was used to help recover the sunken objects. ROVs are unpiloted, and a person operates them at a distance. They can go places that are too deep or too dangerous for people to go.

LIFE SCIENCE
INTEGRATION

Robot Researcher
Dolphins, bats, and barn owls were all models for a new robot named "Rodolph." These animals depend heavily on sound to help them navigate or find prey. The robot emits sound and "listens" for the echoes to detect objects underwater. Rodolph is so sensitive that it can even tell heads from tails on a dime. Infer how this robot can be used underwater to help scientists explore.

Figure 1-2 The submarine Atlantis helps scientists explore the water off the big island of Hawaii.

When Deon had finished, Mr. Hayes looked around at the class. "Let's get back to the point Brianna raised. **Science** is a process used to investigate the world around you, providing you with some possible answers. Does anyone see a connection between looking for shipwrecks and science?"

Scientists as Explorers

Enrique raised his hand. "I think the article does relate to science. People use science to find the answers to questions. The people who explored that shipwreck had questions. They were curious. Scientists are curious about the unknown. There are all sorts of scientists, you know. Explorers are scientists because they are curious about the unknown. I guess, in a way, all scientists are explorers. Hey! When I'm curious about something and I try to search for the answer, maybe that makes me an explorer, too."

Mr. Hayes replied, "I think you're on the right track, Enrique. Scientific exploration and discovery has never been limited to one race, sex, culture, or time period. As in the past, people all over the world make discoveries. These people are not only professional scientists. Often, discoveries are made by people pursuing a hobby. In fact, some important discoveries might be made by one of your classmates. Now, let's go back to your other point, Enrique. Are you saying that scientists and explorers only have curiosity in common? What did the explorers mentioned in the article do?"

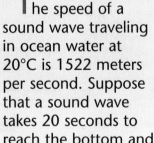

Using Math

The speed of a sound wave traveling in ocean water at 20°C is 1522 meters per second. Suppose that a sound wave takes 20 seconds to reach the bottom and return. How deep is the water at that location?

Enrique thought a moment. "Well, I guess they would have had to use some kind of organized method. They had to pay attention to things like the position of the stars to know where they were headed and cloud formations to predict the weather."

Mr. Hayes asked, "Would the people who found the shipwreck in Deon's article have used some organized or scientific methods?"

Enrique looked confused. "I suppose. But Brianna's right. They didn't do any experiments. They just looked for things."

Sunghee raised her hand. "I think I see how Deon's article relates to science. It's because of the technology they used. I mean, the little robot and stuff. Technology is using science, right? But I have to agree with Brianna and Enrique. Doesn't a scientist always have to do an experiment?"

Mr. Hayes asked, "Well class, does anyone have an answer for Sunghee?"

The class was silent.

Mr. Hayes had an idea he thought might help the class answer his question. He walked to the chalkboard, paused, and began writing. "I have an assignment for you, due next Wednesday. I'd like you to find information that you think shows how scientists are like explorers and how technology helps them. You may look in magazines and books, or use the Internet. Then, list the skills you think the scientists used.

Figure 1-3 This scientist uses technology, such as scientific equipment and instruments, to help her explore.

THE EFFECTS OF CARBON DIOXIDE AND PLANTS ON GLOBAL WARMING

Figure 1-4 Students can be scientists, too. **In what ways have you been a scientific explorer?**

Figure 1-5 What are some things scientists do while searching for new information and solving problems?

Also list the steps they took in searching for new knowledge. Finally, compare the two and come up with your answer to the question, 'Does a scientist always need to use an organized approach to solving problems?'"

Scientific Methods

Scientists use a variety of ways to solve problems. A **scientific method** is an approach taken to try to solve a problem. The steps, as listed in **Figure 1-6,** form a model to solve problems. But, these steps serve only as a guide. Sometimes, several of the steps are used while others are not needed when solving a particular problem. Or, the steps might be performed in a different order. Let's take a look at a possible method that a person might use.

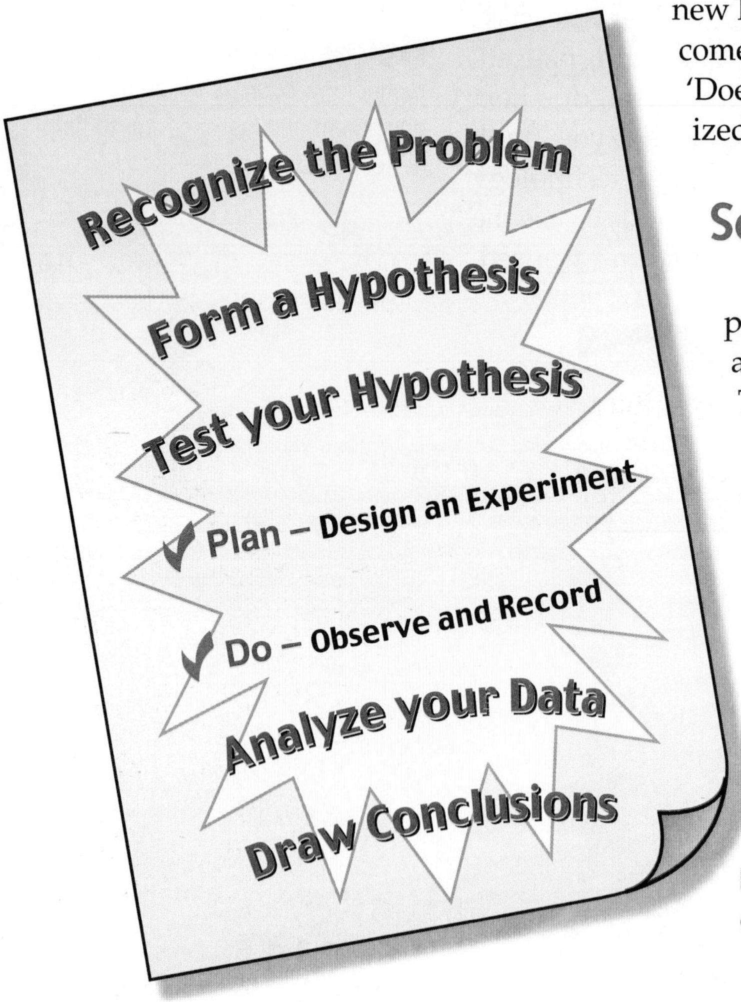

Recognize the Problem

Form a Hypothesis

Test your Hypothesis

✔ Plan – Design an Experiment

✔ Do – Observe and Record

Analyze your Data

Draw Conclusions

Figure 1-6 This poster shows one possible way to solve problems.

Recognize the Problem

The problem-solving process generally begins when you recognize a problem or ask a question. Once you know what you want to study, you then choose the methods that will help you find the answers. Kashanna, shown in **Figure 1-7,** liked to listen to hard rock music as she studied. She and her parents argued about it.

"Kashanna, you can't possibly concentrate with that type of music," her mother would say.

"My grades are okay," Kashanna would argue.

"But I think your grades would be higher if you listened to quiet music, like classical," her mother would reply. "I know that soothing music helps me to think more clearly," she explained.

Kashanna decided to use a scientific method to see whether her mother was right. She asked her friend Hiromi to help.

"You're off to a great start. You've definitely got a problem you want to solve," Hiromi laughed.

Preparing to solve a problem or ask a question often involves making observations and doing research. For example, scientists who develop ways to improve crop yields find out the growth needs of the plant. They learn what has worked and not worked. Many times, scientists identify a real problem only after collecting lots of information from their observations.

*inter***NET**
CONNECTION

Visit the Glencoe Science Web Site at **www.glencoe.com/ sec/science** for more information about the effects of music on concentration. In your Science Journal, compare and contrast the results from different studies.

Figure 1-7 Under what conditions do you study the best?

Often, the next step in solving a problem is to form a hypothesis. A **hypothesis** (hi PAHTH uh sus) is a prediction about a problem that can be tested. A hypothesis may be based upon a variety of things. It can come about from observations, from personal experiences, or from new information gathered during other experiments. Hypotheses are often written as if-and-then statements. For example, a scientist observes that plants, such as those in **Figure 1-8,** that are fertilized grow taller than plants that are not. A scientist may form the following hypothesis: If plants are fertilized more, then they will grow taller. This hypothesis can be tested by an experiment. Scientists are able to form theories from well-tested hypotheses.

A **theory** is an explanation backed by results obtained from repeated tests or experiments. Not all results lead to the formation of a theory. Actually, there are only a few theories and even fewer laws.

A scientific **law** is a well-tested description of how something in nature works. Generally, laws predict or describe a given situation but don't explain why. An example of a law is Newton's first law of motion. According to this law, an object continues in motion, or stays at rest, until it's acted upon by an outside force. Some other laws include the law of conservation of mass, the law of conservation of energy, and the laws of reflection.

Figure 1-8 One scientist might hypothesize that one plant grew taller than the other because it was fertilized more. **What other hypothesis could you make about the plants?**

Kashanna wrote in her Science Journal, "My hypothesis is that if I perform a task while listening to different types of music, then my ability to concentrate will not be affected."

Once a hypothesis is formed, a scientist will find ways to test it. Kashanna must now decide how to test the effects of listening to different types of music on her concentration. Two ways to test a hypothesis are by conducting controlled experiments and by making observational studies.

In order to form conclusions that make sense from your results, you often need a **control**—a standard with which to compare the results. In Kashanna's experiment, she wants to compare the effects of different kinds of music on concentration. The standard that the results will be compared to is her level of concentration when no music is playing. Kashanna's control is to have no music playing during an activity that requires concentration.

Controlled Experiments

A controlled experiment is made up of a series of steps that test a hypothesis in which a control is used. The basic idea of a controlled experiment is to change only one factor, or variable. The variable that is changed is the **independent variable.** The **dependent variable** is the factor being observed or measured. Scientists observe or measure the effect on the dependent variable when they change the independent variable. Kashanna determined that the independent variable is the type of music listened to while performing a task. She chose to test the effects of hard rock, soft rock, classical music, and no music. The dependent variable is how well Kashanna performs the task, which is related to her concentration while the music is playing.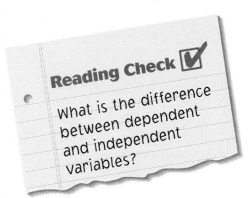

Reading Check ✓

What is the difference between dependent and independent variables?

Plan the Experiment

"How will you know the effect each type of music has on your ability to concentrate?" Hiromi asked. "You need to be able to measure the effect. I don't think you'll convince your parents if you say you felt you concentrated the same with any kind of music."

Kashanna and Hiromi decided to have Kashanna copy various passages out of their science textbook as she listened to each kind of music. Hiromi tried to select passages from the book that wouldn't be any more or less difficult to copy than any of the other passages. Kashanna couldn't copy the same page over and over or she might memorize it, which would affect the results. The number of words written down during a given time period would be the dependent variable.

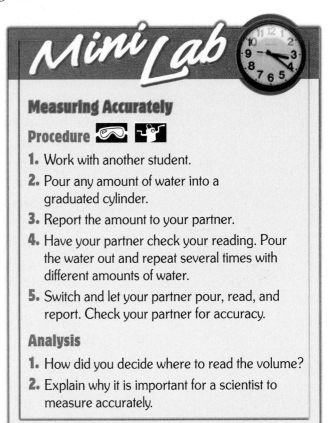

Mini Lab

Measuring Accurately
Procedure 🥽 🧤

1. Work with another student.
2. Pour any amount of water into a graduated cylinder.
3. Report the amount to your partner.
4. Have your partner check your reading. Pour the water out and repeat several times with different amounts of water.
5. Switch and let your partner pour, read, and report. Check your partner for accuracy.

Analysis

1. How did you decide where to read the volume?
2. Explain why it is important for a scientist to measure accurately.

Figure 1-9 What else does Kashanna need to do her experiment?

As they wrote their plan, Kashanna and Hiromi tried to think of other variables that might affect the dependent variable. They knew that these variables should be kept the same while changing only the independent variable. That way, any effect on the dependent variable would be caused only by the independent variable. A variable in an experiment that stays the same is a **constant.** Constants that Kashanna and Hiromi identified were the similar passages in the book to be copied, the amount of time given to copy each passage, the volume of the music, the lighting in the room, and interruptions from people entering the room. They also were careful to select three pieces of music that could each be played uninterrupted for five minutes.

Kashanna thought of something else. "What if I speed up, without even realizing it, when I listen to hard rock to try to prove that hard rock is not harmful to my concentration? I would be influencing the results."

To avoid this problem, they asked their friend Mario to participate in the experiment. They did not tell Mario the hypothesis. An experiment in which some or all information is withheld from a subject (Mario) or the investigator (Kashanna) is called a blind experiment.

Kashanna gathered the materials, shown in **Figure 1-9,** she would need before Mario arrived. An important part of planning an experiment is determining the materials needed. You do not want to be in the middle of conducting an experiment and find you do not have everything you need to complete the experiment.

Do the Experiment

When Mario arrived, Kashanna told him only that he would be listening to music and trying to copy as much of the passage as he could until she told him to stop. She took away his watch and any clocks in the room. She did not want Mario to try to "beat the clock." Mario did not know why Kashanna was doing this experiment. That way, he would not try to make the results come out a particular way. This is why the experiment was a blind experiment.

Look at **Figure 1-10.** Kashanna kept the lighting in the room and the volume of the music the same throughout the experiment. She put headphones on Mario to minimize other noises. When Kashanna said "Go!", Mario copied the science textbook page for five minutes. He copied down a different passage from the textbook each time he listened to each of three types of music and also when no music was played.

Part of doing an experiment is observing and recording data. Observations can include measurements and descriptions that can be written in your Science Journal. Each time five minutes was over, Kashanna observed the number of words Mario wrote. She counted and recorded them in her Science Journal. When the experiment was over, she analyzed the data. Mario had copied the fewest words while listening to hard rock.

"These aren't the results I was looking for!" Kashanna exclaimed.

Figure 1-10 There are many variables to consider before doing an experiment. **What variables might be out of Kashanna's control?**

Hiromi suggested that Kashanna repeat the experiment a few more times. Conducting an experiment once is called a trial. Repeating an experiment several times is making multiple trials. A subject in an experiment will perform slightly differently each time. The scientist takes an average of the results. A multiple trial helps strengthen the support or lack of support for the hypothesis. In Kashanna's experiment, each time a different trial was done, the order of the types of music was changed to help reduce the effect that the tiring of Mario's brain or hand muscles would have on the results.

Kashanna set up a data table to record the results of each trial. Data tables help you organize your observations and test results. **Table 1-1** shows Kashanna's data table.

Table 1-1

Number of Words Copied					
Type of Music	Trial 1	Trial 2	Trial 3	Trial 4	Average
No music	56	60	64	60	
Classical	54	62	60	56	
Soft rock	36	42	38	32	
Hard rock	26	36	42	24	

Problem Solving

Flex Your Brain

Solving problems requires a plan. This plan may be a simple thing that you do in your head, or it may be something more complicated that you actually write down. To the right is a process called *Flex Your Brain*, which is one way to help you organize a plan for solving a problem. Skills that you might find helpful in solving problems can be found in the **Skill Handbook** at the back of your textbook.

Sonar uses sound waves to determine ocean depths and to find unseen objects. Use the *Flex Your Brain* chart to help you explore the other possible uses of sound waves.

Think Critically: How can you use technology to help you find the answer to the problem? Why does *Flex Your Brain* ask you to share what you've learned?

Flex Your Brain

1. **Topic:** _____
2. ❓ *What do I already know?*
   1. _____
   2. _____
   3. _____
   4. _____
3. **Q:** Ask a question
4. **A:** Guess an answer
5. **How sure am I? (circle one)**
   Not sure 1 2 3 4 5 Very sure
6. ❓ *How can I find out?*
   1. _____
   2. _____
   3. _____
   4. _____
7. **Explore**
8. **Do I think differently?** ➤ yes no
9. ❓ *What do I know now?*
   1. _____
   2. _____
   3. _____
   4. _____
10. **SHARE**
   1. _____
   2. _____
   3. _____

Observational Study

Using scientific methods does not always involve doing a controlled experiment. In an observational study, a scientist does not change or control the variables that are already present in a situation or an environment. The scientist observes and records his or her observations, as in **Figure 1-11.** Suppose scientists wanted to learn more about a particular planet. They might observe the planet with powerful telescopes. They might send a probe, a device to gather information. Suppose scientists wanted to learn more about a particular animal. They might want to know how the animal lives in its natural environment. The scientists would observe the animal without changing its living conditions. Or, suppose scientists wanted to find out more about what causes heart disease. They might observe the rate of heart disease in a group of people and note differences between people who develop heart disease and those who do not.

In each of these three cases, a controlled experiment would not help the scientists obtain the information they seek. This is not to say that observational studies never have variables. Suppose a scientist observes the rate of cancer in people who have a low-fat diet compared to those who have a high-fat diet. The scientist classifies people as belonging in one of the two groups. The independent variable is the amount of fat a person eats. The dependent variable is the rate of cancer.

Figure 1-11 Each of these three scientists must decide, or at times guess, which types of experiments will provide the best information.

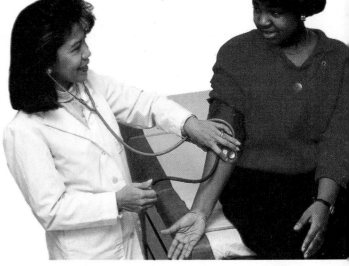

Once a set of data has been collected and organized, it can be analyzed to see if it supports the hypothesis. Data can be analyzed in a number of ways, including performing calculations and making different types of graphs. A **graph** is a diagram that shows the relationship of one variable to another. A graph makes interpretation and analysis of data easier. Look at Kashanna's graph in **Figure 1-12.** Do the results support her hypothesis?

VISUALIZING
Line Graphs

Figure 1-12

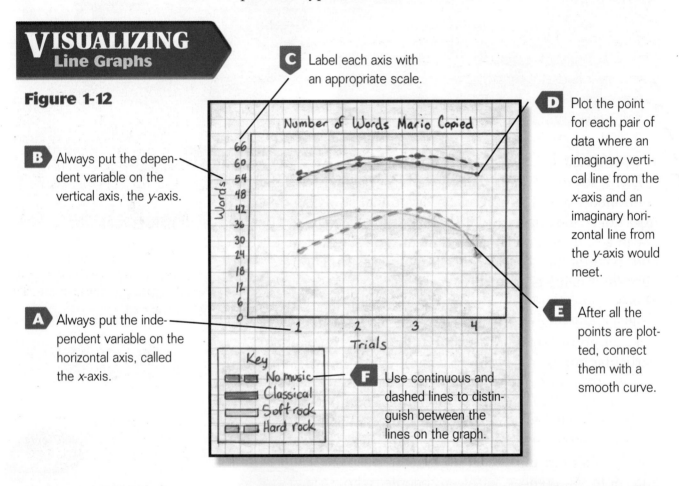

C Label each axis with an appropriate scale.

B Always put the dependent variable on the vertical axis, the *y*-axis.

A Always put the independent variable on the horizontal axis, called the *x*-axis.

D Plot the point for each pair of data where an imaginary vertical line from the *x*-axis and an imaginary horizontal line from the *y*-axis would meet.

E After all the points are plotted, connect them with a smooth curve.

F Use continuous and dashed lines to distinguish between the lines on the graph.

A conclusion is a statement based on the results of the experiment. It might or might not support the hypothesis. Kashanna's hypothesis was not supported. She concluded that the type of music did have an effect on the ability to concentrate. Keep in mind that a hypothesis is not necessarily wrong just because the results do not support it. An experiment might not be designed correctly. A scientist might make errors in observing, measuring, or recording data. An unidentified variable might affect the dependent variable.

As Kashanna and Hiromi reviewed their results, they identified problems in the design. They concluded that more than one variable could have affected Mario's performance. What if some passages contained a greater number of long or difficult words? Or, what if he became bored during the experiment? What if these results could be applied only to Mario? Was his experience typical of everyone's experience? Kashanna and Hiromi decided to conduct more experiments with other classmates.

Scientists who conduct observational studies also draw conclusions from analyzing data. A scientist who observes a higher rate of skin cancer in people who sunbathe often might conclude that frequent sun exposure is a factor in causing skin cancer.

Scientists, like the astronaut in **Figure 1-13,** often must do many experiments and look at problems in different ways to find answers. Scientists have not failed if they do not get answers the first time, or the second, or even the hundredth. They learn a little more each time. Often, results from scientific experiments and observations raise more questions. An important part of doing science is persistence.

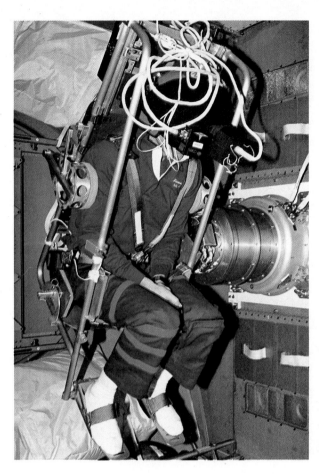

Figure 1-13 This astronaut is using a specially designed chair and helmet to test the effects of space flight on humans.

Section Assessment

1. What are five possible approaches one might take in solving a problem?
2. What is a constant?
3. Why is conducting multiple trials a good idea?
4. **Think Critically:** What else could Kashanna have used as the independent variable in her experiment?
5. **Skill Builder**
   Sequencing Complex tasks are often accomplished by following a series of steps in order. Do the **Chapter 1 Skill Activity** on page 742 to plan a mission to Mars by arranging the steps in the proper sequence.

Using Math

Use the data in **Table 1-1** to find the average number of words copied for each trial. Make a bar graph to show the results of your calculations. Under which conditions would Mario study best?

Follow the Bouncing Ball

Possible Materials

- Balls, such as a baseball, table-tennis ball, golf ball, tennis ball, racquetball, and high-bounce rubber ball
- Meterstick
- Poster paper
- Markers
- Floor materials, such as carpet, foam, hard tile, and wood

Science might be the last thing you are thinking about as you watch a commercial on TV. But, many manufacturers rely on scientists to design and test their products. Suppose you are the owner of a sports store. You want to advertise how high a particular ball bounces. Conduct an experiment to find the surface material on which your ball bounces the highest.

Recognize the Problem

How does the surface of a material affect how high a ball bounces?

Form a Hypothesis

Before a ball is dropped, it has potential energy. Potential energy is energy that is stored. As the ball falls, the potential energy is converted into kinetic energy, which is energy of motion. Some energy is transferred as a ball deforms when it hits the surface. Use this knowledge of potential and kinetic energy to **make a hypothesis** about how the kind of surface material helps determine the bounce of a ball.

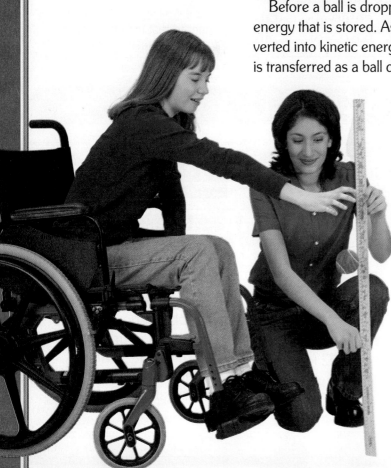

Goals

- **Design an experiment** to find out how high a ball bounces on different surface materials.
- **Separate and control** variables.
- **Measure and record** observations.

Safety Precautions

Do not throw the balls in the classroom.

Test Your Hypothesis

Plan

1. **Decide** how your group will test your hypothesis.

2. **List** the steps that you need to take to test your hypothesis. **Include** in your plan (a) the materials you will use, (b) the dependent variable and how you will **determine** the effect of the independent variable, (c) how you will keep the constants the same, d) the independent variable and how you will **adjust** it, and (e) how many trials you will conduct.

3. **Prepare** a data table in your Science Journal so that it is ready to use as your group collects data. Will the data be summarized in graphs? **Decide** which type of graph to use.

Do

1. Make sure your teacher approves your plan and your data table before you proceed.

2. **Perform** the experiment as planned.

3. **Record** your observations and **complete** the data table in your Science Journal.

Analyze Your Data

1. **Construct** a graph to compare results.

2. **List** the materials in the order that provided the highest bounce to those that provided the lowest bounce. Which surface material provided the highest bounce?

3. **Identify** any other variables that could affect the height of the bounce.

Draw Conclusions

1. **Infer** which surface materials absorb the most energy from the ball.

2. **Explain** why the surface material and the material of the ball are important in how sports, such as tennis and basketball, are played.

3. **Apply** what you learned. Write an advertisement that tells customers how to get the most bounce from the ball.

Using Science to Explore

What You'll Learn

► How remotely operated vehicles help humans to explore
► How scientists use science skills in different ways

Vocabulary
technology
sequence
inference

Why It's Important

► Using science skills and technology helps you gather information about places that you cannot observe directly.

Using Technology

A week had passed since Mr. Hayes's assignment. The students were eager to share what they had found out.

Mr. Hayes opened the discussion. "Before we begin, who can tell us the difference between science and technology?"

Gabriella raised her hand. "Science is the process of trying to understand the world around you. **Technology** is the application of what has been learned through science."

"Excellent," Mr. Hayes said. "Why don't you go first, Gabriella?"

Gabriella stood. "The ocean is a frontier just waiting to be explored like the American West used to be. There's a difference, though. There are few places people may go underwater. It's too deep and the pressure is too great. That's what is known as a hostile environment—an environment in which the conditions are hazardous to people. People need technology to help them."

She continued, "Remotely operated vehicles, or ROVs, can withstand the pressure at several thousand feet. They have cameras and other instruments that gather data about things such as salinity (salt content) and currents. They have manipulators, or arms, that take samples."

Figure 1-14 This manned submersible, MIR I, is used to study and explore to a depth of 6000 m.

"Volcanoes are another frontier on Earth," Jared volunteered. "I read about a spiderlike, walking robot that was designed to explore the inside of an active volcano."

Hiromi spoke next. "Space is another hostile environment," he said. "I read about a robot that NASA developed that's able to travel over rough terrain. They tested it in a desert that resembled the surface of the moon. Once on the moon, scientists would operate it from Earth. But, one thing that makes this robot different is that it has its own navigation system. Suppose it were going toward a cliff. It would take 2.5 seconds for the scientists to signal the robot on the moon, and by that time, the robot might have fallen off. But, this robot can determine what is safe and what is dangerous. It might even ignore the operator's commands if it detects a hazard."

"That's the kind of technology I read about," said Kashanna. "Scientists are making robots to explore hostile environments that don't need someone giving them commands all the time. One robot is called STAR—that's the Spiral Track Autonomous Robot. It travels on two giant screws—that's the 'spiral' part—so it can turn around in tight spaces and climb steep terrain that other robots can't. It has an onboard computer system that allows it to make decisions—that's the 'autonomous' part."

Figure 1-15 The terrain of Mars was photographed and explored by this rover.

Figure 1-16 Technology, such as STAR, is developed to solve specific problems and explore unique environments.

Several students described other uses for technology in hostile environments such as mining and cleaning up nuclear or chemical spills.

Mr. Hayes pointed out that ROVs and robots help people "see" places they cannot visit directly. "Keep in mind," he said, "that people are seeing the data that are sent back, not the environments themselves. Even the camera images aren't the same as directly seeing something."

Using Science to Develop Technology

The class then discussed the science skills they thought would have been used to explore hostile environments. As they talked, Mr. Hayes wrote the science skills on the board. They agreed that the scientists who built the technology used various skills as they followed some scientific method. The scientists recognized a problem for which they wanted to design an ROV or robot. They compared and contrasted different designs and recorded their findings in their Science Journals, as shown in **Figure 1-17**. Comparing is looking for similarities in objects or events. Contrasting is looking for differences in objects or events. They also used math skills to design a model. For example, they might have calculated the energy needed for the machine to function or have drawn a scale model. ✔

Reading Check ✔

What is the difference between comparing and contrasting?

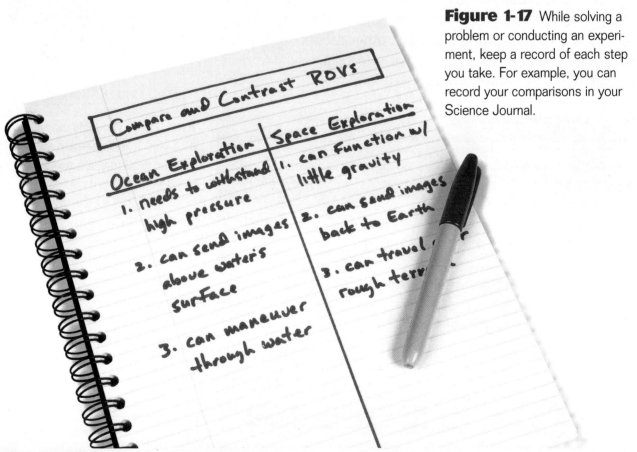

Figure 1-17 While solving a problem or conducting an experiment, keep a record of each step you take. For example, you can record your comparisons in your Science Journal.

Compare and Contrast ROVs

Ocean Exploration
1. needs to withstand high pressure
2. can send images above water's surface
3. can maneuver through water

Space Exploration
1. can function w/ little gravity
2. can send images back to Earth
3. can travel rough terr.

After forming a hypothesis that their design would work, the scientists tested the hypothesis. They planned and conducted a controlled experiment. They used sequencing to test the model. A **sequence** is an arrangement of things or events in a certain order. For example, they might test the ROV's ability to grasp and hold an object, then test how much mass the robot's arm can support before dropping an object. They identified and controlled variables. Only one independent variable was changed at a time so that the scientists could pinpoint the cause of any malfunctions. They carefully observed the model's performance to record accurate data.

As they worked, the scientists constantly made inferences. An **inference** is an attempt at an explanation based on observations. This helped them know how to modify the design. As they worked, they made careful measurements. They might have measured the speed of the model or the size of objects it could lift.

Gravity acts on every particle in an object. The center of mass of an object is the point where an object will balance without tipping over. The position of the center of gravity affects an object's stability. When designing a robot, scientists must make sure the robot remains stable as it moves forward, stops, turns, and moves up or down an incline. If a robot is too heavy near the top, it may tip over easily.

Stability can be increased by lowering the center of gravity and by widening the base. Think of football players. They are harder to knock down if their knees are bent, which lowers their center of gravity, and when their feet are spread apart, which widens their base.

Finally, the scientists organized their data into tables and graphs so they could analyze the results and draw conclusions. Scientists use any number of graphs (line, bar, and circle) to help them interpret data. Communicating was an important skill throughout the process. The scientists worked as a team so they needed to share what they were doing and seeing.

interNET CONNECTION

Visit the Glencoe Science Web Site at **www.glencoe.com/sec/science** for information about ROVs that have been developed recently. In your Science Journal, compare and contrast the designs and functions of several ROVs.

PHYSICS
◀ INTEGRATION

Try at Home

Mini Lab

Inferring Density

Procedure

1. Fill a large, transparent glass or glass jar with warm water. Gently add a drop of food coloring in the center of the water's surface.
2. Carefully float an ice cube on top of the food coloring. Observe for one minute. What happens to the food coloring?
3. Add two drops of food coloring directly on the ice cube to help you see what is happening.

Analysis

1. Record your observations in your Science Journal.
2. Describe where areas of water having different temperatures are located in a lake.

Figure 1-18 When searching and exploring hostile environments, there are no right or wrong methods. Using your imagination and creativity, the world—and beyond—is yours to explore. **What might the researchers on this ocean-research vessel be studying in the Chukchi Sea (between Alaska and Russia)?**

Using Science Skills to Explore

From their assignment, the class decided that the scientists who explore hostile environments using technology do not necessarily follow step-by-step scientific methods. For example, scientists who explore the ocean, as in **Figure 1-18,** might not have a formal hypothesis. The question might be "What's down there?" But, the scientists still use a variety of science skills while following their particular method.

These skills might include observing (looking at the pictures transmitted), inferring (explaining what the pictures are), measuring (determining how much cable to use to lower the ROV in the water), interpreting (using meteorological data to forecast the weather at sea), and communicating (sharing information to position the ROV correctly).

Safe Science

Mr. Hayes emphasized that safety is an important reason for using technology to explore hostile environments. Having equipment become damaged is far less critical than risking a person's life. The class discussed safety rules to follow when conducting science activities or experiments. They designed a poster called SAFE TIPS.

Start a lab activity only with your teacher's permission.
Ask your teacher if you do not understand a procedure.
Follow all safety symbols. Wear goggles during labs.
Engage in responsible behavior.

Tell your teacher immediately of accidents or injuries.
Identify the location of emergency equipment.
Put away chemicals and supplies properly.
Slant test tubes away from you and others when heating.

The students also created the slogan NO TIDE. TIDE stands for **T**asting chemicals, **I**nhaling chemicals, **D**rinking, or **E**ating. This helps them to remember that they should never eat or drink anything in a laboratory. It also reminds them to be cautious around fumes or vapors that could be harmful.

Figure 1-19 Lab equipment, like the test tube shown, must be handled properly.

Section Assessment

1. What are some ways technology is used to explore hostile environments?

2. What are some science skills scientists use to form a hypothesis about the design of an ROV or robot?

3. **Think Critically:** You have read about ways that scientists are like explorers. How are modern scientists different from explorers of the past?

4. **Skill Builder**
   Interpreting Data Suppose you have three plants that are supposed to bloom but are not blooming. You give one plant only water, another plant water and one type of plant fertilizer, and the third plant water and a different type of plant fertilizer. None of the plants bloom. How would you interpret your observations? If you need help, refer to Interpreting Data in the **Skill Handbook** on page 724.

Using Computers

Word Processing
Think of a problem faced by your community such as water pollution. Using a word processor, write a report describing how you would design a robot or an ROV to help solve the problem. If you need help, refer to page 732.

Comparing Densities

Density is a physical property of a substance. It relates to how much material is contained within an object. In general, an object will float if its density is less than the density of the liquid. For example, ice floats in water because ice is less dense than water. How do the densities of various liquids compare?

Materials

- Graduated cylinder (100 mL)
- Balance and masses
- Water
- Cooking oil
- Table salt
- Paper cups
- Plastic spoons or stirrers
- Plastic beverage containers (to dispose of oil)

What You'll Investigate

How do the densities of liquids compare?

Goals

- **Infer** why objects float in some liquids but not in others.
- **Measure** liquids to determine their density.
- **Graph** the densities of the liquids.

Safety Precautions

Never taste anything during a lab activity. Wipe up any spills on the floor immediately.

Procedure

1. **Copy** the data table below for recording your measurements.

2. **Measure** the mass of a paper cup and record.

3. **Measure** 100 mL of water and pour it into the cup. Record the mass.

4. **Make** salt water by dissolving 3.5 g of table salt into 100 mL of tap water. Using a fresh paper cup each time, repeat steps 2 and 3 for the salt water and oil.

5. **Subtract** the mass of the cup to find the mass of the liquid. **Calculate** the density of each liquid using the formula, *density = mass/volume*. The unit used to express density is g/cm^3. One cubic centimeter occupies the same volume as one milliliter.

6. **Graph** your data using a bar graph. How does a graph help you analyze your results?

Conclude and Apply

1. Would a ship be able to carry more cargo in freshwater or salt water? Why?

2. Why might it be harder for aquatic birds to swim in an oil spill than in water?

Liquid's Measurement Data					
Liquid	**Mass of paper cup (g)**	**Mass of liquid in cup (g)**	**Mass of liquid only (g)**	**Volume of liquid (mL)**	**Density (g/cm³)**
Tap water					
Salt water					
Oil					

The Circle of Life
From: *Nature's Numbers* by Ian Stewart

"We live in a universe of patterns. (See sample patterns at left.) Every night the stars move in circles across the sky. The seasons cycle at yearly intervals. No two snowflakes are ever exactly the same, but they all have sixfold symmetry. Tigers and zebras are covered in patterns of stripes, leopards and hyenas are covered in patterns of spots. Intricate trains of waves march across the oceans; very similar trains of sand dunes march across the desert. Colored arcs of light adorn the sky in the form of rainbows, and a bright circular halo sometimes surrounds the moon on winter nights. Spherical drops of water fall from clouds."

Throughout history, people of various cultures have tried to organize and explain the world around them. Long ago, an elder in the Sioux Nation observed the rings within tree trunks, the structure of birds' nests, the shape of raindrops, and other circular patterns around him. He believed that all of nature is like a circle.

In this Native American view of the world, all of the unique communities in nature interact as part of a whole. An elder and teacher of the Chippewa Nation taught that all living creatures are related because they have the same mother (Earth) and share her gifts. For example, plants take in carbon dioxide and release oxygen for organisms to breathe.

Many cultures that have lived close to nature share the world view that nature is based on circular patterns. In recent times, scientists have provided circular models of the solar system and the atom. Thus, we are finding that some native peoples' view of nature corresponds well with the findings of modern science.

Think Critically

Look through your textbook for additional examples of cyclic patterns. Write down these examples and the pages on which they are located in your Science Journal.

Science JOURNAL ▶

Expository Writing: Observe and describe some other examples of circular or cyclic patterns in nature. What other repeating patterns are you familiar with? What responsibility do humans have in "the circle of life"?

For a **preview** of this chapter, study this Reviewing Main Ideas before you read the chapter. After you have studied this chapter, you can use the Reviewing Main Ideas to **review** the chapter.

The Glencoe MindJogger, Audiocassettes, and CD-ROM provide additional opportunities for review.

Section 1-1 SCIENTIFIC PROBLEM SOLVING

A **scientific method** consists of steps taken to try to solve a problem. One step is to recognize a problem. A second step is to form a **hypothesis**—a prediction about a problem that can be tested. In another step, scientists test hypotheses by conducting controlled experiments or observational studies. In a controlled experiment, scientists change the **independent variable** and measure its effect on the **dependent variable.** Scientists who conduct observational studies do not change or control variables. They observe the relationships among variables. Another important step is to analyze data. Scientists organize data into tables or **graphs.** Often, the final step in a scientific method is to draw conclusions. A conclusion may or may not support the hypothesis. This does not necessarily mean the hypothesis is wrong. Sometimes, experiments are not designed correctly or unknown variables produce effects on the dependent variable. Scientists often must do many experiments and look at problems in different ways to find answers. *Why should only one variable at a time be changed in a controlled experiment?*

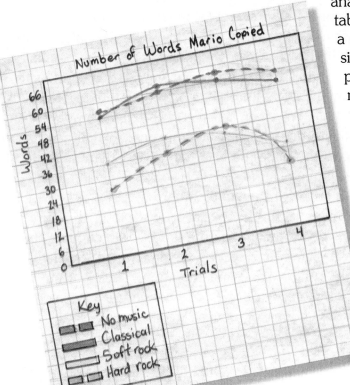

Reading Check ✓

Variables, controls, and trials are used in scientific experiments. Compare the meaning of each word in this context with its meaning in a nonscientific context.

Section 1-2 USING SCIENCE TO EXPLORE

A hostile environment is an environment in which the conditions are hazardous to people. Many places on Earth and in outer space cannot be explored directly by humans. Scientists have constructed robots and remotely operated vehicles, or ROVs, to go to sites of nuclear accidents, deep in the ocean, into volcanoes, into outer space, and into mines. People have increased their knowledge of hostile environments by analyzing data gathered through **technology.** Scientists who design technology to explore hostile environments use various approaches when forming a **scientific method** that will help them solve a particular problem. They design and conduct experiments to test models. Scientists who use technology to explore hostile environments use science skills. In both cases, scientists use science skills to solve a problem or to answer a question. *Does a scientist always have to follow certain steps in a scientific method? Why or why not?*

Career CONNECTION

John Swallow, Forest Technician

John Swallow works in South Dakota's Black Hills National Forest. He is an Oglala Sioux and a forest technician. John determines which trees in the forest can be safely cut down and which trees must be saved. Much of the cutting of trees is done for thinning—to reduce competition between trees for light and nutrients—thus promoting quicker growth. John also works to conserve sensitive or endangered plants in logging areas. *How can science help our understanding of the impact of logging on a forest?*

Chapter 1 Assessment

Using Vocabulary

a. constant
b. control
c. dependent variable
d. graph
e. hypothesis
f. independent variable
g. inference
h. law
i. science
j. scientific method
k. sequence
l. technology
m. theory

Each of the following sentences is false. Make the sentence true by replacing the italicized word with a word from the list above.

1. A *control* is an approach taken to try to solve a problem.
2. An *inference* is a prediction about a problem that can be tested.
3. *Technology* is the process of trying to understand the world around you.
4. A *constant* is a standard to compare with.
5. The *independent variable* is the factor being measured in a controlled experiment.

Checking Concepts

Choose the word or phrase that best answers the question.

6. How is a hypothesis tested?
   A) experiment   C) graph
   B) infer   D) conclude

7. What will a scientist never do in an observational study?
   A) use technology   C) control variables
   B) record data   D) observe variables

8. What does a scientist use to reduce the effect of errors?
   A) observations   C) hypotheses
   B) constants   D) multiple trials

9. You decide to find out which of three cat foods your cat likes the best. What is the cat food that you try each time called?
   A) control   C) independent
   B) dependent   variable
      variable   D) trial

10. How does a blind experiment differ from other experiments?
    A) Data are collected and interpreted.
    B) A hypothesis is formed after observations are made.
    C) Variables are changed to test the hypothesis.
    D) Some or all of the information is withheld from the subject.

11. What does it mean if an experiment does **NOT** support the hypothesis?
    A) The scientist has failed.
    B) The scientist has learned more.
    C) The scientist is not creative.
    D) The scientist did something wrong.

12. Why are ROVs and robots so useful?
    A) They gather information from hostile environments.
    B) They must follow commands from a person.
    C) They allow people to see hostile environments directly.
    D) They make all decisions on their own.

13. How do scientists who build ROVs use scientific methods?
    A) They test the effects of gravity.
    B) They work according to a sequence.
    C) They keep their data secret.
    D) They use every approach in the model.

14. What is a graph **NOT** used for?
    A) conducting an experiment
    B) interpreting data
    C) communicating information
    D) drawing conclusions

15. What is an explanation backed by experimental results?
    A) a control   C) a law
    B) a theory   D) a hypothesis

Thinking Critically

16. You use the skill of sequencing when you get ready for school. What might happen if you changed the order of your actions?

17. A scientist wants to test a new drug that might relieve symptoms for a particular illness. Why is it important to use a control?

18. Give an example of an observational study you can do at home.

19. Why is it important to follow safety rules in the lab?

20. Why do scientists often do research before forming a hypothesis?

Developing Skills

If you need help, refer to the Skill Handbook.

21. **Concept Mapping:** Complete the events chain that shows the order in which science skills might be used in observational studies. Use these phrases: *analyze data, ask a question, draw conclusions, observe,* and *record data.*

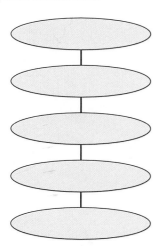

THE PRINCETON REVIEW

Test-Taking Tip

Beat the Clock and Then Go Back As you take a test, pace yourself to finish a few minutes early so you can go back and check over your work. You'll usually find a mistake or two. Don't worry. It's better to make corrections than to hand in a test with wrong answers.

Test Practice

Use these questions to test your Science Proficiency.

1. Michaela set up an experiment to find out if running would help her basketball game. Her basketball game did not improve. What can Michaela conclude from her results?
A) Her hypothesis was wrong.
B) Her results did not support the hypothesis.
C) Running does not help a person do well in sports.
D) A person who plays basketball should not run.

2. Alex eagerly arrived to science class early to begin his experiment. He set up the materials, popped a piece of gum into his mouth, and got right to work by himself, even though he wasn't quite sure of the procedure. What is the safety precaution that he ignored **FIRST**?
A) He didn't put on goggles.
B) He didn't ask questions about the correct procedure.
C) He didn't get the teacher's permission to start the lab activity.
D) He was eating during a lab activity.

Inside the Atom

Reading Check ☑

Before reading this chapter, list the vocabulary terms for each section. As you read, write a definition next to each term.

Explore Activity

By day, they are clear, glass tubes filled with colorless gases. Flip the switch, and they instantly light up the night with their messages. This is advertising magic! Electricity paints pictures that you can't help but notice. What's going on? What are the gases in the tubes? What are they made of, and why do they glow with color at the flick of a switch?

Observe Inside an Atom

1. Your teacher will give you a piece of clay and some pieces of metal. Count the pieces of metal.

2. Bury these pieces in the modeling clay so they can't be seen.

3. Exchange clay balls with another group.

4. With a toothpick, probe the clay to find out how many pieces of metal are in the ball and what shapes they are.

Science Journal

In your Science Journal, sketch the shapes of the metal pieces as you identify them. How does the number of pieces you found compare with the number that were actually in the clay ball? How do their shapes compare?

The Story of the Atom

2•1

What You'll Learn

▶ How scientists discovered subatomic particles
▶ How today's model of the atom developed
▶ The structure of the nuclear atom

Vocabulary
element
electron
proton
neutron
electron cloud

Why It's Important

▶ Atoms make up everything in your world.

An Old Idea

Trying to find out what something looks like when you can't see it is not a new challenge. People began wondering about matter more than 2500 years ago. Some of the Greek philosophers thought that matter was composed of tiny particles. They reasoned that you could take a piece of matter, cut it in half, cut the half-piece in half again, and continue to cut again and again. Eventually, you wouldn't be able to cut any more. You would have only one particle left. They named these particles atoms, a term that means "cannot be divided." Think about matter as being like a string of beads. If you keep dividing the string into pieces, you eventually come to one single bead.

The Greek philosophers didn't try to prove their theories by doing experiments as scientists now do. Today, scientists like the one in **Figure 2-1** will not accept a theory that is not supported by experimental evidence. But even if the Greeks had experimented, they could not have proven the existence of atoms. People had not yet discovered much about what is now called chemistry, the study of matter. The kind of equipment needed to study matter was a long way from being invented. Even 2000 years later, atoms were a mystery.

Figure 2-1 Modern scientists design and carry out experiments to either support or disprove new hypotheses.

Figure 2-2 The 1700s were years of great interest in science. Scientists created laboratories like this one to test their theories by doing experiments.

Dalton's Atomic Model

For a long time after the ancient Greeks, people didn't think much about atoms. Finally, during the eighteenth century, scientists in laboratories like the one in **Figure 2-2** again began debating the existence of atoms. Chemists were learning about matter and how it changes. They were putting substances together to form new substances and taking substances apart to find out what they were made of. They found that there was a limit to how far a substance could be broken down. Certain substances couldn't be broken down into simpler substances. Scientists came to realize that all matter is made up of elements. An **element** is a substance that cannot be broken down into simpler substances. John Dalton, an English schoolteacher, combined the idea of elements with the Greek theory of the atom. He proposed that matter is made up of atoms, that atoms cannot be divided into smaller pieces, and that all the atoms of an element are exactly alike, and different elements are made of different kinds of atoms. For example, iron is an element made of iron atoms. Silver, another element, is made of silver atoms. Dalton pictured an atom as a hard sphere that was the same throughout, something like a tiny marble. His model is shown in **Figure 2-3.**

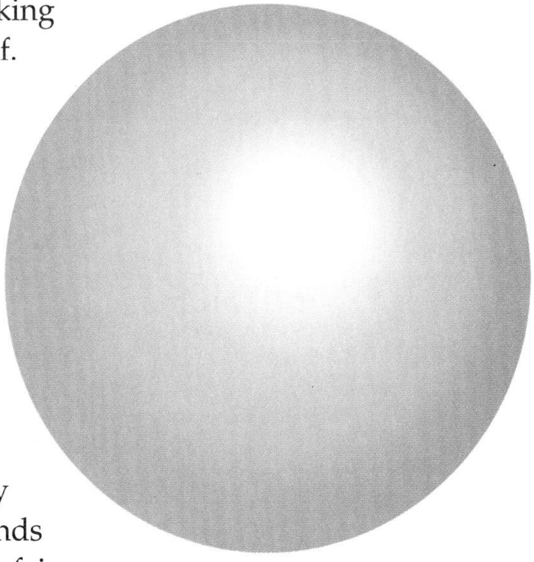

Figure 2-3 Dalton pictured the atom as a hard sphere that was the same throughout.

Where's the proof?

By the second half of the nineteenth century, scientists had equipment to test Dalton's theory of the atom. In 1870, the English scientist William Crookes did experiments with a glass tube that had almost all the air removed from it. The glass tube had two pieces of metal called electrodes sealed in the glass. The electrodes were connected to a battery by wires.

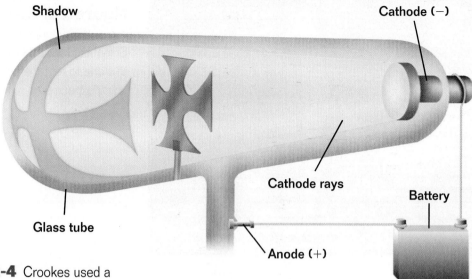

Shadow

Cathode (−)

Cathode rays

Battery

Glass tube

Anode (+)

Figure 2-4 Crookes used a glass tube containing only a small amount of gas. When the glass tube was connected to a battery, something flowed from the negative electrode on the right to the positive electrode. **Was this "something" light or a stream of particles?**

PHYSICS
INTEGRATION ➤

An electrode is a piece of metal that can conduct electric current. One electrode, called the anode, has a positive charge. The other, called the cathode, has a negative charge. In Crookes's tube, the metal cathode was a disk at the right end of the tube. Beyond the anode was an object shaped like a cross, as you can see in **Figure 2-4.** When the battery was connected, the glass tube suddenly lit up with a greenish glow. A shadow of the cross-shaped object appeared at the left end of the tube. The shadow indicated that something was traveling in a straight line from the cathode to the anode, just like the beam of a flashlight. The object was getting in the way of the beam and casting a shadow just like the shadow you would get of your hand if you put it in the beam of a flashlight or movie projector. You can see this in **Figure 2-5.**

Was the greenish glow light? Or, was it a stream of charged particles? This question was answered by placing a magnet beside the tube. In **Figure 2-6,** you can see that the beam is bent by the magnet. Light is not bent by a magnet, so the

Figure 2-5 The shadow cast by the rays in Crookes's tube were just like the shadows cast by light, but it turned out that Crookes's rays were not light.

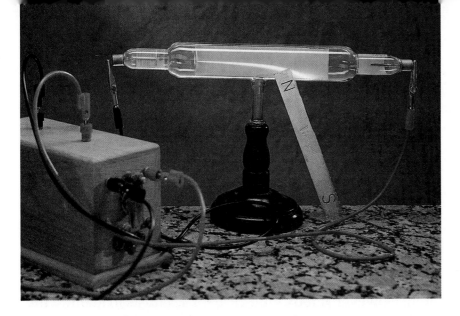

Figure 2-6 When a magnet is placed near a glass tube similar to the one Crookes used, the rays bend. **A magnet cannot bend light, so what must be the "something" that causes the green glow?**

beam is not light. Therefore, the beam must be negatively charged particles of matter that came from the metal of the cathode. How was it posssible to know that the particles were negatively charged? Opposite charges attract each other. These particles were attracted to the positively charged anode, so the particles must be negatively charged. These rays were called cathode rays because they were produced at the cathode. Crookes's tube is known as a cathode-ray tube, or CRT. It's the forerunner of all TV and computer display screens like the one in' **Figure 2-7.**

J. J. Thomson's Contribution

You can imagine how excited scientists were when they heard the results of Crookes's work. But, many scientists were not convinced that the cathode rays were streams of particles. In 1897, J.J. Thomson, an English physicist, repeated the CRT experiment using different metals for the cathode and different gases in the tube. But, the same negatively charged particles were produced regardless of the metal used for the cathode or the gas in the tube. Thomson concluded that cathode rays are negatively charged particles of matter. These particles are now called **electrons.** He also inferred that electrons are a part of every kind of atom because they are produced by every kind of cathode material. Thomson's experiments also proved that atoms are not impossible to divide because atoms are made up of even smaller particles.

Figure 2-7 Crookes's tube became known as a cathode-ray tube because the particles he observed started at the cathode and traveled to the anode. There is a cathode-ray tube or CRT in every TV and computer monitor.

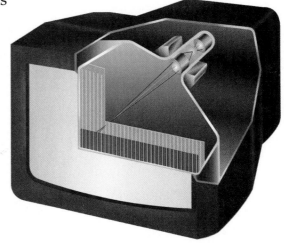

Thomson's Atomic Model

Thomson's experiments answered some of the questions scientists had about atoms. But, they led to another scientific puzzle. If atoms contain one or more negatively charged particles, then matter, which is made of the atoms, also should be negatively charged. But, it isn't. How can this be explained? Could it be that atoms also contain one or more positively charged particles? The negatively charged electrons and the unknown positively charged particles would then neutralize each other in the atom. Thomson continued his experiments and found evidence for the existence of a particle that has the same mass and charge as a positively charged hydrogen atom. However, it took until 1920 for scientists to identify this particle as a proton. A **proton** is a positively charged particle that is present in all atoms. A proton is almost 2000 times heavier than an electron. ✔

Using his new findings, Thomson revised Dalton's model of the atom. Instead of a solid ball that was the same throughout, Thomson pictured a sphere that contained all the positive charge. The negatively charged electrons were spread evenly throughout the sphere. You can compare Thomson's idea of the atom to the ball of raisin-cookie dough shown in **Figure 2-8**. The cookie dough represents the protons, which are most of the mass of the atom. The raisins represent the electrons. They are scattered throughout the dough and make the atom electrically neutral.

Reading Check ✔

What particle has the same mass and charge as a positively charged hydrogen atom?

Figure 2-8 Well-mixed cookie dough is a model for the J.J. Thomson atom.

A The dough contains all the positive charge of the atom. The raisins, which represent the negatively charged electrons, are mixed evenly in the dough.

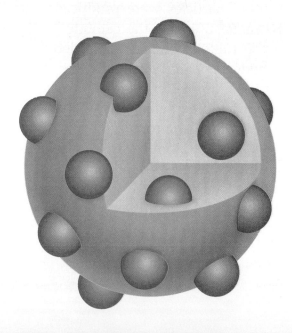

B Thomson pictured the negatively charged electrons as evenly spaced throughout the atom. The negative charges of the electrons and the positive charges of the protons balanced each other.

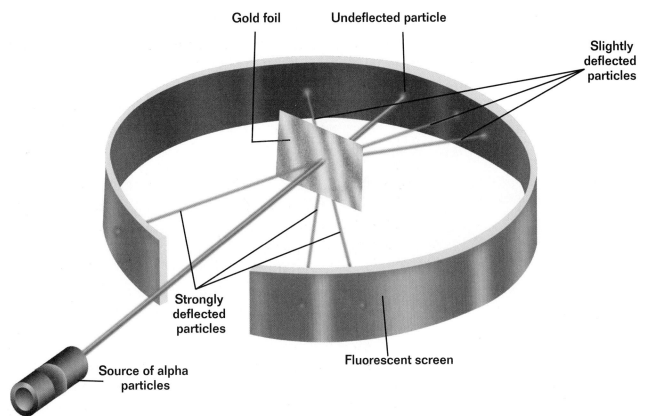

Gold foil   Undeflected particle

Slightly deflected particles

Strongly deflected particles

Source of alpha particles

Fluorescent screen

Rutherford's Atom

Was Thomson's model of the atom correct? In 1906, Ernest Rutherford and his coworkers began an experiment to find out. They wanted to see what would happen when they bombarded a thin film of a metal such as gold with fast-moving bits of matter called alpha particles. Alpha particles come from unstable atoms. Because they are positively charged, alpha particles are repelled by particles of matter with a positive charge.

Figure 2-9 shows how the experiment was set up. A source of alpha particles was aimed at the sheet of thin gold foil. The foil was surrounded by a fluorescent (fluh RES unt) screen that gave a flash of light when it was hit by a charged particle.

Rutherford thought he knew what the results of this experiment would be. He expected that most of the speeding alpha particles would crash right through the foil and hit the screen on the other side, just like a bullet fired through a glass pane. Rutherford reasoned that in the thin gold film, there wasn't enough matter to stop the speeding alpha particle or to change its path. There also wasn't enough charge in any one place in the cookie-dough atom to strongly repel the alpha particle. He thought that the positive charges on the protons in the gold atoms might cause a few minor deflections if an alpha particle happened to come close to a proton. However, he assumed that there would be only a few of these occasions.

Figure 2-9 In Rutherford's experiment, alpha particles bombarded the gold foil. Most particles passed right through the foil or veered slightly from a straight-line path, but some particles bounced right back. The path of a particle is shown by a flash of light when it hits the fluorescent screen.

That was a reasonable assumption to make because in the cookie-dough model, the positive charges of the protons are essentially neutralized by nearby electrons. Rutherford was so sure of what the results would be that he turned the work over to a graduate student.

Surprising Results

Imagine Rutherford's surprise when his student rushed in to tell him that some alpha particles were veering off at large angles. You can see this in **Figure 2-9.** Rutherford expressed his amazement by saying, "It was about as believable as if you had fired a 15-inch shell at a piece of tissue paper, and it came back and hit you." How could an event like the cartoon in **Figure 2-10** be explained? The positively charged alpha particles were moving with such high speed that it would take a large positive charge to cause them to bounce back. But, in the cookie-dough model of the atom, the mass and charges of the electrons and protons are all uniformly mixed.

The Nuclear Atom

Picture in your mind Rutherford and his team wrestling to make sense of this experiment. They might have drawn diagrams like those in **Figure 2-11.** Diagram A, using the cookie-dough model, shows what Rutherford expected. Now and then, an alpha particle might be slightly affected by a positive charge in the atom and turn a bit off course. However, no large changes in direction would be expected. The actual results did not fit this model, so Rutherford proposed a new one. He hypothesized that almost all the mass of the atom and all of its positive charge are crammed into an incredibly small region of space at the center of the atom called the nucleus. The rest of the atom is empty space occupied by the atom's almost-massless electrons. ☑

Diagram B, in **Figure 2-11,** shows Rutherford's new model of the atom and how it fits the experimental data. You could

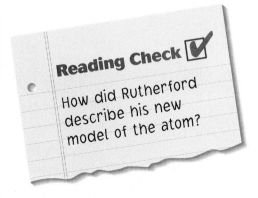

Reading Check ☑

How did Rutherford describe his new model of the atom?

VISUALIZING
The Nuclear Atom

Figure 2-11 Rutherford had to relate his findings to the structure of the atom.

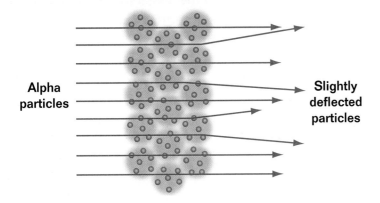

Alpha particles

Slightly deflected particles

A He thought that if the atom could be described by Thomson's cookie-dough model, then only minor bends in the paths of the particles would have occurred. However, some particles bounced back off the foil.

B What could send an alpha particle bouncing off in the opposite direction? Rutherford thought it had to be a tiny nucleus that contains all the positive charge and most of the mass of the atom.

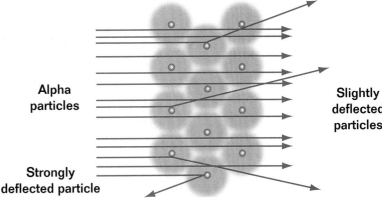

Alpha particles

Slightly deflected particles

Strongly deflected particle

predict that if an alpha particle made a direct hit on the nucleus of a gold atom, which has 79 protons, the alpha particle would be strongly repelled and bounce back. But, most alpha particles could move through the foil with little or no interference because most of the atom is empty space.

The Neutron

Other scientists reviewed Rutherford's nuclear model of the atom with great interest and enthusiasm. However, some data didn't fit. For instance, recall that an atom's electrons have almost no mass. That means that the mass of an atom should be approximately equal to the mass of its protons. But, it isn't. The mass of most atoms is at least twice as great as the mass of its protons. Where does the extra mass come from?

Try at Home

MiniLab

Modeling the Nuclear Atom

Procedure

1. On a sheet of paper, draw a circle with a diameter equal to the width of the paper.
2. Small dots of paper in two colors will represent protons and neutrons. Using a dab of glue on each paper dot, make a model of the nucleus of the oxygen atom in the center of your circle. Oxygen has eight protons and eight neutrons.

Analysis

1. What particle is missing from your model of the oxygen atom?
2. How many of the missing particles should there be, and where should they be placed?

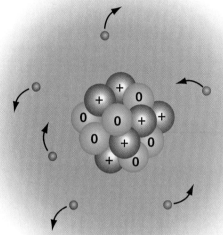

Rutherford reasoned that there must be another particle in the nucleus. The particle, which was later called the **neutron** (NEW trahn), would have the same mass as a proton and be electrically neutral. Proving the existence of neutrons was difficult, however, because a neutron has no charge, so it doesn't respond to magnets or cause fluorescent screens to light up. It took another 20 years before scientists were able to show by experiments that atoms contain neutrons.

The model of the atom was revised again to include neutrons in the nucleus. The nuclear atom, shown in **Figure 2-12**, has a tiny nucleus tightly packed with positively charged protons and neutral neutrons. Electrons occupy the space surrounding the nucleus. The number of electrons in an atom equals the number of protons in the atom.

Comparing Atom and Nucleus

When you look at drawings of atoms such as **Figure 2-12**, be aware that the nuclei are always drawn much larger than they actually are compared to the size of the atom. Picture the nucleus as being the size of a ping-pong ball. Then, the atom would have a diameter of more than 2.4 km. Another way to compare the size of a nucleus with the size of the atom is shown in **Figure 2-13**. You can see that it isn't surprising that in Rutherford's experiment, most of the alpha particles went directly through the gold foil without any interference from the gold atoms. An atom is mostly empty space.

Figure 2-13 If the nucleus of an atom were the size of one poppyseed on your bagel, the atom would have the diameter of this stadium.

What about the electrons?

In the early 1900s, physicists were trying to figure out how the electrons are arranged in an atom. It was natural to think that the negatively charged electrons are attracted to the positive nucleus in the same way Earth's moon is attracted to Earth. Then, electrons would travel in orbits around the nucleus. But, scientists soon learned that electrons are in constant, unpredictable motion and can't be pinned down. It's impossible to know precisely where an electron is at any moment. Instead, scientists talk about where the atom's electrons probably are. Electrons are probably in a region surrounding the nucleus, which is called the **electron cloud.** The model for the electron cloud, shown in **Figure 2-14,** is shaped like a sphere with the nucleus at its center. The electrons are more likely to be close to the nucleus rather than farther away because they are attracted to the positive charges of the protons. Notice the fuzzy outline of the cloud. There is no firm boundary because the electrons could be anywhere.

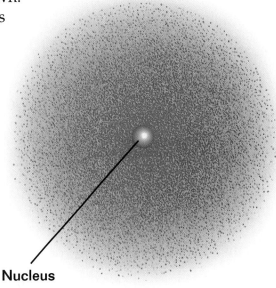

Figure 2-14 The electrons are more likely to be close to the nucleus rather than farther away, but they could be anywhere.

Nucleus

Section Assessment

1. Describe the three kinds of particles found in atoms. Where are they located in the atom and what are their charges?

2. If an atom has 49 protons, how many electrons does it have?

3. How does the nuclear atom differ from the uniform sphere model of the atom?

4. **Think Critically:** In Rutherford's experiment, why wouldn't the electrons in the atoms of the gold foil affect the paths of the alpha particles?

5. **Skill Builder**
   Concept Mapping Make a concept map using all the words in the Vocabulary list for this section. Add any other terms or words that will help create a complete diagram of the section. If you need help, refer to Concept Mapping in the **Skill Handbook** on page 714.

Using Math

The mass of an elec-tron is 9.11×10^{-28} g. The proton is 1836 times heavier. What is the mass of the pro-ton in grams and in kilograms?

Making a Model of the Invisible

Materials

- Sealed box
- Paper and pencil

How do scientists make models of things they can't see? First, they do experiments and gather as much information as possible. Then, they try to fit the information together into some kind of pattern and make inferences. From the data and inferences, they create a model that fits all their data.

What You'll Investigate

How can you determine the inside structure of a box?

Goals

- **Observe** the motion of a marble inside a closed box.
- **Infer** the structure inside the box.

Procedure

1. **Record** the number of the box your teacher gives you. Don't take the lid off the box or look inside.

2. **Lift** the box. **Tilt** the box. Gently **shake** it. In your Science Journal, record all your observations. Make a sketch of the way you think the marble in the box is rolling.

3. Use your observations to **infer** what the inside of the box looks like.

4. **Compare** your inferences with those of students who have the same box as you do. Then, you may want to make more observations or revise your inferences.

5. When you have gathered all the information you can, **sketch** your model in your Science Journal.

6. **Open** your box and **compare** your model with the actual inside structure of the box.

Conclude and Apply

1. How did your model of the inside of the box compare with the actual inside?

2. Is there any other test you could have used to gather more information?

3. How is an observation different from an inference?

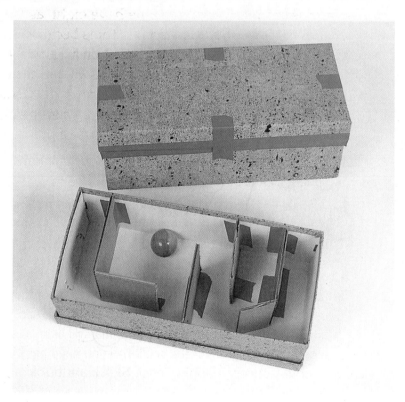

The Nucleus

What's in the nucleus?

The modern idea of the atom pictures all of the protons and neutrons packed into a tiny nucleus that is surrounded by electrons. How does the nucleus in an atom of one element differ from the nucleus of an atom of another element? The atoms of different elements contain different numbers of protons. The **atomic number** of an element is the number of protons in the nucleus of an atom of that element. The smallest of the atoms, the hydrogen atom, has one proton in its nucleus, so hydrogen's atomic number is 1. Chlorine has 17 protons, so chlorine's atomic number is 17. Uranium, the heaviest naturally occurring element, has 92 protons. Its atomic number is 92. Atoms of the same element always have the same number of protons.

Isotopes

The atomic number tells the number of protons, but what about the number of neutrons in an atom's nucleus? Atoms can have the same number of neutrons as protons, or they can have more or fewer neutrons than protons. Most atoms of carbon have six protons and six neutrons. But, some carbon atoms have seven neutrons and some have eight, as you can see in **Figure 2-15.** They are all carbon atoms because they all have six protons. These three kinds of carbon atoms are called isotopes. **Isotopes** (I suh tohps) are atoms of the same element that have different numbers of neutrons. The isotopes of carbon are called carbon-12, carbon-13, and carbon-14. The numbers 12, 13, and 14 are the mass numbers of the isotopes.

Figure 2-15 The three isotopes of carbon differ only in the number of neutrons in each nucleus.

VISUALIZING
Isotopes

Carbon-12

Carbon-13

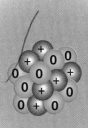

Carbon-14

Table 2-1

Isotopes of Carbon	Carbon-12	Carbon-13	Carbon-14
Mass Number	12	13	14
Number of Protons	6	6	6
Number of Neutrons	6	7	8
Number of Electrons	6	6	6
Atomic Number	6	6	6

Using Math

The atomic number of thorium-234 is 90. The atomic number of uranium-234 is 92. How many neutrons does each isotope have?

The **mass number** of an isotope is the number of neutrons plus protons in the nucleus. **Table 2-1** shows the particles that make up each of the carbon isotopes. You can find the number of neutrons in an isotope by subtracting the atomic number (the number of protons) from the mass number. For example, carbon-14 has 14 – 6 = 8 neutrons.

Nuclear Glue

When you need to hold something together, what do you use? Rubber bands? String? Glue? What do you suppose holds the protons and neutrons together in the nucleus of an atom? Because protons are positively charged, they repel each other just as the north ends of two magnets tend to push each other apart. The uncharged neutrons neither attract nor repel the protons, but they help keep the protons apart and reduce the repelling electric force. So, what force holds the nucleus together? That force is called the strong nuclear force. The strong nuclear force can hold the protons together only if they are nearly touching, as they are in the nucleus of the atom.

Radioactive Decay

Many atomic nuclei are stable when they have about the same number of protons and neutrons. Carbon-12 is the most stable isotope of carbon. It has six protons and six neutrons. Some nuclei are unstable because they have too many or too few neutrons. This is especially true for heavier elements such as uranium and plutonium. In these nuclei, repulsion builds up. The nucleus must release a particle to become stable. When particles are released, energy is given off. The release of nuclear particles and energy is called **radioactive decay.** When particles are ejected from a nucleus, the atomic number of the nucleus can change. One element is changed into another. The changing of one element into another through radioactive decay is called transmutation.

interNET CONNECTION

Visit the Glencoe Science Web Site at **www.glencoe.com/ sec/science** for more information about radioactive decay.

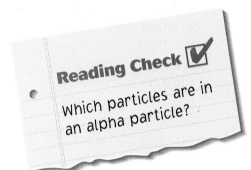

Figure 2-16 This life-saving smoke detector makes use of the radioactive isotope americium-241. The isotope is located inside the slotted chamber. When smoke particles enter the chamber, the alarm goes off.

Some Isotopes Release Alpha Particles

Each year, thousands of homes are saved from fires by smoke detectors like the one in **Figure 2-16.** This device makes use of americium-241, which undergoes transmutation by ejecting an alpha particle. An alpha particle consists of two protons and two neutrons. Energy is released with the alpha particle. Together, the energy and particles are called nuclear radiation. In the smoke detector, the fast-moving alpha particles cause air to conduct an electric current. As long as the electric current is flowing, the smoke detector is silent. When smoke enters the detector, the flow of electric current is interrupted and the alarm is triggered. ☑

The atomic number of americium (a muh RIH shee um) is 95, so americium has 95 protons. When americium expels an alpha particle, it loses two protons and two neutrons. It's no longer americium. It has become the element that has 93 protons, neptunium. In **Figure 2-17,** notice that the mass and atomic numbers of neptunium and the alpha particle add up to the mass and atomic number of americium. All the nuclear particles of americium still exist after the transmutation, but a good deal of energy has been released.

Reading Check ☑

Which particles are in an alpha particle?

Figure 2-17 Americium expels an alpha particle, which is made up of two protons and two neutrons, so americium is changed into the element neptunium which has two fewer protons than americium.

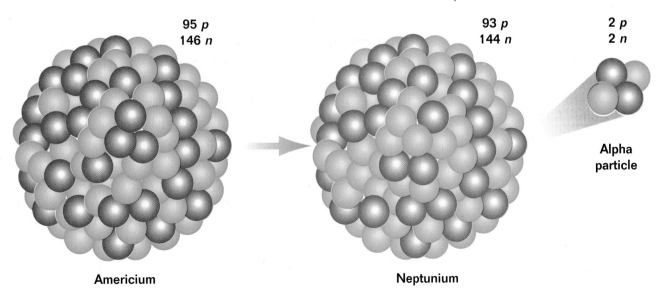

95 *p*
146 *n*

93 *p*
144 *n*

2 *p*
2 *n*

Alpha particle

Americium

Neptunium

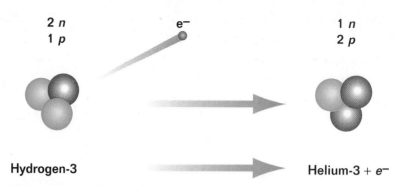

Figure 2-18 The hydrogen-3 isotope converts a neutron into a proton and an electron and tosses out the electron. **What is the element with two protons that remains?**

$2n$
$1p$

e^-

$1n$
$2p$

Hydrogen-3

Helium-3 + e^-

Some Isotopes Release Beta Particles

Some elements undergo transmutations through a different process. Their nuclei emit an electron called a beta particle. A beta particle is a high-energy electron that comes from the nucleus, not from the electron cloud. But, the nucleus only contains protons and neutrons. How can it give off or emit an electron? During this kind of transmutation, a neutron becomes unstable and splits into an electron and a proton. The electron or beta particle is released with a large amount of energy.

Because a neutron has been changed into a proton, the nucleus of the element has an additional proton. The atomic number of the element that results is greater by one. **Figure 2-18** shows the beta decay of the hydrogen-3 isotope. With two neutrons in its nucleus, hydrogen-3 is unstable. One neutron is converted to a proton by beta decay, and an isotope of helium is produced. The mass of the element stays almost the same because the mass of an electron is so small.

Half-Life

How can you tell when a nucleus in a sample will decay? You can't. Radioactive decay is random. It's like watching popcorn begin to pop. You can't predict which kernel will explode or when. But, if you're an experienced popcorn maker, you might be able to predict how long it will take for half the kernels to pop. A convenient way to measure the rate of decay of a nucleus is by half-life. The **half-life** of a radioactive isotope is the amount of time required for half of a sample of the element to decay. For example, iodine-131 has a half-life of eight days. If you start with a sample of 4 g of iodine-131, after eight days you would have only 2 g of iodine-131 remaining. After 16 days, or two half-lives, half of the 2 g would have decayed and you would have only 1 g. After yet another half-life, only 0.5 g would remain. **Figure 2-19** is a diagram of the process.

Figure 2-19 Half-life is the amount of time in which one half of a sample decays. **What happens to the mass of the remaining isotope at the end of each eight days?**

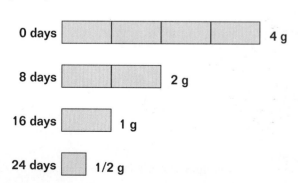

0 days	4 g
8 days	2 g
16 days	1 g
24 days	1/2 g

The radioactive decay of unstable atoms goes on at a steady pace, unaffected by conditions such as weather, pressure, magnetic or electric fields, and even chemical reactions. Half-lives, which are different for each isotope, range in length from fractions of a second to billions of years.

Carbon Dating

Carbon-14 is used to determine the age of dead animals, plants, and humans. The half-life of carbon-14 is 5730 years. In a living organism, the amount of carbon-14 remains in constant balance with the levels of the isotope in the atmosphere or ocean. This balance occurs because living organisms both take in and release carbon. For example, animals take in carbon from food such as plants, and release carbon as carbon dioxide. While life processes go on, any carbon-14 nucleus that decays is replaced by another from the environment. When the plant or animal dies, the decaying nuclei can no longer be replaced. When archaeologists find an ancient item, such as the one in **Figure 2-20,** they can find out how much carbon-14 it has and compare it with the amount of carbon-14 there would have been in the organism when it was alive. Knowing the half-life of carbon-14, they can then calculate when the organism lived.

Mini Lab

Graphing Half-Life
Procedure

1. Make a table with three columns. Label the first column *Number of Half-Lives*. Label the second column *Days Passed* and the third column *Mass of Thorium Remaining*.

2. Thorium-234 has a half-life of 24 days. Fill the first column with the number of half-lives: zero, one, two, and so on up to the number of half-lives that equals 144 days.

3. Fill the second column with the number of days that have passed since the start of the experiment: zero days, 24 days, 48 days, 72 days, and so on up to 144 days.

4. Assume that you have a sample of 64 kg of thorium. Calculate the mass of thorium remaining after each half-life and fill in the third column.

5. Plot the data in the first and third columns on a graph with half-life on the *x*-axis and mass of thorium on the *y*-axis.

Analysis

1. During which 24-day period does the most thorium-234 decay?

2. How much thorium-234 was left in your sample on the 144th day?

3. Compare the mass of thorium-234 after each half-life to the previous mass. How are they related?

Figure 2-20 Using carbon-14 dating techniques, archaeologists can find out when the biological materials in this artifact were living.

Nuclear Waste Products

Waste products from nuclear power plants are a problem because nuclear fuels produce leftover isotopes that still release much radiation. This radioactive waste must be permanently isolated from people and the environment because it continues to produce harmful radiation. Special disposal sites that can contain the radiation must be found. One such site is in Carlsbad, New Mexico, where nuclear waste is buried 655 m below the surface of Earth.

New Elements by Transmutation

Scientists now create elements by smashing atomic particles into a target element. Alpha and beta particles, for example, are accelerated in particle accelerators like the one in **Figure 2-21** to speeds high enough that they can smash into a large nucleus and be absorbed on impact. The absorbed particle converts the target element into another element with a higher atomic number. These artificial transmutations have created new elements that do not exist in nature. Elements with atomic numbers 93 to 112 have been made in this way.

Tracer Elements

The process of artificial transmutation has been adapted so that radioactive isotopes of normally stable elements can be made in hospitals and clinics using specially designed equipment. These isotopes, called tracer elements, are used to diagnose disease and to study environmental conditions. The radioactive isotope is introduced into a living system and then followed as it decays by a device that detects radiation. These devices often present the results as a visual display or photograph. The isotopes chosen for medical purposes have short

LIFE SCIENCE
INTEGRATION

Radiation Therapy
When a person has cancer, cells reproduce rapidly, causing a tumor. When radiation is focused directly on the tumor, it can slow or stop the cell division while leaving healthy surrounding tissue largely unaffected. Find out more about radiation therapy and summarize your findings in your Science Journal.

Figure 2-21 Giant particle accelerators, such as HERA in Hamburg, Germany, are needed to speed up particles to the speeds necessary to cause an atomic transmutation.

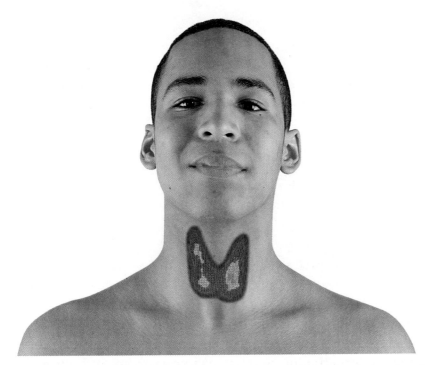

Figure 2-22 Most of the iodine in your diet goes to your thyroid. This image of a healthy thyroid was made by injecting a solution of iodine-131 into the bloodstream. The colors in the image indicate amounts of iodine-131 absorbed at various locations inside the thyroid. **How could this image be used to help diagnose thyroid disease?**

half-lives, which allow them to be used without the risk of exposing living organisms to prolonged radiation.

The isotope iodine-131 has been used to diagnose problems with the thyroid, a gland located at the base of the neck. The radioactive iodine, which is absorbed by the thyroid, creates an image of the thyroid like the one in **Figure 2-22.** Other radioactive isotopes are used to detect cancer, digestion problems, and circulation difficulties.

Problem Solving

Designing a Safe Container

You have been hired to design a container to transport radioactive waste. A whole raw egg will represent the waste. You must consider problems such as accidents, leaks, and ease of transportation. Your design will need to withstand the following tests.

Drop Test: Your teacher will drop your container of radioactive waste from the top of a ladder or a high structure (7 m – 10 m) onto a hard surface.

Side Impact Test: A 1-L plastic bottle filled with sand will be suspended from a door frame. When it is released at a 45 degree angle, it will strike your radioactive waste container.

After each test, open your container to examine the egg. Did it leak? Break apart? Stay in one piece?

Solve the Problem

1. In your Science Journal, write a hypothesis about how you can keep your waste from breaking or spilling.
2. Build your radioactive waste container.
3. Test your hypothesis using the Drop Test and Side Impact Test.
4. Was your hypothesis supported?

Think Critically

1. What could be improved in your design?
2. What other test would you propose?
3. What safety measures must be considered when transporting and storing radioactive waste? Why are these safety measures important?

Figure 2-23 Using fertilizer containing a small amount of a radioactive isotope, scientists can see how the fertilizer is absorbed by the plant.

*inter***NET**
CONNECTION

Visit the Glencoe Science Web Site at **www.glencoe.com/ sec/science** for more information about the use of isotopes in medicine and agriculture.

In the environment, tracers such as sulfur-35 can be placed in pesticides and followed to see what impact the pesticide has as it moves through an ecosystem. As you can see in **Figure 2-23,** fertilizers containing small amounts of radioactive isotopes are used to see how well plants absorb fertilizers.

Section Assessment

1. What are isotopes?
2. How are radioactive isotopes used to detect health problems?
3. Explain what is meant by radioactive decay. How is the rate of radioactive decay measured?
4. **Think Critically:** Suppose you had two samples of the same radioactive isotope. One sample was 25 g. The other was 50 g. Would the same number of particles be ejected from each sample in the first hour? Explain.
5. **Skill Builder**
   Making Models You have learned how scientists used marbles, cookie dough, and a cloud to model the structure of the atom. The poppy seed and the stadium in this chapter modeled the difference in size between the nucleus and atom. Do the **Chapter 2 Skill Activity** on page 743 to make paper-and-pencil models of the electrons, protons, and neutrons in the atoms of different isotopes.

Using Computers

Word Processing Use a word processing program to make a table of the three particles found in atoms. Include columns labeled *Particle, Charge,* and *Mass.* For the masses of the three particles, refer to Using Math in the Section 2-1 Section Assessment. Protons and neutrons have approximately the same mass. If you need help, refer to page 732.

Preserving Food by Irradiation

Eating food contaminated with harmful bacteria, parasites, or fungi can be a serious health risk. According to the Centers for Disease Control and Prevention in Atlanta, Georgia, every year millions of people in the United States become ill from eating contaminated food, and some 9000 Americans die as a result of food-borne illnesses. Worldwide, many more people die of malnutrition and starvation because they don't have enough fresh, high-quality food to eat.

For centuries, people have been preserving food—and in so doing preventing the growth of harmful bacteria and other organisms—by canning, pickling, drying, smoking, freezing, and freeze-drying it. However, all of these methods change the flavor, texture, and consistency of the preserved food in some way. Food irradiation, on the other hand, is a food preservation process that is growing in popularity because it destroys potentially harmful organisms in food without changing the food's quality.

What is irradiation?

In the irradiation process, food is exposed to low-level radiation but never comes into direct contact with the radiation source. Irradiation kills bacteria, prevents cell division in other kinds of organisms, helps prevent spoilage, and slows ripening in fresh vegetables and fruits, such as the papayas at left.

Foods that are commonly irradiated are ground wheat and other cereal grain products, spices, fresh fruits and vegetables, frozen seafood, poultry, and pork.

Are irradiated foods safe?

Many people fear radiation and any nuclear-related technology. Consumers need to understand that food does not become radioactive as a result of exposure to low-level radiation and that the nutritional quality of the food does not change. Based on decades of research, the Food and Drug Administration (FDA) has approved a variety of specific applications of food irradiation. FDA regulations require that irradiated food be labeled as such.

interNET CONNECTION

Visit the Glencoe Science Web Site at **www.glencoe.com/sec/science** to find more information about the debate on food irradiation.

Half-Life

Possible Materials

- Pennies
- Graph paper

The decay rates of most radioactive isotopes range from milliseconds to billions of years. If you know the half-life of an isotope and the size of a sample of the isotope, can you predict how much will remain after a certain amount of time? Is it possible to predict when a specific atom will decay?

Recognize the Problem

How can you use pennies to create a model that will show how half-life can predict the amount of a radioactive isotope remaining after specific periods of time?

Form a Hypothesis

Based on the definition of *half-life*, write a hypothesis that shows how half-life can be used to predict how much of a radioactive isotope will remain after a certain amount of time.

Goals

- **Model** isotopes in a radioactive sample. For each half-life, determine the amount of change in the objects that represent the isotopes in the model.

- **Design an experiment** to test the usefulness of half-life in predicting how much radioactive material still remains after a specific length of time.

Test Your Hypothesis

Plan

1. With your group, **write** the hypothesis statement.

2. **Write** down the steps of the procedure you will use to test your hypothesis. Assume that each penny represents an atom in a radioactive sample. Each coin that lands heads up after flipping has decayed.

3. **List** the materials you will need.

4. In your Science Journal, **make a data table** with two columns. Label one *Half-Life* and the other *Atoms Remaining*.

5. Decide how you can use the pennies to represent the radioactive decay of an isotope.

6. **Determine** (a) what will represent one half-life in your model, and (b) how many half-lives you will investigate.

7. **Decide** (a) what variables there will be in your model, and (b) which variable will be represented on the *y*-axis of your graph and which will be represented on the *x*-axis.

Do

1. Make sure your teacher approves your plan and your data table before you proceed.

2. Carry out your plan.

Analyze Your Data

1. The relationship among the starting number of pennies, the number of pennies remaining (*Y*), and the number of half-lives (*X*) is the following:

$$Y = \frac{\text{(starting number of pennies)}}{2^X}$$

Graph this equation using a graphing calculator. Use your graph to find the number of pennies remaining after 2.5 half-lives.

2. **Compare** your results with those of other groups in your class.

Draw Conclusions

1. Is it possible to use your model to predict which individual atoms will decay during one half-life? Why or why not?

2. Can you predict the total number of atoms that will decay in one half-life? **Explain.**

3. How many half-lives are necessary for the transmutation of the entire sample?

For a **preview** of this chapter, study this Reviewing Main Ideas before you read the chapter. After you have studied this chapter, you can use the Reviewing Main Ideas to **review** the chapter.

The Glencoe MindJogger, Audiocassettes, and CD-ROM provide additional opportunities for review.

Section

2-1 EARLY MODELS OF THE ATOM

The idea that matter is composed of indivisible atoms was first introduced in ancient Greece. In the eighteenth and nineteenth centuries, scientists performed experiments to determine the properties of an atom. John Dalton proposed that an atom is a sphere of matter that is the same throughout. Then, J.J. Thomson discovered that all atoms contain **electrons,** which are tiny, negatively charged particles. Thomson proposed that an atom is a sphere containing all the **protons** with their positive charges. The electrons are mixed uniformly in the sphere like raisins in a ball of cookie dough. *How does the number of protons compare with the number of electrons?*

THE NUCLEAR ATOM

Ernest Rutherford tested Thomson's model by bombarding thin gold foil with speeding, positively charged **alpha particles.** Rutherford expected the alpha particles to pass through the foil because Dalton's model predicted there would be no large concentration of mass or charge to change the paths of the alpha particles. Because some of the alpha particles were deflected from their paths, Rutherford revised the model of the atom again. He hypothesized that almost all the mass and all the positive charge of an atom is concentrated in an extremely tiny nucleus at the center of the atom. *Where are the electrons in this model of the atom?*

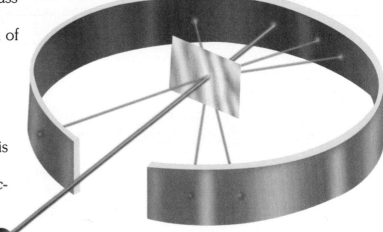

Reading Check ☑

Should the early models of atom structure be labeled as fact or opinion? Explain your answer.

Section 2-2 RADIOACTIVITY

An atom's nucleus contains protons and neutrons held together by the strong nuclear force. If the numbers of neutrons and protons are not approximately equal, the nucleus can become unstable and undergo radioactive decay. Some nuclei decay by emitting an alpha particle. Other nuclei decay by ejecting a **beta particle.** Transmutation is a process in which one element is changed into another through radioactive decay. Some radioactive **isotopes** are made in this way by smashing speeding atomic particles into a target element. These isotopes may be used in medicine and for the study of the environment. *What particles are released from the nucleus in alpha emission and in beta emission?*

HALF-LIFE

Half-life is a measure of the decay rate of a nucleus. It is the time needed for one-half of the mass of a sample of a radioactive isotope to decay. Half-lives vary from fractions of a second to billions of years. *If an isotope has a half-life of 4 s, how many grams remain of a 100-g sample after 8 s have passed?*

Chapter 2 Assessment

Using Vocabulary

a. atomic number   f. isotope
b. electron   g. mass number
c. electron cloud   h. neutron
d. element   i. proton
e. half-life   j. radioactive decay

Explain the difference between terms in each of the following sets.

1. alpha particle, beta particle

2. electron, proton

3. mass number, atomic number

4. element, isotope

5. half-life, radioactive decay

Checking Concepts

Choose the word or phrase that best answers the question.

6. What is the atomic number of an element equal to?
   A) the number of energy levels in an atom
   B) the number of protons in an atom's nucleus
   C) the number of neutrons in an atom's nucleus
   D) the total number of protons and neutrons in an atom's nucleus

7. The atomic number of boron is 5, so boron-11 contains which particles?
   A) 11 electrons
   B) five neutrons
   C) five protons and six neutrons
   D) six protons and five neutrons

8. What are atoms of the same element that have different numbers of neutrons?
   A) protons   C) ions
   B) electrons   D) isotopes

9. In beta decay, a neutron in the nucleus of an isotope is converted to which of the following?
   A) a proton and an electron
   B) a nucleus
   C) an alpha particle
   D) a beta particle

10. What is the process by which an atom of one element changes into an atom of another element?
    A) half-life
    B) a chemical reaction
    C) a chain reaction
    D) transmutation

11. How did William Crookes know that the glow in the cathode-ray tube resulted from a stream of charged particles?
    A) It was green.
    B) It caused a shadow of the anode.
    C) It was deflected by a magnet.
    D) It occurred only when the battery was connected.

12. Why did Rutherford infer that most of the mass and all of the positive charge in an atom is in a tiny nucleus?
    A) All of the alpha particles went straight through the gold foil.
    B) None of the alpha particles went straight through the gold foil.
    C) The positive and negative charges were uniform throughout the atom.
    D) Only a concentrated charge could deflect energetic alpha particles.

13. What did J.J. Thomson's experiment show?
    A) The atom is like a uniform sphere.
    B) Cathode rays are made up of electrons.
    C) All atoms undergo radioactive decay.
    D) Isotopes undergo radioactive decay.

14. A radioactive isotope has a half-life of two years. At the end of four years, how much of the original isotope remains?
    A) one half
    B) one fourth
    C) one third
    D) none

15. How can the model of the nuclear atom be described?
    A) a nucleus that can decay
    B) a ball of raisin cookie dough
    C) an electron cloud
    D) a nucleus in an electron cloud

Thinking Critically

16. How is it possible for atoms of an element to have different masses?

17. Matter can neither be created nor destroyed, but would it be possible for the amounts of some elements in Earth's crust to decrease? Increase?

18. Why must a neutral atom have the same number of protons and electrons?

Developing Skills

If you need help, refer to the Skill Handbook.

19. **Predicting:** If radium-226 releases an alpha particle, what is the mass number of the isotope formed?

20. **Using Graphs:** The radioactive decay of an isotope is plotted in the graph. What is the half-life of the isotope? How many grams of the isotope remain after three half-lives?

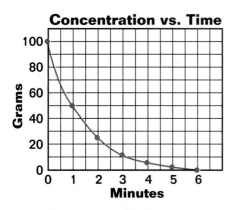

Concentration vs. Time

THE PRINCETON REVIEW

Test-Taking Tip

Use Process of Elimination On any multiple-choice test, you can use a process of elimination to exclude any answers that you know are wrong. Find the ones you know are wrong, eliminate them, and you'll have fewer choices from which to select your answer.

Test Practice

Use these questions to test your Science Proficiency.

1. What did Rutherford's alpha particle experiment show?
   A) Electrons have a negative charge.
   B) Most of the mass and all of the positive charge of an atom is found in a tiny nucleus.
   C) A proton is a hydrogen atom without its electron.
   D) Electrons circle the nucleus of an atom in orbits.

2. What is the difference between chlorine-35 and chlorine-37?
   A) Chlorine-37 has two more electrons than chlorine-35.
   B) Chlorine-37 has two more protons than chlorine-35.
   C) Chlorine-37 has two more neutrons than and chlorine-35.
   D) Chlorine-37 has one more proton and one more neutron than chlorine-35.

The Periodic Table

Chapter Preview

Skills Preview

Skill Builders
- Compare and Contrast
- Observe and Infer

Activities
- Observe
- Compare

MiniLabs
- Design
- Infer

Reading Check ✔

As you read this chapter, list and define the forms of these words that you encounter: *metal, period, element,* and *atom.* Then find more variations of each word in a dictionary and define them.

Explore Activity

Every 29.5 days, the full moon rises over Louisville, Kentucky, and begins to cycle through its phases from full moon to new moon and back again to full moon. This monthly cycle was one of the earliest patterns recognized and recorded by humans. Events that follow a predictable pattern are called periodic events. Modern calendars are based on a different periodic event—Earth's yearly journey around the sun. The opening of school in the fall and the celebration of your birthday are periodic events. What other periodic events can you think of?

Model a Periodic Pattern

1. On a blank sheet of paper, make a grid with four squares across and four squares down. The grid should fill the sheet of paper.

2. Your teacher will give you 16 pieces of paper with different shapes and colors. Identify properties you can use to distinguish one piece of paper from another.

3. Place a piece of paper in each square on your grid. Arrange the pieces on the grid so that each column contains pieces that are similar.

4. Within each column, arrange the pieces to show a gradual change in their appearance.

Science **Journal**

In your Science Journal, describe the patterns you created. Explain how the properties change in the rows across the grid and in the columns down the grid.

Introduction to the Periodic Table

What You'll Learn

▶ The history of the periodic table
▶ How to interpret an element key
▶ How the periodic table is organized

Vocabulary

period   nonmetal
group   metalloid
metal

Why It's Important

▶ The periodic table organizes a lot of information about the elements and makes it easier for you to learn.

Development of the Periodic Table

Early civilizations were familiar with a few of the substances scientists now call elements. They made coins and jewelry from gold and silver. Warriors at the Battle of Troy wore armor and carried shields made from bronze, a mixture of copper and tin. The Assyrians built an empire using steel weapons made by combining iron with carbon. In the nineteenth century, chemists began to search for new elements. By 1830, they had isolated and named 55 different elements. As the list of elements grew, chemists wondered how many elements were left to be discovered.

Mendeleev's Contribution

In 1860, the First International Chemical Congress met in Germany. One of the 140 delegates who attended was the Russian chemist Dmitri Mendeleev (men duh LAY uhf). When he returned to Russia, he used what he had learned at the congress to build a table of the elements. When Mendeleev arranged the elements in order of increasing atomic mass, as shown in **Figure 3-1,** he began to see a pattern. Elements with similar properties fell into groups on the table.

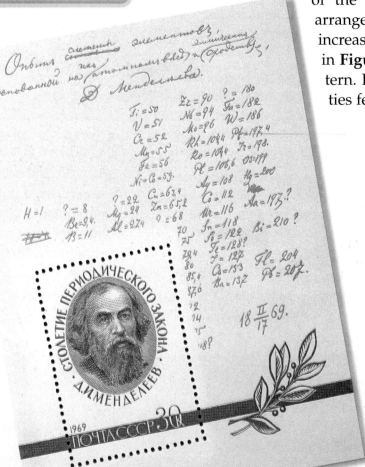

Figure 3-1 Mendeleev continued to work on this table. Notice where he put question marks. He predicted that elements would be discovered to fill these places on the table.

Mendeleev published the first version of his periodic table in the *Journal of the Russian Chemical Society* in 1869. At that time, not all the elements were known. To make his table work, Mendeleev had to leave gaps for undiscovered elements. Based on the groupings in his table, he predicted the properties for six of the unknown elements. Mendeleev's predictions spurred other chemists to look for the missing elements. Within 15 years, three of the missing elements—gallium, scandium, and germanium—were discovered. In **Table 3-1,** you can see that Mendeleev's predictions about germanium were close.

Moseley's Improvement

Although Mendeleev's table correctly organized most of the elements, a few elements seemed out of place. In the early twentieth century, the English physicist Henry Moseley realized that Mendeleev's table could be improved by arranging the elements according to atomic number rather than atomic mass. The atomic number of an element is the number of protons in the nucleus of its atoms. Each element in the table has one more proton than the previous element, so the atomic numbers of missing elements could be filled in by comparing the number of protons in each known element. With Moseley's table, it was clear how many elements were still undiscovered.

The Modern Periodic Table

In the table on the following pages, the elements are organized by increasing atomic number into rows or periods labeled 1-7. A **period** is a row of elements in the periodic table whose properties change gradually and predictably. The first period has only two elements. The second and third periods each have eight elements. Periods 4 and 5 have 18 elements. Period 6 has 32. New elements are still being added to period 7.

Table 3-1

Properties of Germanium

Property	Predicted (1869)	Actual (1886)
Atomic mass	72	72.6
Melting point	very high	937°C
Density	5.5 g/cm³	5.32 g/cm³
Color	dark gray	gray-white

Try at Home

Mini Lab

Designing a Periodic Table

Procedure

1. Collect pens and pencils from everyone in your class.

2. Decide which properties of the pens and pencils you will use to organize them into a periodic table. Consider properties such as color, mass, or length. Then, create your table.

Analysis

1. Explain how your periodic table is similar to the periodic table of the elements.

2. If your classmates brought different pens or pencils to class tomorrow, how would you decide where to place them on the table?

PERIODIC TABLE OF THE ELEMENTS

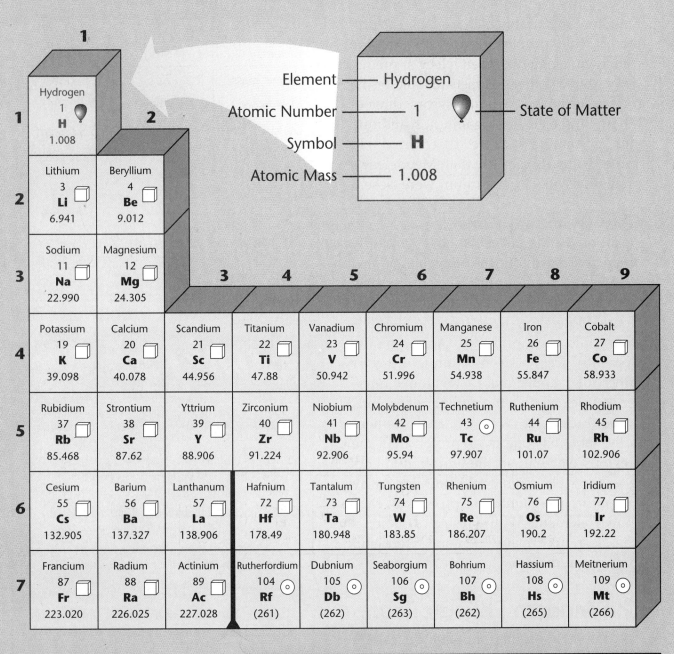

	Element	Hydrogen	
	Atomic Number	1	State of Matter
	Symbol	H	
	Atomic Mass	1.008	

Lanthanide Series

Actinide Series

Metal
Metalloid
Nonmetal

Gas
Liquid
Solid
◉ Synthetic Elements

18

| | | | | | | Helium
2 🎈
He
4.003 |

13	**14**	**15**	**16**	**17**	
Boron 5 ▫ **B** 10.811	Carbon 6 ▫ **C** 12.011	Nitrogen 7 🎈 **N** 14.007	Oxygen 8 🎈 **O** 15.999	Fluorine 9 🎈 **F** 18.998	Neon 10 🎈 **Ne** 20.180
Aluminum 13 ▫ **Al** 26.982	Silicon 14 ▫ **Si** 28.086	Phosphorus 15 ▫ **P** 30.974	Sulfur 16 ▫ **S** 32.066	Chlorine 17 🎈 **Cl** 35.453	Argon 18 🎈 **Ar** 39.948

10	**11**	**12**						
Nickel 28 ▫ **Ni** 58.693	Copper 29 ▫ **Cu** 63.546	Zinc 30 ▫ **Zn** 65.39	Gallium 31 ▫ **Ga** 69.723	Germanium 32 ▫ **Ge** 72.61	Arsenic 33 ▫ **As** 74.922	Selenium 34 ▫ **Se** 78.96	Bromine 35 💧 **Br** 79.904	Krypton 36 🎈 **Kr** 83.80
Palladium 46 ▫ **Pd** 106.42	Silver 47 ▫ **Ag** 107.868	Cadmium 48 ▫ **Cd** 112.411	Indium 49 ▫ **In** 114.82	Tin 50 ▫ **Sn** 118.710	Antimony 51 ▫ **Sb** 121.757	Tellurium 52 ▫ **Te** 127.60	Iodine 53 ▫ **I** 126.904	Xenon 54 🎈 **Xe** 131.290
Platinum 78 ▫ **Pt** 195.08	Gold 79 ▫ **Au** 196.967	Mercury 80 💧 **Hg** 200.59	Thallium 81 ▫ **Tl** 204.383	Lead 82 ▫ **Pb** 207.2	Bismuth 83 ▫ **Bi** 208.980	Polonium 84 ▫ **Po** 208.982	Astatine 85 ▫ **At** 209.987	Radon 86 🎈 **Rn** 222.018
(unnamed) 110 ◉ **Uun**	(unnamed) 111 ◉ **Uuu**	(unnamed) 112 ◉ **Uub**						

Gadolinium 64 ▫ **Gd** 157.25	Terbium 65 ▫ **Tb** 158.925	Dysprosium 66 ▫ **Dy** 162.50	Holmium 67 ▫ **Ho** 164.930	Erbium 68 ▫ **Er** 167.26	Thulium 69 ▫ **Tm** 168.934	Ytterbium 70 ▫ **Yb** 173.04	Lutetium 71 ▫ **Lu** 174.967
Curium 96 ◉ **Cm** 247.070	Berkelium 97 ◉ **Bk** 247.070	Californium 98 ◉ **Cf** 251.080	Einsteinium 99 ◉ **Es** 252.083	Fermium 100 ◉ **Fm** 257.095	Mendelevium 101 ◉ **Md** 258.099	Nobelium 102 ◉ **No** 259.101	Lawrencium 103 ◉ **Lr** 260.105

The periodic table has 18 columns of elements. Each column contains a group, or family, of elements. A **group** contains elements that have similar physical or chemical properties. The human family in **Figure 3-2** has similarities such as facial features, hair color, and build, but the similarities among a family of elements may not always be clear from appearance alone. For example, Group 17 contains a greenish-yellow gas called chlorine, a red-brown liquid called bromine, and a shiny black solid called iodine. Despite these differences, the elements in Group 17 behave in similar ways.

Figure 3-2 Groups of elements can be compared to human families. The members of this family have noticeable family traits. **What traits do they share? How are they different?**

Sections of the Periodic Table

The periodic table can be divided into two sections. One section consists of the first two groups, Groups 1 and 2, plus the elements in Groups 13-18. These eight groups are called the representative elements. They include metals, metalloids, and nonmetals. The elements in Groups 3-12 are called transition elements. They are all metals. Some transition elements, called the inner transition elements, are placed below the main table. These elements are called the lanthanide and actinide series because one series follows the element lanthanum, element 57, and the other series follows actinium, element 89. The lanthanides and actinides are placed below the table so that the table will take up less space. **Figure 3-3** shows what the periodic table would look like with the inner transition elements included.

Figure 3-3 This table shows you how the inner transition elements fit into the periodic table.

	1	**2**	**3**														
1	H																
2	Li	Be															
3	Na	Mg															
4	K	Ca	Sc														
5	Rb	Sr	Y														
6	Cs	Ba	La	Ce	Pr	Nd	Pm	Sm	Eu	Gd	Tb	Dy	Ho	Er	Tm	Yb
7	Fr	Ra	Ac	Th	Pa	U	Np	Pu	Am	Cm	Bk	Cf	Es	Fm	Md	No

A Clean surfaces of metals are shiny and reflect light. This is the property called luster.

B A blacksmith can hammer iron into different shapes because it is malleable.

C Metals are ductile, so they can be pulled or drawn into wires.

Metals, Nonmetals, and Metalloids

Look again at the periodic table. The table is color coded to show which elements are metals, which are nonmetals, and which are metalloids. With the exception of mercury, all the metals are solids, most with high melting points. A **metal** is an element that has luster and is a good conductor of heat and electricity. Other properties of metals are illustrated in **Figure 3-4.**

Figure 3-4 Metals can be distinguished from nonmetals and metalloids by their physical properties—luster, malleability, and ductility.

	4	5	6	7	8	9	10	11	12	13	14	15	16	17	18
															He
										B	C	N	O	F	Ne
										Al	Si	P	S	Cl	Ar
	Ti	V	Cr	Mn	Fe	Co	Ni	Cu	Zn	Ga	Ge	As	Se	Br	Kr
	Zr	Nb	Mo	Tc	Ru	Rh	Pd	Ag	Cd	In	Sn	Sb	Te	I	Xe
Lu	Hf	Ta	W	Re	Os	Ir	Pt	Au	Hg	Tl	Pb	Bi	Po	At	Rn
Lr	Rf	Db	Sg	Bh	Hs	Mt	Uun	Uuu	Uub						

The ability to reflect light is a property of metals called luster. When a metal is polished or cut to expose a fresh surface, it reflects light. Many metals can be pressed or pounded into thin sheets or shaped into objects because they are malleable (MAL yuh bul). Metals are also ductile (DUK tul), which means that they can be drawn out into wires.

Nonmetals are usually gases or brittle solids at room temperature and poor conductors of heat and electricity. Although there are only 16 nonmetals, they include many elements that are essential for life: carbon, sulfur, nitrogen, oxygen, phosphorus, and iodine.

The elements that form a bridge between metals and nonmetals on the periodic table are called metalloids (MET ul oydz). As you might expect from the name, a **metalloid** is an element that shares some properties with metals and some with nonmetals. For example, boron has luster like a metal, but, like a nonmetal, it is a poor conductor of electricity.

The Element Keys

Each element is represented on the periodic table by a box called the element key. An enlarged key for hydrogen is shown in **Figure 3-5.** An element key contains the name of the element, its atomic number, its symbol, and its average atomic mass. Elements that do not occur naturally on Earth are marked with a bull's-eye logo. These are synthetic elements. Element keys for elements that occur naturally on Earth include a logo that tells you whether the element is a solid, a liquid, or a gas at room temperature. All the gases except hydrogen are located on the right side of the table. They are marked by a balloon logo. Most of the other elements are solids at room temperature and are marked by a cube. Locate the two elements on the periodic table that are liquids at room temperature. Their logo is a drop. ✓

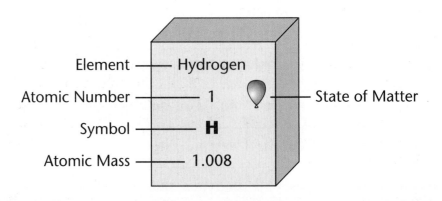

Figure 3-5 As you begin to use the periodic table, the element keys on the periodic table will provide you with useful information.

Symbols for the Elements

The symbols for the elements are either one- or two-letter abbreviations, often based on the element name. For example, V is the symbol for vanadium, and Sc is the symbol for scandium. Sometimes, the symbols don't match the names, for example, Ag for silver and Na for sodium. In those cases, the symbol may come from Greek or Latin names for the elements. Some elements are named for scientists such as Lise Meitner (meitnerium, Mt). Some are named for geographic locations such as France (francium, Fr). The symbols Uun, Uuu, and Uub are temporary symbols for unnamed elements. **Table 3-2** shows the origin of some element names and symbols.

Table 3-2

Chemical Symbols and Their Origins		
Name	Symbol	Origin
Mendelevium	Md	For Dmitri Mendeleev
Lead	Pb	The Latin name for lead is *plumbum.*
Thorium	Th	The Norse god of thunder is Thor.
Polonium	Po	For Poland, where Marie Curie was born
Hydrogen	H	From Greek words meaning "water former"
Mercury	Hg	Hydrargyrum means "liquid silver" in Greek.
Gold	Au	*Aurum* means "shining dawn" in Latin

Section Assessment

1. Use the elements in period 4 to show how the physical state of the elements changes as the atomic number increases across a period.

2. What are the two sections of the periodic table?

3. Where are the metals located in the periodic table? The nonmetals? The metalloids?

4. **Think Critically:** How would the modern periodic table be different if elements were still arranged by average atomic mass instead of atomic number? Give two specific examples.

5. **Skill Builder**

   Classifying Every day, you compare, contrast and classify objects in the world around you. Then, you classify what you have learned. Do the **Chapter 3 Skill Activity** on page 744 to classify some of the elements.

Using Math

Prepare a circle graph of the most abundant elements by weight in Earth's crust. What percent by weight of the crust is from metals? Metalloids? Nonmetals?

Data: oxygen, 46.6%; silicon, 27.7%; aluminum, 8.1%; iron, 5.0%; calcium, 3.6%; sodium, 2.8%; potassium, 2.6%; magnesium, 2.1%; other, 1.5%

Representative Elements

What You'll Learn

▶ Properties of the representative elements

▶ Uses for the representative elements

Vocabulary
alloy
semiconductor

Why It's Important

▶ Many representative elements play key roles in your body, your environment, and in the the things you use every day.

Groups 1 and 2

You probably have friends who like to interact with other people and do so easily and often. They're like the elements in Groups 1 and 2. These two groups of elements are always found in nature combined with other elements. They're called active metals because of their readiness to form new substances with other elements. They are all metals except hydrogen, the first element in Group 1. Although hydrogen is placed in Group 1, it shares properties with the elements in both Group 1 and Group 17.

The Alkali Metals

The Group 1 elements—lithium, sodium, potassium, rubidium, cesium, and francium—have a special family name. They are called the alkali metals. All the alkali metals are silvery solids with low densities and low melting points as shown in **Figure 3-6.** From lithium at the top of the group to francium at the bottom, the elements become more and more ready to combine with other substances to form new substances. Some other properties and uses of the alkali metals are shown in **Figure 3-7.**

1

| 3 Lithium **Li** |
| 11 Sodium **Na** |
| 19 Potassium **K** |
| 37 Rhubidium **Rb** |
| 55 Cesium **Ce** |
| 87 Francium **Fr** |

Figure 3-6 Sodium is so soft, it can be cut with a knife. Sodium chloride, or table salt, contains sodium and chlorine. Sodium chloride is one of the salts left behind when seawater evaporates.

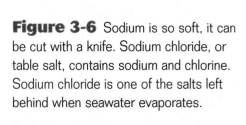

Figure 3-7 The activity of the alkali metals makes them useful elements.

A Potassium is more active than lithium and sodium. Look at what happens when a small piece of potassium is dropped into water. Heat and hydrogen gas are generated. Enough heat is released to cause the hydrogen gas to burst into flames.

B When sodium is added to water, the same kind of reaction occurs. After the reaction, the water contains a substance known as sodium hydroxide or lye. Lye can eat away at grease in clogged drains or digest wood pulp during the manufacture of paper.

C In your body, sodium and potassium have the important job of transmitting nerve impulses. Potassium and sodium are lost from the body in sweat and urine. Most diets contain more than enough sodium. It's more difficult to make sure that you get enough potassium. Bananas and potatoes are good sources of potassium.

The Alkaline Earth Metals

Next door to the alkali metals' family are their Group 2 neighbors, the alkaline earth metals—beryllium, magnesium, calcium, strontium, barium, and radium. The two families have much in common, but some differences. Each alkaline earth metal is denser and harder and has a higher melting point than the alkali metal in the same period. Alkaline earth metals are active, but not as active as the alkali metals.

Magnesium and calcium are the most common elements in Group 2. When magnesium combines with water, a substance called magnesium hydroxide is formed. Magnesium hydroxide is used as the medicine milk of magnesia to soothe an upset stomach. Chlorophyll, the green pigment found in the leaves of trees and plants, contains magnesium atoms. Magnesium is often combined with aluminum to form alloys that resist corrosion. Corrosion can occur when a metal combines with oxygen in the air. An **alloy** (AL oy) is a mixture of two or more elements, one of which is a metal. Some uses of the alkaline earth elements are shown in **Figure 3-8.**

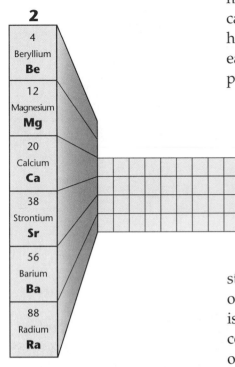

2							
4 Beryllium **Be**
12 Magnesium **Mg**
20 Calcium **Ca**
38 Strontium **Sr**
56 Barium **Ba**
88 Radium **Ra**

Figure 3-8 Alkaline earth metals are a big part of your life.

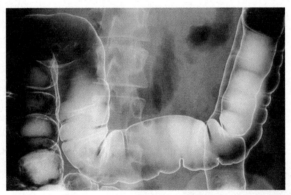

A You have probably been advised to drink milk so that you get the calcium you need for strong bones and teeth. Calcium is also important in controlling your heartbeat and preventing blood clots.

B Barium is used when X rays are taken of the intestinal tract. Ordinarily, the soft tissues of the intestinal tract don't show up on X rays, but when the tract is filled with a substance containing barium, the tissues can be seen on an X ray.

C Alloys of magnesium and aluminum are used to make frames for racing bikes and tennis rackets, and parts for automobile and aircraft engines. An alloy of magnesium and aluminum is not only strong and durable, but lightweight.

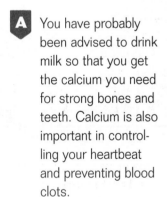

From Metals to Nonmetals

The next group of representative elements is Group 13, located on the other side of the transition elements. Notice that the elements in Groups 13-18 are not all solid metals like the elements of Groups 1 and 2. A single group may contain metals, nonmetals, and metalloids, and have members that are solids, liquids, and gases.

Boron's Family

The elements in Group 13—boron, aluminum, gallium, indium, and thallium—are all metals except boron, which is a brittle, black metalloid. **Figure 3-9** tells you more about this family.

13

| 5 Boron **B** |
| 13 Aluminum **Al** |
| 31 Gallium **Ga** |
| 49 Indium **In** |
| 81 Thallium **Tl** |

Figure 3-9 Here are some of the many uses and properties of the elements of Group 13.

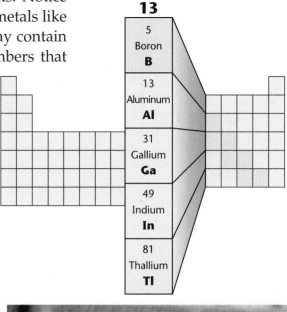

A Cookware made with boron can be moved directly from the refrigerator into the oven without cracking.

B Aluminum is the most common metal in Earth's crust. **What property of metals makes it possible to shape aluminum into soft-drink cans, cookware, aluminum siding, and baseball bats?**

C Gallium follows aluminum in Group 13. Gallium is a solid metal, but its melting point is low enough that it will melt in your hand.

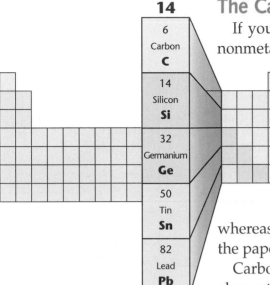

The Carbon Group

If you look down Group 14, you can see that carbon is a nonmetal, silicon and germanium are metalloids, and tin and lead are metals. The nonmetal carbon exists in several forms. You're familiar with two of them—diamond and graphite. A diamond is an array of carbon atoms arranged in an interlocking pattern. Graphite's atoms have a different arrangement, and so graphite and diamond have different properties. Diamond is one of the hardest materials on Earth, whereas graphite is soft. It is soft graphite that rubs off on the paper as you write.

Carbon is followed by the metalloid silicon, an abundant element contained in sand. Sand is ground-up particles of minerals such as quartz, which is composed of silicon and oxygen. Glass is an important product made from sand.

Both silicon and its Group 14 neighbor, germanium, are metalloids. They are used in electronics as semiconductors. A **semiconductor** is an element that doesn't conduct electricity as well as a metal but does conduct electricity better than a nonmetal. Through a process called *doping*, traces of elements such as boron or arsenic are added to silicon to increase its electrical conductivity. One use for doped silicon is shown in **Figure 3-10.**

Tin and lead are the two heaviest elements in Group 14. When you think of the element tin, the tin cans filled with canned fruit and vegetables at the grocery store may come to mind. These cans are actually made of steel coated with tin to protect them from corrosion.

As you can see in **Figure 3-11,** lead is no longer used in gasoline because it is poisonous. Today, the most important use for lead is in car batteries.

Reading Check

What are two elements contained in glass?

Figure 3-10 Doped silicon is used in computer chips and in solar cells, like these that convert sunlight to electricity.

Figure 3-11
Gasoline is unleaded to avoid the health risk of lead in the environment.

Nitrogen's Group

At the top of Group 15 are the two nonmetals nitrogen and phosphorus. Next come two metalloids, arsenic and antimony, and one metal, bismuth. Nitrogen and phosphorus are required by living beings. These elements are parts of the biological materials that store genetic information and energy in living organisms. Although almost 80 percent of the air you breathe is nitrogen, you can't get the nitrogen your body needs by breathing nitrogen gas. Bacteria in the soil must first change nitrogen gas into substances that can be absorbed through the roots of plants. Then, by eating the plants, nitrogen becomes available to your body.

Ammonia is a gas containing nitrogen and hydrogen. When ammonia is dissolved in water, it can be used as a cleaner and disinfectant. You can smell the sharp fumes of ammonia gas when you open a bottle of ammonia cleaning solution. In **Figure 3-12A,** liquid ammonia is being applied directly to soil as a fertilizer. Ammonia also can be converted into solid fertilizers. Ammonia also is used in the making of many products, such as the nylon of the parachute in **Figure 3-12B.**

The element phosphorus comes in two forms—white and red. White phosphorus is so active it can't be exposed to oxygen in the air or it will burst into flames. The heads of matches contain the less active red phosphorus, which ignites from the heat produced by friction when the match is struck. **Figure 3-12C** shows both forms of phosphorus. Phosphorus is an essential ingredient of healthy teeth and bones. Plants also need phosphorus, so phosphorus is one of the nutrients in most fertilizers.

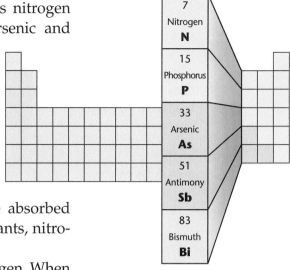

Figure 3-12 Nitrogen and phosphorus are necessary for your body and useful in your daily life.

A Ammonia is a nitrogen-containing substance that can be injected into the soil and used directly by plants.

C Both white and red phosphorus are active. **Why is white phosphorus submerged in a liquid in this photo?**

B Nylon is a tough, light fiber capable of replacing silk in many applications, such as in parachutes.

Figure 3-13 Other members of Group 15 have everyday uses.

A A substance containing gallium and arsenic is responsible for the lighted time display on digital clocks.

B Overhead sprinkler heads use the low melting point of bismuth as a trigger.

The metalloid arsenic and the metal gallium combine to form a substance used to create the lighted display on digital clocks, radios, and VCRs, as you can see in **Figure 3-13A.** Bismuth is used in the sprinkler heads of fire-fighting systems like the one in **Figure 3-13B.** The system turns on automatically when a fire starts because bismuth has a low enough melting point that the heat from a fire causes it to melt. The melting triggers a signal that opens the water valves.

Oxygen's Family

The first two members of Group 16, oxygen and sulfur, are essential for life. Selenium is also necessary for health, but in trace amounts. The heavier members of the group, tellurium and polonium, are both metalloids.

About 20 percent of Earth's atmosphere is the oxygen you breathe. Your body needs oxygen to release the energy from the foods you eat. Ozone, a less common form of oxygen, is formed in the upper atmosphere through the action of electricity during thunderstorms. The presence of ozone is important because it shields living beings from some harmful radiation from the sun. Oxygen is abundant in Earth's rocks and minerals because it readily combines with other elements.

Sulfur is a solid, yellow nonmetal, as you can see in **Figure 3-14.** Large amounts of sulfur are used to manufacture sulfuric acid, one of the most commonly used chemicals in the world. Sulfuric acid is a combination of sulfur, hydrogen, and oxygen. It is used in the manufacture of paints, fertilizers, detergents, synthetic fibers, and rubber.

16

| 8 |
| Oxygen |
| **O** |

| 16 |
| Sulfur |
| **S** |

| 34 |
| Selenium |
| **Se** |

| 52 |
| Tellurium |
| **Te** |

| 84 |
| Polonium |
| **Po** |

Figure 3-14 These piles of sulfur will be used to make sulfuric acid, one of the most important chemicals for making a wide variety of products you use every day.

Selenium conducts electricity when exposed to light, so it is used in solar cells and in light meters. Its most important use is as the light-sensitive component in photocopy machines. You'll find a small amount of selenium in some multivitamin preparations because selenium is one of the trace elements your body needs. Large amounts of selenium, however, can be poisonous.

LIFE SCIENCE
INTEGRATION

A Strand of Evidence
Arsenic disrupts the normal function of an organism by combining with sulfur, which is an essential element. Because arsenic builds up in hair, forensic scientists can test hair samples to confirm or disprove a case of arsenic poisoning. Tests of Napoleon's hair suggest that he was poisoned. Use reference books to find out who Napoleon was and why someone might have wanted to poison him.

Problem Solving

Predicting Periodicity

Comets are large masses of frozen water in which pieces of rock are embedded. Seen through a telescope, a comet has a glowing head and a long, bright tail. Comets orbit the sun just as Earth and the sun's other planets do. To *orbit* means "to follow a path usually shaped like an ellipse." Some comets orbit the sun every few years. Some take thousands of years to complete one trip. The time it takes for a comet to make one trip around the sun is called its period.

People have been watching comets since they first noticed them in the night sky. Early astronomers kept records of unusual events such as eclipses, meteor showers, and the appearance of comets. The famous Comet Halley is named for the eighteenth-century English astronomer Edmund Halley. While researching the records of earlier astronomers, Halley noticed descriptions of bright comets that appeared in 1531, 1607, and 1682. Halley thought these comets might

all be a single comet and that the dates of the three observations were evidence of the comet's periodic motion. He correctly predicted the return of Halley's comet.

Think Critically: What year did Halley predict the comet would return? Approximately how long is the period of Halley's comet—the time it takes to orbit the sun? When was it last seen from Earth? When will it be seen again?

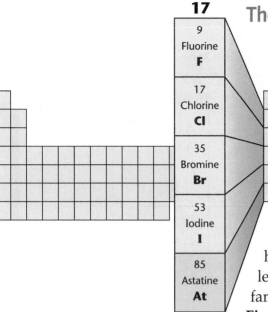

The Halogens

All the elements in Group 17 are nonmetals except for astatine, which is a radioactive metalloid. These elements—fluorine, chlorine, bromine, iodine, and astatine—are called halogens, which means "salt-former." Table salt, sodium chloride, is a substance made from sodium and chlorine. All of the halogens form similar salts with sodium and with the other alkali metals. Fluorine and chlorine are gases. Bromine is a reddish-brown liquid. Iodine is a shiny black solid.

The halogen fluorine is the most active of the halogens in combining with other elements. Chlorine is less active than fluorine, and the trend continues down the family to iodine, which is the least active of the four. **Figure 3-15** shows some of the uses of the halogens.

Figure 3-15 Because they are active, you'll find that the halogens are useful in many ways.

A The halogens are used to fight bacteria. For example, chlorine is at work in this swimming pool.

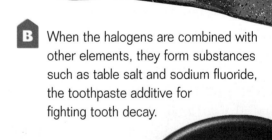

B When the halogens are combined with other elements, they form substances such as table salt and sodium fluoride, the toothpaste additive for fighting tooth decay.

Mini Lab

Inferring the Presence of Chlorine

Procedure

1. Place 2 mL of salt water, 2 mL of distilled water, and 2 mL of tap water into separate test tubes.
2. Carefully add 5 drops of silver nitrate solution to each test tube and stir. **CAUTION:** *Silver nitrate solution can stain skin and clothing.*

Analysis

1. What happened when you added silver nitrate to the salt water?
2. What happened in the test tube with distilled water?
3. Does your tap water contain chlorine? Explain.

C Some pots and pans are easier to clean up than others because they have a nonstick surface made from a substance containing fluorine.

The Noble Gases

Why are the Group 18 elements called the noble gases? The answer is because they rarely combine with other elements. Like the nobility, they stand apart from the crowd. All the Group 18 elements—helium, neon, argon, krypton, xenon (ZEE nawn), and radon—are colorless gases.

Helium is a lighter-than-air gas, so it's great for all kinds of balloons, from party balloons to blimps that carry television cameras high above sporting events. Helium balloons, such as the one in **Figure 3-16A,** lift instruments into the upper atmosphere to measure atmospheric conditions. Even though hydrogen is lighter than helium, helium is preferred for these purposes because helium will not burn.

The "neon" lights you see in advertising signs, like the one in **Figure 3-16B,** may actually contain any of the noble gases, not just neon. In the glass tubes that make up the sign, electricity is passed through the noble gas and the electricity causes the gas to glow. Each noble gas produces its own color. Helium glows pink, neon glows red-orange, and argon produces a purple color.

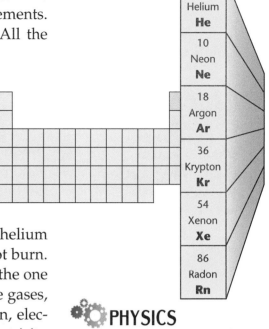

18

| 2 Helium **He** |
| 10 Neon **Ne** |
| 18 Argon **Ar** |
| 36 Krypton **Kr** |
| 54 Xenon **Xe** |
| 86 Radon **Rn** |

PHYSICS
◄ **INTEGRATION**

Figure 3-16 Scientists used to call the noble gases inert gases because they were never found combined with other elements.

A Instruments carried by weather balloons contain helium that gathers information about the conditions in the upper atmosphere around the world. **How might this information be helpful to you?**

B Each color in this advertising sign is caused by a different noble gas.

Argon, the most abundant of the noble gases on Earth, was first found in 1894. Krypton is used with nitrogen in ordinary lightbulbs because these gases keep the glowing filament from burning out. When a mixture of argon, krypton, and xenon is used, a bulb can have a life ten times longer than bulbs available today. Krypton lights are used to illuminate landing strips at airports, and xenon is used in strobe lights and photographic flash cubes.

At the bottom of the group is radon, a radioactive gas produced naturally as uranium in rocks and soil decays. If radon seeps into a home, the gas can be harmful because it continues to emit radiation. When people breathe the gas over a period of time, it can cause lung cancer. People in regions where granite and shale are abundant are encouraged to have their homes tested for radon.

Chemists originally thought that it was impossible for any of the noble gases to combine with other elements. However, in 1962, a new substance was formed that contained xenon, platinum, and fluorine. Since then, chemists have succeeded in making combinations of xenon and krypton with fluorine.

interNET CONNECTION

Visit the Glencoe Science Web Site at **www.glencoe.com/ sec/science** for more information about representative elements.

Section Assessment

1. What do the elements in Group 1 have in common with the elements in Group 17? How are Group 1 elements different from the elements in Group 18?

2. Explain how silicon's role as a semiconductor confirms that silicon is a metalloid.

3. List the five most important elements for life and tell what groups on the periodic table they are in.

4. **Think Critically:** Francium is a rare radioactive alkali metal at the bottom of Group 1. Its properties have not been studied carefully. Would you predict that francium would combine with water more or less readily than cesium?

5. **Skill Builder**
   Predicting Predict how readily astatine would form a salt compared to the other elements in Group 17. If you need help, refer to Predicting in the **Skill Handbook** on page 730.

Using Computers

Using a Database
Search an on-line database for recent articles on the environment. Pick one area of concern such as water quality, air quality, or global warming. Then track the impact of one representative element. If you need help, refer to page 717.

Preparing an Alloy

Many of the most important materials in the world are mixtures of elements called alloys. Bronze is an alloy of copper and tin. Brass is an alloy of copper and zinc. Many types of steel are produced by adding carbon and other metals to iron.

What You'll Investigate

How can two metals be combined to form an alloy?

Goals

- **Observe** the changes that occur during the preparation of an alloy.
- **Compare** the plating of a metal to the formation of an alloy.

Safety Precautions

CAUTION: *Nitric acid and sodium hydroxide can cause burns. If you spill nitric acid or sodium hydroxide on your skin, notify your teacher immediately. Rinse the affected area with large amounts of tap water.*

Procedure

1. Carefully **pour** dilute nitric acid into one evaporating dish until the dish is half full. Using tongs, **hold** the penny in the nitric acid for about 20 s.

2. Still using the tongs, **remove** the penny from the acid and rinse it in the beaker of cold water.

3. **Place** one teaspoonful of 30-mesh zinc in the second evaporating dish.

4. Slowly **pour** dilute sodium hydroxide into the dish to a depth of about 2 cm above the zinc.

5. Using tongs, gently **place** the penny on top of the zinc. Rinse the tongs in cold water.

6. Gently **heat** the contents of the evaporating dish on a hot plate until the penny turns a silver color.

Materials

- Copper penny
  *copper wire
- Zinc, 30-mesh
- Hot plate
- Nitric acid, dilute
- Sodium hydroxide, dilute
- Evaporating dishes
  *beakers (2)
- Tongs
- Beaker of cold tap water

  *Alternate Materials

7. Set the control on the hot plate to medium high. Using tongs, **remove** the penny from the dish and rinse it in the cold tap water.

8. Dry the penny and **place** it directly on the hot plate until the penny turns a golden color.

9. Your teacher will dispose of the contents of the two evaporating dishes.

Conclude and Apply

1. What caused the change in the appearance of the penny when it was placed in the nitric acid?

2. When one metal is coated with a layer of a second metal, the process is called plating. At which point in this activity did plating occur?

3. What alloy formed when the penny was heated on the hot plate?

4. **Infer** why heat is necessary for the alloy to form.

Transition Elements

The Metals in the Middle

What You'll Learn

▶ Properties of some transition elements
▶ How to distinguish lanthanides from actinides

Why It's Important

▶ Without transition elements, your electrical appliances wouldn't work, there would be no magnets on your refrigerator, and the world would be a less colorful place.

What about that large block of elements sandwiched between Group 2 and Group 13? Groups 3-12 are called the transition elements. All transition elements are metals. Across any period from Group 3 through Group 12, the properties of the elements change less noticeably than they do across a period of representative elements. Most transition elements are found combined with oxygen, sulfur, or other elements in ores such as malachite shown in **Figure 3-17**. A few transition elements such as gold, silver, and copper are sometimes found as pure elements in Earth's crust.

Figure 3-17 Many substances that contain transition elements are colored.

The Iron Triad

Three elements in period 4—iron, cobalt, and nickel—have such similar properties that they are known as the iron triad. A triad is a group of three. The elements in the iron triad have magnetic properties. Industrial magnets are made from an alloy of nickel, cobalt, and aluminum. Nickel is used in batteries along with cadmium. Iron is a necessary part of hemoglobin, the substance that transports oxygen in the blood.

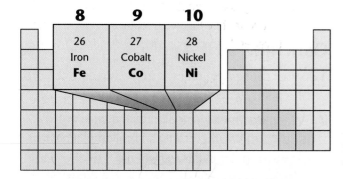

Iron is the most important of the transition elements. Usually, iron is mixed with other metals and with carbon to create a variety of steels with different properties. Structures such as bridges and skyscrapers like the one shown in **Figure 3-18** depend upon steel for their strength. But, structures made from steel can be eaten away by rust, which results when iron and steel are

Figure 3-18 The strength of a tall building is in its skeleton, which is made from steel.
What qualities of steel are important in its use in buildings and bridges?

exposed to oxygen in the air. Iron or steel can be painted to protect the metal from rusting. Iron structures also can be coated with zinc for protection from corrosion.

The Coinage Metals

Ancient civilizations made coins from copper, silver, and gold, so these three elements came to be called the coinage metals. They are often found uncombined in nature because they don't readily combine with other elements. **Figure 3-19** illustrates some uses for the coinage metals.

Figure 3-19 Today, copper, silver, and gold are no longer used for coins, but they have many other uses.

A From earliest times, silver and gold were used for jewelry and precious objects of art.

B Photographic film is coated with a thin layer of gelatin that contains a substance composed of silver and bromine or silver and iodine. These substances release silver when they are exposed to light. The amount of silver released depends upon the intensity of the light and the length of exposure. The silver atoms form a pattern that emerges when the film is developed.

C Copper is a good conductor of both electricity and heat. Copper wires carry electricity, and copper-bottomed pans distribute heat evenly. Copper resists corrosion so it used to be the preferred choice for plumbing pipes. Now copper is getting scarcer and more expensive. Plastic piping is being used instead.

Figure 3-20 You can see that the tungsten filament can be heated to a high temperature but it doesn't melt. **What happens to the filament after long use?**

Other Transition Metals

Most of the transition metals have higher melting points than the representative elements. The filaments of lightbulbs like the one in **Figure 3-20** are made of tungsten, element 74, because it has the highest melting point of any metal (3410°C) and will not melt with the heat of the bulb.

Mercury, which has the lowest melting point of any metal (–39°C), is used in thermometers and in barometers. Mercury is the only liquid metal at ordinary temperatures. Like many of the heavy metals, mercury is poisonous to living beings.

Chromium's name comes from the Greek word for color, *chroma*, and the element lives up to its name. Two substances containing chromium are shown in **Figure 3-21.** Many other transition elements combine to form substances with equally brilliant colors.

Ruthenium, rhodium, palladium, osmium, iridium, and platinum are sometimes called the platinum group because they have similar properties. They do not combine easily with other elements, so they can be used for electrodes and as catalysts. A catalyst is a substance that can cause changes to occur faster but is not changed itself. The catalytic converters in automobiles, like the one in **Figure 3-22,** help change pollutants into harmless substances before they are exhausted from the tailpipe into the air.

Figure 3-21 These two substances containing chromium are typical of many substances containing transition elements. They are used to make brightly colored paints.

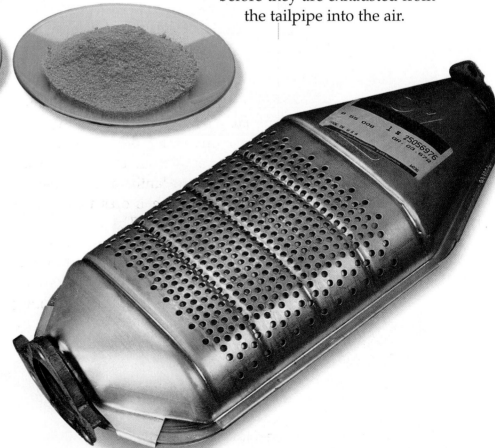

Figure 3-22 The presence of catalytic converters in all recently manufactured cars has improved the quality of the air you breathe.

Inner Transition Elements

Do any of the elements in the two rows located below the table seem familiar to you? Except for uranium, which you may have heard about, they are not the metals that you find in most of the things you use every day. But, some inner transition elements have important uses, particularly when combined with other metals.

There are two series of inner transition elements. The first series, from cerium to lutetium, is called the lanthanides. The lanthanides also are called the rare earths because at one time they were thought to be scarce. The word *earth* is an old-fashioned word that refers to a substance formed when a metal combines with oxygen. The lanthanides are usually found combined with oxygen in Earth's crust. The second series of elements, from thorium to lawrencium, are called the actinides.

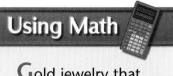

Using Math

Gold jewelry that is 100 percent pure gold is called 24-carat gold. How much gold is in 18-carat gold? In 12-carat gold?

58 Ce	59 Pr	60 Nd	61 Pm	62 Sm	63 Eu	64 Gd	65 Tb	66 Dy	67 Ho	68 Er	69 Tm	70 Yb	71 Lu
90 Th	91 Pa	92 U	93 Np	94 Pu	95 Am	96 Cm	97 Bk	98 Cf	99 Es	100 Fm	101 Md	102 No	103 Lr

The Lanthanides

The lanthanides are soft metals that can be cut with a knife. The elements are so similar that they are hard to separate when they occur in the same ore, which they often do. The element dysprosium gets its name from the Greek word meaning "hard to get at." Three of the lanthanides are named for a town in Sweden, Ytterby, where their ores are mined— erbium (Er), ytterbium (Yb), and terbium (Tb). ☑

Reading Check ☑

Why is dysprosium hard to get at?

Despite the name *rare earth*, the lanthanides are not as rare as originally thought. Earth's crust contains three times as much cerium as lead. Cerium makes up 50 percent of an alloy called misch metal. The other ingredients are lanthanum, neodymium, and iron. Flints in lighters, like the one in **Figure 3-23**, are made from misch metal.

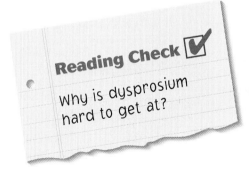

Figure 3-23 The flint in this lighter is made of an alloy called misch metal, whose principal ingredient is the lanthanide cerium.

Neodymium and praseodymium are added to the glass used in welders' masks to absorb high-energy radiation that could damage eyes. The glass used in television screens and computer monitors contains yttrium and europium, both combined with oxygen. When these substances are struck by a beam of electrons, they produce a bright red color. Compounds of lanthanides are also used in high-intensity searchlights, lasers, and movie projectors. Some lanthanides are used in the control rods of nuclear reactors to absorb excess neutrons.

The Actinides

All the actinides are radioactive. The nuclei of atoms of radioactive elements are unstable and decay to form other elements. Thorium, protactinium, and uranium are the only actinides that are now found naturally on Earth. All the others are synthetic elements. They may have existed on Earth at one time, but because most decay within a few days, none can be found today. Uranium is still found in Earth's crust because its half-life is long—4.5 billion years. The synthetic elements have many uses. Plutonium is used as a fuel in nuclear power plants. Americium is used in some home smoke detectors. Some actinide isotopes have medical uses. For example, californium-232 is used to kill cancer cells.

*inter*NET CONNECTION

Visit the Glencoe Science Web Site at **www.glencoe.com/ sec/science** for more information about transition elements.

Section Assessment

1. What is the major difference between the lanthanides and actinides? Would you expect neodymium and uranium to have similar properties? Explain.

2. How do the elements in the iron triad differ from other transition metals?

3. What is one drawback to using steel for structures such as skyscrapers, and how can that drawback be overcome?

4. **Think Critically:** Of the elements iridium and cadmium, predict which is likely to be toxic and which could act as a catalyst. Explain.

5.  **Skill Builder**
   Observing and Inferring How does the appearance of a burned-out lightbulb compare to a new bulb? What could explain the difference? If you need help, refer to Observing and Inferring in the **Skill Handbook** on page 720.

Science **Journal**
In your Science Journal, discuss the term *valuable* as it relates to elements. How do relative abundance, number of uses, and durability contribute to value?

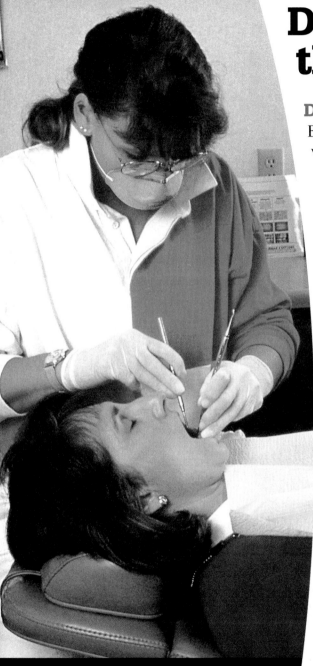

Dentistry and the Elements

Dental Materials

Before dentistry became a science, a person's decayed tooth would eventually fall out or have to be pulled. Since the 1930s, dentists, like the one at left, have successfully used elements found in the periodic table to repair and replace decayed teeth. The elements mercury and silver traditionally have been used to fill cavities. Mercury is a poisonous liquid metal, but mixing it with silver, copper, and zinc forms a hard substance that has been considered safe to put in people's mouths. Today, other materials also are used for fillings.

A combination of gold, silver, and copper is used to make gold coverings, called crowns, for damaged or weakened teeth. If a tooth is broken off at the root and needs single-tooth replacement, the element titanium is used as a post to support a replacement tooth made from plastic.

The framework for dentures—replacements for teeth that have fallen out—is made from the elements chromium and cobalt. When mixed together, these metals are flexible, strong, and rust resistant.

Elements and the Orthodontist

Orthodontists, dentists who are specialists in the positioning of teeth, use braces (see below) or retainers to reposition crowded or misplaced teeth. Braces are often made of stainless steel, a combination of iron, nickel, and carbon. The stainless steel is mixed with chromium to keep the braces from rusting.

With all these materials available for fixing teeth, dentists still emphasize prevention: regular brushing, flossing, and checkups.

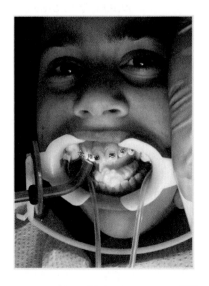

Science JOURNAL

In your Science Journal, write a paragraph summarizing some of the advantages of modern materials in dentistry. Base your summary on library or online research.

Activity 3•2

Health Risks from Heavy Metals

Whether it's lip balm that blocks UV rays from the sun or cream cheese with lower fat, society benefits from using chemicals in many products. But, chemicals, such as heavy metals, can be dangerous if they are used incorrectly or leak into the environment where they are not meant to be.

Recognize the Problem

Do heavy metals and other chemicals pose a threat to the health of humans? One way to reduce any threat is to know as much as possible about the chemical, its source, and its environmental impact.

Form a Hypothesis

Could health problems be caused by exposure to heavy metals, such as lead, or a radioactive chemical element, such as radon? Is the incidence of these problems higher in one area than another? Form a hypothesis as to the potential health risk of a chemical in your area.

Goals

- **Organize and synthesize** information on a chemical or heavy metal thought to cause health problems in your area.
- **Communicate** your findings with others in your class.

Data Sources

Go to the Glencoe Science Web Site at **www.glencoe.com/sec/science** to obtain information, hints, and data from other students.

Health Risk Data Table				
Location	Chemical or Heavy Metal	How People Come in Contact with Chemical	Potential Health Problem	Who is affected

Test Your Hypothesis

Plan

1. **Read** general information concerning heavy metals and other potentially hazardous chemicals.

2. Use the sites listed on the Glencoe Science Web Site to **research** possible health problems in your area caused by exposure to chemicals or heavy metals.

3. Check the Glencoe Science Web Site to see what others have learned.

Do

1. Make sure your teacher approves your plan before you proceed.

2. **Search** for resources that can help you find out about health risks in your area.

3. **Organize** your information in a data table like the one shown.

4. **Write** a report in your Science Journal about the results of your research.

5. **Post your data** in the table provided on the Glencoe Science Web Site.

Analyze Your Data

1. Did all your sources agree on the health risk of the chemical or heavy metal?

2. Analyze all your sources for possible bias. Are some sources more reliable than others?

3. How did the health risk differ for adults and children?

Draw Conclusions

1. Were the same substances found to be health risks in other parts of the country? From the data on the Glencoe Science Web Site try to predict what chemicals or heavy metals are health risks in different parts of the country.

2. From your report, what information do you think is the most important for the public to be aware of?

3. What could be done to decrease the risk of the health problems you identified?

Section
3-1 PERIODICITY

When organized according to atomic number in a table, elements with similar properties occupy the same column, called a **group** or family. The properties of the elements change gradually across a horizontal row called a **period. Metals** are usually shiny, malleable, and ductile. They are good conductors of heat and electricity. Many **nonmetals** are gases. Solid nonmetals are often brittle and poor conductors of heat and electricity. **Metalloids** have properties between those of metals and nonmetals. The periodic table can be divided into representative elements and transition elements. *What do families on the periodic table have in common with human families?*

Section
3-2 ALKALI AND ALKALINE EARTH METALS

Atoms of elements in Groups 1 and 2 readily combine with atoms of other elements. The ease with which the atoms of the elements combine with other atoms increases down the two groups. Each element in Group 2 combines less readily than its neighbor in Group 1. Each alkaline earth metal is denser and has a higher melting point than the alkali metal in its period. Sodium, potassium, magnesium, and calcium have important biological roles. *What element is magnesium mixed with to form strong, lightweight alloys?*

Reading Check ✔

Construct a chart that shows what each symbol in an element key represents. What other feature could be indicated with a symbol?

ELEMENTS IN GROUPS 13–18

Aluminum, the most common metal in Earth's crust, has many uses. Carbon is found in two common forms— diamond and graphite. Nitrogen, oxygen, sulfur, and phosphorus are essential for life. Ammonia and sulfuric acid are important chemicals in manufacturing. Silicon is a metalloid used as a semiconductor in electronics. The halogens combine with other elements to form a variety of substances such as table salt and sodium fluoride. The noble gases have many uses that depend upon the fact that they do not combine with other elements. *What are the two groups of elements that together form common salts?*

Section 3-3 TRANSITION ELEMENTS

Iron is the most important transition element because of its strength and durabilty, but it must be protected from corrosion. Magnets contain elements from the iron triad. The coinage metals are fairly unreactive, malleable elements. The uses of copper depend upon its superior ability to conduct heat and electricity. Substances containing silver are in the coating on photographic film. Platinum is used as electrodes and as a catalyst. The lanthanides are naturally occurring elements with similar properties. The actinides are radioactive elements. All actinides except thorium, proactinium, and uranium are synthetic. *Why is it dangerous to handle the mercury that is spilled when a thermometer or barometer breaks?*

Chapter 3 Assessment

Using Vocabulary

a. alloy
b. group
c. metal
d. metalloid
e. nonmetal
f. period
g. semiconductor

Answer the following questions about the Vocabulary words.

1. What is the difference between a group and a period?
2. What is the connection between a metalloid and a semiconductor?
3. How are a metal and an alloy alike?
4. Arrange the terms *nonmetal, metal,* and *metalloid* according to increasing electrical conductivity.
5. How is a metalloid like a metal? How is it different?

Checking Concepts

Choose the word or phrase that best answers the question.

6. Which of the following groups combines most readily with other elements?
   A) coinage metals
   B) alkaline earth metals
   C) alkali metals
   D) iron triad

7. Which element is located in Group 6, period 4?
   A) tungsten   C) titanium
   B) chromium   D) hafnium

8. Which element is **NOT** found uncombined in nature?
   A) gold   C) silver
   B) calcium   D) copper

9. Which group contains only nonmetals?
   A) Group 1   C) Group 2
   B) Group 12   D) Group 18

10. Which of the following elements is likely to be contained in a substance with a brilliant yellow color?
    A) chromium   C) iron
    B) carbon   D) tin

11. Which halogen is radioactive?
    A) astatine   C) bromine
    B) chlorine   D) iodine

12. Which of the following is unlikely to happen to zinc?
    A) It is rolled into sheets.
    B) It is used to coat a steel hull.
    C) It is used in a battery.
    D) It is used as an insulator.

13. Which of the following describes the element tellurium?
    A) alkali metal   C) metalloid
    B) transition metal D) lanthanide

14. Which element has the highest melting point?
    A) bromine   C) mercury
    B) iodine   D) tungsten

15. Which of these elements is **NOT** essential for living organisms?
    A) strontium   C) sodium
    B) sulfur   D) selenium

Thinking Critically

16. Why is it important that mercury be kept out of streams and waterways?

17. If you were going to try to get the noble gas argon to combine with another element, would fluorine be a good choice for the other element? Explain.

18. Hydrogen, which is lighter than helium, used to be used in blimps that carried passengers. Why is helium a better choice?

19. Why is water **NOT** used for putting out some chemical fires?

20. It's possible that some of the actinides beyond uranium were once present in Earth's crust. If that is true, how would their half-lives compare with the half-life of uranium, which is 4.5 billion years?

Developing Skills

If you need help, refer to the **Skill Handbook.**

21. **Recognizing Cause and Effect:** Why do photographers work in low light when they develop film?

22. **Predicting:** How would life on Earth be different if the atmosphere were 80 percent oxygen and 20 percent nitrogen instead of the other way around?

23. **Making and Using Graphs:** Make a bar graph of the representative elements that shows how many of the elements are solids, liquids, and gases at room temperature.

24. **Concept Mapping:** Draw a concept map of the periodic table. Make the first division between representative elements and transition elements.

25. **Making and Using Tables:** The periodic table below shows the locations of a few elements. For each element shown, give the element's period and group number; whether the element is a metal or a nonmetal; and whether it is a solid, liquid, or gas at room temperature.

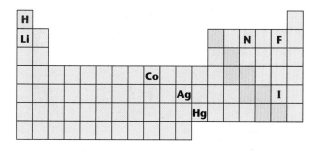

Test-Taking Tip

When Eliminating, Cross It Out List the answer choice letters on the scratch paper. Use your pencil to cross out choices you've eliminated. You'll stop yourself from choosing an answer you've mentally eliminated.

Test Practice

Use these questions to test your Science Proficiency.

1. Diamond is one of the hardest substances on Earth. Graphite is soft. Which is the best explanation for the difference in hardness?
   A) Graphite and diamond are made from different elements.
   B) Graphite is a mixture of elements.
   C) The atoms in diamond and graphite are arranged in different patterns.
   D) Diamond is made from carbon-14 atoms. Graphite contains mainly carbon-12 atoms.

2. Which is the best description of sulfur?
   A) period 2, Group 16, transition element, important industrial element
   B) period 3, oxygen family, representative element, biologically important
   C) period 5, oxygen family, representative element, poisonous
   D) period 6, inner transition element, radioactive, metal

CHAPTER

4 Chemical Bonds

Chapter Preview

Section 4-1
- Why do atoms combine?

Section 4-2
- Ionic and Covalent Bonds

Skills Preview

Skill Builders
- Classify
- Map Concepts

Activities
- Hypothesize
- Design an Experiment

MiniLabs
- Make and Use a Table
- Make a Model

Reading Check ☑

Before you read this chapter—and all the other ones—read the What You'll Learn feature at the beginning of each section. Explain why each section includes this feature.

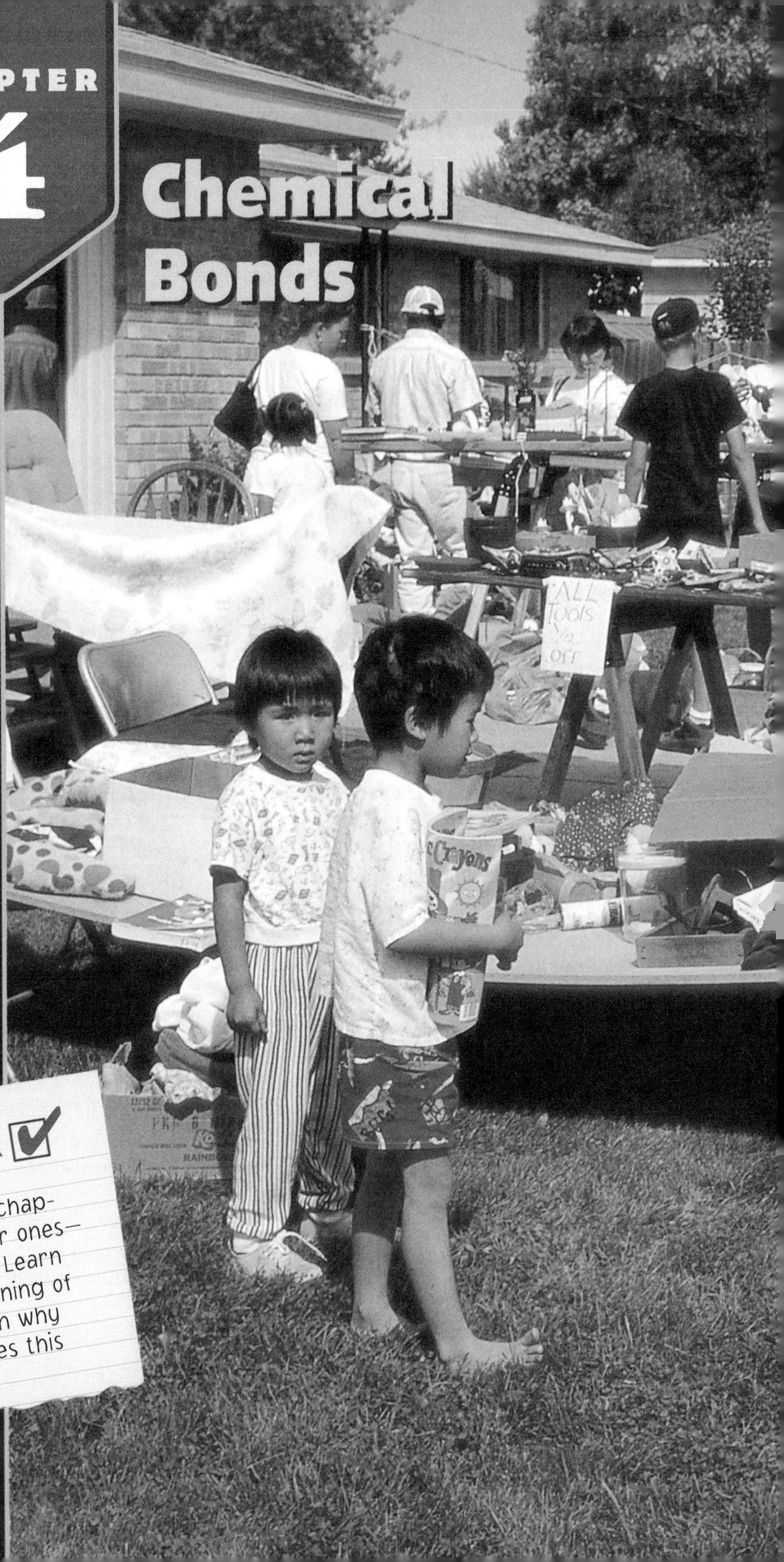

Explore Activity

It's time to clean out the garage and attic and get rid of stuff. Look at it all—stuff made out of wood, glass, plastic, metal, cloth, and even paper. Where do all the different materials that make up everyday things come from? There are fewer than 100 different kinds of naturally occurring atoms on Earth. They combine with each other in countless ways to make countless different substances. Why is this so? What makes elements combine with other elements? The answer is in their electrons.

Model the Energy of Electrons

1. Pick up a paper clip with a magnet. Touch the paper clip to another paper clip and pick it up.

2. Continue to pick up paper clips until you have a strand of them and no more will attach.

3. One by one, gently pull off the paper clips.

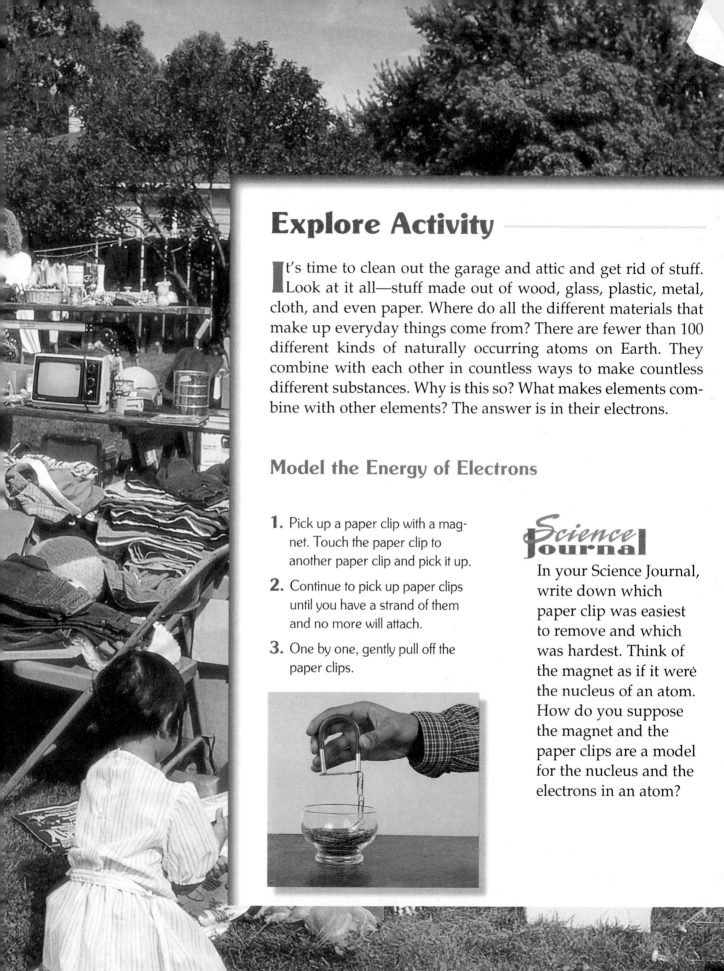

Science Journal

In your Science Journal, write down which paper clip was easiest to remove and which was hardest. Think of the magnet as if it were the nucleus of an atom. How do you suppose the magnet and the paper clips are a model for the nucleus and the electrons in an atom?

Why do atoms combine?

What You'll Learn

► How the electrons are arranged in an atom
► The energy of electrons in atoms
► How the arrangement of electrons in an atom is related to the periodic table

Vocabulary
electron dot diagram
chemical bond

Why It's Important

► When you know about an atom's electrons, you can predict how the atom will behave.

Atomic Structure

At the center of an atom is a tiny nucleus containing the atom's protons and neutrons. The rest of the space in the atom is empty, except for the atom's electrons. The electrons are in constant motion around the nucleus. Scientists know that they cannot say exactly where the electrons are at any time. They use a model, the electron cloud model, which tells where the electrons are most likely to be. They are most likely to be clustered around the nucleus because their negative charges are attracted to the positively charged nucleus. But, the electrons could be anywhere. That's why the model for an electron cloud in **Figure 4-1** has a fuzzy outline.

How many electrons are in the electron cloud of an atom, and how are they arranged? Each element has a different number of protons and electrons, so each has a different atomic structure. For example, lithium has three protons in its nucleus, and three electrons move around lithium's nucleus.

The Periodic Table

When the elements are arranged in order of increasing atomic number, they fall into groups in which the members share common properties. Could those common properties depend upon similarities in the way electrons are arranged in the atoms?

Electron Arrangements and Energy

All the electrons in an atom are in the electron cloud, but within the cloud, some electrons are closer to the nucleus than others. How do scientists know this? Think about the Explore Activity. It took more energy on your part to pull off the paper clip closest to the magnet than it took to remove the one farthest away. That's because the closer a paper clip is to the magnet, the stronger

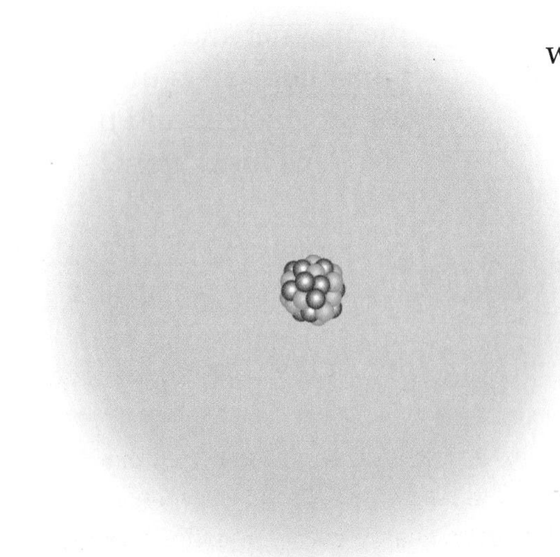

Figure 4-1 In the electron cloud model, the electrons are more likely to be in the heavily shaded area than in the lightly shaded area, but they could be anywhere. **Why is there no definite boundary for an atom?**

the magnet's attractive force on the clip. Scientists have found that the closer an electron is to the nucleus, the stronger the attractive force between the positively charged nucleus and the negatively charged electrons. So, removing electrons that are close to the nucleus takes more energy than removing those farther away from the nucleus. A diagram of how the electrons might be arranged in energy levels around the nucleus of an atom is shown in **Figure 4-2**. Notice that the electrons are arranged in spheres at different distances from the nucleus. That means that each sphere must represent a different energy.

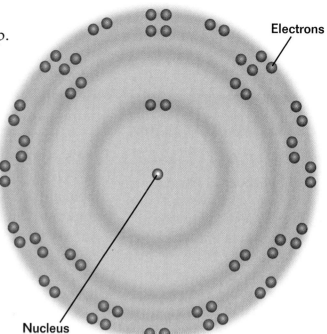

Figure 4-2 The energy of an electron is different depending upon which energy level it occupies.

An Energy Stairway

The stairway, shown in **Figure 4-3,** is a model for picturing the energy differences among electrons in the electron cloud. Think of the nucleus as being at floor level. The difference in heights of the steps represents the difference in energy between electrons on different steps. Electrons in the sphere closest to the nucleus are in the lowest energy level. They are on the first energy step. These electrons are held most tightly to the nucleus because they occupy the space closest to the nucleus. Electrons in the next sphere are on the second energy step. They are at a higher energy level because they are farther from the nucleus. Electrons in the outermost sphere have even higher energy because they are still farther from the attractive force of the positively charged nucleus.

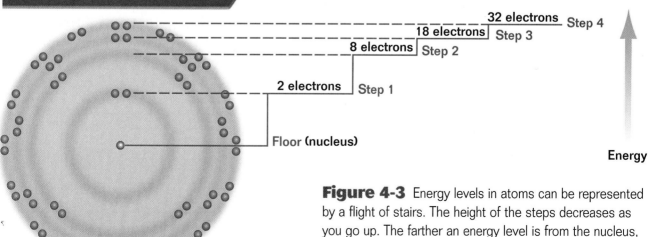

Figure 4-3 Energy levels in atoms can be represented by a flight of stairs. The height of the steps decreases as you go up. The farther an energy level is from the nucleus, the higher its energy and the more electrons it can hold.

interNET
CONNECTION

Visit the Glencoe Science Web Site at **www.glencoe.com/ sec/science** for more information about electrons in atoms.

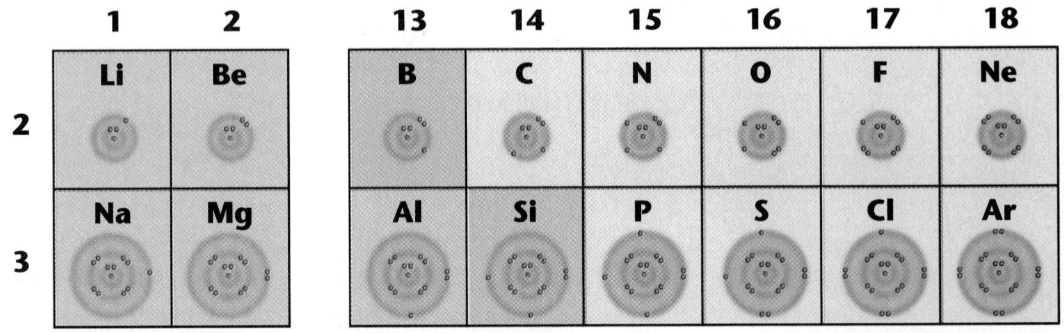

Figure 4-4 Lithium and carbon have their outermost electrons in the second energy level. **In what level do sodium and chlorine have theirs?**

How many electrons?

You can see in **Figure 4-3** that the farther an energy level is from the nucleus, the bigger its sphere. The bigger the sphere, the more electrons it can hold. **Figure 4-3** shows the maximum number of electrons that each of the first four energy levels can hold. The first energy level can hold only two electrons. Notice in the periodic table in **Figure 4-6** that there are two elements in the first period. The periods of the periodic table are the horizontal rows. Period 1 contains only hydrogen and helium. These elements have electrons only in the first energy level. Hydrogen has one electron. Helium has a completed outer energy level with two electrons. The second energy level holds eight electrons. In **Figure 4-4,** you can see that eight elements are in the second period. These elements have two electrons in the first energy level, plus different numbers of electrons in the second energy level. Starting with lithium, each element in the second period has one more electron in the second energy level than the element that comes before it. The final element in this period, neon, has a completed outer energy level with eight electrons.

Electron Arrangement and Groups

The elements in the same column of the periodic table are called a group or a family of elements. Fluorine, chlorine, and bromine are three members of Group 17, the halogen family. Just as people in a family may have similar smiles, noses, or eating habits, elements in the same family have similar properties. This is because they all have the same number of electrons in their outer energy levels. **Figure 4-5** shows the electron arrangements of sodium, Group 1, and chlorine, Group 17. Notice that sodium has one electron in its outer energy level and chlorine has seven. Compare the diagrams of these elements in **Figure 4-5** with the diagrams of lithium and fluorine in **Figure 4-4.** You can see that the Group 1 elements, lithium and sodium, have one electron in their outer energy levels. Fluorine and chlorine both have seven electrons in their outer energy levels. You know that bromine is in the same family as fluorine and chlorine, so

	1	2		13	14	15	16	17	18
2	Li	Be		B	C	N	O	F	Ne
3	Na	Mg		Al	Si	P	S	Cl	Ar

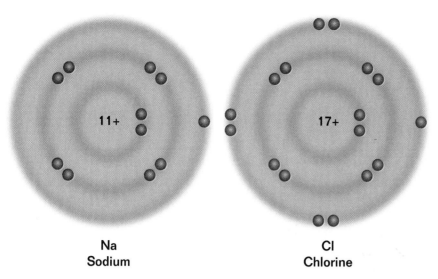

Na
Sodium

Cl
Chlorine

Figure 4-5 Compare the electron arrangements of sodium and chlorine with the electron arrangements of lithium and fluorine in Figure 4-4. **What can you conclude about elements that are in the same families?**

you can predict that bromine also has seven electrons in its outer energy level. The number of electrons in an atom's outer energy level determines how the element will combine with other elements. ☑

Look at the elements in Group 18 of the periodic table in **Figure 4-6.** The number of electrons in the outer energy level of each group is shown at the top of the column. The members of Group 18, the noble gases, have eight electrons in their outer energy levels. They do not combine easily with other elements. The noble gases are stable, which means that they resist change. The reason for their stability is that their outer energy levels are filled.

Reading Check ☑
How many electrons are in the outer energy level of bromine?

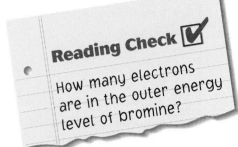

Using Math

An atom of copper has an effective volume of 1.18×10^{-23} cm³. The volume of a penny is 0.314 cm³. Calculate the number of copper atoms in a pure copper penny.

1e⁻ 1								8e⁻ 18
	2e⁻ 2	3e⁻ 13	4e⁻ 14	5e⁻ 15	6e⁻ 16	7e⁻ 17		

1	Hydrogen **H** 1							Helium **He** 2
2	Lithium **Li** 3	Beryllium **Be** 4	Boron **B** 5	Carbon **C** 6	Nitrogen **N** 7	Oxygen **O** 8	Fluorine **F** 9	Neon **Ne** 10
3	Sodium **Na** 11	Magnesium **Mg** 12	Aluminum **Al** 13	Silicon **Si** 14	Phosphorus **P** 15	Sulfur **S** 16	Chlorine **Cl** 17	Argon **Ar** 18
4	Potassium **K** 19	Calcium **Ca** 20	Gallium **Ga** 31	Germanium **Ge** 32	Arsenic **As** 33	Selenium **Se** 34	Bromine **Br** 35	Krypton **Kr** 36
5	Rubidium **Rb** 37	Strontium **Sr** 38	Indium **In** 49	Tin **Sn** 50	Antimony **Sb** 51	Tellurium **Te** 52	Iodine **I** 53	Xenon **Xe** 54
6	Cesium **Cs** 55	Barium **Ba** 56	Thallium **Tl** 81	Lead **Pb** 82	Bismuth **Bi** 83	Polonium **Po** 84	Astatine **At** 85	Radon **Rn** 86
7	Francium **Fr** 87	Radium **Ra** 88						

Figure 4-6 You can see that the number of electrons (e⁻) in the outer energy levels increases from one to eight across a period of these groups.

Drawing Electron Dot Diagrams

Procedure

1. Draw a periodic table that includes the first 18 elements. These are the elements from hydrogen through argon. Make each block a 3-cm square.
2. Fill in each block with the electron dot diagram of the element.

Analysis

1. What do you observe about the electron dot diagram of the elements in the same family?
2. Describe any changes you observe in the electron dot diagrams across a period.

Electron Dot Diagrams

As you're probably beginning to understand, the number of electrons in an element's outer energy level tells you a lot about the element's behavior. Different atomic structures result in different physical properties such as color; hardness; and whether an element is a solid, liquid, or gas. Atomic structure also determines the chemical properties of an element, such as how the element behaves with other elements. If you want to predict how atoms of one element will behave in the presence of atoms of another element, it would help to have an easy way to represent the atoms and show how many electrons are in their outer energy levels. You can do this with electron dot diagrams. An **electron dot diagram** is the chemical symbol for the element surrounded by as many dots as there are electrons in its outer energy level.

Writing Dot Diagrams

How do you know how many dots to make? For Groups 1, 2, and 13–18, you can use a periodic table. Group 1 has one outer electron. Group 2 has two. Group 13 has three, Group 14, four, and so on to Group 18, which has eight. Helium is an exception. It has only two electrons in its single energy level. How many electrons are in the outer energy level of the oxygen family? These elements are in Group 16, so the answer is six.

How would you write a dot diagram for the element phosphorus? First, write the symbol for the element phosphorus—P. Then, find phosphorus in the periodic table. Next, ask what group it is in. It's in Group 15. This means that it has five electrons in its outer energy level. The completed dot diagram with the five electrons is shown in **Figure 4-7.**

What happens when atoms form chemical bonds with each other? A **chemical bond** is a force that holds two atoms together. Chemical bonds form when atoms combine in ways that give them eight electrons in their outer energy levels. When this happens, the atoms have outer energy levels that are filled, just like the noble gases. Each atom then has greater stability than before it interacted. A chemical

Figure 4-7 The electron dot diagram shows the symbol for phosphorus and the five electrons in its outer energy level.

Phosphorus

Figure 4-8 Chemical bonds hold atoms together like friends linking arms. **Why do atoms form chemical bonds?**

bond is like friends linking arms as in **Figure 4-8.** In the next section, you'll learn how gaining, losing, or sharing electrons provides the link that holds atoms together.

Section Assessment

1. How many electrons does nitrogen have in its outer energy level? How many does bromine have?

2. How many electrons does oxygen have in its first energy level? Second energy level?

3. Which electrons in oxygen have the higher energy, those in the first energy level or those in the second?

4. **Think Critically:** Atoms in a group of elements increase in size as you move down in the periodic table. Explain why this is so.

5. **Skill Builder**
   Classifying Use the periodic table to organize the following elements into families: K, C, Sn, Li, F, Na, Pb, and I. Then, write the electron dot diagram for each element and compare the diagrams in each family. What can you conclude? If you need help, refer to Classifying in the **Skill Handbook** on page 713.

Using Math

Make a scale model for an atom. The diameter of an atom is about 1×10^{-8} cm, and the diameter of the nucleus is about 1×10^{-13} cm. Calculate the size an atom would be if its nucleus were the size of a penny (about 2 cm). Compare the size of your model atom to the size of a football field, which is about 100 m long.

Atomic Structure

Possible Materials

- Magnetic board
- Rubber magnetic strips
- Paper
- Marker
- Half-inch squares of paper
- Grapes
- Candy-coated peanuts
- Coins

As more information has become known about the structure of the atom, scientists have developed new models of the atom. Making your own model and studying the models of others will help you learn how protons, neutrons, and electrons are arranged in an atom.

Recognize the Problem

Can an element be identified based on a model that shows the arrangement of the protons, neutrons, and electrons of an atom?

Form a Hypothesis

Write a hypothesis that explains how your group will construct a model of an element that others will be able to identify.

Goals

- **Design an experiment** to create a model of a chosen element.

- **Observe** the models made by others in the class and identify the elements they represent.

Safety Precautions

Never eat any food used in a laboratory experiment. Dispose of all food after your experiment.

Test Your Hypothesis

Plan

1. Choose an element from periods 2 or 3 of the periodic table. How can you find out the number of protons, neutrons, and electrons in an atom?

2. What materials will you use to represent the electrons of the atom? How will you represent the nucleus? How can you show the difference between protons and neutrons?

3. How will you model the arrangement of electrons in the atom? Will the atom have a charge? Is it possible to identify an atom by the number of protons it has?

Do

1. Make sure your teacher approves your plan before you proceed.

2. Construct your model, then **record** your observations in your Science Journal and include a sketch.

3. Construct a model of another element.

4. Observe the models made by your classmates. **Identify** the elements they represent.

Analyze Your Data

1. What elements did you identify using your hypothesis?

2. In a neutral atom, **identify** which particles are always present in equal numbers.

3. Predict what would happen to the charge on an atom if one of the electrons were removed. What happens to an atom if one proton and one electron are removed?

4. Compare and contrast your model with the electron cloud model of the atom.

Draw Conclusions

1. What is the minimum amount of information you need to know to identify a neutral atom of an element?

2. If you made models of the isotopes boron-10 and boron-11, how would these models be different?

Ionic and Covalent Bonds

What You'll Learn

▶ How to describe ionic and covalent bonds

▶ The difference between polar and nonpolar covalent bonds

▶ Chemical shorthand

Vocabulary
ion
ionic bond
compound
covalent bond
molecule
formula

Why It's Important

▶ Everything in the world is held together by bonds.

Ionic Bonds—Loss and Gain

Some metal atoms can obtain the stable atomic structure of a noble gas by losing an electron. This is easy for elements in Group 1. Think about sodium as an example. Sodium has one electron in its outer energy level. If a sodium atom loses that electron, the energy level occupied by the electron becomes empty as you can see in **Figure 4-9**. The energy level below that is filled. By losing one electron, sodium's atomic structure becomes the same as the stable noble gas neon.

Other nonmetal atoms can acquire the stable structure of a noble gas by gaining an electron. Elements in Group 17, such as chlorine and fluorine, have seven electrons in their outer energy levels. These elements readily gain an electron. In doing so, they fill their outer energy levels. For example, if an atom of chlorine gains an electron, its atomic structure becomes the same as the noble gas argon. The diagram in **Figure 4-9** shows the chlorine atom as it gains an electron.

Positive and Negative Ions

When a sodium atom loses an electron, the atom becomes positively charged because there is one electron less in the atom than there are protons in the nucleus. Similarly, when a chlorine atom gains an electron, it becomes negatively charged because there is one more electron in the atom than there are protons in the nucleus. An atom that is no longer neutral because it has lost or gained an electron is called an **ion** (I ahn). A sodium ion is represented by the symbol Na⁺. A chlorine ion

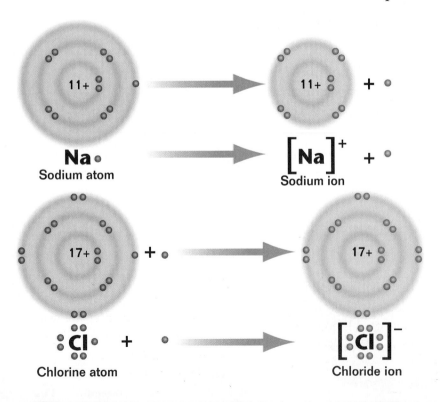

Na
Sodium atom

[Na]⁺
Sodium ion

Cl
Chlorine atom

[Cl]⁻
Chloride ion

Figure 4-9 When sodium loses an electron and chlorine gains an electron, their outer energy levels become full.

Figure 4-10 The symbols in brackets represent the sodium ion and the chloride ion. These ions form when sodium loses an electron and chlorine gains one. When sodium loses an electron and chlorine gains it, ordinary table salt, sodium chloride, is the result.

Na • ⟶ [Na]⁺ + •

:Cl• + • ⟶ [:Cl:]⁻

Na • + :Cl• ⟶ [Na]⁺[:Cl:]⁻

Sodium   Chlorine   Sodium chloride

is represented by the symbol Cl⁻. **Figure 4-10** shows dot diagrams for the formation of the two ions.

The positive sodium ion and the negative chlorine ion are attracted to each other. This attraction, which holds the ions close together, is a chemical bond called an **ionic bond.** In **Figure 4-10,** you can see that when sodium and chlorine ions form an ionic bond, the compound sodium chloride, ordinary table salt, is formed. A **compound** is a pure substance that contains two or more elements.

PHYSICS
◄**INTEGRATION**

Ionic Salts

Sodium chloride, the stuff that comes out of your salt shaker, is an example of an ionic salt. An ionic salt is a hard, crystalline (KRIH stuh lihn) compound in which positive ions of metal atoms and negative ions of nonmetal atoms are lined up in a regular pattern as shown in **Figure 4-11.** When ionic salts are dissolved in water, the ions separate. A solution of an ionic salt will conduct an electric current because the charged particles can move through the solution. Pure water is a poor conductor of electric current.

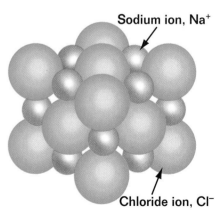

Sodium ion, Na⁺

Chloride ion, Cl⁻

Figure 4-11 In ionic compounds such as sodium chloride, the positive and negative ions line up in regular fashion. Each positive ion is surrounded by negative ions, and each negative ion is surrounded by positive ions.

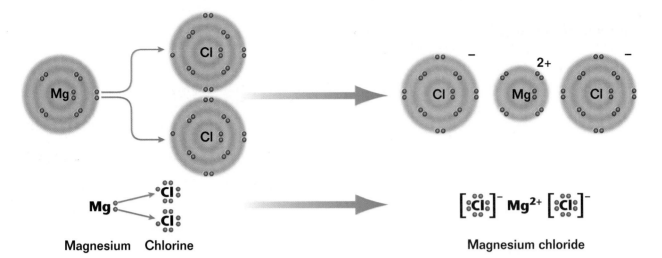

Magnesium   Chlorine

$$\left[:\overset{..}{\underset{..}{Cl}}: \right]^{-} \quad Mg^{2+} \quad \left[:\overset{..}{\underset{..}{Cl}}: \right]^{-}$$

Magnesium chloride

Figure 4-12 Magnesium divides up its two electrons between two chlorines to form $MgCl_2$, but it also could give two electrons to one atom, as it does in MgO.

Using the periodic table, you can predict that ionic salts similar to sodium chloride would form between all the elements of the alkali metals family and all of the halogens. Some examples are sodium fluoride, the anticavity ingredient in some toothpastes, and potassium iodide, which is frequently added to table salt to prevent iodine deficiency.

More Gains and Losses

You have seen what happens when elements gain or lose one electron. Now see what happens when elements gain or lose more than one. The element magnesium, Mg, in Group 2 has two electrons in its outer energy level. Magnesium can lose these two electrons and have the same structure as a stable neon atom. The two electrons can be gained by two chlorine atoms. As you can see in **Figure 4-12,** a single magnesium ion represented by the symbol Mg^{2+} and two chlorine ions are produced. The two negatively charged chlorine ions are attracted to the positively charged magnesium ion. The compound magnesium chloride is produced.

The two electrons released by magnesium could be gained by a single atom such as oxygen. When oxygen gains two electrons to form the ion O^{2-}, it can combine in a one-to-one ratio with a positive ion in Group 2. If the positive ion is Mg^{2+}, magnesium oxide (MgO) is formed.

Covalent Bonds—A Matter of Sharing

Some atoms of nonmetals are unlikely to lose or gain electrons. For example, carbon has six protons and six electrons. Four of the six electrons are in its outer energy level. To obtain a noble gas structure, carbon would either have to gain four electrons or lose four electrons. If carbon gained four electrons, that would mean that the carbon nucleus, with its charge of 6+, would have to hold its own six electrons plus four more—a total of ten negatively charged electrons. That would take too much energy. Too much energy also would be needed to remove four electrons. Each time an electron is removed, the nucleus holds the remaining electrons even more tightly. So, how do atoms of an element like carbon form bonds with other atoms?

The Covalent Bond

Atoms that do not gain or lose electrons become more stable by sharing electrons. The chemical bond that forms between atoms when they share electrons is called a **covalent** (koh VAY luhnt) **bond.** Shared electrons are attracted to the nuclei of two atoms at the same time. They move between the outer energy levels of each atom in the covalent bond so that each atom has a full outer energy level some of the time. The atoms in a covalent bond form a neutral particle, which means that the particle contains the same numbers of positive and negative charges. The neutral particle formed when atoms share electrons is called a **molecule** (MAH luh kyewl). You can see a model of electron sharing and molecule formation in **Figure 4-13.** Notice that no charged particles are involved because no electrons are gained or lost.

Figure 4-13 The sharing of electrons allows each atom to have a filled outer energy level. **Which noble gas is hydrogen similar to? Which is chlorine similar to?**

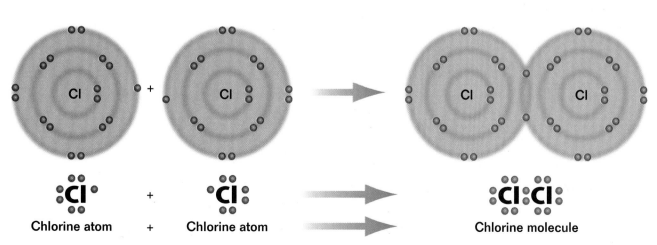

Hydrogen atom + Hydrogen atom → Hydrogen molecule

Chlorine atom + Chlorine atom → Chlorine molecule

Figure 4-14 Convince yourself, by counting the electrons, that all of carbon's four electrons and all of the two oxygens' 12 electrons are present in the electron dot diagram of CO_2. **Does each atom in the two covalent compounds have eight electrons around it?**

Carbon atom   Oxygen atoms

Carbon dioxide molecule

Nitrogen atoms

Nitrogen molecule

Reading Check ☑

How many pairs of electrons are shared in a double bond?

Sometimes an atom shares more than one electron with another atom. In the molecule carbon dioxide, shown in **Figure 4-14,** each of the oxygen atoms shares two electrons with the carbon atom. When two pairs of electrons are involved in a covalent bond, the bond is called a double bond. **Figure 4-14** also shows the sharing of three pairs of electrons between two nitrogen atoms in the nitrogen molecule. When three pairs of electrons are shared by two atoms, the bond is called a triple bond. Nitrogen molecules make up about 80 percent of the air in the atmosphere. ☑

Problem Solving

Beyond Diamond and Graphite

Is there no end to the variety of nature? Bursting onto the scene in 1985 came a new form of carbon. If you could see this new kind of carbon, you might say that it looks like a soccer ball. In fact, it's called a buckyball, which is a nickname for buckminsterfullerene. Buckminster Fuller is the architect who designed the first geodesic dome. The dome at right is located at EPCOT near Orlando, Florida. Buckminsterfullerene looks a lot like the dome created by its namesake. This amazing form of carbon is a molecule containing 60 carbon atoms bonded together in a hollow sphere.

In early 1990, *Science* magazine named buckminsterfullerene the "Molecule of the Year" because it held so much yet-to-be-developed promise. Medical applications were proposed in which disease-attacking agents would be attached to the outside of the molecule or radioactive isotopes would be carried inside the molecule. The molecule could then be injected into a patient. Another application concerned the separation of mixtures. How might that work?

Solve the Problem

1. Fill a tall, glass cylinder with glass marbles. The marbles will represent the spherical buckyballs. The mixture to be separated could be sand or salt mixed with barley or rice. These substances represent two different chemical compounds.

2. Pour the sand and barley mixture over the marbles and observe.

Think Critically

1. Did the mixture change as a result of being poured over the marbles? How do you think the packing of the marbles helped with the separation?

2. How might buckyballs be used to separate a mixture of chemical compounds?

3. Can you think of any other uses for buckyballs?

Figure 4-15 The balloon became electrically charged by rubbing it on someone's hair. Now, it attracts a stream of water. The two pairs of electrons in the two bonds between oxygen and hydrogen spend more time near the oxygen than near the hydrogen. This makes oxygen slightly negative and hydrogen slightly positive.

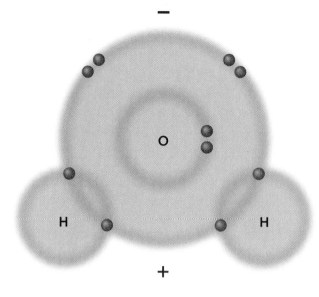

Polar and Nonpolar Molecules

You have seen that atoms often share electrons to become more stable. Do the atoms always share electrons equally? The answer is no. Some atoms have a greater attraction for electrons than others do. Oxygen, for example, attracts electrons more strongly than hydrogen does. When a covalent bond forms between hydrogen and oxygen, the shared pair of electrons tends to spend more time near the oxygen atom than the hydrogen atom.

The Polar Water Molecule

Water molecules are formed when hydrogen and oxygen share electrons. **Figure 4-15** shows evidence of the unequal sharing of electrons by hydrogen and oxygen in water. Because the oxygen atom has a greater share in the electron pair, the oxygen end of a water molecule has a slight negative charge, and the hydrogen end has a slight positive charge. This type of bond is a polar bond. *Polar* means having two opposite ends or poles. Often, one or more polar bonds result in a polar molecule such as the water molecule. Molecules that do not have these unbalanced charges are called nonpolar molecules. Because all atoms have different atomic structures, they all have different attractions for electrons, so the only truly nonpolar bonds are bonds between the same two atoms. The nitrogen molecule, which has two nitrogen atoms joined in a covalent bond, is an example of a nonpolar bond.

*inter*NET
CONNECTION

Visit the Glencoe Science Web Site at **www.glencoe.com/ sec/science** for more information about polar molecules.

A The alchemist studied matter and communicated with others using symbols.

B Symbols make chemical communication shorter and easier. Although the ancient symbols are interesting, modern symbols are easier to remember and use.

	Sulfur	Iron	Zinc	Silver	Mercury	Lead
Ancient	⧍	♂	⧋	☽	☿	♄
Modern	S	Fe	Zn	Ag	Hg	Pb

Figure 4-16 The alchemist was the forerunner of today's chemist.

Chemical Shorthand

The medieval alchemist (AL kuh mist) in **Figure 4-16A** looks quite different from a modern chemist, but like the ancient alchemists, today's chemist investigates matter, records results to share with others, and uses symbols to represent the elements. Some of the symbols used by alchemists are shown in **Figure 4-16B.** The modern chemist knows that the black tarnish that forms on silver is a compound made up of the elements silver and sulfur. She uses symbols to represent the compound: Ag_2S. If the alchemist knew the composition of tarnish, how might he have used his symbols to represent it? Modern symbols make it easy to write down chemical information and have other people understand it.

Formulas for Molecules

Figure 4-17 Two hydrogen atoms make up one hydrogen molecule. The formula for the hydrogen molecule makes that clear by placing the subscript 2 after the H.

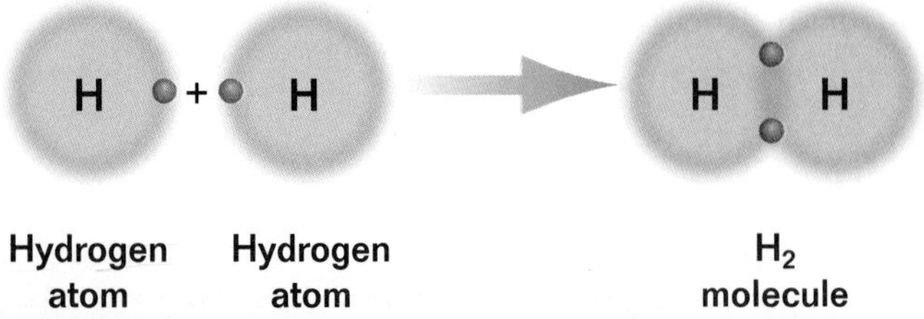

When you write Ag_2S, chemists everywhere know exactly what you mean. Chemical formulas allow scientists to communicate and share research. **Figure 4-17** shows a model of the way a hydrogen molecule is formed. Two hydrogen atoms join together in a covalent bond. The resulting molecule is represented by the chemical formula H_2. The small 2 after the H in the formula is called a subscript. *Sub-* means "below" and *script* means "write," so a subscript is a number that is written below. The subscript 2 means that two atoms of hydrogen are in the molecule.

H + H → H H

Hydrogen atom   Hydrogen atom H_2 molecule

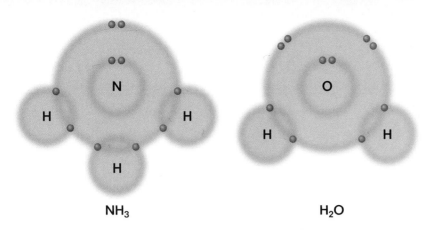

NH₃   H₂O

Figure 4-18 Ammonia has three hydrogen atoms and one nitrogen atom, so its formula is NH₃. The water molecule, H₂0, has two hydrogen atoms and one oxygen atom.

A chemical **formula** is a combination of chemical symbols of the elements that tells what elements are present in a molecule and how many atoms of each element are present. Similarly, the formula for the molecule containing two chlorine atoms is Cl_2. When there is no subscript, the number of atoms is understood to be one.

Covalently bonded molecules also can be compounds like ammonia and water shown in **Figure 4-18.** These molecules have more than one kind of atom joined together in covalent bonds. Ammonia has the formula NH_3, and the formula for water is H_2O. The formula for silver tarnish, Ag_2S, tells you that silver tarnish is a compound that contains two silver atoms and one sulfur atom.

Using Math

A container holds a gas made up of molecules that contain carbon and hydrogen. Of the atoms in the container, 20 percent are carbon. Determine the chemical formula of the gas molecules.

Section Assessment

1. Use the periodic table to decide whether lithium would form a positive or a negative ion. Would fluorine form a positive or a negative ion? Write the formula for the compound the two elements would form.

2. What is the difference between a polar and a nonpolar bond?

3. What does a chemical formula tell you?

4. **Think Critically:** Most laundry detergents are long molecules with one end that is soluble in grease and the other end soluble in water. What is the most probable type of molecule in detergents? Explain.

5. **Skill Builder**
   Predicting Scientists use what they have learned to predict what they think will happen. Do the **Chapter 4 Skill Activity** on page 745 to predict the type of bond that will form between elements.

Using Computers

Spreadsheet Design a table using spreadsheet software to compare and contrast ionic, polar covalent, and nonpolar covalent bonds. If you need help, refer to page 738.

Ionic Compounds

Materials

- Paper (8 different colors)
- Tacks (2 different colors)
- Corrugated cardboard
- Scissors

Metals in Groups 1 and 2 often lose electrons and form positive ions. Nonmetals in Groups 15, 16, and 17 often gain electrons and become negative ions. What are the possibilities for the formation of compounds between these five groups of elements?

What You'll Investigate

How do different atoms combine with each other to form compounds?

Goals

- **Construct** models of electron gain and loss.
- **Write** formulas for the ions that form when electrons are gained or lost.
- **Determine** the formulas of compounds formed between positive and negative ions.

Procedure

1. **Cut** three paper disks to represent each of these elements: Li, S, Mg, O, Ca, N, Al, and I. The disks should be about 7 cm in diameter. Use a different color of paper for each element.

2. On each disk, **write** the symbol of the element it represents.

3. Lay circles that represent an atom of lithium and an atom of sulfur side by side on a piece of corrugated cardboard.

4. **Choose** a color of thumbtack to represent the outer electron of lithium. Choose another color of thumbtack to represent the outer electrons of sulfur. **Place** one tack for each electron around the outside of each disk. Space the tacks evenly.

5. **Move** one or more electrons from the metallic atom to the nonmetallic atom so that both elements achieve a noble gas arrangement of electrons. If necessary, add more atoms of one or the other element.

6. Write the formulas for each of the ions in the ionic compound.

7. Repeat steps 3 through 6 for the remaining combinations of atoms: Mg and O, Ca and N, Al and I.

Conclude and Apply

1. **Draw** electron dot diagrams for all of the ions produced.

2. **Identify** the noble gas elements that have the same electron arrangements as the ions you produced.

3. How many lithium atoms combine with one sulfur atom?

4. Why did you have to use more than one atom in some cases? Why couldn't you just take more electrons from one metal atom or add extra ones to a nonmetal atom?

How it Works

Metallic Bonding

Knowing the type of bonding in a substance can help you predict many of its physical properties. An ionic compound may form a solid with a high melting point that conducts electricity in the liquid state or when it is dissolved in water. Many covalent compounds are gases, liquids, or soft solids at room temperature. They do not conduct electricity or easily dissolve in water.

Bonding in metals is not due to the formation of compounds. Metallic bonding is the sharing of electrons between all the atoms in the metal. This type of bonding explains why some metals have the strength to support a high-rise office building (left), why other metals can be formed into the thin wire filaments within lightbulbs, and why still other metals can be rolled or shaped into soft drink cans or hammered into horseshoes.

IN METALLIC BONDING

1 The outer electrons of each atom in the metal are not held tightly to the nucleus. Instead, they are free to move from one nucleus to another.

2 The metal atoms are bonded together in a large network. A sea of electrons surrounds each positively charged nucleus.

3 The bonding in metals is not rigid. Each nucleus can slide through the sea of electrons to new positions and stay connected to the other nuclei. As a result, metals can be hammered into thin sheets or pulled into long, thin wires.

4 The electrons can easily flow through the metal to conduct electricity.

Thinking Critically

1. How does metallic bonding differ from ionic bonding? From covalent bonding?

2. Explain why a metal with three outer electrons would be a better conductor than a metal with one outer electron.

Career
CONNECTION

Use the library to research the difference between a metallurgist and a metalsmith.

For a **preview** of this chapter, study this Reviewing Main Ideas before you read the chapter. After you have studied this chapter, you can use the Reviewing Main Ideas to **review** the chapter.

The Glencoe MindJogger, Audiocassettes, and CD-ROM provide additional opportunities for review.

Sodium ion, Na⁺

Chloride ion, Cl⁻

Section 4-1 ELECTRON ARRANGEMENT

The electrons in the electron cloud of an atom are arranged in energy levels. Each energy level contains a definite number of electrons. The number of electrons in the outer energy level of the atom increases across any period of the periodic table. The noble gas elements are stable because they have filled outer energy levels. *How many electrons are in the outer energy level of fluorine?*

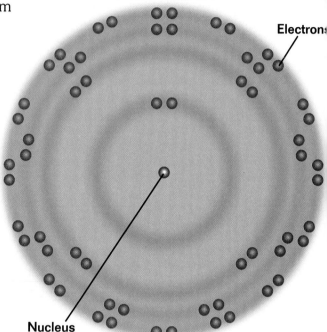

Electrons

Nucleus

Section 4-2 IONIC AND COVALENT BONDS

Atoms can become more stable if they gain, lose, or share electrons until their outer energy level is filled with electrons. **Ionic bonds** are created when a metal atom loses one or more electrons and a nonmetal atom gains one or more electrons. **Covalent bonds** are created when nonmetal atoms share one or more electrons. The unequal sharing of electrons results in a polar covalent bond. *How does the number of electrons in the outer energy level determine the type of bond that will be formed?*

CHEMICAL SYMBOLS AND FORMULAS

In order to communicate clearly about elements and combinations of elements, chemists created chemical symbols and **formulas.** This chemical language tells what elements are in **molecules** and **compounds,** and how many atoms of each element are present. The formula for silver sulfide, Ag_2S, shows there are two silver atoms and one sulfur atom in *every molecule of silver sulfide. How many hydrogen atoms and how many nitrogen atoms are in one molecule of ammonia, NH_3?*

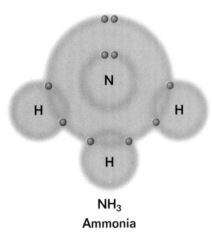

NH_3
Ammonia

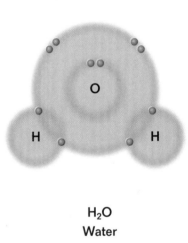

H_2O
Water

Career
CONNECTION

Dr. Brenna Flaugher, Particle Physicist

As a particle physicist, Brenna Flaugher uses a supercollider to study the particles that make up protons and neutrons, and the forces that bind these particles together. Though these particles are small, they can help understand big things, like why matter has mass, why gravity works, and how the universe was formed. Brenna chose a career in particle physics because it represents an exciting scientific frontier. *How does studying atoms help us understand chemical interactions?*

Chapter 4 Assessment

Using Vocabulary

a. chemical bond   e. formula
b. compound   f. ion
c. covalent bond   g. ionic bond
d. electron dot diagram   h. molecule

Distinguish between the terms in each of the following pairs.

1. ion, molecule
2. molecule, compound
3. electron dot diagram, formula
4. formula, molecule
5. ionic bond, covalent bond

Checking Concepts

Choose the word or phrase that best answers the question.

6. Which term is used to represent a molecule?
   A) equation   C) chemical symbol
   B) formula   D) number

7. Which of the following is a covalently bonded molecule?
   A) Cl_2 C) Ne
   B) air   D) salt

8. Which of the following is represented by the symbol Cl^-?
   A) an ionic compound
   B) a polar molecule
   C) a negative ion
   D) a positive ion

9. Which phrase describes what happens to electrons when a polar covalent bond forms?
   A) They are lost.
   B) They are gained.
   C) They are shared equally.
   D) They are shared unequally.

10. Which of the following compounds is unlikely to contain ionic bonds?
    A) NaF   C) LiCl
    B) CO   D) $MgBr_2$

11. Which term describes the units that make up compounds with covalent bonds?
    A) ions   C) salts
    B) molecules   D) acids

12. In the chemical formula CO_2, the subscript 2 shows which of the following?
    A) There are two oxygen ions.
    B) There are two oxygen atoms.
    C) There are two CO_2 molecules.
    D) There are two CO_2 compounds.

13. Which term describes the units that make up substances formed by ionic bonding?
    A) ions   C) acids
    B) molecules   D) atoms

14. Which is **NOT** true about the molecule H_2O?
    A) It contains two hydrogen atoms.
    B) It contains one oxygen atom.
    C) It is a polar covalent compound.
    D) It is an ionic compound.

15. What is the number of the group in which the elements have a filled outer energy level and are stable?
    A) 1   C) 16
    B) 13   D) 18

Thinking Critically

16. Groups 1 and 2 form many compounds with Groups 16 and 17. Explain.

17. What would you need to know about the atoms in a covalent bond in order to decide if the bond is polar?

18. When salt is dropped into a glass of water, the salt dissolves in the water and the sodium and chlorine ions are separated. Explain why this might occur.

19. Cesium in period 6 is more reactive than lithium in period 2. Both elements are in the alkali metals family. Explain the difference in reactivity on the basis of the outer energy levels of the two atoms.

20. Use the fact that water is a polar molecule to explain why water has a much higher boiling point than other molecules of the same size.

Developing Skills

If you need help, refer to the Skill Handbook.

21. **Predicting:** Suppose that equal masses of CuCl and $CuCl_2$ are decomposed into their component elements, copper and chlorine. Predict which compound will yield more copper. Explain your answer.

22. **Concept Mapping:** Draw a concept map starting with the term *chemical bond* and use all the vocabulary words.

23. **Recognizing Cause and Effect:** A helium atom has only two electrons. Why does helium behave as a noble gas?

24. **Observing and Inferring:** Suppose you have a sample of an element. You identify it as iron. List observations that you made that allowed you to infer that it is iron.

25. **Making and Using a Table:** Fill in the second column of the table with the number of metal atoms in one unit of the compound. Fill in the third column with the number of atoms of the nonmetal in one unit.

Formulas of Compounds		
Compound	Number of Metal Atoms	Number of Nonmetal Atoms
Cu_2O		
Al_2S_2		
NaF		
$PbCl_4$		

THE PRINCETON REVIEW

Test-Taking Tip

Your Answers Are Better Than the Test's When you know the answer, answer the question in your own words before looking at the answer choices. Often, more than one answer choice will look good, so arm yourself with yours before looking.

Test Practice

Use these questions to test your Science Proficiency.

1. Which of the following statements is true?
   A) A molecule also can be a compound.
   B) A compound can contain only two different kinds of atoms.
   C) A compound can contain only one kind of atom.
   D) A molecule can contain only one kind of atom.

2. Which statement below **BEST** explains why atoms react chemically with each other?
   A) When atoms react, they lose all of their electrons and become more stable.
   B) When atoms react, they lose, gain, or share electrons to reach a full outer energy level and are then more stable.
   C) When atoms react, they gain protons and are then more stable.
   D) When atoms react, they lose, gain, or share electrons and are then less stable.

Chemical Reactions

Chapter Preview

Skills Preview

Skill Builders

- Predict
- Interpret Data

Activities

- Design an Experiment
- Make a Model

MiniLabs

- Observe and Infer
- Compare and Contrast

Reading Check ✔

As you read, use context clues to figure out unfamiliar terms. For example, what clues help you understand the term *jostling* in the caption for Figure 5-12A? *Proteases* in the caption for Figure 5-13?

Explore Activity

An unfortunate accident caused this awful scene. Dramatic changes are going on as chemical reactions rage. When the action stops, the matter that existed before the chemical reactions will not be the same as before. It may look different, smell different, have a different physical state, or have different chemical properties. A chemical reaction is a change in matter, sometimes complex, as in this photo, and sometimes simple, as you will see in this Explore Activity.

Observe a Chemical Reaction

1. Pour 50 mL of vinegar into the bottom of a small plastic bag with a zipper closing. Have your partner hold the bag open so that you can pour the vinegar without getting any on the sides of the bag.

2. Cinch the bag together in the middle and tie it off with a twist tie.

3. Put one teaspoonful of baking soda into the top of the bag. Force out as much air as possible and zip the bag.

4. Untie the tie and shake the baking soda down into the vinegar. Observe.

Science **Journal**

In your Science Journal, draw a sketch of what happened after you mixed the vinegar and baking soda. Write a paragraph explaining your picture.

Describing a Chemical Reaction

Evidence of Chemical Reactions

You can smell a rotten egg and the smoke from a campfire. These are signs of chemical reactions. It's easy to tell when these chemical reactions occur. They give off smoke or smell bad. Other reactions are less obvious, but you can usually tell they have occurred.

Physical and Chemical Changes

Matter undergoes two kinds of changes—physical changes and chemical changes. Physical changes in a substance are those that affect its physical properties, such as its size and shape or its state (solid, liquid, or gas). For example, when water is frozen into ice, its physical state changes from liquid to solid, but it's still water. Chemical changes in a substance result in the formation of new substances that have properties different from those of the original substance. For example, a chemical change has occurred when a spot of rust appears on the steel body of a car, when an egg is fried, or when the leaves turn red in the fall. A process in which chemical changes occur is called a **chemical reaction.**

The same substance can undergo both physical and chemical changes. Look at the newspaper shown in **Figure 5-1.** If you take a piece of newspaper in your hands and crumple it

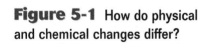

Figure 5-1 How do physical and chemical changes differ?

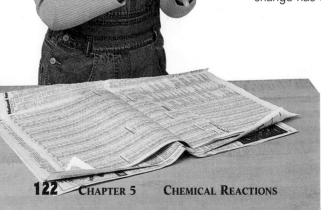

A Tearing or crumpling a piece of newspaper doesn't really change its substance. It's still newspaper, so only a physical change has occurred.

B The energy of the sun causes changes in the color of the newspaper. A chemical change has occurred.

Figure 5-2 Look for evidence of chemical change. It's all around you.

A The texture of fresh, raw eggs is permanently changed by the heat of the frying pan as these eggs are fried sunny-side up.

B Bubbles stream from an antacid tablet when it dissolves in water. Bubbles also formed in the chemical reaction of vinegar and baking soda.

C Soap scum is an example of a precipitate, which is sometimes a product of a chemical reaction.

D Smoke and ash are left after a newspaper burns as kindling for these logs. Heat is also evidence that a chemical reaction is occurring.

up, you change its size and shape, but you still have a piece of newspaper. Crushing the paper is a physical change. If you leave that piece of newspaper in sunlight for a long time, it will turn yellow. If you use it as kindling in a campfire and touch a match to it, it will burst into flames. These processes are chemical reactions. The final substances are chemically different from the starting substances. How can you tell that a chemical reaction has occurred? Sometimes it is obvious, sometimes not. **Figure 5-2** shows several clues to look for to determine whether or not a change is chemical.

Mini Lab

Observing a Chemical Change

Procedure

1. Place about ¼ teaspoon of baking soda in an evaporating dish. Add 2 mL of white vinegar.
2. Allow the mixture to dry.
3. Examine the result and compare it with baking soda. Do they look the same?
4. To further investigate the residue, add 2 mL of vinegar and observe.

Analysis

1. Did a chemical reaction occur in step 1? In step 4? Explain.
2. Are the chemical properties of the residue the same as those of baking soda? Explain.

interNET
CONNECTION

Visit the Glencoe Science Web Site at **www.glencoe.com/ sec/science** for more information about chemical reactions.

Chemical Equations

In order to describe a chemical reaction, you must know what substances react. The substances that react, called the **reactants** (ree AK tunts), are substances that exist before the reaction begins. The substances that are formed by the reaction are called the **products.**

When you mix baking soda and vinegar, a vigorous chemical reaction occurs. Bubbles form. The reaction mixture foams up inside the container. Baking soda and vinegar are the common names for the reactants in this reaction. They also have chemical names. Baking soda is the compound sodium hydrogen carbonate, and vinegar is acetic (uh SEE tihk) acid in a water solution. These are the reactants. What are the products? You saw bubbles form when the reaction occurred, but is that enough of a description? There are many kinds of bubbles. Are bubbles the only product, or do some atoms from the vinegar and baking soda end up forming something else? What goes on in the chemical reaction may be more than what you can see with your eyes. Chemists try to find out everything that happens in a chemical reaction. Then, they record it in a shorthand known as a chemical equation.

Word Equations

One way to describe a chemical reaction is with an equation that uses words to describe the reactants and products. The reactants are listed on the left side of an arrow, separated from each other by plus signs. The products are placed on the right side of the arrow. They also are separated by plus signs. The arrow between the reactants and products represents the changes that occur during the chemical reaction. When reading the equation, the arrow is read *produces.* How would you write a word equation for the reactants and products in the chemical reaction between baking soda and vinegar, shown in **Figure 5-3?**

Chemical names rather than common names are used in word equations. In the baking soda and vinegar reaction, you already know the chemical names of the reactants—sodium hydrogen carbonate and acetic acid. The names of the products are sodium acetate, water, and carbon dioxide gas. The word equation for the reaction is as follows.

acetic acid + sodium hydrogen carbonate → sodium acetate + water + carbon dioxide

Equations with Formulas

The word equation for the reaction of baking soda and vinegar is long. That's why chemists use chemical formulas to represent the chemical names of pure substances in the equation. You can convert a word equation into a chemical equation by substituting chemical formulas for the chemical names. For example, the chemical equation for the reaction between baking soda and vinegar can be written as follows.

$$HC_2H_3O_2 + NaHCO_3 \rightarrow NaC_2H_3O_2 + H_2O + CO_2$$

| acetic acid (vinegar) | sodium hydrogen carbonate (baking soda) | sodium acetate | water | carbon dioxide |

Figure 5-3 Observing a reaction is the first step toward writing a chemical equation to describe it.

Remember that in these formulas, the subscripts tell you the number of atoms of a particular element in that molecule. The subscript 2 in CO_2 means that each molecule of carbon dioxide has two oxygen atoms. If an atom has no subscript, it means that there is only one atom of that element in the molecule.

Conservation of Mass

What happens to the atoms in the reactants when the reactants are converted into products? Do they disappear? No, they don't. According to the *law of conservation of mass,* the mass of the products of a chemical reaction is always the same as the mass of the reactants in that reaction.

In your math class, you have seen equations with equal signs. In these math equations, the right side of the equation is numerically equal to the left side. But, in a chemical equation, it is the number and kind of atoms that are equal on the two sides. Every atom that appears on the reactant side of the equation also appears on the product side.

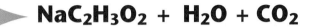

HCCHHHOO   NaHCOOO   NaCCHHHOO HHO COO

$$HC_2H_3O_2 + NaHCO_3 \longrightarrow NaC_2H_3O_2 + H_2O + CO_2$$

Figure 5-4 Count all the carbon atoms, all the hydrogen atoms, all the oxygen atoms, and all the sodium atoms on each side of the balance. **Are there equal numbers of each kind of atom on each side?**

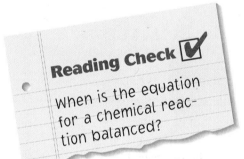

Reading Check

When is the equation for a chemical reaction balanced?

Atoms are not lost or created in a chemical reaction. They just change partners, as old chemical bonds in the reactants break and new chemical bonds form in the products.

Balancing Chemical Equations

When you write the chemical equation for a reaction, you must observe the law of conservation of mass. Sometimes, this is easy, as in the vinegar and baking soda reaction. All that you needed to do was write down the chemical formulas for the reactants and products. Look at **Figure 5-4.** It shows that when you count the number of carbon, hydrogen, oxygen, and sodium atoms on each side of the arrow in the equation, you find that the numbers of each kind of atom are equal, or balanced.

Not all chemical equations are balanced so easily. For example, here is the equation for the reaction that occurs when silver tarnishes.

$$Ag + H_2S \rightarrow Ag_2S + H_2$$
silver hydrogen silver   hydrogen
        sulfide   sulfide

Count the number of atoms of each type in the reactants and in the products. Two hydrogen atoms are on the reactant side, and two hydrogen atoms are on the product side. One sulfur atom is on the reactant side and one sulfur atom is on the product side. Notice that one silver atom is on the reactant side and two silver atoms are on the product side. The law of conservation of mass says this cannot be true. A chemical reaction cannot create a silver atom, so the equation as it is written does not represent the reaction correctly. The equation must show that two atoms of silver react. Check to see that the equation is balanced when it is written as follows with a 2 in front of the reactant Ag.

$$2Ag + H_2S \rightarrow Ag_2S + H_2$$

Energy in Chemical Reactions

Recall that atoms form chemical bonds because they become more stable by gaining, losing, or sharing electrons. When atoms become more stable, they have a lower total energy. This means that when atoms form bonds, energy is released. The reverse is also true. When bonds break, energy must be added. This energy is taken up by the atoms that form the products of such a reaction.

In a chemical reaction, some bonds in the reactant molecules break while new bonds in the products form, so changes in energy are a part of every chemical reaction. Noticeable amounts of energy often are released or absorbed during a chemical reaction, as you can see in the example of an energy-releasing reaction shown in **Figure 5-5.**

Energy Is Absorbed

In some chemical reactions, the energy needed to break the old bonds in the reactants is greater than the energy released when the new bonds form in the products. Energy must be absorbed if these reactions are to occur. A reaction in which energy is absorbed is called an **endothermic reaction.** In the equation for an endothermic (en duh THUR mihk) reaction, the word *energy* is sometimes written along with the reactants in the chemical equation. Think of energy as a necessary reactant in the reaction. An example of an endothermic reaction is the reaction that breaks down water into hydrogen and oxygen.

$$2H_2O + energy \rightarrow 2H_2 + O_2$$
$$\text{water} \qquad\qquad \text{hydrogen} \quad \text{oxygen}$$

*inter*NET
CONNECTION

Visit the Glencoe Science Web Site at **www.glencoe.com/ sec/science** for more information about energy in chemical equations.

EARTH SCIENCE
INTEGRATION

The Sun's Energy
Without energy from the sun, life on Earth, as we know it, could not exist. Infer whether the reactions that occur inside the sun are exothermic or endothermic.

Figure 5-5 Energy is released immediately when a highway emergency flare is activated. **What observation might tell you that a reaction absorbs energy?**

Energy Is Released

If the energy needed to break the old bonds in the reactants is less than the energy released when the new bonds form in the products, then the reaction will release energy. A reaction in which energy is released is called an **exothermic reaction.** Some examples of reactions in which energy is being released or absorbed are shown in **Figure 5-6.** Can you identify each of them as exothermic or endothermic?

When writing a chemical equation for a reaction that releases energy, the word *energy* is sometimes written along with the products. An example of an exothermic (ek soh THUR mihk) reaction is the reaction that occurs when you burn propane in a gas grill.

$$C_3H_8 + 5O_2 \rightarrow 3CO_2 + 4H_2O + \text{energy}$$
$$\text{propane} \quad \text{oxygen} \quad \text{carbon} \quad \text{water}$$
$$\text{dioxide}$$

But, it's not always necessary to include energy in a chemical equation. Usually, it's included only when it's important to know whether a reaction absorbs or releases energy. A fuel like propane, for example, is burned for the purpose of

Figure 5-6 Some reactions require energy or they won't happen. Others release energy as they take place.

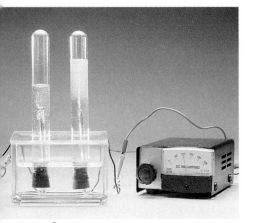

A Electrical energy is being used to break apart water molecules. The two gases, hydrogen and oxygen, are being collected in separate test tubes.

C You can infer that the release of energy occurred because of the motion created by this explosion. Sound and heat also were produced.

B The chemical process that takes place when a cold compress is activated requires energy. **Where does the energy come from?**

D The glow of a firefly is energy in the form of light produced by a chemical reaction.

obtaining energy to cook food, as shown in **Figure 5-7.** Therefore, energy is included in the equation. For the breakdown of water, energy is included so that you know the reaction will not occur unless energy is provided. In a reaction such as the tarnishing of silver, energy may be released or absorbed, but because this is not the most useful thing to know about this reaction, energy is not included in the equation at this time.

Figure 5-7 Burning propane is an exothermic reaction. **What other fuels can you list that are important because they provide energy?**

Section Assessment

1. Are the following chemical equations balanced? Why or why not?

   a. $Ca + Cl_2 \rightarrow CaCl_2$

   b. $Zn + Ag_2S \rightarrow ZnS + Ag$

   c. $Cl_2 + NaBr \rightarrow NaCl + Br_2$

2. What evidence might tell you that a chemical reaction has occurred?

3. What is the difference between an exothermic and an endothermic reaction?

4. **Think Critically:** After a forest fire, the ashes left over have less mass and take up less space than the trees that lived there before the fire. How can this be explained in terms of the law of conservation of mass?

5. 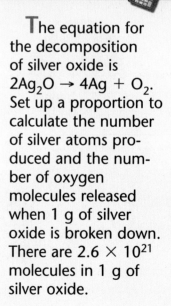 **Skill Builder**
   Comparing and Contrasting
   The energy released when hydrogen and oxygen combine to form water can supply the energy that takes the space shuttle into orbit. The reaction is $2H_2 + O_2 \rightarrow 2H_2O$ + energy. When water is broken down into the elements H_2 and O_2, the reaction is $2H_2O$ + energy $\rightarrow 2H_2 + O_2$. Compare the energy released in the first equation with the energy absorbed in the second equation. If you need help, refer to Comparing and Contrasting in the **Skill Handbook** on page 720.

Using Math

The equation for the decomposition of silver oxide is $2Ag_2O \rightarrow 4Ag + O_2$. Set up a proportion to calculate the number of silver atoms produced and the number of oxygen molecules released when 1 g of silver oxide is broken down. There are 2.6×10^{21} molecules in 1 g of silver oxide.

Exothermic or Endothermic?

Possible Materials

- Test tubes (8)
- Test-tube rack
- Hydrogen peroxide solution (3%)
- Raw liver
- Raw potato
- Thermometer
- Stopwatch
  * *clock with second hand*
- Graduated cylinder (25-mL)
  * *Alternate Materials*

Energy is always a part of a chemical reaction. Some reactions must have energy supplied to them from the environment or they won't happen. An example is the cold packs you may have used when you were injured in sports. The endothermic reaction inside the cold pack cools you by taking energy away from you. Other reactions release energy into the environment.

Recognize the Problem

Does a reaction give off heat if it is exothermic or endothermic? What evidence can you find to show that a reaction between hydrogen peroxide and liver or potato is exothermic?

Form a Hypothesis

Think about the difference between endothermic and exothermic reactions. Consider the goals of the experiment and **make a hypothesis** that describes how you can use the reactions between hydrogen peroxide and liver or potato to determine if a reaction is exothermic or endothermic.

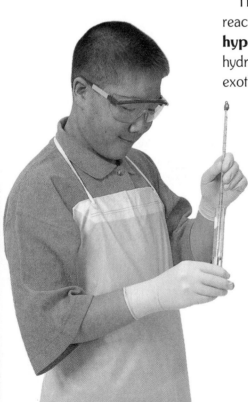

Goals

- **Design an experiment** to test whether a reaction is exothermic or endothermic.
- **Measure** the energy released in a chemical reaction.

Safety Precautions

Wear a lab apron and goggles at all times. Be careful when handling glass thermometers. Test tubes containing hydrogen peroxide should be placed and kept in racks. Dispose of materials as directed by your teacher. Wash your hands when you complete this activity. **CAUTION:** *Hydrogen peroxide can irritate skin and eyes and damage clothing.*

Test Your Hypothesis

Plan

1. As a group, look at the list of materials. **Decide** (a) what procedure you will use to test your hypothesis, and (b) what measurements you will make.

2. **Decide** how you will measure the heat released to the environment while a reaction is going on. **Determine** how many measurements you will need to make during a reaction.

3. You will get more accurate data if you repeat each experiment several times. Each repeated experiment is called a trial. Use the average of all the trials as your data for supporting your hypothesis.

4. Copy the data table in your Science Journal before you begin your experiment.

Do

1. Make sure your teacher approves your plan and your data table before you proceed.

2. Carry out your plan.

3. **Record** your measurements immediately in your data table.

Analyze Your Data

1. Can you **infer** that a chemical reaction took place? If so, what evidence did you observe?

2. **Identify** the variables in this experiment.

Draw Conclusions

1. Do your observations allow you to distinguish between an exothermic reaction and an endothermic reaction? Use your data to **explain** your answer.

2. Where did the energy in this experiment come from?

3. Suppose you had used smaller pieces of liver and potato. **Predict** what changes you would have observed.

Temperature After Adding Liver/Potato				
Trial	**Temperature after adding liver (˚C)**		**Temperature after adding potato (˚C)**	
	Starting	After ___ min	Starting	After ___ min
1				
2				
3				
4				
Total				
Average				

Rates of Chemical Reactions

Figure 5-8 Some reactions are so slow you don't realize they are happening. Others happen explosively.

How fast?

Fireworks explode in the summer sky. A tree lies rotting in a forest. Two sets of chemical reactions are happening here—one fast and one slow. You've seen other examples of chemical reactions that take different amounts of time: the baking soda and vinegar reaction, a burning match, the gradual rusting of a car's fender. Why does one reaction in **Figure 5-8** take longer than the other? Can you measure how fast a reaction proceeds? Can anything be done to speed up or slow down a reaction?

Activation Energy

If a chemical reaction is to occur between two substances, the particles of those substances must bump into each other or collide. That makes sense, because to form new chemical bonds, atoms must be close together. But, not just any collision will do. The collision must be strong enough to cause a change to take place. This means that the reaction particles must smash into each other with a certain minimum amount of energy. Anything less, and the reaction will not occur. Why is this true? A reaction involves breaking bonds in the reactants and then recombining the atoms to form products. The process of breaking the bonds requires energy, so for the reaction to get underway, energy must be present at the beginning. This minimum amount of energy is called the activation energy of the reaction.

A It takes decades for the soft green coating to develop on copper statues. This coating is the result of exposure of copper to other elements in the air.

B The disappointing thing about fireworks is that these chemical reactions are over so quickly.

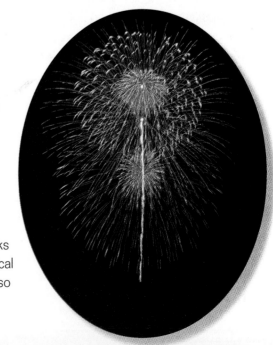

What about exothermic reactions? Is there an activation energy for reactions that release energy? In both exothermic and endothermic reactions, enough energy must be present at the start to break the original bonds, so even exothermic reactions have an activation energy. Consider the exothermic reaction between gasoline and oxygen gas. You know that gasoline burns readily to provide a lot of energy to move vehicles such as cars and buses. But, if gasoline is spilled when a car's gas tank is being filled, the gasoline doesn't burst into flames when it is exposed to air. It just forms a puddle on the ground and, in time, evaporates. In this case, the necessary activation energy is not available. But, if someone ignores the No Smoking sign in **Figure 5-9** or leaves the car's ignition on so that it creates a spark, it could be enough to supply the necessary activation energy and start an explosive reaction. Then, the energy that the reaction releases is enough to keep the reaction going.

Figure 5-9 A spark from a car's ignition or a cigarette could supply the activation energy needed to ignite spilled gasoline.

Reaction Rate

Many physical quantities are measured in terms of a rate. A rate tells you how much something changes over time. For example, speed is the rate at which you might run or ride your bike. It's the amount of distance you move divided by the time during which you were moving. Maybe you jog at a rate of 8 km per hour. Chemical reactions have rates, too. The **rate of reaction** is a measure of how fast a reaction occurs.

To find the rate of a reaction, you can measure either how quickly one of the reactants is disappearing or how quickly one of the products is appearing, as in **Figure 5-10.** Both measurements tell how the amount of a substance changes per unit of time. Reaction rate is important because the faster the product can be made, the lower the cost. However, sometimes fast rates of reaction are not desirable. In the case of the spoilage of food, the slower the rate, the longer the food will stay edible. What conditions control the rate of a reaction, and what can be done to change the rate?

Figure 5-10 As a population of green chameleons turns red, the rate of appearance of red chameleons is equal to the rate of disappearance of green chameleons.

Figure 5-11 Some fresh foods can be stored for a week or more at the temperature of the refrigerator. Other foods are still edible after storing for six months or a year at freezing temperatures. **How does temperature affect spoilage?**

Temperature Makes a Difference

What can you do to keep the food you buy at the store from spoiling? You can put it in the refrigerator or the freezer, as in **Figure 5-11.** The spoiling of food is a chemical reaction, and the temperature of the food affects the rate of this reaction. Most chemical reactions speed up at higher temperatures. This is because atoms and molecules are always in motion and the higher the temperature, the faster they move. Faster molecules collide with each other more often and with greater energy than slower molecules, so collisions are more likely in which there is enough energy to break the old bonds. This energy is the activation energy. The high temperature inside an oven speeds up the chemical reactions going on as the liquid batter of a cake changes into a spongy product. Lowering the temperature slows down most reactions. For example, if you caught a fish in the summer and put it into the freezer, you could eat it in the winter.

Concentration Affects Rate

The more reactants that are present, the greater the chance of collisions between them and the faster the reaction rate. It's like the situation in **Figure 5-12.** When you try to walk along a street that is full of people hurrying here and there, you're

Figure 5-12 Reactions occur faster when there are more particles to collide with each other.

 A Bumping and jostling are bound to happen when the sidewalk gets this crowded.

B As molecules whiz back and forth, they are much more likely to collide with each other if there are more of them packed into the same space.

liable to bump into other people. The amount of substance present in a certain volume is called the concentration of the substance. If you increase the concentration, you increase the number of particles of a substance per unit of volume. The particles are more crowded, so more collisions occur, which increases the rate of reaction.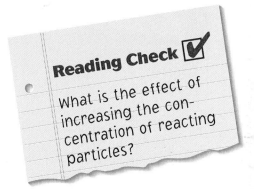

Reading Check

What is the effect of increasing the concentration of reacting particles?

Particle Size Can Change the Rate

The size of the reactant particles also affects how fast the reaction can occur. Only the atoms or molecules on the outside of the piece of reactant material are in contact with the other reactants and can take part in the reaction. If the particles are large, most of the atoms are stuck inside and can't participate in the reaction. If the particles are small, more of the reactant atoms are at the surface and can react. When more atoms can take part in the reaction, the rate of reaction increases. Think about how easily you can start a campfire with thin, dry twigs. Even a large pile of twigs will easily catch fire and burn completely in a few minutes. Could you start a fire if you just had large logs and no tinder to burn? Probably not, but once started, a campfire of logs will burn more slowly, and sometimes die down with one log still slowly smoldering.

Problem Solving

Changing Rates of Reaction

Chemists often try to make reactions go more quickly. The faster the reaction, the more product can be made in a given period of time and the lower the cost. In their search for faster reaction rates, chemists experiment with the conditions of the reaction such as the temperature, the concentration of the reactants, and the particle size of the reactants.

Examine the table that lists the conditions for two trials for each of the three reactions in column 1. List the factors that affect the rate of a reaction. Next, use your list to decide which of the trials for each reaction was faster.

Think Critically: In reaction 1, what additional change could be made in a third trial? Would it increase the reaction rate if the baking soda in reaction 2 were dissolved in water? In reaction 3, what more could the chemist do to get more oxygen gas from hydrogen peroxide more quickly? What could be done to slow down reaction 3? Explain your answers.

Conditions for Reactions		
Chemical Reaction	**Trial 1**	**Trial 2**
1. Zinc reacts with hydrochloric acid.	The zinc is in chunks.	The zinc is powdered.
2. Baking soda reacts with acetic acid.	10% acetic acid is used.	5% acetic acid is used.
3. Three percent hydrogen peroxide breaks down into oxygen gas and water.	The reaction takes place at 50°C.	The reaction takes place at 25°C.

Try at Home

Mini Lab

Uncovering Inhibitors

Procedure

1. Cereals and crackers would be stale soon after you bought them if it were not for some common inhibitors that increase the shelf life of these products. The long chemical names for three such inhibitors are usually shortened to BHT, TBHQ, and tocopherols. Look at the ingredient lists on packages on your kitchen shelves and list products that contain one of these inhibitors.

2. A date on the top of the box tells you how long the product is considered fresh. Compare that date with the approximate date when the product was purchased to estimate shelf life.

Analysis

1. What is the average estimated shelf life of the products you examined?

2. Why is increased shelf life important?

Using Math

At the beginning of a reaction, there is no CO_2 present. After 50 s, the concentration of CO_2 is 66 g per liter. Calculate the average rate of reaction during this time in units of grams per liter per second.

LIFE SCIENCE
INTEGRATION ➤

Inhibitors—Slowing Down

Sometimes, reactions occur too quickly. Food and medications, for example, undergo chemical reactions that cause them to spoil or lose their effectiveness. Can these reactions be slowed down? A substance that slows down a chemical reaction is called an **inhibitor.** An inhibitor doesn't completely stop a reaction, but it makes the formation of a certain amount of product take longer. The boxes in which many cereals are sold contain the compound butyl hydroxytoluene, BHT. The presence of BHT in the packaging material slows the spoiling of the cereal and increases shelf life.

Catalysts—Speeding Up

Is it possible to speed up a chemical reaction? You could add a catalyst (KAT uh lihst). A **catalyst** is a substance that speeds up a chemical reaction but doesn't appear in the chemical equation because it is not permanently changed or used up. A reaction using a catalyst will not produce more product than a reaction without a catalyst, but it will produce the same amount of product faster. How does a catalyst work? Visualize catalysts as hands that hold molecules in the best possible position for the reaction to take place. By holding molecules in the best position for the reaction, the catalyst reduces the activation energy needed to start the reaction. When the activation energy is reduced, the reaction rate increases.

Enzymes Are Catalysts

Some of the most effective catalysts are at work in your body. These catalysts, called enzymes, speed up reactions needed for efficient cell functioning. They help your body convert food to fuel, build bone and muscle tissue, and convert extra energy to fat.

These are complex reactions. Without enzymes, they would occur at rates that are too slow to measure or they would not occur at all. Enzymes make it possible for your body to function. Enzymes function as catalysts by positioning the reacting molecules so that their structures fit together properly. One class of enzymes called proteases (PROH tee ays es) functions within cells to break down proteins and recycle the materials. Proteins are large, complex molecules that perform many important functions in living things. Proteases are used in common products, such as meat tenderizer and contact lens-cleaning solution, as shown in **Figure 5-13.** Why do you think these products would need to break down proteins?

Figure 5-13 Proteins from the eye collect on contact lenses and can cloud your view. Proteases in lens-cleaning solutions speed up the decomposition of proteins so that they can be removed from a lens.

Section Assessment

1. How would you measure the rate of a reaction?

2. For the following general reaction, A + B + energy → C, where A and B are gases, what will be the effect on the reaction rate of the following?
   a. increasing the temperature
   b. increasing the pressure
   c. adding more of A without adding more of B

3. **Think Critically:** Jars of spaghetti sauce are stored on shelves at the grocery store waiting to be purchased. When you take a jar home and use it, you break the air-tight seal on the top. These jars are labeled "refrigerate after opening." Explain why the jar can be stored on the shelf in the market but must be placed in the refrigerator after it is opened.

4. **Skill Builder**
   Observing and Inferring The rate of a reaction is affected by several factors. For example, the temperature of the reaction mixture can either speed up or slow down the reaction. Do the **Chapter 5 Skill Activity** on page 746 to investigate a chemical reaction. Then, infer the type of reaction you have observed and the effect temperature has on it.

Using Math

A chemical reaction is proceeding at a rate of 2 g of product per 45 s. How long will it take to obtain 50 g of product from the reaction?

Speeding Up a Reaction

Materials

- Test tubes (2)
- Test-tube rack
  beaker to hold test tubes
- Graduated cylinder (25 mL)
- Small plastic spoon
- Hot plate
- Wooden splint
- Hydrogen peroxide, 3%, H_2O_2
- Manganese dioxide, MnO_2
- Beaker of hot water
- Bunsen burner
  lighter
  Alternate Materials

The equation for a chemical reaction tells you nothing about how fast the reaction occurs. One slow reaction is the breakdown of hydrogen peroxide, H_2O_2, into oxygen gas, O_2, and water. Is there a way to make this reaction go faster?

Chemists measure the rate of a chemical reaction by observing how quickly the reactants are used up or the products are formed. Testing the production of oxygen is a handy way to observe the rate of a reaction. A glowing wooden splint will relight and burn brightly when placed in oxygen.

What You'll Investigate

How is the rate of the breakdown of hydrogen peroxide affected when manganese dioxide, MnO_2, is added as a catalyst?

Goals

- **Observe** the decomposition of hydrogen peroxide.
- **Infer** how a catalyst changes the reaction rate.

Safety Precautions

CAUTION: *Hydrogen peroxide can irritate skin and eyes. Wear goggles, an apron, and gloves. Do not use more than 5 mL of hydrogen peroxide.*

Procedure

1. Pour 5 mL of hydrogen peroxide into each of two test tubes.
2. Place about ¼ teaspoonful of manganese dioxide in one of the test tubes.
3. Light the wooden splint. Blow out the flame and insert the glowing splint first into the test tube containing only hydrogen peroxide and then into the test tube containing the manganese dioxide.

4. Record your observations.
5. Place the two test tubes in a beaker of hot water and heat them on a hot plate until all the liquid has disappeared. Record your observations.

Conclude and Apply

1. **Describe** what happened when manganese dioxide was added to one of the test tubes.
2. In which test tube was gas produced more rapidly? How do you know?
3. How did you identify the gas?
4. What remained in the two test tubes after the liquid was driven off?
5. Does manganese dioxide fit the description of a catalyst? Give reasons for your answer.
6. The word *catalyst* is used in everyday conversation to describe special people. Write a sentence that illustrates what effect such people might have on others around them.

Using Proportions

The Mole

One job of a chemist is to determine the number of atoms needed to combine with other atoms or molecules to make new products. In real life, large numbers of atoms are involved in chemical reactions. So, chemists invented the mole to use as a counting unit, the way a baker uses the word *dozen*, meaning 12 of something. A mole of atoms contains 6.02×10^{23} atoms, and a mole of molecules contains 6.02×10^{23} molecules. This huge quantity is known as Avogadro's number. If you counted out 1 mole of peas, your pile would cover the United States to a depth of about 6 km. Let's see how chemists use the mole to solve problems.

Problem and Solution

Ammonia gas is made from nitrogen gas and hydrogen gas. This reaction is written as follows.

$$N_2 + 3H_2 \rightarrow 2NH_3$$

This balanced equation shows a chemist that 1 mole of nitrogen molecules reacts with 3 moles of hydrogen molecules and that 2 moles of ammonia molecules will be produced. If you wanted to produce 6 moles of ammonia from this reaction, how would you know how much hydrogen you needed?

1. From the balanced equation, you now know that the ratio of hydrogen molecules to ammonia molecules is 3:2.

2. The easiest way to find out your answer is to set up a proportion and calculate the cross product. Start with the ratio that is known. Set it equal to the ratio that has the unknown quantity. Then, solve the proportion.

$$\frac{3 \text{ moles } H_2}{2 \text{ moles } NH_3} = \frac{x}{6 \text{ mole } NH_3}$$

$$x = \frac{(3 \text{ moles } H_2)(6 \text{ moles } NH_3)}{2 \text{ moles } NH_3}$$

$$x = 9 \text{ moles } H_2$$

You would start with 9 moles of H_2 to produce 6 moles of NH_3.

Practice
PROBLEMS

1. How many moles of N_2 would be needed to produce 9 moles of NH_3 ?

2. How many moles of NH_3 would you produce if 5 moles of N_2 were used?

For a **preview** of this chapter, study this Reviewing Main Ideas before you read the chapter. After you have studied this chapter, you can use the Reviewing Main Ideas to **review** the chapter.

The Glencoe MindJogger, Audiocassettes, and CD-ROM provide additional opportunities for review.

Section 5-1 EVIDENCE FOR CHEMICAL REACTIONS

Reactions are always occurring all around you. Many observable signs show that **chemical reactions** have occurred, including changes in color or odor, the release or absorption of heat or light, and the release of a gas. Sometimes, a solid called a precipitate forms when two clear liquids are mixed. Observations of the changes that occur are the basis for writing equations that describe chemical reactions. *Write down an example of a chemical reaction and describe the evidence that shows it has occurred.*

BALANCED CHEMICAL EQUATIONS

A chemical equation is a shorthand way of describing what happens in a chemical reaction. In a chemical equation, chemists use symbols to represent the **reactants** and **products** of a reaction. The reactants are placed on the left side of the equation with an arrow pointing toward the products on the right. The law of conservation of mass requires that chemical equations be balanced, meaning that the same number of atoms of each element must be found on each side of the equation. The chemical equation sometimes shows whether a reaction is **endothermic** or **exothermic**. *What is the difference between an endothermic and an exothermic reaction?*

HCCHHHOO NaHCOOO   NaCCHHHOO HHO COO

$$HC_2H_3O_2 + NaHCO_3 \longrightarrow NaC_2H_3O_2 + H_2O + CO_2$$

5-2 RATE OF REACTION

The **rate of reaction** is a measure of how quickly a reaction occurs. All reactions have an activation energy, which is a minimum amount of energy required to start the reaction. Reactions with low activation energies occur rapidly. Those with high activation energies occur slowly or not at all. Other factors that influence the rate of a chemical reaction are the temperature at which the reaction occurs, the concentration of the reactants, and the size of the particles of reactant. **Catalysts** are substances that can speed up a reaction without being used up. **Inhibitors** slow down the rate of reaction. *Why do many reactions occur more quickly at higher temperatures?*

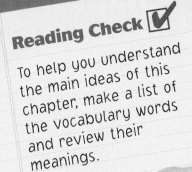

Reading Check ✓

To help you understand the main ideas of this chapter, make a list of the vocabulary words and review their meanings.

Career

CONNECTION

Dr. Lynda Jordan, Biochemist

Dr. Lynda Jordan is a biochemist working at North Carolina Agricultural and Technical State University. Dr. Jordan studies the enzyme phospholipase, an enzyme isolated from the cells of the human placenta. She is interested in finding out about the structure and function of the enzyme. Many people have diseases, such as diabetes, that are associated with this enzyme, so understanding how the enzyme functions is important. *How might an enzyme cause a disease in an organism?*

Chapter 5 Assessment

Using Vocabulary

a. catalyst
b. chemical reaction
c. endothermic reaction
d. exothermic reaction
e. inhibitor
f. product
g. rate of reaction
h. reactant

Explain the differences between terms in each of the following sets.

1. exothermic reaction, endothermic reaction
2. catalyst, rate of reaction
3. reactant, product
4. catalyst, inhibitor
5. chemical reaction, rate of reaction

Checking Concepts

Choose the word or phrase that best answers the question.

6. A balanced chemical equation must have the same number of atoms of each of these on both sides.
   A) atoms
   B) elements
   C) molecules
   D) compounds

7. Which is **NOT** a balanced equation?
   A) $CuCl_2 + H_2S \rightarrow CuS + 2HCl$
   B) $AgNO_3 + NaI \rightarrow AgI + NaNO_3$
   C) $2C_2H_6 + 7O_2 \rightarrow 4CO_2 + 6H_2O$
   D) $MgO + Fe \rightarrow Fe_2O_3 + Mg$

8. Which is a chemical change?
   A) Paper is shredded.
   B) Liquid wax turns solid.
   C) A raw egg is broken.
   D) Soap scum forms.

9. Reactions that release energy are which of the following?
   A) unbalanced
   B) balanced
   C) exothermic
   D) endothermic

10. Which is a false statement about the law of conservation of mass?
    A) The mass of reactants must equal the mass of products.
    B) All the atoms on the reactant side of an equation are also on the product side.
    C) It is not always necessary to have the same elements present on both sides of the equation.
    D) No atoms are lost, but only rearranged.

11. What is a way to decrease the rate of a chemical reaction?
    A) increase the temperature
    B) reduce the concentration of a reactant
    C) increase the concentration of a reactant
    D) add a catalyst

12. In order to slow down a chemical reaction, what should you add?
    A) catalyst
    B) salt
    C) inhibitor
    D) enzyme

13. Which is **NOT** evidence that a chemical reaction has occurred?
    A) The leaves turn red in fall.
    B) Steam condenses on a cold window.
    C) A strong odor comes from the exhaust pipe of a car.
    D) Bubbles of gas form when a tablet is placed in water.

14. What does **NOT** affect reaction rate?
    A) the law of conservation of mass
    B) activation energy
    C) particle size
    D) concentration

15. Which of the following does NOT describe a catalyst?
    A) It can be recovered after the reaction.
    B) It speeds up a reaction.
    C) It does not appear in the chemical equation.
    D) It can be used in place of an inhibitor.

Thinking Critically

16. Pickled cucumbers remain edible much longer than fresh cucumbers. Explain.
17. A test tube containing a substance becomes warmer when you add another substance to it. What can you infer from this observation?
18. A beaker of water standing in the sunlight becomes warm. Has a chemical reaction occurred? Explain.
19. Is $2Ag + S$ the same as Ag_2S? Explain.

Developing Skills

If you need help, refer to the Skill Handbook.

20. **Interpreting Data:** At 25°C, you measure the rate of a chemical reaction. You then increase the temperature to 100°C and find that the reaction rate is half as large as before. Does this reaction absorb or release energy? Explain.
21. **Interpreting Scientific Illustrations:** The two curves on the graph represent the concentrations of compounds A (blue) and B (red) during a chemical reaction.
    A) Which compound is a reactant?
    B) Which compound is a product?
    C) During what time period is the concentration of the reactant changing most rapidly?

Rate of Reaction

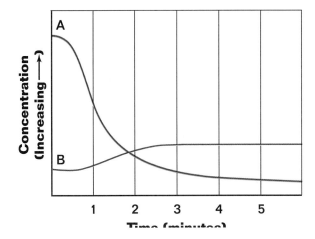

Test-Taking Tip

Plan Your Work and Work Your Plan
Set up a study schedule for yourself well in advance of your test. Plan your workload so that you do a little each day rather than a lot all at once. The key to retaining information is to repeatedly review and practice it.

Test Practice

Use these questions to test your Science Proficiency.

1. Which of the following is **NOT** true.
   A) All chemical reactions either release or absorb energy.
   B) In all chemical equations, energy must be included either on the reactant or the product side.
   C) Some reactions are important because they produce energy.
   D) Reactions that produce energy are called exothermic.

2. In a balanced equation for a chemical reaction, each side of the equation must have all of the following except one. Choose the one that should **NOT** be included.
   A) the same number and kind of elements
   B) the same number of each kind of atom
   C) the same number of molecules
   D) the same mass

2

Forces and Motion

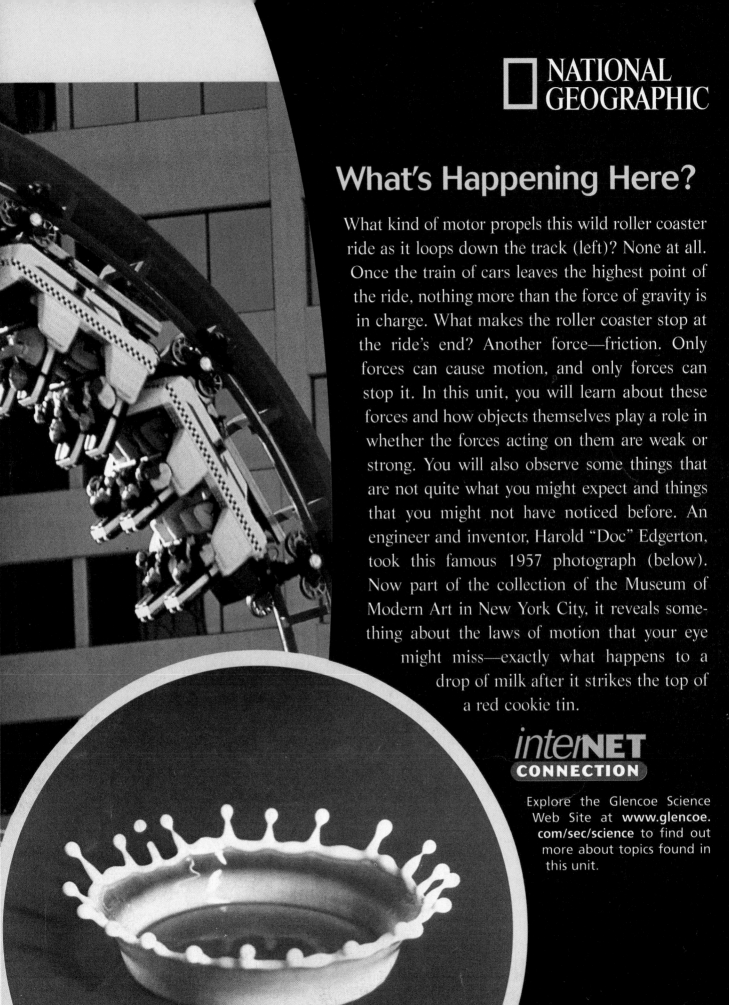

What's Happening Here?

What kind of motor propels this wild roller coaster ride as it loops down the track (left)? None at all. Once the train of cars leaves the highest point of the ride, nothing more than the force of gravity is in charge. What makes the roller coaster stop at the ride's end? Another force—friction. Only forces can cause motion, and only forces can stop it. In this unit, you will learn about these forces and how objects themselves play a role in whether the forces acting on them are weak or strong. You will also observe some things that are not quite what you might expect and things that you might not have noticed before. An engineer and inventor, Harold "Doc" Edgerton, took this famous 1957 photograph (below). Now part of the collection of the Museum of Modern Art in New York City, it reveals something about the laws of motion that your eye might miss—exactly what happens to a drop of milk after it strikes the top of a red cookie tin.

interNET CONNECTION

Explore the Glencoe Science Web Site at **www.glencoe. com/sec/science** to find out more about topics found in this unit.

CHAPTER

6

Motion

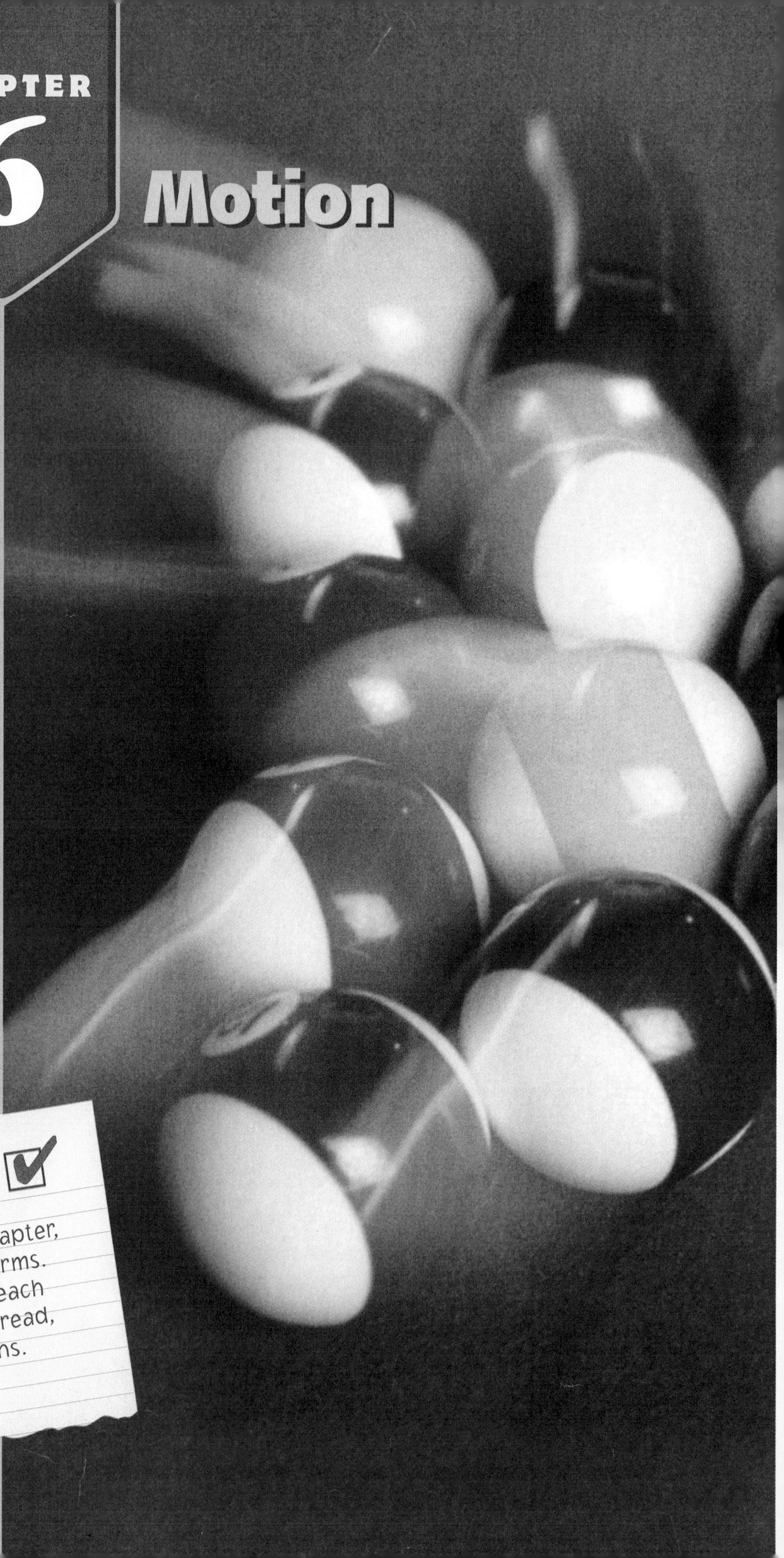

Chapter Preview

Section 6-1
What is motion?

Section 6-2
What is momentum?

Section 6-3
What is energy?

Skills Preview

Skill Builders
- Measuring in SI
- Observe and Infer

Activities
- Use Numbers
- Design an Experiment

MiniLabs
- Use Numbers
- Observe and Infer

Reading Check

Before reading the chapter, list the vocabulary terms. note what you think each word means. As you read, revise your definitions.

Explore Activity

I t's your turn. You chalk up the end of your pool cue and take aim. If you make the break just right, the balls will scatter just how you want them to. You might have observed the collision of two or more balls when playing pool, croquet, or pinball. With practice and understanding, players learn to control the motions of the balls. Science can explain the motion.

Compare Collisions

1. Use a piece of paper with a fold in the middle to make a track and a ruler with a groove to make a ramp.

2. Lean the ruler against a binder or a book to give it a slope. Place the base of the ramp on the track.

3. Put a target marble at the bottom of the ramp. Mark its starting position.

4. Let a second marble, the shooter, roll down the ramp from about 10 cm up and hit the target marble. Mark on the paper where both marbles go.

5. Repeat the experiment, starting the shooter higher up the ramp.

Science Journal

In your Science Journal, describe your experiment and what you discovered. Did both marbles always move? When did they move farthest?

6•1 What is motion?

Change in Position

What You'll Learn

► How to calculate speed
► How to calculate velocity and acceleration

Vocabulary
speed
displacement
velocity
acceleration

Why It's Important

► Most of the changes you observe are the result of matter in motion.

As you stand on a street corner, you can sense how fast all the vehicles and pedestrians are moving by watching them change position. If something is moving slowly, such as a snail crossing a wall, its slow motion is obvious. By observing for just a short time, you know it will take hours for it to change its position from one end of the wall to the other. At the other extreme, a race car changes its position in a flash. A car can be moving so fast that you have a hard time following it. By observing for a short time, you know it can cover a lot of track in a hurry. It is easy to get a rough idea of an object's motion from familiar experiences, as shown in **Figure 6-1.**

To better describe an object's motion, numbers are used. The rate of change of position is called **speed.** You can describe an object's motion with its speed at one instant, as police radar does. Or, you can describe the average speed for a journey. Average speed is found by dividing the total distance traveled by the time it takes.

$$\text{average speed} = \frac{\text{distance}}{\text{time}}$$

If you ran 50 m in 20 s, the average speed was as follows.

$$\frac{50 \text{ m}}{20 \text{ s}} = 2.5 \text{ m/s}$$

Your average speed was 2.5 m/s.

In the example above, you might have started out slowly, at a steady speed, slowed to turn around, and

Figure 6-1 Speed is the rate of change of position.

A This rhinoceros beetle might walk 0.08 m in 10 s, for an average speed of 0.008 m/s.

B This cheetah might run 300 m in 10 s, for an average speed of 30 m/s

148 CHAPTER 6 MOTION

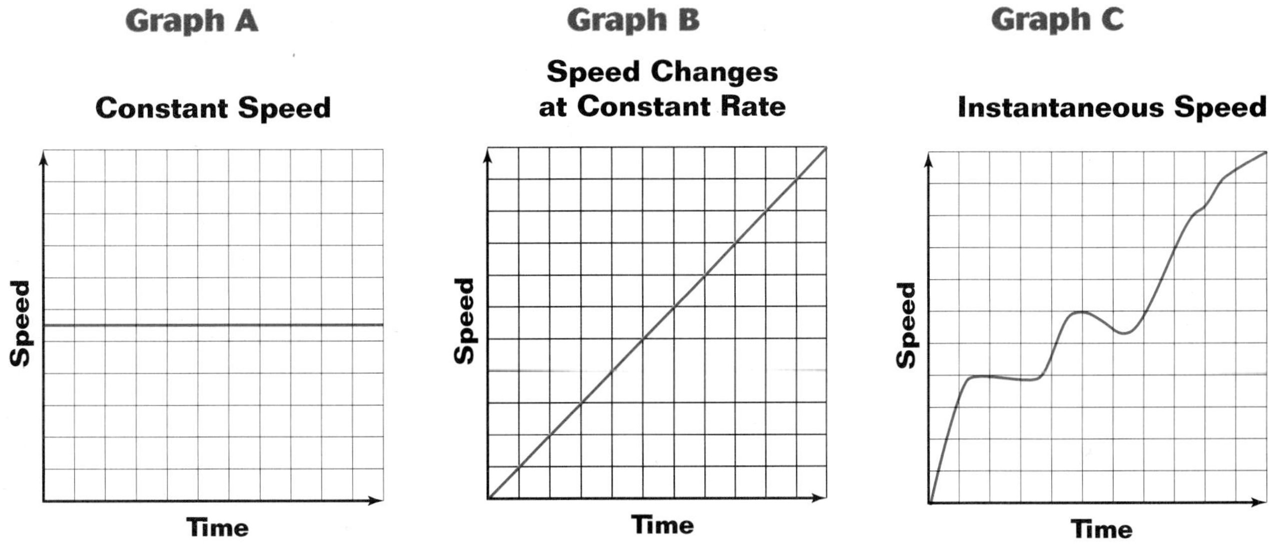

Graph A

Constant Speed

Speed | Time

Graph B

Speed Changes at Constant Rate

Speed | Time

Graph C

Instantaneous Speed

Speed | Time

stopped suddenly to avoid hitting a wall. If you were concerned with the details of your motion, you might record your speed every few seconds over the course of the run. You might also record the direction at those times, tell where you ran, and indicate when you speeded up or slowed down. In this chapter, you will usually be concerned with average speed, or with speed that is increasing or decreasing in a steady, predictable way. You can compare the ways of describing motion in the graphs in **Figure 6-2**.

Displacement

Saying you ran 2.5 m/s is often all you need to know. But where did you go? The direction of motion can be important. **Displacement** measures the change in position of an object. It includes direction. Only the starting and ending points are used to find displacement. This is illustrated in **Figure 6-3**. If you tell a friend you moved 20 m to the left, you are describing your displacement.

Figure 6-2 Graph A shows constant speed. When you use average speed to make calculations, you treat it as a constant speed. Constant acceleration is illustrated in Graph B. The actual speed increases over time. In this case, the average speed is the same as the constant speed in Graph A. Graph C shows the details of a speed changing over time. **Compare the initial and final speeds in Graphs B and C.**

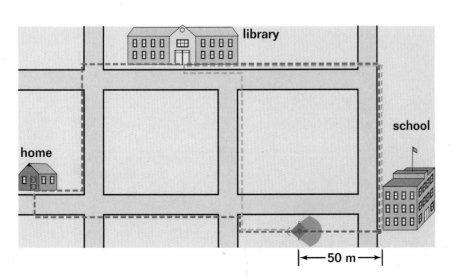

Figure 6-3 Three students (red line, blue line, orange line) walk from school to the ball diamond. In each case, the displacement is 50 m west. The distances traveled depend on the routes each student chose. **How does the distance traveled in each case compare to the displacement?**

Velocity

The rate of change of displacement is **velocity** (vel AH seh TEE). Velocity includes both speed and direction. For example, you might say, "We drove west at 30 km/h." In this case, 30 km/h is the speed and west at 30 km/h is the velocity. *Velocity* is often used as a synonym for *speed,* but in science velocity and speed mean two different things.

Reading Check

What is the difference between velocity and speed?

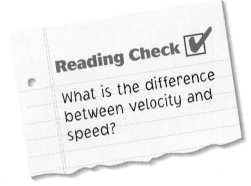

$$\text{average velocity} = \frac{\text{displacement}}{\text{time}}$$

$$v = \frac{d}{t}$$

In this equation, v stands for average velocity and d for displacement.

Average speed is not always equal to average velocity. For example, if you run around a 1-km track in six minutes (0.1 hour), your distance traveled is 1 km. However, your displacement for the whole trip around the track is 0 because you end up where you started. Your initial and final positions are identical. So, despite the fact that you ran the whole track, there is no change in position.

$$\text{average speed} = \frac{\text{distance}}{\text{time}} \qquad \text{average velocity} = \frac{\text{displacement}}{\text{time}}$$

$$= \frac{1 \text{ km}}{0.1 \text{ h}} \qquad\qquad\qquad = \frac{0 \text{ km}}{0.1 \text{ h}}$$

$$= 10 \text{ km/h} \qquad\qquad\qquad = 0 \text{ km/h}$$

Your average speed is 10 km/h, but your average velocity is 0 km/h.

Velocity gives much more information than speed when measuring motion. The directional part is important. You have seen examples of velocity. For example, when weather reporters track a hurricane, they give its position and its velocity. The direction is needed for someone to determine if he or she is in the path of the hurricane and should leave the area.

When the *Pathfinder* spacecraft landed on Mars in 1997, it released a small robot named Sojourner, shown in **Figure 6-4.** The robot had to be guided

Figure 6-4 Controllers gave Sojourner careful instructions on how to roll away from the *Pathfinder* spacecraft after its cushioned landing on Mars. **Why was the robot's speed important? Why was its direction important?**

around large boulders and then moved up against rocks in order to study them. Sojourner could not carry out its mission without ground controllers on Earth knowing both its position and its velocity.

Relative Motion

Motion is always described relative to a frame of reference. For example, the *Sojourner* robot in **Figure 6-4** starts at the spacecraft *Pathfinder*. A displacement might be described as "4 m north of *Pathfinder*." Another reference frame, such as the rock Scooby Doo, could have been chosen. People also must agree on directions. *Forward* and *left* can have different meanings, depending on which way you are facing.

For motion back and forth along a line, people sometimes use positive and negative numbers. For example, +3 would mean three steps forward, and –5 would mean five steps back. If you make both displacements, you will be two steps back from where you started, as shown in **Figure 6-5**. This is true no matter which order you do the displacements.

Velocity is also relative. Imagine watching a train moving 20 km/h north relative to the ground. If you are standing on the sidewalk, the train appears to be moving at 20 km/h north. If you are riding in a car going north at 15 km/h, the train appears to be moving more slowly, at 5 km/h north. If you are riding in a car going south at 15 km/h, the train appears to zip by at 35 km/h. The motion of the train relative to the ground is the same in each case. Only your frame of reference changes.

Positive and negative numbers are used to indicate motion forward and backward or right and left. **Figure 6-6** shows an example of how to compute relative velocity.

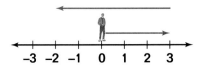

Figure 6-5 If you take 3 steps forward and 5 steps back, you will be 2 steps back from your starting point. **What happens if you take 4 steps left and 1 step right?**

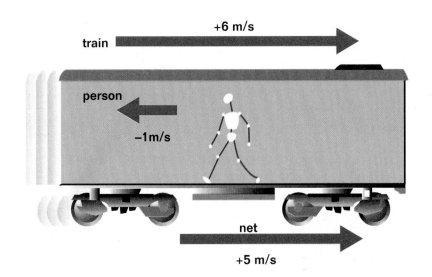

Figure 6-6 The velocity of the walker relative to the ground is 5 m/s forward.

Acceleration

When you're riding in a car that takes off quickly from a stop sign, you feel your body press back against the seat. When you stop, your body is pushed forward against the seat belt. You can sense motion when you accelerate. **Acceleration** is the rate of change of velocity. Speeding up, slowing down, and turning are all forms of acceleration. To find the average acceleration, use the following formula.

$$\text{average acceleration} = \frac{\text{change in velocity}}{\text{time}}$$

$$a = \frac{v_2 - v_1}{t}$$

For example, if an object takes 2 s to go from velocity 0 to velocity +4 m/s, the average acceleration is found as follows.

$$\frac{4 \text{ m/s} - 0 \text{ m/s}}{2 \text{ s}} = +2 \text{ m/s}^2$$

The average acceleration is +2 m/s².

You can rearrange the formula to find the change in velocity given the acceleration and time, as illustrated in **Figure 6-7.** The direction of the acceleration is important.

When an object accelerates in the direction it is moving, the object speeds up, as shown in **Figure 6-7A.** If an object is moving to the right and you accelerate it to the right, it goes to the right at a greater velocity.

Acceleration in the direction opposite to its motion slows an object down, as shown in **Figure 6-7B.** If an object is moving forward and you accelerate it backward, its velocity decreases. For example, friction accelerates an object opposite to the direction of motion, slowing it down.

Acceleration and Distance

When an object accelerates in the direction of motion, it covers more distance in each second than it did in the previous second. An object that starts at rest and accelerates at a for time t covers a distance given by the following formula.

$$\text{distance} = 0.5(\text{acceleration})(\text{time})^2$$

$$d = 0.5at^2$$

Mini Lab

Calculating Acceleration

Procedure

1. Mark off a course. Place tape at the following number of meters from start: 0, 0.1, 0.4, 0.9, 1.6, 2.5, and 3.6.

2. Work with a partner. While one of you claps a slow, steady beat, the other should move along the course, stepping on one piece of tape for each clap.

3. Measure the time between claps.

4. Experience negative acceleration by moving through the course from 3.6 to 0 while your partner claps a steady beat.

Analysis

1. As you move through this course forward and backward, how does your velocity change?

2. Calculate the change in displacement (velocity) and the change in velocity (acceleration) for each time interval. For example, if your claps were about 3 s apart, then you would go from 0 to 0.1 m in 3 s for a velocity of 0.03 m/s, and the acceleration would be (0.03 m/s − 0)/(3 s) = 0.01 m/s².

Figure 6-7 Determine the direction of acceleration and velocity. Find the change in velocity. Then, find the new velocity.

A You are biking at 2 m/s and accelerate forward 0.3 m/s^2 for 2 s.

change in velocity = acceleration × time

= (0.3 m/s^2) (2 s)

= 0.6 m/s

Add the change in velocity to the initial velocity.

2 m/s + 0.6 m/s = 2.6 m/s

Your new velocity is 2.6 m/s forward.

What would your velocity be if you now accelerated at 0.1 m/s^2 for 5 s?

B You are biking at 2 m/s and accelerate backward (brake) at –0.5 m/s^2 for 2 s.

change in velocity = acceleration × time

= (–0.5 m/s^2) (2 s)

= –1 m/s

Add the change in velocity to the initial velocity.

2 m/s – 1 m/s = 1 m/s

Your new velocity is 1 m/s forward. **If you now accelerate at –0.3 m/s^2 for 1.5 s, what will your new velocity be?**

Table 6-1

Accelerating from Rest at $1 \ m/s^2$		
Time (s)	Velocity (m/s) $v = at$	Distance (m) $d = 0.5at^2$
0	0	0.0
1	1	0.5
2	2	2.0
3	3	4.5
4	4	8.0

The velocity and distance of an object accelerating at a constant rate of $1 \ m/s^2$ are given in **Table 6-1.** Note that if the acceleration is opposite to the direction of motion, the object will cover less and less distance in each time interval until it comes to a stop.

Graphing Motion

Graphs can help to explain motion. For example, the graph in **Figure 6-8** describes a bike ride along a street.

a. You start at rest.

b. You accelerate at $0.3 \ m/s^2$ for 10 s.

c. You are now biking at 3 m/s. You maintain this speed for 30 s, until you come to a hill.

d. You start uphill. You slow down at $-0.2 \ m/s^2$ until you come to a stop. How long does this take?

e. You remain stopped for 5 s.

f. When you let off the brakes, you start to coast backward. You accelerate backward at $-0.2 \ m/s^2$ for 2 s.

g. You squeeze hard on the brakes with an acceleration of $0.4 \ m/s^2$ until you come to a stop. Note that the acceleration is positive because it is opposite to a negative velocity.

Figure 6-8 The graph shows velocity vs. time for a bike ride. **When is acceleration positive? When is it negative? When is it zero? How can you tell?**

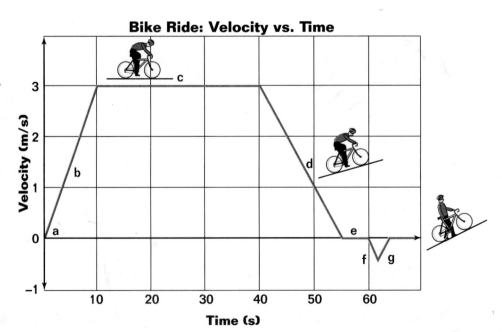

Bike Ride: Velocity vs. Time

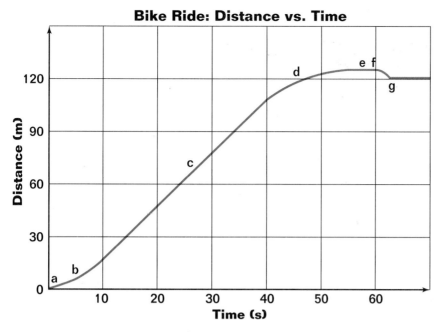

Bike Ride: Distance vs. Time

Distance (m) vs. *Time (s)* with points labeled a, b, c, d, e, f, g.

Figure 6-9 The information in **Figure 6-8** also can be conveyed in a distance-time graph, as shown here. Notice that when the acceleration is 0, the distance-time graph is a straight line. When you find the slope of the line (the rate of change of distance), you find the velocity. **What is the acceleration in part c of the graph?**

Compare the velocity-time graph in **Figure 6-8** with the distance-time graph in **Figure 6-9.** Both convey information about the same bike ride. The distance-time graph shows your displacement and how it changed (velocity). The velocity-time graph shows your speed and how it changed. Both describe your motion.

Section Assessment

1. Belayneh Dinsamo of Ethiopia set a world's record in the 1988 Rotterdam Marathon. He ran the 42.2-km course in 2.114 hours. What was his average speed?

2. A bicyclist starts at rest. She starts to pedal, and after 8 s she is traveling forward at 4 m/s. Find her acceleration, including the direction.

3. The bicyclist in question 2 continues to pedal at 4 m/s. Draw a velocity-time graph of her motion from 0 s to 15 s.

4. **Think Critically:** Suppose you are in-line skating forward at 1.5 m/s. Suddenly, another person bumps you, giving you an acceleration of 0.5 m/s² for 1 s. What other information do you need to determine your velocity after the push?

5. **Skill Builder**
   Using Numbers Do the **Chapter 6 Skill Activity** on page 747 to calculate average velocity based on measurements from a scientific illustration.

Using Math

A car is traveling due north at 20 m/s. It brakes with an acceleration of –4 m/s² for 3 s. What is its final velocity?

The Tortoise and the Hare

Possible Materials

- Stopwatch
  clock or watch with second hand
- Meterstick or another way of measuring position
- Calculator
  Alternate Materials

The tortoise and the hare is an old fable. The tortoise and the hare have a race. The tortoise plods slowly and steadily along. The hare alternately zips ahead, then stops for a while. Even though the hare is faster, the tortoise wins the race. The hare's velocity at any moment can be higher than the tortoise's, but over the course of the race, the tortoise's average velocity is greater than the hare's.

Recognize the Problem

You will design two racing strategies. One will involve slow, steady movement. The other will involve rapid starts, stops, and pauses. Compare and contrast the two types of motion.

Form a Hypothesis

Based on what you know about motion, state a hypothesis about how the tortoise's average speed and average velocity compare to those of the hare.

Goals

- **Measure** the positions of two different racers.
- **Calculate** their average speeds.
- **Use** a position-time graph.

Safety Precautions

Work where there is enough space to jog safely.

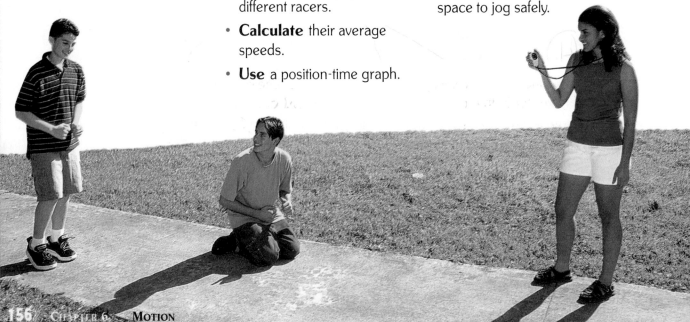

Test Your Hypothesis

Plan

1. **Find** a location for your race. Measure the distance.

2. Choose a racer to play the tortoise and one to be the hare. The tortoise should walk the course slowly. **Time** the tortoise and **calculate** the average velocity.

3. The hare will have two different strategies. Both will involve jogging part of the time at a constant speed. **Find** a reasonable speed for the jogging hare.

4. **Design** the first hare strategy. The hare will either jog at constant speed or stand still. For

example, the hare might jog for 5 s, rest for 10 s, and so on. Try to make a plan that lets the tortoise win the race.

5. **Design** a second hare strategy. This time, the hare will jog forward and backward. For example, the hare might jog forward 5 s, back 5 s, and so on. Again, try to let the tortoise win the race.

6. In both plans, ignore the hare's acceleration. Assume that the hare is moving at constant speed or is at rest.

Do

1. Make sure your teacher approves your plan before you proceed.

2. **Run** the two races of hare vs. tortoise. One person should use a timer to call out *start, 5, 10,* and so on at 5-s intervals.

(Longer intervals are fine if you have a long course.)

3. While doing the experiment, **record** your observations. Who won? When was the tortoise ahead? When was the hare ahead?

Analyze Your Data

1. **Calculate** the average velocity of each racer for both races.

2. **Calculate** the average speed of each racer for both races.

3. Use a distance-time graph to **compare and contrast** the distances the hare ran in the two races.

Draw Conclusions

1. If you know the speed of two racers at any moment, can you **predict** the outcome of a race? Explain.

2. **Compare and contrast** the different types of motion seen in the races.

6·2 What is momentum?

What You'll Learn

▶ How to find an object's momentum

▶ How to use the law of conservation of momentum to understand collisions

Vocabulary

mass
inertia
momentum
law of conservation
    of momentum

Why It's Important

▶ The conservation of momentum explains collisions between objects, whether they are pool balls or atoms.

Mass and Inertia

The universe consists of matter in motion. **Figure 6-10** shows some familiar examples. The stars you see, the air you breathe, the ground you walk on, and the eyes you read with all are made of matter. The quantity of matter is measured as **mass.** The unit of mass is the kilogram. From the tiniest particles, such as atoms, to the largest objects, such as stars, all are made of matter.

Mass plays an important role when you study motion. In the 1600s, Galileo Galilei studied motion. He noticed that objects with a lot of mass were more difficult to move and, once moving, were just as difficult to stop. If you have ever had to help push a stalled car out of the road, you know just how difficult it can be to get it moving. Once it's moving, it's easy to keep it moving as long as the ground is flat. The effort to stop the car is just as great as the effort to get it moving.

Compared to pushing a car, pushing your bicycle is easy. It hardly takes any effort because the bicycle has a small mass. Galileo used the word inertia (in ER sha) to describe how easy or difficult it is to change an object's motion. **Inertia** measures an object's tendency to remain at rest or stay in constant motion. A measure of the inertia of an object is its mass. By pushing on different objects, you can compare their masses by seeing how easy they are to move.

Figure 6-10 Your world is filled with matter in motion.

A People can move their bodies, as well as objects such as this bat and ball.

B Steam lifts the lid off a pot.

Momentum

When Sir Isaac Newton began to organize his ideas to explain force and motion, he kept returning to the same two quantities—mass and velocity. He decided that these two quantities are the most important things to know when you want to understand an object's motion. He called the product of mass and velocity **momentum.** Momentum has the symbol p. Using m for mass, the formula is as follows.

$$\text{momentum} = \text{mass} \times \text{velocity}$$
$$p = mv$$

Because momentum includes velocity, it has direction. Momentum points in the direction of motion, just like velocity. Positive and negative signs are used to indicate momentums in opposite directions. You can add momentums, as shown in **Figure 6-11.**

Momentum, Newton said, was the quantity of motion. If you know this quantity, then you can begin to understand exactly how objects move.

When a fast-moving baseball is zipping straight toward your head, you know you'd better duck! Moving at up to 200 km/h (56 m/s), the speeding ball could seriously injure you. Even if you caught the ball with a glove, your hand

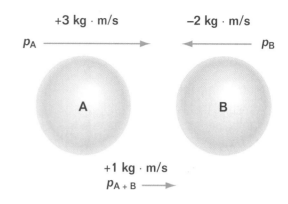

Figure 6-11 The momentum of this system, balls A and B, is the sum of the individual momentums.

C Natural processes control the movement of clouds and air, which we recognize as weather, and more dramatic movements, like earthquakes and volcanic eruptions.

D Satellites are in motion around Earth.

would feel a sting when it hit. That ball has momentum. The momentum of a baseball with a mass of 0.125 kg moving at this speed is found using the momentum formula.

$$\text{momentum} = \text{mass} \times \text{velocity}$$

$$p = mv$$

$$= (0.125\ \text{kg}) \times (56\ \text{m/s})$$

$$= 7.0\ \text{kg} \cdot \text{m/s}$$

The ball's momentum is 7.0 kg · m/s. An answer that includes direction might say the ball is moving toward the spectator in Section 1A, Row 7, Seat 23 with a momentum of 7.0 kg · m/s.

Momentum does not have a standard unit. You can use kg · m/s, g · m/s, kg · km/h, or whatever combination of mass and velocity units is most useful. (The symbol · means "times.") But, if you are making calculations with more than one momentum, be sure to use the same units for each.

Table 6-2 is a list of common objects that all have a momentum of 7 kg · m/s. Compare these objects with the speeding baseball. You can see that a mosquito with little mass needs a lot of velocity to have the same momentum. At the other extreme, a massive truck has the same momentum when barely moving. This is why, when you ride in a car on the highway, a collision with a truck is more dangerous than an insect colliding with your windshield.

Table 6-2

Common Objects with a Momentum of 7 kg · m/s		
Object	Mass (kg)	Speed (m/s)
mosquito	0.000001	7 000 000
Ping-Pong ball	0.005	1 400
bullet	0.02	350
bowling ball	7	1
seventh grader	50	0.14
18-wheeler	12 000	0.0006

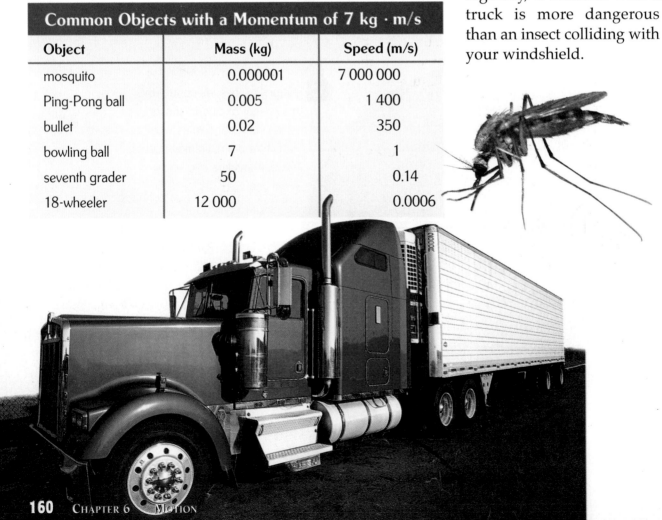

Conservation of Momentum

When you hit a ball with a bat, you change the ball's motion. If the ball has a great deal of inertia, its velocity will not change quickly. For example, if you hit a bowling ball with a bat in the same way you would hit a baseball, the bowling ball's velocity will not change much. The baseball has much less inertia, so it's easier to change its motion. Newton discovered that in both cases, however, the momentum is the same. The two balls get the same quantity of motion from the bat as long as the action (or push) is the same and lasts for the same amount of time.

Once moving, which ball is easier to stop? It takes just as much force, applied for the same amount of time, to stop each ball. It would be like running a movie backward. Force applied in one direction gives a certain momentum, and force in the opposite direction during an equal amount of time stops that momentum.

Momentum is conserved. In every situation you can imagine, from atoms smashing in particle accelerators to stars exploding in a galaxy, the momentum of the collection of objects involved does not change. If no outside forces act on a group of objects, the momentum of the whole group will never change. This is called the **law of conservation of momentum.** If one object slows down, it's because it hit another object. The object it hit then moves faster. The one object lost just as much momentum as the other one gained, so there's no change overall. This law is illustrated in **Figure 6-12.** ✔

Reading Check ✔

What is the law of conservation of momentum?

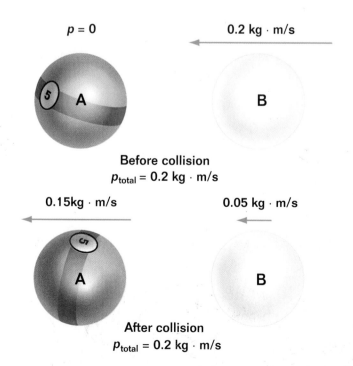

$p = 0$ 0.2 kg · m/s

A   B

Before collision
p_{total} = 0.2 kg · m/s

0.15kg · m/s   0.05 kg · m/s

A   B

After collision
p_{total} = 0.2 kg · m/s

Figure 6-12 The total momentum is 0.2 kg · m/s before and after the balls collide because momentum is conserved. **How could you predict the white ball would slow down after the collision?**

Figure 6-13 The student-skateboard systems in A and B have a momentum of 0. When the student jumps, the momentum of the system is conserved.

p_{student} $p_{\text{skateboard}}$

interNET CONNECTION

Visit the Glencoe Science Web Site at **www.glencoe.com/ sec/science** for more information about meteors.

Examples of Momentum Conservation

The system of skateboard and rider in **Figure 6-13** has a momentum of 0 before and after the skateboarder jumps. In **Figure 6-13B,** the momentum of the person is equal and opposite to the momentum of the board, so they cancel. The opening pages of this chapter show a rack of pool balls being scattered by a cue ball. The shooter applies an outside force on the cue ball when he or she hits it. The cue ball gains momentum from the stick. When the cue ball hits the rack, it slows down as it collides with the other balls. The cue ball loses momentum as the other balls gain a nearly equal amount of momentum. In a perfect system, the balls would bounce around the table without stopping until an outside force acted. When you play pool, the outside force of friction causes the balls to slow down and eventually stop.

Problem Solving

Observing Inertia

Mass is usually measured with a beam balance or a spring scale. A beam balance compares a known mass to an unknown mass. A spring scale measures the pull (or push) of the mass on a spring. Sometimes, you need to measure mass without these simple lab tools. For example, scientists who study meteor craters can't weigh the meteor. Astronomers can't weigh a comet. They need other ways to determine mass.

Get a number of balls that are about the same size. Place them on a flat surface. Make a hypothesis about their relative masses without handling them. (For

example, blue is heaviest, then red, then silver, and green is lightest.) Use one of the balls as a control ball. Place the other balls one at a time at the bottom of a ramp. Launch the control ball from the same point on a ramp to collide with each of these balls. (Launching from the same point ensures that the control ball will have approximately the same velocity each time.) Observe the collisions and the inertia of each ball.

Think Critically: How can you tell the mass order with this method? What can you do to make this more accurate?

The law of conservation of momentum can help you figure out what happens in a collision. Using the break in pool as an example, you could calculate where every ball is going to go if you knew the momentum of the cue ball and the exact position of all the balls before the collision. You might need a computer to help with the calculations, but you would not need to know anything else.

The particles in a gas are sometimes modeled as tiny billiard balls. The particles have an average speed, which is determined by the temperature of the gas. But, individual particles might have speeds higher or lower than this value. If the system is at rest, the sum of the momentums of the individual particles is zero. In this model, momentum is conserved in each collision. When a fast particle hits a slow molecule, the momentum of each may change, but the total momentum for the pair remains constant. **Figure 6-14** illustrates how the collisions of the particles with the walls of the container provide the pressure of the gas.

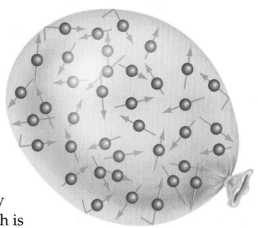

Figure 6-14 The particles in a gas can be modeled as colliding balls. When the particles collide with the balloon, they give the balloon its shape.

CHEMISTRY
◄ **INTEGRATION**

Section Assessment

1. A 140-kg lineman from your favorite team comes charging at you. He is running at full speed of 10 km/h. Suppose your mass is 50 kg. How fast must you be moving to stop his forward motion?

2. You see a film where one pool ball rolls forward and hits another. The first ball stops and the second moves off with the same momentum as the first ball. Can you tell whether the film is being run backward or forward?

3. **Think Critically:** Every day, Earth is hit by 1 million kg of matter from outer space. Most of this is in the form of grains of dust that hit Earth with an average speed of about 10 km/s. Give some reasons why we don't notice a change in the motion of Earth.

4. **Skill Builder**
   Interpreting Scientific Illustrations The illustration shows the momentums before and after a collision. What is the momentum of B after the collision? If you need help, refer to Interpreting Scientific Illustrations in the **Skill Handbook** on page 726.

Science **Journal** Explain how your momentum changes over the course of a bike ride around your block.

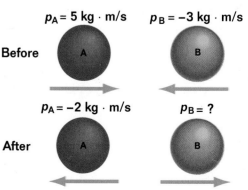

$p_A = 5$ kg · m/s $p_B = -3$ kg · m/s

Before   A   B

$p_A = -2$ kg · m/s $p_B = ?$

After   A   B

Materials

- Small marbles (5)
- Large marbles (2)
- Metersticks (2)

Comparing Collisions

You've played games that involve bouncing balls against each other, the walls and floor, and various pieces of sports equipment. How do these collisions work?

What You'll Investigate

How do the masses and velocities of marbles before a collision affect the velocities of the marbles after a collision?

Goals

- **Make** a hypothesis about how momentum changes.
- **Compare and contrast** different collisions.

Procedure

1. You want to limit this study to motion along a straight line. Use the metersticks to make a track, as shown in the photo. The sticks should be a little farther apart than the width of the largest marble you are using in each collision.

2. Set a small marble in the center of the track. Shoot another small marble as fast as you can down the track. Repeat. **Describe** the collision.

3. Repeat step 2 with two large marbles.

4. Repeat step 2 with a small shooter marble and a large target.

5. Repeat step 2 with a large shooter marble and a small target.

6. Repeat step 2 shooting two small marbles at each other.

7. Repeat step 2 shooting one small and one large marble at each other.

8. Repeat step 2 using four small, touching marbles as the target and one small marble as the shooter.

Conclude and Apply

1. **Compare and contrast** the various types of collisions.

2. How did you **separate and control variables?**

What is energy?

Energy

A final way to describe motion is with energy. **Energy** is the ability to cause change. If you look back at all the examples of motion in this chapter, you will see that all involve change.

The energy of matter in motion is **kinetic energy.** Where does kinetic energy come from? It comes from other forms of energy. Chemical energy is found in the bonds between atoms. You use it to move your body, as in **Figure 6-15.** Nuclear energy is contained in the bonds in the nucleus. Electromagnetic energy includes electricity, magnetism, and light. Heat is the transfer of thermal energy. All of these can cause change.

Energy can be transferred between objects. A soccer player has chemical energy in her muscles from the food she ate. The chemical energy is released as she accelerates her leg. Her leg now has kinetic energy. When her foot kicks the ball, the kinetic energy of her foot is used to accelerate the ball. Her foot and leg lose kinetic energy as the ball gains the same amount of kinetic energy. The ball soars downfield and eventually stops. The ball's kinetic energy turns to heat energy as it heats up the atoms and molecules of the ball, air, and ground. Eventually, these hot particles will bounce into other particles and spread the heat everywhere.

It can be difficult to follow the trail of energy. People became especially interested in defining and understanding energy when steam engines started to be used to do work. James Joule discovered the **law of conservation of energy,** which states that energy cannot be created or destroyed, but is only transformed from one form to another. ☑

What **You'll Learn**

► What energy is, and some of its forms
► How to find kinetic and gravitational potential energy
► What the law of conservation of energy is and how to use it

Vocabulary
energy
kinetic energy
law of conservation
of energy
gravitational potential
energy

Why **It's Important**

► Natural processes involve the transfer of energy.

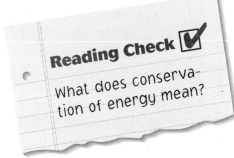

Reading Check
What does conservation of energy mean?

Figure 6-15 Chemical energy is contained in your muscles. It is transformed to kinetic energy when you use your muscles to produce motion.

Figure 6-16 Heat energy from the sun is transformed to chemical energy in the bamboo. When the animal eats the bamboo, it gains chemical energy, which it can transform to kinetic energy.

The total amount of energy in the whole universe never changes. Only the different forms in which energy appears change, as shown in **Figure 6-16.** As you study the flow of energy, as in the case of the soccer ball, you will eventually find that all the energy has been transformed into heat and seems to have disappeared. It really hasn't, but it has been lost from the object that had it at first.

To show how energy is transferred by friction, drop a basketball from shoulder height. After it bounces on the ground, it will not return to the height of your shoulders. When it bounces a second time, it won't return to the height of the first bounce. The bounces will keep getting shorter and shorter until the ball lies still on the ground. If there were no friction, the ball would bounce up and down from the same height forever.

Calculating Kinetic Energy

Kinetic energy is the energy an object has due to its motion. It depends on the object's mass and velocity. You can calculate the amount of kinetic energy using the following formula.

kinetic energy $= \frac{1}{2}$ (mass)(velocity)^2

$$KE = \frac{1}{2} mv^2$$

KE represents kinetic energy; *m*, mass; and *v*, velocity. The unit of energy is the joule (J), 1 J = 1 kg · m^2/s^2. It is named for James Joule.

Mini Lab

Observing Energy Transfer

Procedure

1. Tie a weight to a long string. Hang the string and weight from the ceiling. Adjust the string until the weight is just above the floor.
2. Pull the weight to one side until it is 1 m high. Gently let go of the weight. Do not push it.
3. Observe the motion of the weight.

Analysis

1. Calculate the gravitational potential energy of the weight before it was released.
2. Where did the weight have the greatest kinetic energy? The least?
3. What happened as *GPE* decreased? Increased? Explain.

Potential Energy

Potential energy is the stored energy of position or condition. Many forces can store energy this way. A book on the edge of a desk has potential energy due to gravity. If you knock it off, it will accelerate toward the ground. A paper clip held near a magnet also has potential energy. If you let go of it, it will accelerate toward the magnet. The positive and negative charges in a battery have potential energy. When you run a wire between them, the negative charges move. A squashed spring has potential energy. If you release it, it will accelerate.

Anything that can fall has the ability to create change. **Gravitational potential energy,** or *GPE,* is the energy an object could change to kinetic energy if it falls. An object's *GPE* depends on its mass, *m,* and the height it can fall, *h.*

$$GPE = \text{(force of gravity)(height)}$$

$$GPE = mgh$$

The *g* represents the acceleration due to gravity, 9.8 m/s^2.

You have experience with gravitational potential energy. How many times have you held your arms over your head to protect it from something falling? The more massive the object or the farther it falls, the more you cringe, hoping it does not hit you on the head.

Figure 6-17 shows how energy changes when a ball is dropped. When you first release the ball, it has a certain gravitational potential energy, *mgh,* and no kinetic energy. Just before it hits the ground, its *GPE* is 0. All the *GPE* has been converted to kinetic energy. At any point along the way, it's part *GPE* and part *KE.* But everywhere the total amount of energy is the same.

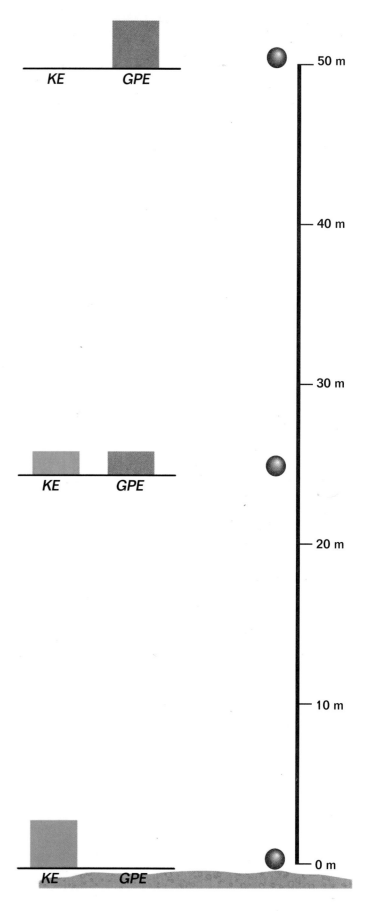

Figure 6-17 As the ball falls, gravitational potential energy is converted to kinetic energy.

Figure 6-18 Energy is transferred on a long slide. **Where is a rider's potential energy least? Greatest? Where is a rider's kinetic energy least? Greatest? Does the total energy change?**

interNET
CONNECTION

Visit the Glencoe Science Web Site at **www.glencoe.com/ sec/science** for more information about energy.

Figure 6-18 shows a slide. As you ride down, potential energy is transferred to kinetic energy. When you climb back up, you use kinetic energy to gain potential energy. Because this is a real system, some energy is transferred to heat. But none is lost or gained: energy is conserved.

Section Assessment

1. Suppose you and your bicycle have a total mass of 70 kg. You are moving at 10 m/s. How much kinetic energy do you and the bicycle have?

2. When you bring your bicycle to a stop, where does the kinetic energy it had go?

3. **Think Critically:** Suppose you hold a strong magnet 1 cm away from the refrigerator door. Is there potential energy in this system? What happens when you let go of the magnet?

4. **Skill Builder**
   Observing and Inferring Use the conservation of energy to explain what happens when you drop a ball and it bounces back up. If you throw the ball downward instead of dropping it, do you expect it to bounce higher or lower than when you dropped it? Why? If you need help, refer to Observing and Inferring in the **Skill Handbook** on page 720.

Using Computers

Database Use on-line databases to investigate a particular source of energy, such as oil, solar, or alternative fuels. If you need help, refer to page 733.

Discovery of the Neutrino

The law of conservation of momentum states that when no outside forces act on a system, the momentum of the system is conserved. The law of conservation of energy states that energy is not created or destroyed, only transferred from one object to another. These seemingly simple ideas are behind some of the most important scientific discoveries, including that of a tiny particle called a neutrino.

Tracking Particles

To find the momentum and energy of small particles, scientists study the tracks the particles leave in detectors (left). A track depends on the mass, charge, and initial momentum of the particle.

Around 1930, scientists discovered that one type of particle track (lower right) showed a sudden change of direction and speed. When the particle turned, it did not hit anything and no new outside force acted on it. Scientists predicted that a new particle, one they couldn't detect, was being ejected, carrying off momentum and energy. The new particle was called a neutrino, which means "little neutral particle."

The Mysterious Neutrino

Scientists thought the neutrino had no electric charge and no mass. Neutrinos leave no track in detectors. Direct evidence for the neutrino did not come until 1956. In 1998, scientists in Japan showed that neutrinos do have mass, though that mass has not yet been measured. Neutrinos are a topic of current research in science. Yet, they still obey the basic laws you learn in science class.

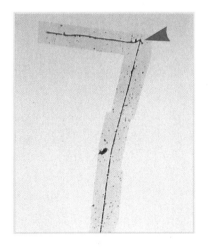

Science
JOURNAL

The track at right was made by a particle in a high-energy accelerator. Scientists used the law of conservation of momentum to propose that the particle must have thrown off another particle, called a neutrino, which doesn't leave a track. In your Science Journal, explain why the conservation of momentum law suggests this is so.

Chapter 6 Reviewing Main Ideas

For a **preview** of this chapter, study this Reviewing Main Ideas before you read the chapter. After you have studied this chapter, you can use the Reviewing Main Ideas to **review** the chapter.

The Glencoe MindJogger, Audiocassettes, and CD-ROM provide additional opportunities for review.

Section 6-1 VELOCITY AND ACCELERATION

An object's motion can be described by **velocity.** Velocity gives the rate of change of position, or **speed,** and the direction of motion. An object's change in motion is described with **acceleration,** the rate of change of velocity. Acceleration can act in the direction of motion, opposite to the direction of motion, or at an angle. *How are speed and velocity related to position and time?*

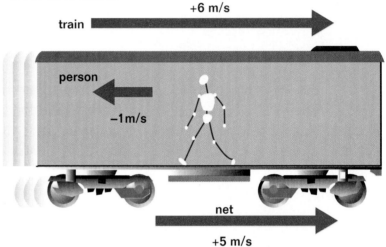

Section 6-2 MASS AND INERTIA

Mass is the amount of matter in an object and it is a measure of the object's **inertia.** *How does the inertia of a freight train moving at 10 km/h compare with your inertia while you bicycle at the same speed?*

MOMENTUM

Momentum is the quantity of motion for an object. Knowing this value gives you an idea of how powerfully the object could collide with another object. *If your mass is 60 kg and you travel in a car moving at 100 km/h, what is your momentum?*

$+3$ kg · m/s -2 kg · m/s

p_A p_B

A   B

$+1$ kg · m/s

p_{A+B}

Reading Check ✔

Explain how direction plays a role in the different concepts studied in this chapter.

CONSERVATION OF MOMENTUM

If no outside forces act on a group of objects, the momentum of the group will not change. The momentum of individual objects in the group may change, as collisions transfer momentum between objects, but the total momentum of the group remains unchanged. *What happens to the momentum of a small ball that strikes a large ball and stops?*

Section 6-3 CONSERVATION OF ENERGY

Energy is the ability to cause change. It takes many forms. **Gravitational potential energy, kinetic energy,** and heat are familiar examples. Energy cannot be created or destroyed, only transferred from one form to another. *A bouncing ball eventually comes to a stop. Where did the kinetic energy go?*

Chapter 6 Assessment

Using Vocabulary

a. acceleration
b. displacement
c. energy
d. gravitational potential energy
e. inertia
f. kinetic energy
g. law of conservation of energy
h. law of conservation of momentum
i. mass
j. momentum
k. speed
l. velocity

For each set of terms below, explain the relationship that exists.

1. inertia, mass
2. displacement, velocity
3. velocity, acceleration
4. kinetic energy, gravitational potential energy
5. mass, momentum

Checking Concepts

Choose the word or phrase that best answers the question.

6. When an object accelerates, what can it do?
   A) speed up
   B) slow down
   C) change direction
   D) all of the above

7. What is the rate of change of position?
   A) velocity
   B) acceleration
   C) displacement
   D) momentum

8. Where is the kinetic energy of a falling object greatest?
   A) top of fall
   B) bottom of fall
   C) middle of fall
   D) it doesn't change

9. What is the rate of change of velocity called?
   A) momentum
   B) mass
   C) acceleration
   D) force

10. When no outside forces act on a system of objects, what do the objects do?
    A) conserve momentum
    B) do not conserve momentum
    C) come to rest
    D) continue with the same velocity

11. What is a possible unit of momentum?
    A) kg
    B) kg · m
    C) kg · m/s^2
    D) kg · m/s

12. What is the gravitational potential energy of a 3-kg object 8 m above the ground?
    A) 24 J
    B) 36 J
    C) 96 J
    D) 235 J

13. Which of the following is **NOT** conserved?
    A) mass
    B) acceleration
    C) energy
    D) momentum

14. What is the momentum of an object with mass 50 kg moving at 20 km/h?
    A) 1000 kg · km/h
    B) 2000 kg · km/h
    C) 5000 kg · km/h
    D) 20 000 kg · km/h

15. What is the kinetic energy of a 60-kg diver falling at 10 m/s?
    A) 300 J
    B) 600 J
    C) 3000 J
    D) 5880 J

Thinking Critically

16. When a wrecking ball hits a wall, it is usually moving at about 10 km/h, which is not very fast. Explain how this ball can knock down a solid wall.

17. When you rub your hands together, what energy was transformed to produce heat?

18. An 80-kg person decides to jump off the back end of a 30-kg canoe. His friend measures the speed of the canoe after he jumps to be 0.8 m/s. The canoe was initially at rest. What rule would you use to find the speed of the person who jumped?

19. If the canoe accelerates from 0 to 0.8 m/s in 0.2 s, what is the acceleration?

20. A ball has a potential energy of 180 J and a kinetic energy of 0 J. After falling 2 m, it has a potential energy of 135 J. What is its kinetic energy at this point?

Developing Skills

If you need help, refer to the Skill Handbook.

21. Using Numbers: An in-line skater is going north at 2 m/s. After accelerating smoothly for 9 s, she is going south at 1 m/s. What was her acceleration, including direction?

22. Concept Mapping: Complete the concept map with the following phrases: *kinetic energy, chemical energy (plant), chemical energy (animal),* and *solar energy.*

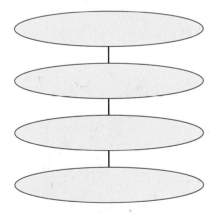

23. Recognizing Cause and Effect: Before a collision, a 1-kg ball is moving left at 0.4 m/s and a 2-kg ball is at rest. After the balls collide, only the 2-kg ball is in motion. What is its velocity? How do you know?

24. Making and Using Graphs: Make a distance-time graph for an object moving with constant velocity 4 m/s. Go from 0 s to 5 s.

THE PRINCETON REVIEW

Test-Taking Tip

Warm Up Before the Race On the day of your exam, arrive at the site early enough to relax, get settled, and go over your notes. It will give you time to relax and prepare your mind for the test.

Test Practice

Use these questions to test your Science Proficiency.

1. Before a collision, a system of three balls has a momentum of +8 kg · m/s. After the collision, one ball has a momentum of –2 kg · m/s and one ball has a momentum of +5 kg · m/s. What is the momentum of the third ball?
A) +5 kg · m/s
B) +13 kg · m/s
C) +1 kg · m/s
D) –1 kg · m/s

2. An object is displaced from a position 2 m north of you to a position 6 m south. The displacement takes 2 s. What is the velocity of the object?
A) 1 m/s north
B) 2 m/s north
C) 3 m/s south
D) 4 m/s south

3. A rock falls 10 m down a cliff. Where is its gravitational potential energy greatest?
A) at the top of the fall
B) at the bottom of the fall
C) at the midpoint of the fall
D) no change in *GPE*

CHAPTER

7

Force and Newton's Laws

Chapter Preview

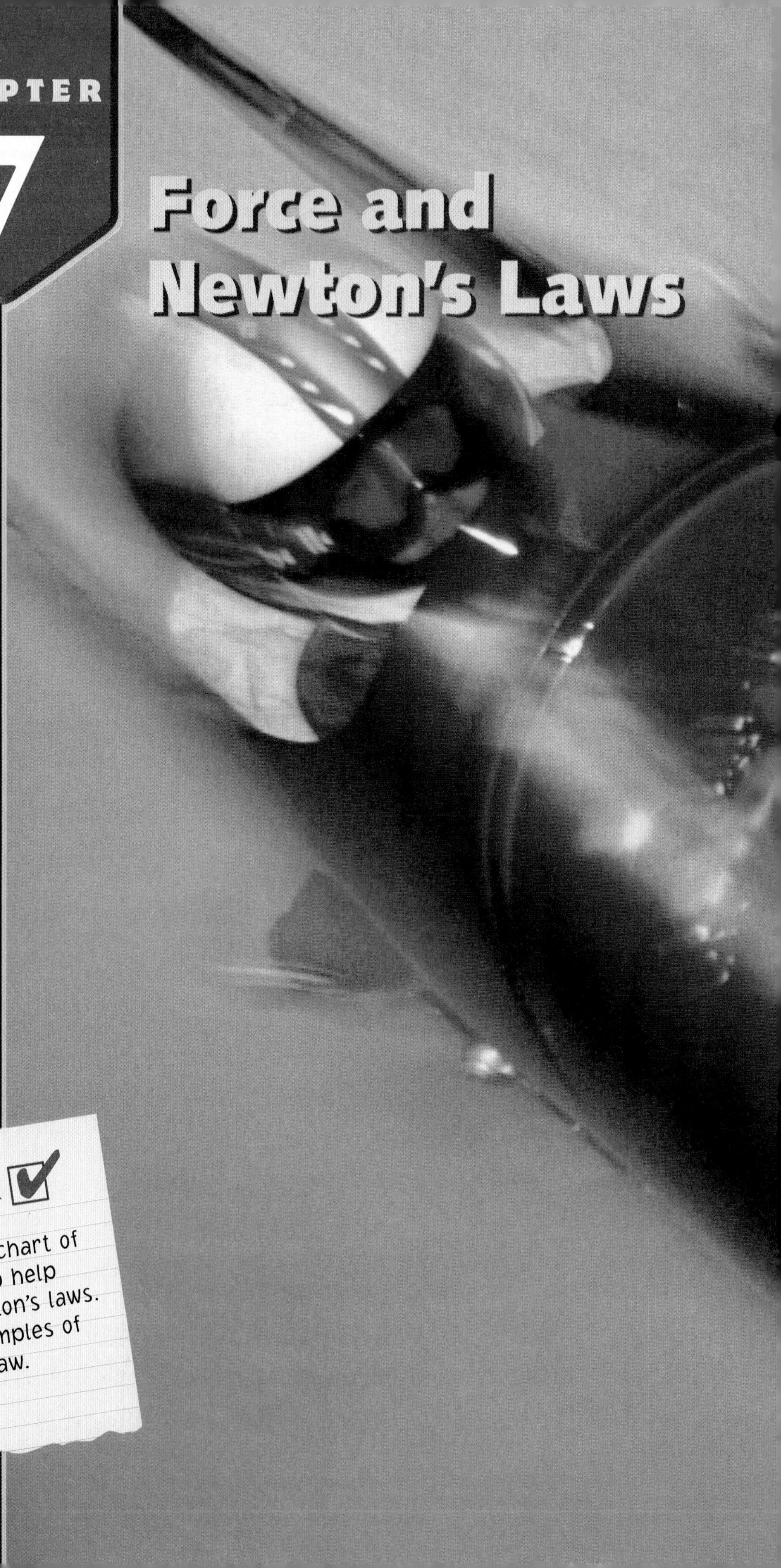

Skills Preview

Skill Builders
- Concept Mapping

Activities
- Design an Experiment

MiniLabs
- Measure in SI

Reading Check

As you read, make a chart of the examples used to help explain each of Newton's laws. Add one or two examples of your own for each law.

Explore Activity

Bobsleds go fast—very fast, as you know if you've ever watched one speed down its icy run. At the top of the run, the bobsledders exert a force on the sled to accelerate it. Then they jump in, and the force of gravity accelerates them down. The team members use their bodies as well as the brakes and steering mechanism to change the sled's motion, slowing it or turning it. The motion of the sled can be understood with Newton's laws of motion.

Define Motion

1. Lean one end of a meterstick on top of three books. This is your ramp. Put one side of the ramp against a wall so the marbles won't roll off.

2. Tap a marble so it rolls up the ramp. Measure how far up the ramp it travels before rolling back.

3. Repeat step 2 using two books, one book, and zero books. The same person should tap the marble each time, trying to keep the force constant.

Science Journal

Make a table and record the motion of the marble for each ramp height. What do you think would happen if you could send a marble along a perfectly smooth, flat path?

Force

When an object accelerates, it changes its motion. It can speed up, slow down, or turn. If an object accelerates, a force must be acting on it. A **force** is a push or a pull. Some examples of forces are shown in **Figure 7-1.** For example, when you throw a ball, your hand exerts a force on the ball, and you accelerate the ball forward. After the ball leaves your hand, gravity exerts a force on it, causing its path to curve downward. When the ball hits the ground, the ground exerts a force, stopping the ball and perhaps bouncing it back up.

The force of a magnet can move a paper clip. Earth's gravitational field can also move the paper clip. Or, you can move the paper clip by picking it up. All of these are examples of forces acting on the paper clip.

Suppose you hold a paper clip near a magnet. You, the magnet, and gravity all exert forces on the clip. A **net force** is the total force felt by an object. The object will accelerate in the direction of the net force. The clip does not move because the net force is zero.

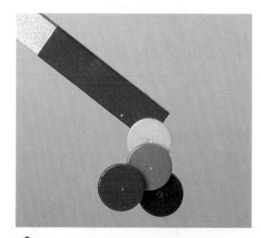

B The force of the magnet on the metal disks is strong enough to pull them off the table.

C The force stored in the spring will stop the door as it opens.

Figure 7-1 Each of these pictures shows a force working.

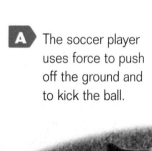

A The soccer player uses force to push off the ground and to kick the ball.

If you push gently on one side of the book in **Figure 7-2,** and a friend pushes hard on the other side, the net force is toward you, so the book will move toward you.

A force can act on an object without causing it to accelerate. Right now gravity is pulling you down and your chair is pushing you up. Your motion isn't changing, so the forces are *balanced.* Two or more forces are **balanced forces** if their effects cancel each other and they do not cause a change in an object's motion. An example is shown in **Figure 7-3.** If the forces on an object are balanced, the net force is zero. If the forces are **unbalanced forces,** the net force is not zero, and the object accelerates. An object can be in motion and have no net force acting on it. If you push a hockey puck across the ice, your hockey stick accelerates it by exerting a force. When you stop exerting that force, the puck keeps moving at constant speed across the ice until the force of friction slows it down. All the forces acting on the puck are balanced while its motion doesn't change.

Figure 7-2 The sum of all the forces acting on an object is the net force.

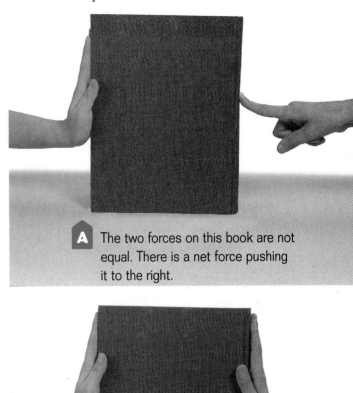

A The two forces on this book are not equal. There is a net force pushing it to the right.

B When the two forces are equal and in opposite directions, the net force is zero. The book does not move.

Figure 7-3 Acrobats exert forces to hold each other in position. All the forces are balanced, so the acrobats do not move. **What will happen if the forces become unbalanced?**

CHEMISTRY
INTEGRATION

Electric Force
A neutral atom has balanced electric forces. An ion has charge and can accelerate other ions or electrons. It has a net electric force. When two negatively charged ions repel each other, is this an example of force? How do you know?

Newton's First Law of Motion

In 1635, when Galileo Galilei was 70 years old, he was placed under house arrest for claiming that the planets, including Earth, orbit the sun and that Earth rotates once each day. His claim troubled many people. "How can Earth be moving?" they thought. "If it does, then our water glasses should fall over!" Galileo's view was revolutionary. He spent the remaining seven years of his life confined to his home. About thirty years later, Isaac Newton would build on Galileo's work and begin to change the way people thought about the world.

Galileo said the reason the water glass does not fall over is because Earth has always been moving around the sun and spinning on its axis in a smooth manner. If Earth suddenly stopped rotating, everything that is not strongly attached to the ground would spill. **Figure 7-4** gives another example.

Newton used Galileo's ideas about motion in what is now called **Newton's first law of motion.** It states, "An object will remain at rest or move with constant velocity until it is acted upon by a net force." This also is called Newton's law of inertia.

A Thought Experiment

Galileo discovered this scientific law by thinking about a ball rolling up a ramp, as in the Explore Activity. If the ramp is steep, the ball will not travel far before it stops. As the ramp

Figure 7-4 An object in motion remains in motion.

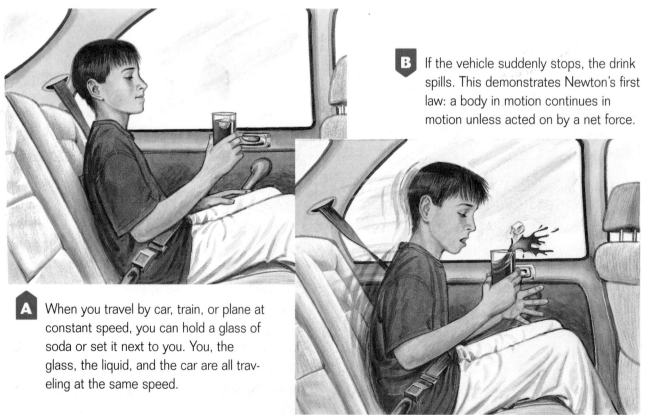

B If the vehicle suddenly stops, the drink spills. This demonstrates Newton's first law: a body in motion continues in motion unless acted on by a net force.

A When you travel by car, train, or plane at constant speed, you can hold a glass of soda or set it next to you. You, the glass, the liquid, and the car are all traveling at the same speed.

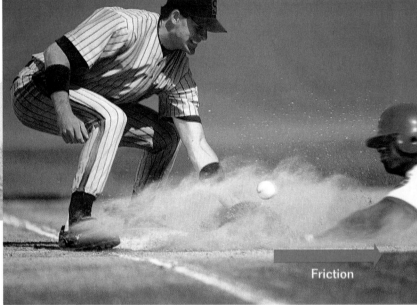

Figure 7-5 Friction acts against the motion between objects.

A Without friction, the climber would slide down the slope.

is lowered closer and closer to level, the ball will go farther and farther up the ramp. If the ramp is then made perfectly smooth and level, the ball should continue moving forever if nothing disturbs it.

You can try this by rolling a bowling ball on a large, level surface, like your school gymnasium floor. A slight push will easily send the ball across the room at nearly constant speed.

What happens when you repeat the experiment on a rough or uneven surface, like grass or a thick carpet? The ball slows down. Something disturbs the ball's motion. A force must be acting on the ball.

Friction

Galileo said an object in motion remains in motion until a net (or unbalanced) force acts on it. The unbalanced force that brings nearly everything to a stop is **friction,** the rubbing force that acts against motion between two touching surfaces. There are a number of different forms of friction, but they all have one thing in common. They always act against an object's direction of motion, as shown in **Figure 7-5.** Friction will never speed up an object. If you rub your hand against a tabletop, you can feel the friction push against the direction your hand is moving. If you rub back the other way, you can feel the direction of friction change so it is again acting against your hand's motion. ☑

B If you are in motion, friction slows you down, like this baseball player.

Reading Check ☑

What is friction?

Older Ideas About Motion

It took a long time to understand force. People once thought the natural state of an object was rest. For an object to be in motion, something had to be continuously moving it. As soon as the force stopped, nature would bring the object to rest.

Galileo understood that constant motion is as natural as rest. If he could remove friction, an object would continue to move with constant motion. He did a series of experiments where he pushed an object across smoother and smoother surfaces and found that the object would go farther and farther. He reasoned that if he could make the surface perfectly smooth and flat, the object would never slow down. You can repeat this experiment yourself at home or at school.

Static Friction

Another experiment can demonstrate static friction. Place an eraser on your ruler. Start to tip the ruler, as shown in **Figure 7-6.** The eraser does not start to slide right away, but stays in place until the ruler reaches a certain angle. The friction that prevents an object from moving when a force is applied is called static friction. It is static friction that makes it possible to walk. Every step taken pushes against Earth. Without friction, you'd slip and fall.

Have you ever tried to push something heavy, like a refrigerator? When you begin to push, nothing happens. Static friction balances your force. As you push harder and harder, the object will suddenly give way and move. When the object begins to move, you are exerting a force too great for static friction to balance.

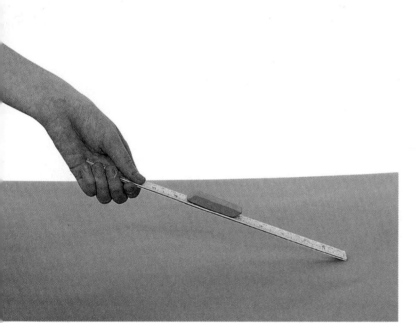

Figure 7-6 Static friction holds the eraser in place on the ruler. **What will happen when the net force due to gravity is greater than the force of static friction?**

Sliding Friction

Static friction keeps an object at rest. Sliding friction slows down an object that slides. If you push an object across the room, there is sliding friction between the bottom of the object and the floor. You have to keep pushing to overcome the force of sliding friction. The brake pads in a car use sliding friction against the wheels to slow the car. Bicycle brakes, shown in **Figure 7-7A,** work the same way. Skidding tires, shuffling shoes, and rubbing hands are all common forms of sliding friction.

Figure 7-7 A bicycle uses sliding friction and rolling friction.

A Sliding friction is used to stop this bicycle tire. Friction between the brake pads and the wheel brings the wheel to a stop.

B Rolling friction with the ground pushes the bottom of the bicycle tire back so the wheel rolls forward.

Rolling friction

Rolling Friction

The wheel helps reduce sliding friction, but even the best wheel cannot completely remove this force. In fact, another kind of friction, rolling friction, is needed to make a wheel turn. There is friction between the ground and the part of a bike tire in contact with the ground, as shown in **Figure 7-7B.** Rolling friction pushes back so that the tire rolls forward. Sometimes, when a bike hits a patch of ice or wet leaves, there is not enough friction between the tire and ground to spin the tire, and the bike skids.

Spin a wheel with your hand and you can feel the friction between your hand and the wheel. If the wheel were coated in oil, your hand would slip off and it would be difficult to get enough friction to start the wheel in motion.

Air Resistance

When you ride a bicycle, the air pushes your hair and clothes back. Whether you are biking, walking, or riding in a car, air pushes against you. This is air resistance. Air resistance acts on the forward moving part of an object, such as the front of a car. It acts against the direction of motion and gets stronger as an object goes faster.

When you first start to pedal, your legs provide the force to push the bicycle forward. The air resistance is low, and you can accelerate fairly quickly. As you go faster, the air resistance gets stronger. Eventually, the air resistance (and road friction) balance your pedaling force, so you move at constant velocity.

Mini Lab

Defining Rolling Friction

Procedure

1. Attach a spring scale to a wheeled object such as a skateboard.
2. Pull the skateboard across the room at a steady speed. Observe the reading on the spring scale.

Analysis

1. What did the spring scale read when you started? What did it read as you moved at constant speed? When you stopped?
2. What is the force of rolling friction in this example? (Assume air resistance is so small it can be ignored.)

Figure 7-8 Engineers design cars, bike helmets, and other items so that they have as little air resistance as possible.

Whatever type, friction plays a role in nearly every real-life situation, as shown in **Figure 7-8.** It is one key in understanding and applying Newton's laws. Friction is a force that is always present, though it can be reduced and sometimes ignored.

A When you bike, air resistance pushes against you to slow you down.

Air resistance

B When driving a car at high speed, overcoming the force of air resistance takes most of the energy used in gas.

Section Assessment

1. A car maintains a speed of 20 km/h as it turns to the left. Is a force acting on the car? Explain.

2. Explain why friction made it difficult to discover Newton's first law of motion.

3. **Think Critically:** In the following situations, are the forces balanced or unbalanced? How can you tell?

   a. You push a box of books until it is moving at 0.5 m/s.

   b. You continue to push the box of books across the floor at 0.5 m/s.

   c. You stop pushing the box, and it comes to a stop.

4. **Skill Builder**
   Comparing and Contrasting
   Compare and contrast static friction, sliding friction, and rolling friction. If you need help, refer to Comparing and Contrasting in the **Skill Handbook** on page 720.

Science Journal

Most of the meteors that reach Earth's atmosphere burn up on the way down. Friction between the meteor and the atmosphere produces a huge amount of heat. Research how the space shuttle is protected from friction when it reenters Earth's atmosphere. Report your findings in your Science Journal. If you need help, refer to page 733.

Newton's Second Law

Force and Acceleration

Are you ever afraid to share your ideas in class? Newton did not like to write about his discoveries because he was afraid he would be criticized. A fellow scientist encouraged Newton to publish his discoveries about motion. Newton reluctantly agreed and wrote *The Principia*.

The central theme for *The Principia* was Newton's description of forces and how they act, now called Newton's laws of motion. If you know how a force acts on an object, you can calculate anything you would like to know about its motion in the future as well as the past. Newton used the laws to calculate the motions of the planets.

Newton presented the answers to many complex problems. He calculated the orbits of the planets around the sun and the effect of Jupiter's gravity pulling on Saturn. He then asked an astronomer if he had noticed Saturn's motion change unexpectedly when it passed near Jupiter. The motion had changed and by just the amount Newton calculated. Newton's laws are still used to understand and predict motion today.

The change in Saturn's motion depended on the direction of Jupiter's force. As **Figure 7-9** shows, you must know the direction of a force to know what effect it will have.

What You'll Learn

► Newton's second law of motion
► Why the direction of force is important

Vocabulary
Newton's second law of motion
normal force

Why It's Important

► Newton's second law explains how any object, from a swimmer to a satellite, moves when any force acts on it.

Figure 7-9 The boy is moving at constant speed. When the girl gives him a gentle push, will he speed up, slow down, or turn to one side? You have to know the direction of a force to understand how it will affect motion.

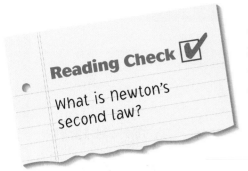
Newton's first law of motion describes the motion of an object with no net force acting on it. **Newton's second law of motion** states, "An object acted upon by a net force will accelerate in the direction of the force according to the following equation." ✓

$$\text{acceleration} = \frac{\text{net force}}{\text{mass}}$$

$$a = \frac{F_{net}}{m} \quad \text{or} \quad F_{net} = ma$$

In this equation, a is the acceleration, m is the mass, and F_{net} is the net force. Force is measured in newtons, abbreviated N; $1 \text{ N} = 1 \text{ kg} \cdot \text{m/s}^2$. If force acts on a small mass and a large mass, the small mass accelerates more. For example, if you try to push an empty box across the floor, you can accelerate it faster than if the box is packed with books.

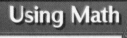

Using Math

A force of 30 N acts on a 6-kg mass. What is the acceleration? If a 0.5-kg mass accelerates at 9.8 m/s², what is the force?

Newton's Second Law and Momentum

Momentum is equal to mass times velocity. When a net force acts on an object, the object's momentum changes. For example, when the bicyclist in **Figure 7-10** brakes, he exerts a force to reduce his velocity. When he reduces his velocity, he reduces his momentum.

The longer a net force acts the greater the change in momentum. The change in momentum, $p_2 - p_1$, is the difference between the object's momentum before and after the force acts. This is described by the following formula.

$$\text{Force} \times \text{time} = \text{change in momentum}$$

$$Ft = p_2 - p_1.$$

Because $p_1 = mv_1$ and $p_2 = mv_2$, you can substitute mv_1 and mv_2 in the equation above.

$$Ft = mv_2 - mv_1$$

The force that acts on an object is related to the initial velocity, v_1, and final velocity, v_2, of the object.

Notice that the force can be positive or negative. Force is defined relative to a frame of reference. In the example in **Figure 7-10,** the positive direction is defined as forward. A force that slows the bike is directed backward, so such a force is negative.

Figure 7-10 This bicyclist uses the brakes to slow down. His velocity before and after he brakes is forward. **In what direction is the force?**

Balanced Forces

While you are reading this sentence, you are probably sitting in a chair. Are forces acting on you now? Newton's first law says that if you're at rest, all the forces acting on you are balanced. Gravity is pulling you down. Your chair is pushing you up. The outward force from a surface, such as the upward force provided by your chair, is called the **normal force.** *Normal* means at a right angle. On a flat surface, the normal force is straight up and balances your weight. The normal force is supplied by the strength of the surface—in this case, the chair. If you put a heavy weight on a rickety chair, the chair might not be able to provide enough normal force to balance the weight. Then, the chair breaks.

When the surface is tilted, the normal force is reduced, as shown in **Figure 7-11.** The normal force no longer balances the weight. If friction doesn't balance this net force (look back at **Figure 7-5A**), you will start moving downhill.

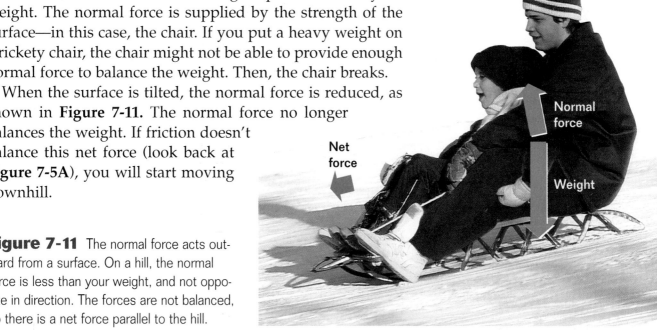

Figure 7-11 The normal force acts outward from a surface. On a hill, the normal force is less than your weight, and not opposite in direction. The forces are not balanced, so there is a net force parallel to the hill.

Using Math

Force and Change in Momentum

Example Problem

A bicyclist exerts a net force of 24 N and accelerates from 2 m/s to 4 m/s. Find the time needed to do this if the bicycle and rider have a mass of 90 kg.

Problem-Solving Steps

1. What is known? velocity before and after, $v_1 = 2$ m/s and $v_2 = 4$ m/s, mass $m = 90$ kg, force $F = -24$ N
2. What is unknown? time t
3. Use the equation $Ft = mv_2 - mv_1$.
4. **Solution:** $\qquad Ft = mv_2 - mv_1$
$$(24 \text{ N})t = (90 \text{ kg})(4 \text{ m/s}) - (90 \text{ kg})(2 \text{ m/s})$$
$$(24 \text{ kg} \cdot \text{m/s}^2)t = 180 \text{ kg} \cdot \text{m/s}$$
$$t = 7.5 \text{ s}$$

The bicyclist takes 7.5 s to reach the new speed.

Practice Problem

The same bicyclist exerts a force on the brakes to slow from 4 m/s to 0 m/s. This takes 12 s. What was the force?

Strategy Hint: Is the force positive or negative?

Figure 7-12 The force of air resistance on these skydivers pushes them up. The force of gravity pulls them down. When the forces are equal, the skydivers fall at a constant speed. This speed is called terminal velocity.

Another example of balanced forces is an object moving at constant speed, such as the bicyclist in **Figure 7-8**. Even falling objects eventually reach a constant speed due to air resistance. *Terminal velocity* is the speed an object reaches when the force of gravity is balanced by the force of air resistance, as shown in **Figure 7-12**. When parachutists jump from an airplane, they will fall for a long time before opening the parachutes. As they accelerate downward, the air resistance against each parachutist's body gets stronger until terminal velocity is reached. If a jumper falls spread eagle, the terminal velocity is about 215 km/h. If a jumper falls in a jack knife, the terminal velocity could be 320 km/h. Although this is very fast, it is still constant. When the speed is constant, the forces acting must be balanced.

Once the parachute is opened, the upward force of air resistance on the open parachute is much greater than the downward force of gravity. The forces are unbalanced and the increased air resistance will slow the parachutist down to a safer terminal velocity of about 18 km/h.

Unbalanced Forces

When the forces acting on an object are not balanced, the object accelerates in the direction of the net force. It might speed up, slow down, or turn.

Figure 7-13 The force and acceleration are to the left. **If the puck has a mass of 0.2 kg and the hockey stick exerts a force of 100 N for 0.1 s, what is the final speed of the puck, v_2?**

Speeding Up

If you look back at all of the examples of objects speeding up, you'll notice there's something pushing or pulling the object in the direction it is moving. The direction of the push or pull is the direction of the force. It is also the direction of the acceleration. Force is in the same direction as the velocity if the object is speeding up, as shown in **Figure 7-13**.

For example, if an object is at rest or moving in a positive direction, and it is accelerated at +4 m/s², it will go +4 m/s faster every second the force acts. You accelerate like this when you fall. Your velocity increases downward by 9.8 m/s every second. This is a rapid change that

v_2 *F*

Figure 7-14 When you catch a ball, you exert a force opposite to the direction of the ball's motion. **If you exert a force of 40 N on a 0.5-kg ball moving at 10 m/s, how long does it take to stop the ball?**

produces high speeds in just seconds. If you have ever jumped off a high-diving platform, you know how quickly you speed up.

Slowing Down

To slow down an object you have to push or pull it against the direction it is moving. An example is given in **Figure 7-14.** This time the force is opposite to the velocity. If the velocity is positive, then the acceleration is negative and makes the velocity less and less.

When a platform diver hits the water, the water provides a large force that slows the diver down. If the diver doesn't have the correct form when entering the water, this force can hurt. You may have experienced this. Water normally seems easy to move around, but when you hit it quickly, its tendency is to remain at rest. It pushes up against you as you enter the water. The force of the water against your body can stop it about five times faster than the pull of gravity accelerated it.

Turning

Sometimes forces and motion are not in a straight line. If a net force acts at an angle to the direction of motion, an object will follow a curving path. Its velocity will change because the direction of motion changes. The object might be going slower, faster, or at the same speed after the turn.

If you jump straight forward from a diving board you will not continue straight across the pool at that height. The force of gravity accelerates you downward, at a right angle to your direction of motion.

Measuring Buoyant Force

Procedure

1. Collect several small objects made of different materials. Weigh them on a spring scale and record the weights. If your scale measures in kilograms rather than newtons, multiply by 10 m/s^2 to get the force in newtons.

2. Now, attach each object to the spring scale and place the object in water. Compare the force reading on the scale with the weights you found in step 1.

Analysis

1. Compare the differences in the weights.

2. How would you find the buoyant force exerted upward on each object by the water?

Your body follows a curving path in the air, as shown in **Figure 7-15.**

Acceleration makes motion exciting because you can feel the change. Pushing then pulling, fast then slow, up then down—these are the action words of force and acceleration. They are what make a day at the amusement park or the swimming pool so much fun.

Figure 7-15 When a diver jumps forward, she doesn't keep moving in a straight line. Gravity exerts a force perpendicular to her motion, turning her.

Section Assessment

1. A human cannonball with a mass of 80 kg is fired out of a cannon with a force of 6400 N. The force lasts for 0.32 s. Find the acceleration and final speed.

2. You are riding on your bicycle at a speed of 20 km/h when you decide to stop pedaling. Draw a simple picture of you on your bicycle. Using arrows to represent forces, draw and label all the forces acting on you as you coast along. If it takes you a minute to stop, at what rate did you accelerate?

3. **Think Critically:** Explain how you can determine the direction of a force by watching an object's change in motion.

4. 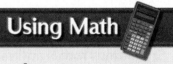 **Skill Builder**
   Making and Using Tables The gravitational force on the surface of each planet in our solar system is different. Do the **Chapter 7 Skill Activity** on page 748 and use a table to find out what you would weigh on different planets.

Using Math

A ball of mass 5 kg is moving at 2 m/s. A force takes 4 s to stop the ball. Find the force.

1. A plane is flying north at 500 km/h. A wind is blowing toward the east at a speed of 60 km/h. What is the actual speed of the plane?

2. You push on the front of a box with a force of 5 N. Your friend pushes on the left side of the box with a force of 12 N. What is the total force on the box? Use an arrow to show the direction of the force.

3. A ball is thrown with a forward velocity of 4 m/s and an upward velocity of 1 m/s. Find the total velocity of the ball.

Applying the Pythagorean Theorem

One way to represent a force is with a vector. A vector is an arrow that points in the direction of the force and is proportional in length to the size of the force. For example, a 3-N force to the left can be represented on paper by a 3-cm arrow pointing left. Vectors also can represent other quantities that have number and direction, such as displacement, velocity, momentum, and acceleration.

Adding Vectors

You can represent all the forces acting on an object with vectors. When all the vectors are connected tip-to-tail, the vector for the total force is drawn from the end of the chain to the head, as follows.

Problem

A boat is moving east at 10 km/h relative to the water. The water is flowing south at 6 km/h relative to the shore. Find the velocity of the boat relative to the shore.

Solution

1. Make a sketch of the situation. Note that the vectors are at right angles.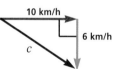

2. The two velocities form two sides of a right triangle. To find the boat's actual velocity, find the length of the hypotenuse. Use the Pythagorean theorem, $c^2 = a^2 + b^2$.

3. Substitute 10 and 6 for a and b, and solve for c.

$$c^2 = a^2 + b^2$$
$$= (10 \text{ km/h})^2 + (6 \text{ km/h})^2$$
$$= 136 \text{ (km/h)}^2$$
$$c = \sqrt{136 \text{ km}^2/\text{h}^2} = 11.7 \text{ km/h}$$

So, the boat is moving at about 12 km/h relative to the land.

Modeling Motion in Two Directions

Possible Materials

- Masking tape
- Stopwatch
  *watch or clock with a second hand
- Meterstick
  *metric tape measure
- Spring scales marked in newtons (2)
- Plastic lid
- An egg in its shell
  *Alternate Materials

When you move a computer mouse across a mouse pad, how does the rolling ball tell the computer cursor to move in the direction you push the mouse? Inside the housing for the mouse's ball, there are two or more rollers that the ball rubs against as you move the mouse. They measure up-and-down motion and back-and-forth motion. What happens to the rollers when you move diagonally and at different angles?

Recognize the Problem

Place an egg on something that will slide, such as a plastic lid. The container is called a *skid*. Lay out a course to follow on the floor. Can you move an egg from one point to another using forces in only two directions?

Form a Hypothesis

How can you combine forces to move in a straight line, along a diagonal, or around corners? Write a plan for moving your egg along the path.

Goals

- **Move** the skid across the ground using two forces.
- **Measure** how fast the skid can be moved.
- **Determine** how smoothly the direction can be changed.

Safety Precautions

Be careful not to drop the egg.

Test Your Hypothesis

Plan

1. **Lay out** a course that involves two directions, such as the course shown in the photo.

2. **Attach** two spring scales to the skid. One will always pull straight forward. One will always pull to one side. You cannot turn the skid. If one scale is pulling toward the door of your classroom, it must always pull in that direction. (It can pull with zero force, if needed, but it can't push.)

3. How will you handle movements along diagonals and turns?

4. How will you measure speed?

5. **Experiment** with your skid. How hard do you have to pull to counteract sliding friction at a given speed? How fast can you accelerate? Can you stop suddenly without spilling the egg, or do you need to slow down?

6. **Write a plan** for moving your egg along the course by pulling only forward and to one side. Be sure you understand your plan and have considered all the details.

Do

1. Make sure your teacher approves your plan before you proceed.

2. **Try** moving your egg along the path.

3. **Modify** your plan, if needed.

4. **Organize** your data so it can be used to run your course.

5. **Test** your results with a new route.

Analyze Your Data

1. What was the difference between the two routes? How did this affect the forces you could use on the egg?

2. How did you **separate and control variables** in this experiment?

3. Was your hypothesis supported? Explain.

Draw Conclusions

1. What happens when you combine two forces at right angles?

2. If you could pull on all four sides (front, back, left, right) of your skid, could you move anywhere along the floor? **Make a hypothesis** to explain your answer.

What You'll Learn

▶ Newton's third law of motion

Vocabulary
Newton's third law of motion

Why It's Important

▶ Newton's third law can help you understand motion from walking to launching rockets.

Action and Reaction

Newton's first two laws explain everything about the motion of a single object. If the forces acting on the object are balanced, the object will remain at rest or stay in motion with constant velocity. If the forces are unbalanced, the object will accelerate in the direction of the net force.

Newton's final law describes the connection between the object supplying the force and the object receiving the force. **Newton's third law of motion** states, "Forces always act in equal but opposite pairs." Another way of saying this is "For every action, there is an equal but opposite reaction." This means that one object can't supply a force (action) without the object it is acting on causing a return force (reaction), as shown in **Figure 7-16.**

Figure 7-16 When one ice-skater pulls on the second, the second pulls back just as hard. The forces are equal and opposite.

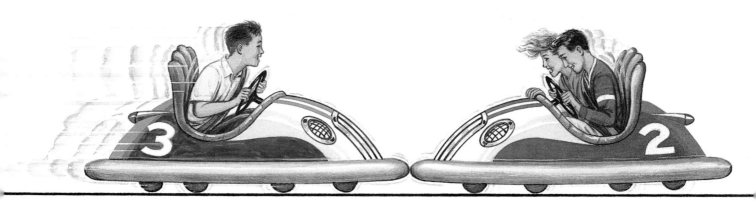

Figure 7-17 In this collision, the first car exerts a force on the second. The second exerts the same force in the opposite direction on the first car. **Which car do you think accelerates more?**

Fun with Newton

Imagine you're driving a bumper car and are going to ram into your two friends in another car, head-on, as shown in **Figure 7-17.** Initially, your friends are at rest. When your bumper meets theirs, its surface pushes against their bumper's surface. Their car accelerates in the direction you forced it to move—backwards. By Newton's third law, their car pushes you with an equal and opposite force, which is directed toward you. This causes your car to slow down because the force was against your motion. Action-reaction forces are always the same size but are in opposite directions and act on different objects.

There is no delay in time between the action and the re-action. They occur at the same time. If you touch your nose with your finger, your nose and finger sense the touch at exactly the same time. These are action-reaction forces. As soon as you remove your finger, the nerves in both your fin-ger and nose will sense this. Also, when you touch your nose, your head moves in the direction of the finger's push, and the finger slows down as the nose pushes back. Why doesn't your head's motion change as drastically as your finger's motion?

Usually, you don't notice the action-reaction that goes on as you move about. You know how to use these forces from experience. You have been learning this since you learned to sit up or roll over. When you start looking, you notice action-reaction pairs all around you.

Using Math

Two students pull on each other. The 45-kg student has an acceleration of 0.2 m/s². What is the acceleration of the 50-kg student? Use action force = reaction force.

*inter***NET**
CONNECTION

Visit the Glencoe Science Web Site at **www.glencoe.com/ sec/science** for more information about the physics of living things.

Force of ground against shoe

Force of shoe against ground

Figure 7-18 The force of the ground on your foot is equal and opposite to the force of your foot on the ground. If you push down harder, the ground pushes up harder.

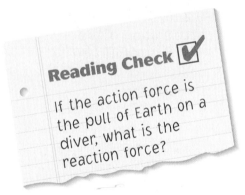

Reading Check ✓

If the action force is the pull of Earth on a diver, what is the reaction force?

LIFE SCIENCE
INTEGRATION ➤

Large and Small

Another reason it's easy to miss the action-reaction pair is because one of the objects is often much more massive and appears to remain motionless when a force acts on it. It has so much inertia, or tendency to remain at rest, that it hardly accelerates. Walking is a good example. When you walk forward, you push backward on the ground. Your shoe pushes Earth backward, and Earth pushes your shoe forward, as shown in **Figure 7-18.** Earth has so much mass, it does not noticeably move when you push it. You have very little mass compared to Earth. Earth pushes you forward with enough acceleration to make you move. The forces are the same but in opposite directions. If you step on something that can move easily, like a skateboard, you can see it being pushed back.

One subtle example of action-reaction is falling to the ground after jumping off a diving board or a step. Earth's gravity pulls a diver down with an acceleration of 9.8 m/s². The reaction is the diver pulling Earth up. The forces are equal but opposite. Why don't you notice Earth being moved by this force? The person's mass is a tiny fraction of Earth's mass, so Earth's acceleration is a tiny fraction of the person's acceleration. ✓

More Examples of Newton's Third Law

Have you ever stuck your hand out a car window and felt the wind push your hand back? Did it take a lot of strength to keep your hand steady? Why was it hard to hold your hand still? The answer is because air has mass. Your hand exerts a force forward on the air, and the air exerts an equal and opposite force back against your hand. The faster the car is going, the more force you have to exert to equal the force of the air.

When a bird flies, its wings push the air down and backward along a diagonal. In reaction, the air pushes the bird upward and forward, as shown in **Figure 7-19A.** If you could see the air, you would see it accelerate quickly as the bird pushes it. Air has little inertia. The bird is more massive than the air and does not accelerate as much.

When you paddle a canoe, there is little friction between the canoe and the water. To move the canoe forward, you push water back with your paddle. The paddle has a large enough surface to push a lot of water. Although it is hard to

Figure 7-19 When a bat flies or a fish swims, they also push on the air or water around them. **What pushes back?**

A The bird's wings push down on the air, which pushes up on the wing. In a wind tunnel, you could see how the bird's wings push on the air. Without air to push on, the bird couldn't fly.

see the water move, you can see currents form on the surface as the water is pushed backwards, as in **Figure 7-19B.** The water accelerates backwards and reacts by pushing forward on the paddle. Because the paddle is attached to you and you are attached to the canoe, the canoe accelerates in the forward direction. The same thing happens when you use your arms to swim. Can you think of another example of action-reaction?

B The paddle pushes back on the water, and the water pushes forward on the paddle.

Section Assessment

1. You sit on the floor and push a skateboard with a force of 6 N. If your mass is 60 kg, what is the force the skateboard exerts on you? In what direction is the force?

2. A hockey puck is at rest on the ice. What two forces are acting on it? You now hit the puck across the ice. While you are hitting the puck, what forces act on it? What else has a change of motion when the puck is hit?

3. **Think Critically:** Suppose you are an astronaut on the space shuttle. What would happen if you pushed against a chair that was not bolted to the floor? Why is pushing against a chair that is bolted down different?

4. **Skill Builder**
   Using Numbers A person standing on a canoe throws a cement block over the side. The action force on the cement block is 60 N. The reaction force is on the person and canoe. Their total mass is 100 kg. What is their acceleration? If you need help, refer to Using Numbers in the **Skill Handbook** on page 731.

Science Journal
Some people have trouble understanding Newton's third law. They reason, "If every action has an equal and opposite reaction, nothing will ever move." Explain why objects can still move. (Consider whether the forces act on the same object or on different objects.)

Balloon Races

Materials
- Balloons of different sizes and shapes
- Drinking straws
- String
- Tape
- Meterstick
- Stopwatch or clock

Going into space captures people's imaginations. Rockets use Newton's third law to propel them. In this experiment, you will compare different balloon rocket designs. The balloon rocket is powered by escaping air, using Newton's third law. Its motion is determined by Newton's first and second laws.

What You'll Investigate

How does Newton's third law accelerate different balloon rockets?

Goals
- **Measure** the speed of a balloon rocket.
- **Describe** how Newton's laws explain a rocket's motion.

Procedure

1. Run a string across the classroom to make a rocket path. Leave one end loose so you can easily place the rockets on the string.
2. **Make** a balloon rocket according to the photo. Don't tie the balloon closed. Let it run down the track. **Measure** its distance and time.
3. Repeat step 2 with different balloons.

Conclude and Apply

1. **Compare and contrast** the distances traveled. Which rocket went the greatest distance?
2. **Calculate** the average speed for each rocket. **Compare and contrast** them. Which rocket has the greatest average speed?
3. **Infer** what aspects of these rockets made them travel far or fast.
4. **Draw** a diagram showing all the forces acting on a balloon rocket.
5. Use Newton's laws of motion to **explain** the motion of a balloon rocket from launch until it comes to a stop.

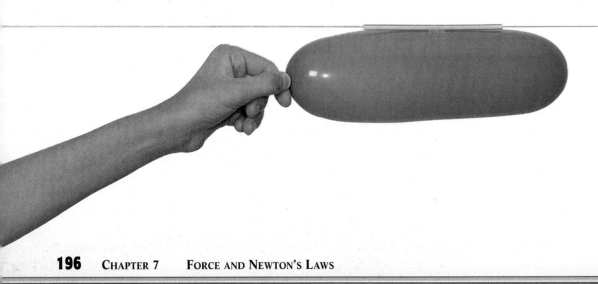

Describing Motion

7·4

The Laws of Motion

With Newton's laws and the law of conservation of momentum, summarized in **Table 7-1,** almost any motion problem can be solved. In most everyday problems, if you know an object's motion and all the forces acting on it, you can figure out how the object will move in the future and how it moved in the past. It can be exciting to make a prediction using Newton's laws and then see your prediction confirmed by experiment. **Figures 7-20** and **7-21** give examples of complex motions that can be analyzed with Newton's laws.

What **You'll Learn**

► How to use the law of conservation of momentum and Newton's laws of motion to describe and analyze motion

Why **It's Important**

► All the motion you observe, whether the moon in orbit or a fast-turning in-line skater, can be understood with these laws.

Table 7-1

The Laws of Motion	
Newton's first law	An object will remain at rest or continue moving with constant velocity until it is acted upon by a net force.
Newton's second law	An object acted upon by a net force will accelerate in the direction of the force according to the following equation. $$a = \frac{F_{net}}{m}$$
Newton's third law	Forces occur in equal but opposite pairs. (For every action, there is an equal but opposite reaction.)
Law of conservation of momentum	In a system where no outside forces act, the total momentum before and after a collision stays the same.

Figure 7-20 When the child pushes off the wall, the wall pushes against the child—Newton's third law. Conservation of momentum explains why the adult will be pushed back when she catches and slows the child. They glide back together. This demonstrates Newton's first law. Eventually friction with the water will slow them according to Newton's second law. **Can you find another example of Newton's third law?**

VISUALIZING
Newton's Laws

Figure 7-21 Athletes don't do calculations before they jump, run, or throw, but understanding how the laws of motion work can help you improve your game. Newton's laws are all seen on a bobsled run.

A The two bobsledders push against the ground as they run—Newton's third law. Newton's second law explains the acceleration of the sled.

B To turn, the sled must be acted on by a force at an angle to its motion, as explained by Newton's second law.

C The net force determined by gravity and the normal force will keep accelerating the sled downhill according to Newton's second law.

D At the bottom, the track is level. According to Newton's first law, the sled continues forward in a straight line until a force (the brakes) slows it.

Throwing and Catching a Ball

What happens when you can't use friction to hold yourself in one spot? Imagine you are standing on ice skates and the effect of friction is small. Suppose your friend exerts a forward force of 60 N for 1 s to throw a 15-kg ball, as shown in **Figure 7-22.** You can find the forward velocity of the ball.

$$\text{force} \times \text{time} = \text{mass} \times \text{velocity}$$

$$Ft = mv$$

$$(60 \text{ N})(1 \text{ s}) = (15 \text{ kg})(v)$$

$$60 \text{ kg} \cdot \text{m/s} = (15 \text{ kg})(v)$$

$$v = 4 \text{ m/s}$$

The ball is moving at 4 m/s.

What happens when you catch the ball? Use the law of conservation of momentum. Assume you have a mass of 50 kg.

$$\text{momentum before} = \text{momentum after}$$

$$\begin{array}{c}\text{momentum of} \\ \text{ball before}\end{array} = \begin{array}{c}\text{momentum of you} \\ \text{and ball after}\end{array}$$

$$m_1 v_1 = m_2 v_2$$

$$(15 \text{ kg})(4 \text{ m/s}) = (15 \text{ kg} + 50 \text{ kg})(v_2)$$

$$60 \text{ kg} \cdot \text{m/s} = (65 \text{ kg})(v_2)$$

$$v_2 = 0.9 \text{ m/s}$$

You and the ball go backward at about 0.9 m/s.

Mini Lab

Measuring Force Pairs

Procedure

1. Work in pairs. Each person needs a spring scale.
2. Hook the two scales together. Each person should pull back on a scale. Record the two readings. Pull harder and record the two readings.
3. Continue to pull on both scales, but let the scales move toward one person. Do the readings change?
4. Try to pull in such a way that the scales have different readings.

Analysis

1. What can you conclude about the pair of forces in each situation?
2. Explain how this experiment demonstrates Newton's laws.

Figure 7-22 When you try to catch a ball without friction to hold you still, the law of conservation of momentum describes how you and the ball move backwards with the same momentum the ball alone had before the collision. **What would happen to your speed if you threw the ball back to your friend?**

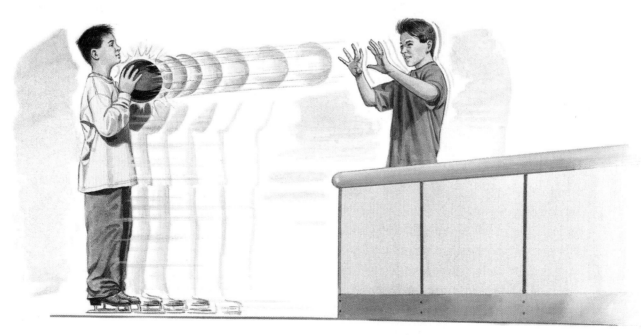

Figure 7-23 If the engine compartment were closed, the gas inside would collide evenly with all sides, and it would stay at rest. But, the opening at the bottom of the engine lets the gas moving down escape. To get out, the gas must first bounce off the top of the compartment. The force down is equal to the force up.

Rocket Launch

The launching of the space shuttle is a spectacular use of Newton's third law. Three rocket engines supply the force of lift, called thrust. Just before launch, the shuttle's weight is about 20 million N. Nearly all of this is highly explosive rocket fuel.

When the rocket fuel is ignited, the burning creates a hot, fast-moving gas. Particles of gas push against the inside of the engine but can only escape out the bottom of the engine, as shown in **Figure 7-23.** The hard wall of the engine pushes the gas molecules downward when they bounce off of it. The upward push on the shuttle is the action. The downward push on the gas is the reaction. The forces are equal but opposite.

Gas particle

Engine compartment

Problem Solving

Modeling Motion in Space

Astronaut Jim Lovell, who flew on *Gemini 7* and *12* and *Apollo 8* and *13,* explains how underwater training for astronauts started.

The attempts to work outside a spacecraft on *Gemini* flights *9, 10,* and *11* were disasters. Every time the astronauts touched the spacecraft it seemed to repel them, and the astronauts became fatigued and hot, fighting to maintain position. We forgot Newton's third law of motion: "For every action there is an equal and opposite reaction." On Earth, gravity is so overwhelming that we don't notice the reaction. But in zero gravity the reaction is noticeable.

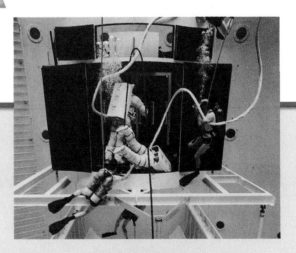

. . . Someone had the brilliant idea that a person. . . underwater would be a good substitute for an astronaut in zero gravity . . . [With this technique] we established the proper handholds and footholds, tools, and movement techniques that are still used today.

Think Critically: Explain how each of Newton's laws would affect your motion working outside a spacecraft in orbit.

Steering a Rocket

The space shuttle steers using the same principle that it does to launch. Little engines located all around its surface can fire in different directions. When the pilot wants to turn the shuttle's nose to the right, he or she will fire an engine on the front left and back right. The action-reaction is due to Newton's third law. According to Newton's second law, the reaction force will move the nose to the right and the tail to the left, as shown in **Figure 7-24A.**

The astronauts also have a backpack that works the same way, shown in **Figure 7-24B.** It uses cold rather than hot gas. Remember Newton's first law—once turning, how does an astronaut stop from turning?

Newton's laws are the keys to understanding motion. They aren't complicated, but you must think carefully to fully understand how they work. As you see how these laws are used to explain familiar motions, you can start to use them to analyze more complicated motions.

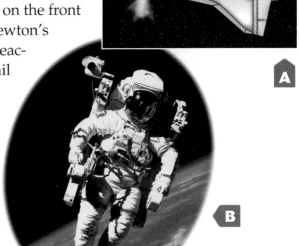

A

B

Figure 7-24 A stream of gas in one direction moves the shuttle (A) or astronaut (B) in the opposite direction.

Section Assessment

1. You catch a 0.2-kg baseball moving at 30 m/s. It takes you 0.4 s to bring it to a stop. What force did you use? If the ball is moving in a positive direction, is the force in a positive or negative direction?

2. A player throws a baseball. The ball flies forward and downward toward another player. The second player catches the ball. Explain how Newton's laws are involved in each of these three motions.

3. **Think Critically:** You can use the law of conservation of momentum to analyze a collision in which two balls roll together, collide, then roll apart. Explain what is happening in this collision using Newton's laws of motion.

4. **Skill Builder**
   Recognizing Cause and Effect Explain how cause and effect apply to Newton's second law. If you need help, refer to Recognizing Cause and Effect in the **Skill Handbook** on page 721.

Using Math

Look at **Figure 7-22.** Suppose the ball has a mass of 10 kg. Find its velocity if the throw is still 60 N for 1 s. Find your velocity after catching the ball.

For a **preview** of this chapter, study this Reviewing Main Ideas before you read the chapter. After you have studied this chapter, you can use the Reviewing Main Ideas to **review** the chapter.

The Glencoe MindJogger, Audiocassettes, and CD-ROM provide additional opportunities for review.

Section 7-1 FORCE

A **force** is a push or a pull. *How can you tell that a net force is acting on an object?*

NEWTON'S FIRST LAW

Newton's first law states that objects in motion tend to stay in motion and objects at rest tend to stay at rest unless acted upon by a **net force.** *Why don't we see objects in motion on Earth tending to stay in motion forever?*

Section 7-2 NEWTON'S SECOND LAW

Newton's second law states that an object acted upon by a net force will accelerate in the direction of this force according to the equation $a = F_{net}/m$. *If a baseball bat hits a bowling ball, why doesn't the bowling ball accelerate as quickly as a baseball that is hit just as hard?*

Reading Check ☑

List three questions someone might ask about force and the changes it causes. Then answer the questions.

Section

7-3 NEWTON'S THIRD LAW

Newton's third law states that forces are always applied in equal but opposite pairs between two objects. *What is meant by "equal but opposite pairs?" Use an example to explain.*

Section

7-4 LAWS OF MOTION

The laws of motion can be used to completely describe and understand most of the motion you observe. *Explain how each of Newton's three laws is involved when you jump off a diving board into a pool.*

Chapter 7 Assessment

Using Vocabulary

a. balanced forces
b. force
c. friction
d. net force
e. Newton's first law of motion
f. Newton's second law of motion
g. Newton's third law of motion
h. normal force
i. unbalanced forces

Each phrase below describes a science term from the list. Write the term that matches the phrase describing it.

1. the outward force a surface supplies to support an object
2. the forces acting on a body cancel each other
3. forces occur in equal and opposite pairs
4. the sum of the forces on an object
5. the force needed to turn a wheel

Checking Concepts

Choose the word or phrase that best answers the question.

6. How can Newton's third law be simply stated?
   A) action-reaction   C) inertia
   B) balanced-unbalanced   D) before-after

7. What is the rubbing when one surface moves against another surface called?
   A) terminal velocity   C) normal force
   B) friction   D) inertia

8. What is the combination of units for the newton?
   A) m/s^2 C) kg · m/s^2
   B) kg · m/s   D) kg/m

9. Which of the following has no direction?
   A) force   C) momentum
   B) acceleration   D) mass

10. What is a push or a pull a simple definition of?
    A) force   C) acceleration
    B) momentum   D) inertia

11. What is the type of friction important to walking?
    A) static friction
    B) sliding friction
    C) rolling friction
    D) air resistance

12. An object is accelerated by a net force in what direction?
    A) at an angle to the force
    B) in the direction of the force
    C) in the direction opposite to the force
    D) Any of these is possible.

13. If you exert a net force of 8 N on a 2-kg object for 3 s, what is the object's change in momentum?
    A) 12 kg · m/s   C) 24 kg · m/s
    B) 13 kg · m/s   D) 48 kg · m/s

14. You push against a wall with a force of 5 N. What is the force vector of the wall on your hands?
    A) 0 N   C) 5 N
    B) 2.5 N   D) 10 N

15. You are on a bike. Which of the following is an example of balanced forces?
    A) You pedal to speed up.
    B) You turn at constant speed.
    C) You coast to slow down.
    D) You pedal at constant speed.

Thinking Critically

16. A baseball is pitched east at 40 km/h. The batter hits it west at 40 km/h. Did the ball accelerate? Explain.

17. Frequently, we don't notice the pair of forces acting between two objects because one of the objects is Earth. How are the forces acting on Earth hidden?

18. A car is parked on a hill. The driver starts the car, accelerates until the car is driving at constant speed, drives at constant speed, then brakes to put the brake pads in contact with the spinning wheels. Explain how static friction, sliding friction, rolling friction, and air resistance are seen in this example.

19. You hit a hockey puck and it slides across the ice at constant speed. Is there a force keeping it in motion? Explain.

20. Newton's third law describes the forces between two colliding objects. Use this connection to explain the forces acting when you kick a soccer ball.

Developing Skills

If you need help, refer to the Skill Handbook.

21. **Making Models:** Explain why Galileo's thought experiment of rolling balls along a flatter and flatter ramp is a model of motion. Could the predicted motion ever be seen in a real experiment?

22. **Interpreting Scientific Illustrations:** Is there a net force acting on the object shown?

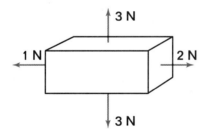

23. **Using Numbers:** An object of mass 0.4 kg accelerates at 2 m/s². Find the force.

24. **Recognizing Cause and Effect:** Use Newton's third law to explain why a rocket accelerates on takeoff.

Test-Taking Tip

Become an Expert on What You Fear Most If you think you can't remember all of the information, don't run away. Instead, consider it a challenge, meet the problem head-on, and you'll be surprised at how easy it is to conquer even the toughest concepts.

Test Practice

Use these questions to test your Science Proficiency.

1. Two students, Molly and Brian, are sitting in identical desk chairs with rollers. Molly weighs 40 kg and Brian weighs 60 kg. Brian quickly shoves Molly's chair, causing both chairs to move. During the push, while Brian's hand touched Molly's chair, which of the following is true?
   A) Neither student exerts a force on the other.
   B) Brian's force on Molly is larger.
   C) Molly's force on Brian is larger.
   D) Both students exert the same amount of force on each other.

2. You are standing in an elevator that is moving upward with constant velocity. What can you conclude about the forces acting on your body?
   A) The normal force of the floor is greater than the gravitational force.
   B) The normal force of the floor is less than the gravitational force.
   C) The normal force of the floor is equal to the gravitational force.
   D) No forces are acting.

3

Earth's Interior

What's Happening Here?

The earth beneath your feet is not as solid as it feels. Earth's surface is, in fact, broken into massive, shifting plates. Along the edges of these plates, molten rock finds its way to the surface, creating volcanoes that can erupt with tremendous force. The people in this truck (left) narrowly escaped the explosion of Mount Pinatubo on the Philippine island of Luzon in 1991. Some 800 inhabitants of Luzon did not escape. When Mount Pinatubo awoke from its 600-year slumber, it spewed out more gas and debris than most other volcanic eruption of this century. Earth's internal processes also cause earthquakes. The twisted wreckage of a train in Kobe, Japan (below), illustrates the terrible destructive power unleashed by the quake of 1995. In this unit, you will learn how understanding the forces that originate deep within Earth helps us to predict the destruction they can cause.

*inter*NET CONNECTION

Explore the Glencoe Science Web Site at **www.glencoe.com/sec/science** to find out more about topics found in this unit.

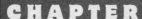

CHAPTER

8 Earthquakes

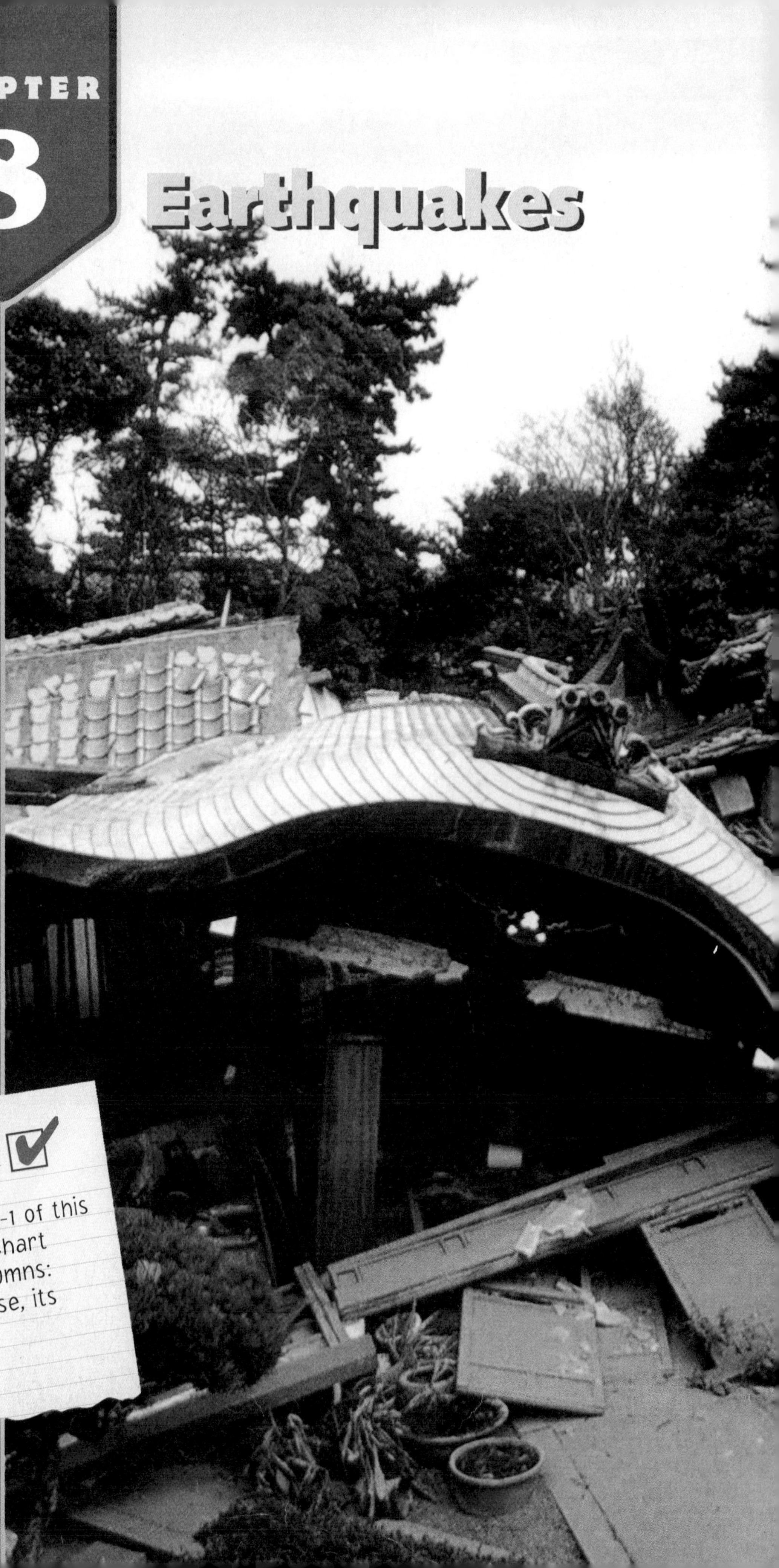

Chapter Preview

Section 8-1
Forces Inside Earth

Section 8-2
Earthquake Information

Section 8-3
Destruction by Earthquakes

Skills Preview

Skill Builders
- Compare and Contrast
- Make and Use a Table

Activities
- Interpret Data
- Make and Use a Graph

MiniLabs
- Interpret a Graph
- Make a Model

Reading Check

As you read Section 8-1 of this chapter, complete a chart with these three columns: type of fault, its cause, its effects.

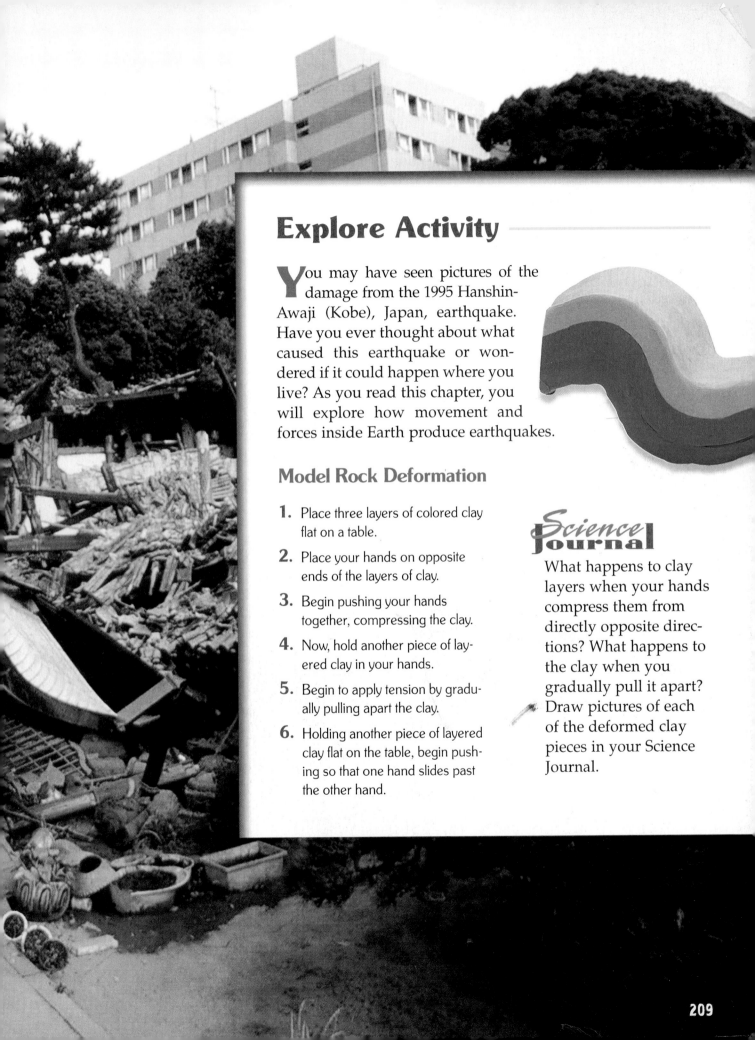

Explore Activity

You may have seen pictures of the damage from the 1995 Hanshin-Awaji (Kobe), Japan, earthquake. Have you ever thought about what caused this earthquake or wondered if it could happen where you live? As you read this chapter, you will explore how movement and forces inside Earth produce earthquakes.

Model Rock Deformation

1. Place three layers of colored clay flat on a table.

2. Place your hands on opposite ends of the layers of clay.

3. Begin pushing your hands together, compressing the clay.

4. Now, hold another piece of layered clay in your hands.

5. Begin to apply tension by gradually pulling apart the clay.

6. Holding another piece of layered clay flat on the table, begin pushing so that one hand slides past the other hand.

Science Journal

What happens to clay layers when your hands compress them from directly opposite directions? What happens to the clay when you gradually pull it apart? Draw pictures of each of the deformed clay pieces in your Science Journal.

Forces Inside Earth

Causes of Earthquakes

Think about the last time you used a rubber band to hold a roll of papers together. Rubber bands stretch when you use force on them. Because they are elastic, they return to their original shape once the force is released. A wooden ice-cream–bar stick behaves in much the same way. When force is first applied to the stick, it will bend and change shape, as shown by the student on the left in **Figure 8-1.** The energy needed to bend the stick is stored inside the stick as potential energy. If the force keeping the stick bent is removed, the stick will return to its original shape, and the stored energy will be released as energy of motion.

Passing the Elastic Limit Causes Faulting

There is a limit to how far a rubber band will stretch or to how far a wooden ice-cream–bar stick will bend. Once this elastic limit is reached, the rubber band or wooden stick breaks. Rocks near Earth's surface behave in much the same way. Up to a point, applied forces cause rocks to bend and stretch, undergoing elastic deformation. Once their elastic limit is passed, the rocks may break. This is demonstrated with an ice-cream–bar stick by the student on the right in **Figure 8-1.** When bent rocks break, they move along surfaces called **faults.**

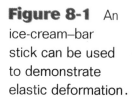

What You'll Learn

▶ To explain how earthquakes result from the buildup of stress in Earth's crust
▶ The differences between normal, reverse, and strike-slip faults

Vocabulary

fault
earthquake
normal fault
reverse fault
strike–slip fault

Why It's Important

▶ Studying the causes of earthquakes will help you tell where they can occur.

Figure 8-1 An ice-cream–bar stick can be used to demonstrate elastic deformation.

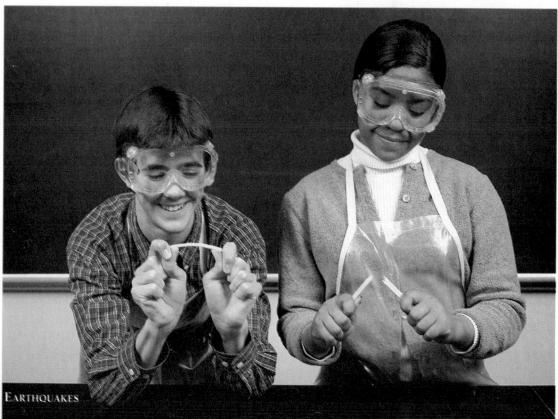

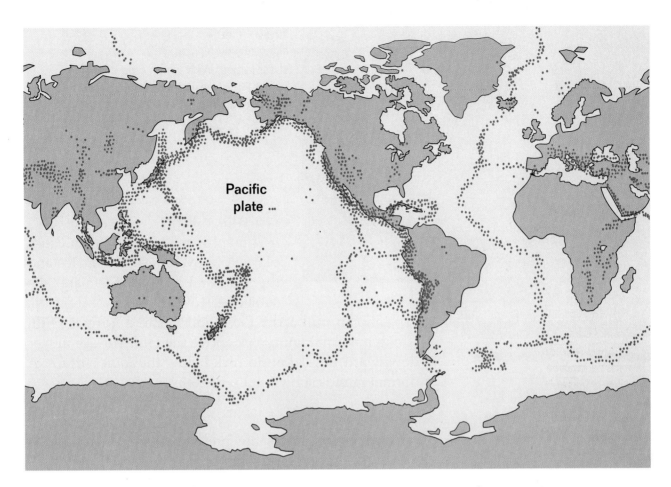

Pacific
plate ...

Figure 8-2 The dots represent the locations of major quakes over a ten-year period. Eighty percent of earthquakes occur along the edges of a section of Earth known as the Pacific plate.

What causes faults to form? Something must be forcing rocks to move. Otherwise, the rocks would just rest quietly. Earth's crust is in constant motion because of forces inside Earth. These forces cause sections of Earth's crust, called plates, to move, putting stress on rocks. Because of this stress, rocks tend to bend and stretch. However, if the force is great enough, rocks break. This breaking releases stored energy to produce the vibrations that we call **earthquakes. Figure 8-2** shows how the locations of earthquakes outline the sections of Earth's crust.

Types of Faults

Rocks go through several types of forces where sections or plates of Earth's crust and upper mantle meet. When you played with the layers of clay in the Explore Activity, you experimented with three forces—compression, tension, and shear. Compression is a force or stress that squeezes and compresses, while tension is the force that causes rocks to stretch and become longer. Shear is the force that causes rocks on either side of a fault to move past each other. Let's take a look at these three forces and the types of faults they create.

PHYSICS
◄ **INTEGRATION**

Figure 8-3 Rock layers are affected differently by tension, compression, and shear forces. **With which type of force would Earth's crust be stretched and thinned? With which type would Earth's crust be folded and thickened?**

Normal Faults

Some forces inside Earth cause plates to move apart. The plates and the rocks that compose them are then subjected to the force of tension. Tension can pull apart rocks and create a **normal fault.** Along a normal fault, rock above the fault surface moves downward in relation to rock below the fault surface. A normal fault is shown in **Figure 8-3A.**

Reverse Faults

Compression forces are present where Earth's plates move together. Compression pushes on rocks from opposite directions and causes them to bend and sometimes break. Once they break, the rocks continue to move along the fault surface. At a **reverse fault,** the rocks above the fault surface are forced up and over the rocks below the fault surface, as shown in **Figure 8-3B.**

A When rock moves along a fracture caused by tension forces, the break is called a normal fault. Rock above the fault moves downward in relation to the rock below the fault surface. Normal faults can form mountains such as the Sierra Nevada, which border California on the east.

B When compression forces break rock, the rock above the fault surface moves upward in relation to the rock below the fault surface. The mountains shown, in Banff National Park in the Canadian Rocky Mountains, contain many reverse faults.

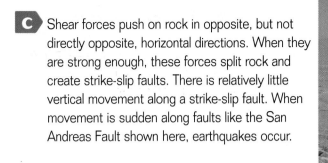

C Shear forces push on rock in opposite, but not directly opposite, horizontal directions. When they are strong enough, these forces split rock and create strike-slip faults. There is relatively little vertical movement along a strike-slip fault. When movement is sudden along faults like the San Andreas Fault shown here, earthquakes occur.

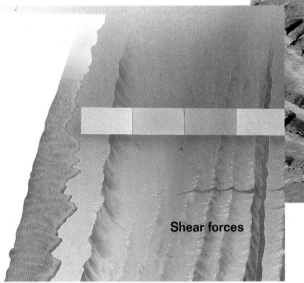

Shear forces

Strike-Slip Faults

You have probably heard about the San Andreas Fault in California. At this fault, shown in **Figure 8-3C,** two of Earth's plates are moving sideways past each other because of shear forces. This type of fault is called a strike-slip fault. At a **strike-slip fault,** rocks on either side of the fault surface are moving past each other without much upward or downward movement. Compare the faults in **Figure 8-3.** How do they differ? ☑

As the rocks move past each other at a strike-slip fault, their ragged surfaces catch each other, and the rocks are twisted and strained. Not only do they change shape, but the catching of their surfaces prevents movement along the faults. As forces keep driving the plates to move, energy builds up and the rocks reach their elastic limit. When the rocks are stressed past their elastic limit, they may break and an earthquake may result.

Some earthquakes can be dramatic—even devastating— events, while others go almost unnoticed. Regardless of their sizes, most earthquakes result from plates moving over, under, and past each other. If these plates simply slid smoothly by each other, tension, compression, and shear forces would not build up energy. But, rocks do experience these stresses and energy builds up in them, causing small

Reading Check ☑

What is a strike-slip fault?

PHYSICS
INTEGRATION

Fault Forces
Explain what types of faults are produced by compression and by tension. How does the type of stress determine the nature of the fault in each case?

Figure 8-4
Geologists use surface evidence like these cracks in Costa Rica when searching for dangerous hidden fractures or faults.

changes in shape. When rocks break, as shown in **Figure 8-4,** energy is released along fault surfaces, and we observe the effects in the form of earthquakes.

Section Assessment

1. What type of force usually generates strike-slip faults?

2. The Appalachian Mountains formed when two of Earth's plates collided. What type of faults would you expect to find in these mountains? Why?

3. What happens to rocks when an earthquake occurs?

4. **Think Critically:** Why might it be easier to predict *where* an earthquake will occur than it is to predict *when* it will occur?

5. **Skill Builder**
   Concept Mapping Make a cycle concept map that shows why many earthquakes occur along the San Andreas Fault. Use the following terms and phrases: *rocks, stress, bend and stretch, elastic limit reached,* and *earthquakes.* If you need help, refer to Concept Mapping in the **Skill Handbook** on page 714.

Using Computers

Graphics Use the graphics capabilities of a computer to make simple working models of the three types of faults: normal, reverse, and strike-slip. Have your computer model show how the forces that cause each fault differ. If you need help, refer to page 734.

Earthquake Information

Types of Seismic Waves

Have you ever seen a coiled-spring toy? When children play with a coiled-spring toy, they send energy waves through it. **Seismic** (SIZE mihk) **waves** made by an earthquake are like the waves of the toy. Where are seismic waves formed? How do they move through Earth, and how can we use the information that they carry? Let's investigate how scientists have answered these questions.

Earthquake Focus

As you have learned, when rocks move along a fault surface, energy is released and damage occurs, as seen in **Figure 8-5**. The point in Earth's interior where this energy release occurs is the **focus** of the earthquake. Seismic waves are produced at and travel outward from the earthquake focus.

What You'll Learn

► To compare and contrast primary, secondary, and surface waves
► How an earthquake epicenter is located
► The structure of Earth's interior

Vocabulary
seismic wave
focus
primary wave
secondary wave
epicenter
surface wave
inner core
outer core
mantle
crust

Why It's Important

► Seismic waves help scientists locate earthquakes and give information about Earth's interior.

Figure 8-5 This photograph shows buildings damaged during the 1989 Loma Prieta, California, earthquake. This earthquake was caused by the Pacific plate slipping past the North American plate by only 2 m.

Seismic Waves

Waves that cause particles in rocks to move back and forth in the same direction the wave is moving are called **primary waves.** If you squeeze together several coils on one end of a coiled-spring toy and then release them, they compress and then stretch as the wave travels through the toy. Particles in rocks also squeeze together and stretch apart as primary waves move through them.

Now, if you and a friend stretch the coiled-spring toy between you and then move one end up and down, a different type of wave will pass through the toy. The spring will move up and down as the wave moves along it. **Secondary waves** move through Earth by causing particles in rocks to vibrate at right angles to the direction of the wave.

VISUALIZING
Seismic Waves

Figure 8-6 Primary and secondary waves travel outward from the focus. Surface waves move outward from the epicenter.

A Sudden movement along a fault releases energy that causes an earthquake. The point beneath Earth's surface where the movement occurs is the focus of the earthquake.

B Primary waves and secondary waves originate at the focus and travel outward in all directions. Primary waves travel faster than secondary waves.

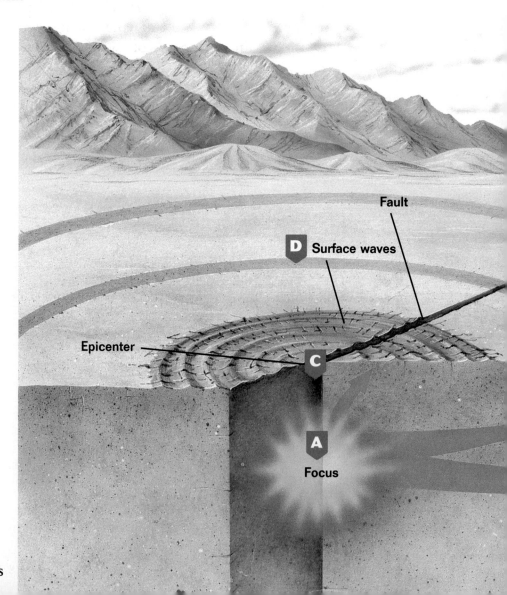

Fault

D Surface waves

Epicenter

C

A
Focus

The point on Earth's surface directly above an earthquake's focus is the **epicenter** (EP ih sent ur), as shown in **Figure 8-6.** Energy that reaches the surface of Earth makes waves that travel outward from the epicenter. These waves, called **surface waves,** move particles up and down and side to side in a swaying motion.

Surface waves cause most of the destruction during an earthquake. Because most buildings are stiff and hard, they begin to fall apart when surface waves pass. The waves cause different parts of a building to move in different directions. This is because part of the surface wave motion is up and down, and part of the motion is side to side. ☑

Locating an Epicenter

Primary, secondary, and surface waves don't travel through Earth at the same speed. Primary waves are the fastest. Surface waves are the slowest. Can you think of a way this information could be used to determine how far away an earthquake epicenter is? Think of the last time you and two friends rode your bikes to the store. You were fastest, so you arrived first. In fact, the longer you rode, the farther ahead of your friends you became. Scientists use the different speeds of seismic waves to find the distance to an earthquake epicenter.

Reading Check ☑

Which seismic waves cause most of the damage during an earthquake?

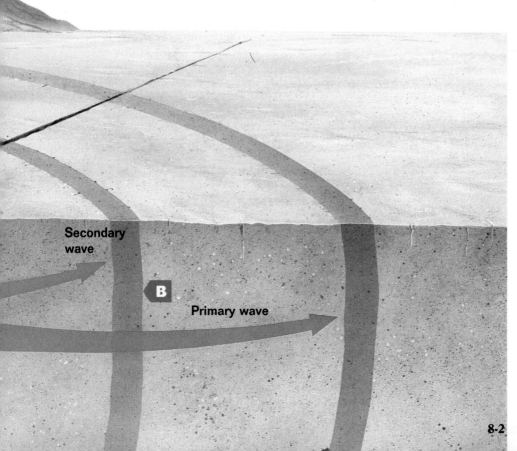

Secondary wave

B

Primary wave

C The place on Earth's surface directly above the earthquake focus is called the epicenter. Surface waves radiate, or spread, outward from the epicenter in much the same way that ripples travel outward from a stone thrown into a pond.

D The amplitude, or height, of surface waves is greater than the amplitudes of primary and secondary waves. Surface waves cause the most damage during an earthquake.

Making and Using Tables and Graphs

Procedure

1. Use the graph in **Figure 8-7** to determine the difference in arrival times for primary and secondary waves at the distances listed in the data table below. Two examples are provided for you.

2. Use the graph to determine the differences in arrival times for at least two other distances of your choice.

Analysis

1. Interpret what happens to the difference in arrival times as the distance from the earthquake increases.

2. Explain how the distances you chose fit with what you interpreted in question 1.

Arrival Times	
Distance (km)	Difference in Arrival Time
1500	2 minutes; 50 s
2250	
2750	
3000	
4000	5 minutes; 45 s
7000	
9000	

Seismograph Stations

Based on their different speeds, primary waves arrive first at recording stations, secondary waves second, as shown in **Figure 8-7**, and surface waves last. This allows scientists to determine the distance to an earthquake epicenter. The farther apart the wave arrivals, the farther away the epicenter is. When epicenters are far from the seismograph station, the primary wave has more time to put distance between it and the secondary and surface waves.

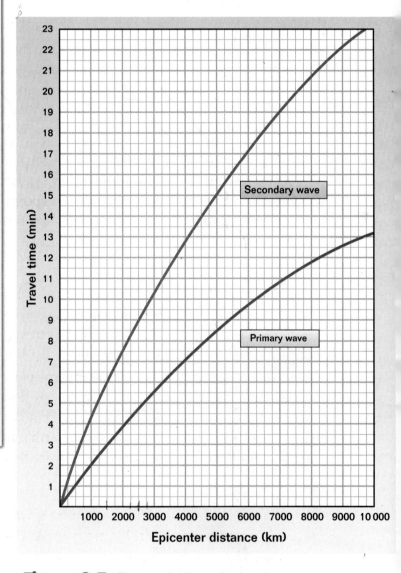

Figure 8-7 This graph shows the distance that primary and secondary waves travel over time. By measuring the difference in arrival times, a seismologist can determine the distance to the epicenter.

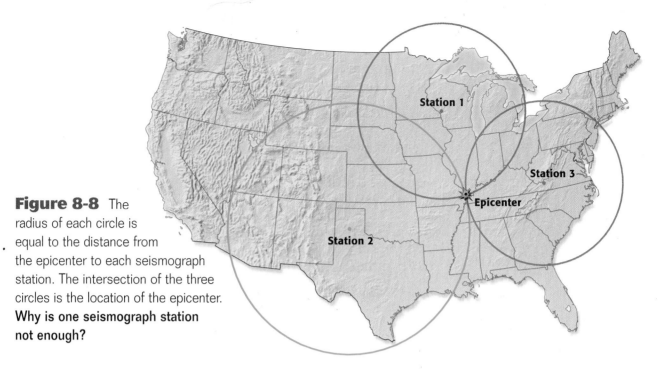

Figure 8-8 The radius of each circle is equal to the distance from the epicenter to each seismograph station. The intersection of the three circles is the location of the epicenter. **Why is one seismograph station not enough?**

Epicenter Location

If seismic wave information is recorded from at least three seismograph stations, the location of the epicenter can be determined, as shown in **Figure 8-8.** To locate an epicenter, scientists draw circles around each station on a map. The radius of each circle equals that station's distance from the earthquake epicenter. The point where all three circles meet is the location of the earthquake epicenter.

Mapping Earth's Interior

Scientists have found that at certain depths within Earth, the speed and path of seismic waves change. These changes mark the boundaries of the layers in Earth with different densities. Recall that the density of a material is mass per unit volume. In general, material in Earth's layers becomes denser toward the core as pressures increase. Using information from seismic waves, scientists have learned about Earth's interior without ever having been there, as shown in **Figure 8-9.**

Structure of Earth

Seismic wave studies allow scientists to make a model of Earth's interior, as shown in **Figure 8-10.** At the very center of Earth is a solid, dense **inner core** made mostly of iron with some nickel and smaller amounts of oxygen, silicon, and sulfur. Above the solid inner core lies the liquid **outer core,** also made mainly of iron. Earth's **mantle** is the largest layer, lying directly above the outer core. It is made mostly of silicon, oxygen, magnesium, and iron. Earth's thinnest, outermost layer is the **crust.**

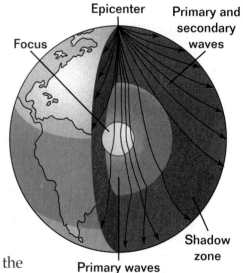

Figure 8-9 Primary waves bend when they contact the outer core (orange-red), and secondary waves are stopped completely. Primary waves also bend and speed up when they enter the inner core (yellow). In fact, as shown, seismic waves gradually bend and change speed as the density of rock changes.

Compared to the mantle, the crust contains more silicon and aluminum and less magnesium and iron. The crust is separated from the mantle by the Moho discontinuity.

Moho Discontinuity

Seismic waves speed up when they reach the bottom of the crust. This boundary between the crust and the mantle is called the *Moho discontinuity* (dis kahnt un EW ut ee). The boundary was discovered by the Yugoslavian scientist Andrija Mohorovičić, who inferred that seismic waves speed up because they're passing into a denser layer of Earth.

This denser layer is called the upper mantle, as shown in **Figure 8-10.** It is made up of minerals that are denser, on average, than minerals found in the crust.

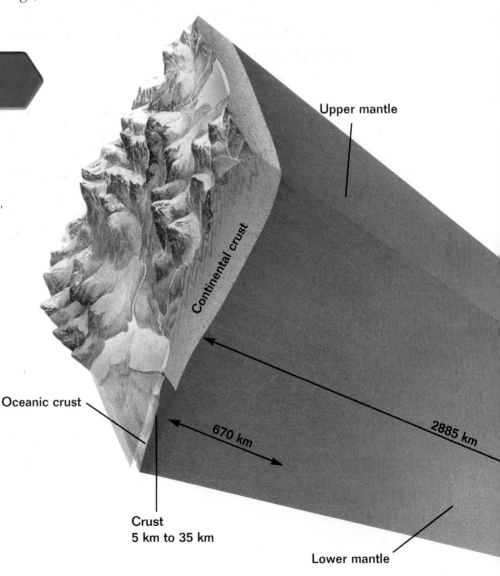

VISUALIZING
Layers of Earth

Figure 8-10 This wedge shows the layers inside Earth from the inner core. The inner core, outer core, and mantle are shown at the correct scale, but the crust is shown much thicker than it actually is.

A The crust of Earth varies in thickness. It is greater than 60 km in some mountainous regions, and less than 5 km thick under some oceans.

Upper mantle

Continental crust

Oceanic crust

670 km

2885 km

Crust
5 km to 35 km

Lower mantle

B There is a layer in the upper mantle where rock material is described as plasticlike. It is like a solid but also flows like a liquid when under pressure. Some parts of this layer are thought to be molten.

Plasticlike Layer

Primary and secondary waves slow down when they hit a plasticlike layer that is part of the upper mantle. Then, seismic waves speed up again as they pass through the solid lower mantle. The denser the layer, the faster the seismic waves can travel through that layer.

Shadow Zone

An area exists on Earth where no seismic waves are detected after they are released by an earthquake. This area is called the *shadow zone*. Secondary waves don't pass through liquid, so they're stopped completely when they hit the liquid outer core. Primary waves are slowed and bent but not stopped by the liquid outer core. The bending of the primary waves and the stopping of the secondary waves create the shadow zone, as shown in **Figure 8-9.** These primary waves speed up again as they travel through the solid inner core. ☑

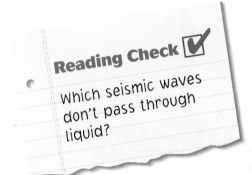

Reading Check ☑

Which seismic waves don't pass through liquid?

Mantle Samples

You can see that scientists learn a lot about Earth's interior by studying the behavior of seismic waves. But, did you ever wonder if anyone has ever held a piece of Earth's mantle or core in his or her hands? Some volcanic materials are a window to Earth's interior, containing minerals that scientists suggest are pieces of the upper mantle. Magma can break off and bring up pieces of the mantle as it forces its way to the surface as lava.

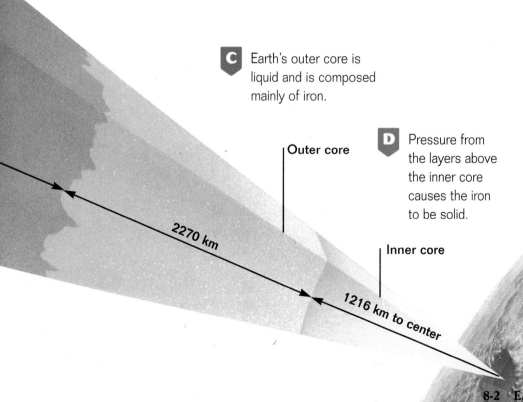

C Earth's outer core is liquid and is composed mainly of iron.

Outer core

D Pressure from the layers above the inner core causes the iron to be solid.

2270 km

Inner core

1216 km to center

Meteorites

Samples of the deep mantle and core have never been collected. However, the rocky materials that make up our solar system, which includes Earth and meteorites, are thought to have formed at about the same time. Therefore, we can compare the composition of meteorites with that of Earth. Some meteorites have certain minerals that we know from rock formations and volcanic materials to be mantle minerals. Some meteorites are heavy and rich in iron, which studies show are the same materials in Earth's core. Scientists hypothesize that meteorites, such as the examples shown in **Figure 8-11,** contain samples that are like different parts of Earth's interior.

Figure 8-11 Meteorites are made of minerals that are like those in different layers of Earth.

Problem Solving

Interpreting Data

Your teacher has placed five closed and sealed boxes in front of the class. The sizes of the five boxes are the same and equal to a sixth box that is empty. Your teacher has challenged you to complete problem-solving exercises in order to earn points. To earn all the points available, you must list at least three facts about the contents of each box. You are permitted to do anything you wish except open the boxes and look directly at the enclosed objects. The other rule is that you cannot damage any of the boxes in any way.

Determine what tests you will perform on each box that will reveal facts about its contents. You may wish to work with another student in case any of your tests require more than one person. In your Science Journal, make a table similar to the one above. Record all observations about the unknown box contents. List any inferences you have made concerning the contents of each box.

Box Number	Observations			Inferences
	Fact 1	Fact 2	Fact 3	
1				
2				
3				
4				
5				

Box Interpretations

Think Critically:
Compare the facts you discovered with those listed by your teacher. How is the challenge presented by your teacher related to a study of seismic waves and mapping of Earth's interior?

Using Math

Calculating Time

Example Problem: Primary waves travel at about 6 km/s through continental crust. The distance from Phoenix, Arizona, to Los Angeles, California, is about 600 km. How long would it take primary waves to travel between the two cities?

Problem-Solving Steps

1. What is known?
   distance, d = 600 km; average speed, v = 6 km/s
2. What is unknown? time, t
3. Use the equation, $t = d/v$
4. **Solution:** $t = d/v$
   t = 600 km/6 km/s = 100 s (1 minute, 40 s)

Practice Problem

Secondary waves travel at about 3.6 km/s through continental crust. How long would it take secondary waves to travel from Phoenix to Los Angeles?

Section Assessment

1. Which type of seismic wave does the most damage to property? Explain why.

2. Why is a seismic record from three locations needed to determine the position of an epicenter?

3. **Think Critically:** Suppose an earthquake occurs at the San Andreas Fault. What area on Earth would experience no secondary waves? Would China experience primary and secondary waves? Explain your answers.

4. **Skill Builder**
   Making and Using Graphs Use the data table below to make a graph of some travel times of earthquake waves. Which line represents primary waves? Which line represents secondary waves? If you need help, refer to Making and Using Graphs in the **Skill Handbook** on page 717.

Earthquake Wave Travel Times						
Distance from Earthquake (km)	1500	2000	5000	5500	8600	10 000
Time (minutes)	5.0	2.5	14.0	7.0	11.0	23.5

Science Journal

When sound is produced, waves move through the air by pressing molecules together and then spreading them apart. Research sound waves and compare them to the types of seismic waves you have learned about. Relate what you learn to the fact that people report loud noise when earthquakes occur.

Epicenter Location

Materials

- **Figure 8-7**
- String
- Metric ruler
- Globe
- Chalk
- Paper

Try this activity to see how to plot the distance of several seismograph stations from the epicenters of two earthquakes and how to use these data to interpret where the earthquake epicenters were located.

What You'll Investigate

Can plotting the distance of several seismograph stations from two earthquake epicenters be used to interpret the locations of the two epicenters?

Goals

- **Plot** the distances of several seismograph stations based on primary and secondary wave arrival times.
- **Interpret** the location of earthquake epicenters from these plots.

Procedure

1. **Determine** the difference in arrival time between the primary and secondary waves at each station for each quake from the data table below.

2. Once you determine the arrival times of seismic waves for each seismograph station, use the graph in **Figure 8-7** to determine the distance in kilometers of each seismograph from the epicenter of each earthquake. **Record** these data in a data table provided by your teacher. The difference in arrival times in Paris for earthquake B is 9 minutes and 30 seconds. On the graph, the primary and secondary waves are separated along the vertical axis by 9 minutes and 30 seconds at 8975 km.

3. Using the string, **measure** the circumference of the globe. Determine a scale of centimeters of string to kilometers on Earth's surface. (Earth's circumference = 40 000 km.)

4. For each earthquake, A and B, place one end of the string at each seismic station location on the globe. Use the chalk to draw a circle with a radius equal to the distance from the earthquake's epicenter.

5. **Identify** the epicenter for each quake.

Conclude and Apply

1. How is the distance of a seismograph from the earthquake related to the arrival time of the waves?

2. What is the location of each earthquake epicenter?

3. How many stations were needed to accurately locate each epicenter?

4. **Predict** why some seismographs didn't receive secondary waves from some quakes.

Earthquake Wave Arrival Times			
Location of Seismograph	Wave	Wave Arrival Times	
		Earthquake A	Earthquake B
(1) New York	P	2:24:05 P.M.	1:19:42 P.M.
	S	2:29:15 P.M.	1:25:27 P.M.
(2) Seattle	P	2:24:40 P.M.	1:14:37 P.M.
	S	2:30:10 P.M.	1:16:57 P.M.
(3) Rio de Janeiro	P	2:29:10 P.M.	—
	S	2:37:50 P.M.	—
(4) Paris	P	2:30:30 P.M.	1:24:57 P.M.
	S	2:40:10 P.M.	1:34:27 P.M.
(5) Tokyo	P	—	1:24:27 P.M.
	S	—	1:33:27 P.M.

Destruction by Earthquakes

Measuring Earthquakes

On January 25, 1999, a major earthquake struck Colombia, South America, leaving over 1900 dead or missing. On February 4, 1998, and then again on May 30, 1998, major earthquakes of magnitudes 6.1 and 6.9 occurred at the Afghanistan-Tajikistan border. More than 6300 people were killed. On May 10, 1997, a magnitude-7.3 earthquake killed at least 1567 people in northern Iran. On January 17, 1995, a major earthquake occurred in Kobe, Japan, causing about $100 billion of property damage and 5502 deaths. On January 17, 1994, a major earthquake occurred in Northridge, California, causing billions of dollars of property damage, as seen in **Figure 8-12,** and 57 deaths. What determines the amount of damage done by an earthquake, and what can you do to protect yourself from the effects? With so many lives lost and such destruction, as shown in **Table 8-1,** it is important for scientists to learn as much as possible about earthquakes to try to reduce their damage.

What **You'll Learn**

▶ Definitions of *magnitude* and the *Richter scale*
▶ Ways to make your classroom and home more earthquake-safe

Vocabulary

seismologist
seismograph
magnitude
tsunami

Why **It's Important**

▶ People can prepare for earthquakes by building seismic-safe structures.

Figure 8-12
Several major highways were damaged in the January 17, 1994, earthquake in Northridge, California. **What happens during an earthquake that causes so much damage to highway overpasses?**

Seismology

Scientists who study earthquakes and seismic waves are **seismologists.** They use an instrument called a **seismograph** to record primary, secondary, and surface waves from earthquakes all over the world.

One type of seismograph has a drum holding a sheet of paper on a fixed frame. A pendulum with an attached pen is suspended from the frame. When seismic waves occur at the station, the drum vibrates but the pendulum remains at rest. The pen on the pendulum traces a record of the vibrations on a sheet of paper. The height of the lines traced on the paper is a measure of the energy released, or **magnitude,** of the earthquake.

Earthquake Magnitude

Not all seismographs measure vibrations in the same way. The Richter scale measures only local intensity on one kind of seismograph. However, seismologists also study magnitude in other ways.

The Richter magnitude is based on seismic waves that travel through Earth. It deals mainly with the strength of the break, not with the length or width of the fault. The Richter scale describes how much energy is released by the earthquake. For each increase of 1.0, the amplitude, or height, of the largest surface waves is ten times greater. However, about 32 times as much energy is released for every increase of 1.0 on the scale. For example, a magnitude-8.5 earthquake releases about 32 times as much energy as a magnitude-7.5

Table 8-1

Large-Magnitude Earthquakes			
Year	Location	Richter Value	Deaths
1556	Shensi, China	?	830 000
1737	Calcutta, India	?	300 000
1755	Lisbon, Portugal	8.8	70 000
1811–12	New Madrid, MO	8.3	few
1886	Charleston, SC	?	60
1906	San Francisco, CA	8.3	700–800
1920	Kansu Province, China	8.5	180 000
1923	Tokyo, Japan	8.3	143 000
1939	Concepción, Chile	8.3	30 000
1960	Southern Chile	8.6	5700
1964	Prince William Sound, AK	8.5	131
1970	Peru	7.8	66 800
1975	Laoning Province, China	7.5	few
1976	Tangshan, China	7.6	240 000
1985	Mexico City, Mexico	8.1	9500
1988	Armenia	6.9	28 000
1989	Loma Prieta, CA	6.9	63
1990	Iran	7.7	50 000
1990	Luzon, Philippines	7.8	1621
1993	Guam	8.1	none
1993	Marharashtra, India	6.4	30 000
1994	Northridge, CA	6.8	57
1995	Kobe, Japan	6.9	5502
1997	Northern Iran	7.3	>1500
1998	Afghanistan	6.1 & 6.9	>6300

earthquake. **Table 8-2** shows how often various magnitude earthquakes are expected to occur.

Another magnitude used by seismologists is based on Earth movement or surface waves. Seismologists also use a magnitude called the moment magnitude. It comes from multiplying the length of the fault break by the amount of rock movement and then again by the rock stiffness. The moment magnitude depends on the strength and size of fault movement.

Tsunamis

Most earthquake damage happens when surface waves cause buildings, bridges, and roads to collapse. People living near the seashore, however, have another problem. An earthquake under the sea causes a sudden movement of the ocean floor. The movement pushes against the water, causing a powerful wave that can travel thousands of kilometers in all directions, as shown in **Figure 8-13.** Far from shore, a wave caused by an earthquake is so long that a large ship may ride over it without anyone noticing. But, when one of these waves breaks on a shore, it forms a towering crest that can reach 30 m in height. Ocean waves caused by earthquakes are called seismic sea waves, or **tsunamis** (soo NAHM eez).

Table 8-2

Earthquake Occurrences	
Richter Magnitude	Number Expected per Year
1.0 to 3.9	> 949 000
4.0 to 4.9	6200
5.0 to 5.9	800
6.0 to 6.9	120
7.0 to 7.9	18
8.0 to 8.9	< 2

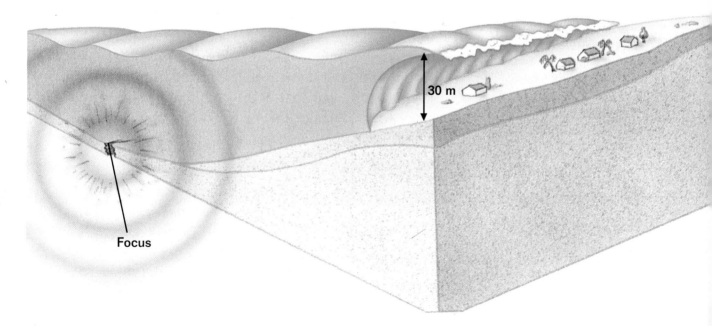

30 m

Focus

Figure 8-13 A tsunami begins over the earthquake focus. **What might happen to towns located near the shore?**

Figure 8-14 On July 17, 1998, a powerful tsunami swept away trees and houses along the northern coast of Papua, New Guinea. At least 2000 people died.

interNET
C O N N E C T I O N

Visit the Glencoe Science Web Site at **www.glencoe.com/ sec/science** for more information about tsunamis.

Just before a tsunami crashes on shore, the water along a shoreline may move rapidly toward the sea, exposing a large portion that is normally underwater. This should be taken as an immediate warning sign that a tsunami could strike. **Figure 8-14** shows some damage that was caused by the tsunami that struck Papua, New Guinea, on July 17, 1998.

Earthquake Safety

You've seen the destruction that earthquakes can cause. However, there are ways to minimize the damage and loss of life.

One of the first steps in earthquake safety is to study the earthquake history of a region, such as the one illustrated in **Figure 8-16.** If you live in an area that's had earthquakes in the past, you can expect them to occur there in the future. As you know, most earthquakes happen along plate boundaries. **Table 8-1** shows where severe earthquakes have happened. Being prepared is an important step in earthquake safety.

Quake-Proofing Your Home

Make your home as earthquake-safe as possible. Take heavy objects down from high shelves and place them on lower shelves. Reduce the chance of fire from broken gas lines by checking that hot-water heaters and gas appliances are held securely in place. During an earthquake, keep away from windows and avoid anything that could fall on you. Watch for fallen power lines and possible fire hazards. Stay clear of rubble that could contain sharp edges.

Seismic-Safe Structures

Seismic-safe structures stand up to vibrations that occur during an earthquake. **Figure 8-15** shows how buildings can be built to resist earthquake damage.

Today in California, some new buildings are held together by flexible, circular moorings placed under the buildings. The moorings are arranged in layers of steel plates and rubber parts. The rubber acts like a cushion to absorb earthquake waves.

Mini Lab

Modeling Seismic-Safe Structures

Procedure

1. Obtain a set of building blocks from your teacher.
2. On a tabletop, build one structure out of the blocks by simply placing one block on top of another.
3. Build a second structure by wrapping sections of three blocks together with rubber bands. Then, wrap larger rubber bands around the entire completed structure.
4. Set the second structure on the tabletop and pound on the side of the table with a steady rhythm.

Analysis

1. Which of your two structures was better able to withstand the "earthquake" caused by pounding on the table?
2. How might the idea of wrapping the blocks with rubber bands be used in construction of supports for elevated highways?

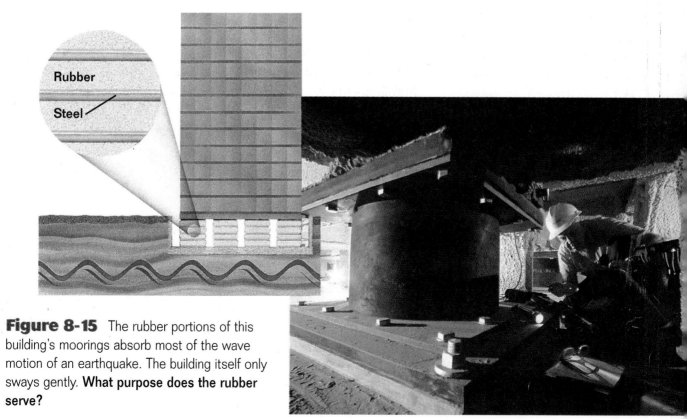

Figure 8-15 The rubber portions of this building's moorings absorb most of the wave motion of an earthquake. The building itself only sways gently. **What purpose does the rubber serve?**

Rubber

Steel

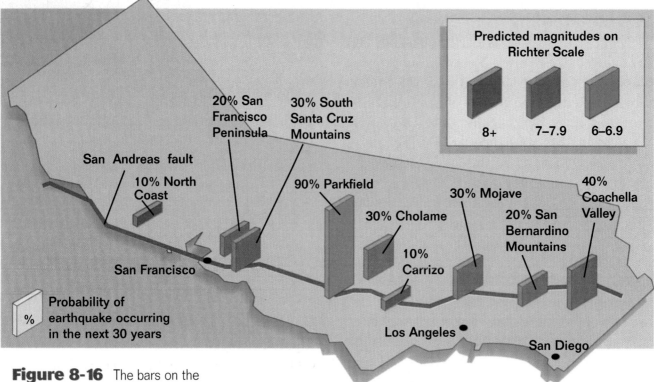

Figure 8-16 The bars on the graphic show the likelihood that an earthquake of a certain magnitude will strike these areas within the next 30 years. California residents are preparing for the major earthquakes predicted there.

Figure 8-15 shows how they work. Tests have shown that buildings supported in this way should be able to withstand an earthquake measuring up to 8.3 on the Richter scale without major damage.

Section Assessment

1. How do rubber moorings in a building help minimize damage during an earthquake?

2. Research how animal behavior has been studied to predict earthquakes. What changes may be occurring in the environment to cause animals to act differently?

3. **Think Critically:** Explain why a seismograph wouldn't work if the pen vibrated along with the rest of the machine.

4. 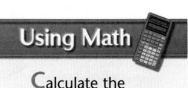 **Skill Builder**
   Using Numbers Have you ever wondered what you would need to have stored up at home in the event of an earthquake? To find out what's important, and how much it costs, do the **Chapter 8 Skill Activity** on page 749.

Using Math

Calculate the difference in energy released between an earthquake of Richter magnitude 7.5 and one of magnitude 5.5.

Science
JOURNAL

Using what you have learned about earthquakes in this chapter, write your own story to explain why earthquakes occur. Use your stories to explain things about earthquakes that are still not well understood. Read your classmates' stories to find out what questions they still have about earthquakes. Make a list of these questions in your Science Journal.

Why We Have Earthquakes— A Korean Folktale

An earthquake is a shaking of Earth caused by the release of energy as rock suddenly breaks or shifts under stress. Most quakes happen along faults— breaks in Earth's crust along which rocks on either side can move. The Korean Peninsula is relatively stable compared to Japan, which is situated on a plate boundary. Of the nearly 2000 earthquakes that have been historically or scientifically recorded in Korea since 2 A.D., only 48 have been destructive.

Traditional Korean folktales, which have been passed on orally from generation to generation, explain natural events such as earthquakes. The tales also are told to teach moral lessons. Like the folktales and myths of other cultures throughout the world, Korean folktales reflect the peculiarities of the environment where they are told.

A Shoulder to Lean On

One Korean folktale tells of a time when one corner of Heaven began to sag. The King of Heaven took a gigantic pillar of red copper and placed one end on Earth and the other end under the sagging corner of Heaven.

The ground on Earth was soft, and, since Heaven was heavy, the pillar began to sink into Earth. The king sent the strongest man in Heaven to hold the pillar on his shoulder. This was the only way to keep the great weight of Heaven from sagging.

The man is still holding the pillar. He can't let it slip from his shoulder or all of Heaven will come crashing down. But, the great weight becomes painful for the man to hold on just one shoulder. So, from time to time, he shifts the pillar from one shoulder to the other. Every time the man shifts the weight of the pillar, the ground on Earth shakes with his efforts. According to the folktale, this is why we have earthquakes.

Materials
- Graph paper
- Pencil

Earthquake Depths

You learned earlier in this chapter that Earth's crust is broken into sections called plates. Stresses caused by movement of these plates generate energy within rocks that must be released. When this release is sudden and rocks break, an earthquake occurs.

What You'll Investigate

Can a study of the foci of earthquakes tell us anything about how strain builds up in rocks and how it may be released?

Goals

- **Observe** any connection between earthquake-focus depth and epicenter location using the data provided on the next page.

- **Describe** any observed relationship between earthquake-focus depth and the movement of plates at Earth's surface.

Procedure

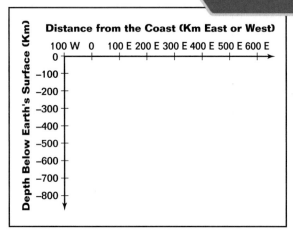

1. Use graph paper and the data table on the next page to make a line graph plotting the depths of earthquake foci and the distances from the coast of a continent for each earthquake epicenter.

2. **Place** "Distance from the coast" on the horizontal axis. Begin labeling at the far left with 100 km west. To the right of it should be 0 km, then 100 km east, 200 km east, 300 km east, and so on through 700 km east. What point on your graph would represent the coast?

3. Label the vertical axis "Depth below Earth's surface." **Label** the top of the graph 0 km to represent Earth's surface. **Label** the bottom of the vertical axis −800 km.

4. **Plot** the focus depths against the distance and direction from the coast for each earthquake in the table on the next page.

Conclude and Apply

1. **Describe** any observed relation between the location of earthquake epicenters and the depth of earthquake foci.

2. Based on the graph you have completed, **hypothesize** what is happening to the plates at

Earth's surface in the vicinity of the plotted earthquake foci.

3. **Infer** what process is causing the earthquakes you plotted on your graph paper.

4. **Hypothesize** why none of the plotted earthquakes occurred below 700 km.

Focus and Epicenter Data		
Quake	Focus Depth	Distance of Epicenter from Coast (km)
A	−55 km	0
B	−295 km	100 E
C	−390 km	455 E
D	−60 km	75 E
E	−130 km	255 E
F	−195 km	65 E
G	−695 km	400 E
H	−20 km	40 W
I	−505 km	695 E
J	−520 km	390 E
K	−385 km	335 E
L	−45 km	95 E
M	−305 km	495 E
N	−480 km	285 E
O	−665 km	545 E
P	−85 km	90 W
Q	−525 km	205 E
R	−85 km	25 W
S	−445 km	595 E
T	−635 km	665 E
U	−55 km	95 W
V	−70 km	100 W

For a **preview** of this chapter, study this Reviewing Main Ideas before you read the chapter. After you have studied this chapter, you can use the Reviewing Main Ideas to **review** the chapter.

GLENCOE TECHNOLOGY

The Glencoe MindJogger, Audiocassettes, and CD-ROM provide additional opportunities for review.

Section 8-1 FORCES INSIDE EARTH

Plate movements put stress on rocks. To a point, the rocks bend and stretch. But, if the force is great enough and the rock's elastic limit is passed, the rocks will remain bent and may break. When the rocks break, they can move along surfaces called **faults.** Breaking rocks produce vibrations called **earthquakes.** *How do rocks move relative to each other in a reverse fault?*

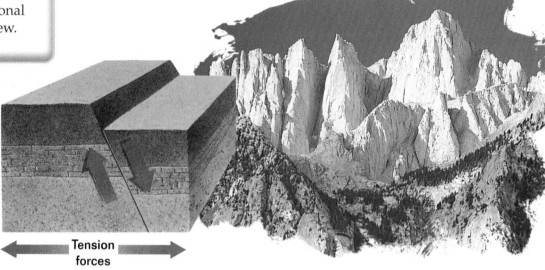

Tension forces

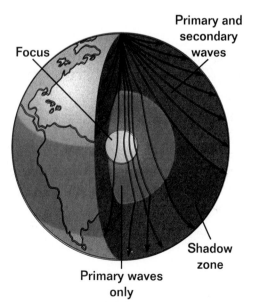

Focus

Primary and secondary waves

Shadow zone

Primary waves only

Section 8-2 EARTHQUAKE INFORMATION

Primary waves compress and stretch rock particles as the waves move. **Secondary waves** move by causing particles in the rocks to move at right angles to the direction of the waves. **Surface waves** move rock particles up and down and from side to side. Scientists can locate earthquake **epicenters** by measuring **seismic wave** speeds. By observing the speeds and paths of seismic waves, scientists are able to determine the boundaries among Earth's layers. *What happens to the path and speed of seismic waves as they move from one layer to another inside Earth?*

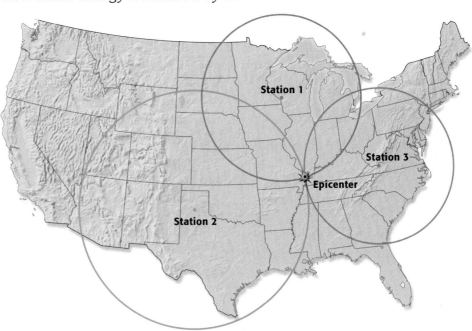

Reading Check ✓

Write your own summary of Section 8-3 before reading the text on this page. Try to keep your summary within three to five sentences.

Section 8-3 DESTRUCTION BY EARTHQUAKES

Seismologists study **earthquakes** and the waves produced by earthquakes. The **magnitude** of an earthquake is a measure of the energy released by the earthquake. The Richter scale describes how much energy is released by an earthquake. For each difference of one on the Richter scale, an earthquake releases about 32 times more energy. *How much more energy is released by an earthquake of magnitude 8.5 than an earthquake of magnitude 6.5?*

SEISMIC-SAFE STRUCTURES

Most lives lost during an earthquake are due to destruction of human-made structures. Seismic-safe structures are resistant to vibrations that occur during an earthquake. Buildings in areas with such structures are damaged during an earthquake but are less likely to collapse. *Give suggestions for how to quake-proof your home.*

Using Vocabulary

a. crust
b. earthquake
c. epicenter
d. fault
e. focus
f. inner core
g. magnitude
h. mantle
i. normal fault
j. outer core
k. primary wave
l. reverse fault
m. secondary wave
n. seismic wave
o. seismograph
p. seismologist
q. strike-slip fault
r. surface wave
s. tsunami

Distinguish between the terms in each of the following pairs.

1. surface wave, tsunami
2. fault, focus
3. normal fault, reverse fault
4. seismologist, seismograph
5. inner core, outer core

Checking Concepts

Choose the word or phrase that best answers the question.

6. Earthquakes can occur when which of the following is passed?
   A) tension limit
   C) elastic limit
   B) seismic limit
   D) shear limit

7. When the rock above the fault surface moves down relative to the rock below the fault surface, what kind of fault forms?
   A) normal
   C) reverse
   B) strike-slip
   D) shearing

8. Primary and secondary waves move outward from which of the following?
   A) epicenter
   C) Moho discontinuity
   B) focus
   D) tsunami

9. What kind of waves stretch and compress rocks?
   A) surface
   C) secondary
   B) primary
   D) shear

10. What are the slowest seismic waves?
    A) surface
    C) secondary
    B) primary
    D) pressure

11. What is the fewest number of seismograph stations that are needed to locate the epicenter of an earthquake?
    A) two
    C) four
    B) three
    D) five

12. What happens to primary waves when they go from liquids into solids?
    A) slow down
    C) stay the same
    B) speed up
    D) stop

13. What part of a seismograph remains still?
    A) sheet of paper
    C) drum
    B) fixed frame
    D) pendulum

14. An earthquake of magnitude 7.5 has how much more energy than a quake of magnitude 6.5?
    A) 32 times more
    C) twice as much
    B) 32 times less
    D) about half as much

15. How are most lives lost during an earthquake?
    A) tsunamis
    C) collapse of buildings
    B) primary waves
    D) broken gas lines

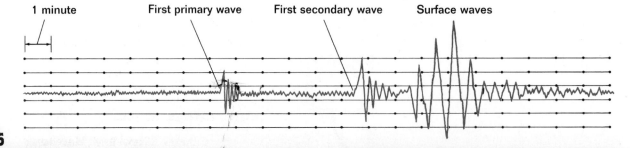

1 minute   First primary wave   First secondary wave   Surface waves

Assessment

Thinking Critically

16. What kind of faults would you expect to be most common along the Mid-Atlantic Ridge? Explain.

17. Tsunamis often are called tidal waves. Explain why this is incorrect.

18. Which would probably be more stable during an earthquake—a single-story wood-frame house or a brick building? Explain.

Developing Skills

If you need help, refer to the Skill Handbook.

19. Interpreting Scientific Illustrations: The illustration on the opposite page is a typical record of earthquake waves made on a seismograph. How many minutes passed between the arrival of the first primary wave and the first secondary wave?

20. Concept Mapping: Complete the concept map below showing what faults result from the three forces. Use the following terms: *tension, compression, shear, normal faults, reverse faults,* and *strike-slip faults.*

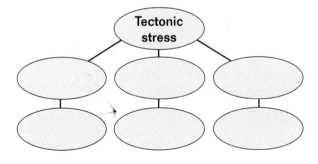

Test-Taking Tip

Work Weak Areas, Maintain Strong Ones It's sometimes difficult to focus on all the concepts needed for a test. So, ask yourself "What's my strongest area?" and "What's my weakest area?" Focus most of your energy on your weak areas. But, also put in some upkeep time in your best areas.

Test Practice

Use these questions to test your Science Proficiency.

1. Normal faults occur when tension is applied to rocks. Which of the following statements **BEST** supports this fact?

A) As tension is applied, Earth's crust thins and can crack.

B) When Earth's crust thins and cracks due to tension, the rock above the fault moves down relative to the rock below the fault.

C) Tension causes Earth's crust to fold and eventually develop faults.

D) When Earth's crust thins and cracks due to tension, the rock above the fault moves up relative to the rock below the fault.

2. Seismic records show that primary waves slow down and secondary waves stop when they reach Earth's outer core. What does this tell you about Earth's outer core?

A) The density of Earth material increases in the outer core.

B) Earth's outer core is solid.

C) Earth's outer core is liquid and has a lower density than rock material at the bottom of the mantle.

D) Earth's inner core is solid and more dense than the mantle.

CHAPTER

9

Volcanoes

Chapter Preview

Skills Preview

Skill Builders
- Map Concepts

Activities
- Measure
- Interpret Data

MiniLabs
- Make a Model

Reading Check ✓

Before you begin this chapter, look up the word origins of unfamiliar terms like *tephra*, *batholith*, and *caldera*. Knowing the origins will help you understand these words.

Explore Activity

The explosive eruptions of Soufrière Hills volcano on the Caribbean island of Montserrat began in July 1995 and have blanketed much of the island with volcanic ash. Clouds of ash rose to heights of 12 000 m and covered much of the capital city of Plymouth. Volcanoes can be spectacular and dangerous. Massive eruptions of volcanic ash into Earth's atmosphere can cause drastic changes in the environment. On a smaller scale, and definitely in the case of Montserrat island's population, volcanic eruptions affect humans in many ways. List harmful and also helpful effects that volcanoes have.

Model a Volcano

1. Use clay to make a small model volcano with a crater at the top.

2. Place a small amount of baking soda (less than 1/4 teaspoon) and a drop of red food coloring in the crater.

3. Add approximately 20 mL of vinegar to the baking soda in the crater.

Science Journal

In your Science Journal, write a paragraph that explains what happens to the baking soda and food coloring when the vinegar is added. Hypothesize how your model eruption is similar to an actual eruption and how it is different.

What causes volcanoes?

What You'll Learn

▶ How volcanoes can affect people
▶ Conditions that cause volcanoes
▶ The relationship between volcanoes and Earth's moving plates

Vocabulary
volcano
vent
crater
hot spot

Why It's Important

▶ You'll understand why volcanoes are common in certain regions on Earth.

Volcanoes and You

A **volcano** is an opening in Earth's surface. It often forms a mountain when layers of lava and volcanic ash erupt and build up. Most of Earth's volcanoes are dormant, which means that they are not currently active, but more than 600 are active now. Active volcanoes sometimes erupt smoke, steam, ash, cinders, and flows of lava.

In 1980, Mount St. Helens in Washington state erupted. It was one of the largest recent volcanic eruptions in North America. Geologists warned people to leave the area surrounding the mountain. Most people left, but a few stayed. A total of 59 people were killed as a result of the eruption. Heat from the eruption melted snow, which also caused mudslides and flooding in the area.

Active Volcanoes

For centuries, the Kilauea volcano in Hawaii has been erupting, but not explosively. Most of the town of Kalapana Gardens was destroyed in May 1990. No one was hurt because the lava moved slowly. The most recent series of eruptions from Kilauea, as seen in **Figure 9-1,** began in January 1983.

Figure 9-1 Kilauea in Hawaii has been continually erupting since January 3, 1983, becoming the most active volcano on Earth. Living with volcanoes as active as Kilauea can create serious problems for home owners. Losses have reached 61 million dollars as at least 181 homes have been destroyed.

Figure 9-2 Volcanic ash covered several buildings in Iceland during an eruption in 1973. **Why might people continue to live close to a volcano despite the danger?**

Kilauea is the world's most active volcano. Iceland is also famous for its active volcanoes and is known as the land of fire and ice. An Icelandic eruption is shown in **Figure 9-2.**

Eruptions of the Century

The largest volcanic eruption of the twentieth century occurred on the Alaska Peninsula. Beginning on June 6, 1912, Mount Katmai erupted an estimated 30 times greater volume of material than was expelled during the 1980 eruption of Mount St. Helens. In June 1991, Mount Pinatubo erupted in the Philippines, killing nearly 900 people. The eruption is considered the largest of any volcano in more than half a century. Millions of tons of sulfur dioxide and ash were thrown into Earth's upper atmosphere. It's possible that this material was the cause of the lowered global temperatures and record ozone losses that were observed as recently as 1993.

Just prior to the eruption of Mount Pinatubo, Mount Unzen in Japan erupted. Forty-four people lost their lives, including several volcanologists who were studying the erupting volcano and producing an educational program.

Using Math

Approximately 7000 quickly moving flows of hot gas and volcanic debris have occurred on Mount Unzen in Japan from 1991 through 1994. As long as Mount Unzen remains active, how many such flows, on average, can be expected to occur on Mount Unzen each month?

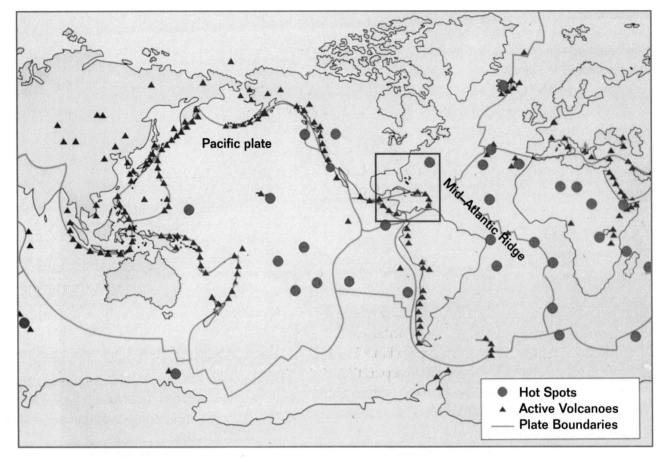

Figure 9-3 The diagram above shows the locations of active volcanoes, hot spots, and plate boundaries around the world. The squared-off area is shown in depth in Figure 9-4B. **How are the locations of active volcanoes related to the locations of hot spots and plate boundaries?**

Reading Check ✓

Why is magma forced upward toward Earth's surface?

How do volcanoes form?

What happens inside Earth to create volcanoes? Why are some areas of Earth more likely to have volcanoes than others? Deep inside Earth, heat and pressure cause rock to melt and form magma. Some deep rocks already are melted. Others are hot enough that a small rise in temperature or drop in pressure can cause them to melt to form magma.

Magma Forced Upward

Magma is less dense than the rock around it, so it is slowly forced upward toward Earth's surface. You can see this process if you turn a bottle of cold syrup upside down. Watch the dense syrup force the less-dense air bubbles slowly toward the top of the bottle. ☑

After many thousands or even millions of years, magma reaches Earth's surface and flows out through an opening called a **vent.** As lava flows out, it cools quickly and becomes solid, forming layers of igneous rock around the vent. The steep-walled depression around a volcano's vent is the **crater.**

Where do volcanoes occur?

Volcanoes form in places that are directly related to the movement of Earth's plates. Volcanoes occur where plates are moving apart, where plates are moving together, and at locations called hot spots. You can find locations of active volcanoes along with plate boundaries and hot spots on the map in **Figure 9-3.** There are many examples of volcanoes around the world at these three different areas. Let's explore volcanoes in Iceland, the Caribbean island of Montserrat, and Hawaii.

Plates Moving Apart

Iceland is a large island in the North Atlantic Ocean. It is near the Arctic Circle and has some glaciers. But, as seen in **Figure 9-2,** it also has volcanoes. Iceland has volcanic activity because it sits on top of the Mid-Atlantic Ridge.

The Mid-Atlantic Ridge is an area where Earth's plates are moving apart. Where plates separate, they form long, deep cracks called rifts. Magma flows from rifts as lava and is quickly cooled by seawater. **Figure 9-4A** shows how magma rises at rifts to form new volcanic rock. As more lava flows, it builds up from the seafloor. Sometimes, the volcanoes and rift eruptions rise above sea level, forming islands such as Iceland.

Plates Moving Together

Soufrière Hills volcano is located on the island of Montserrat, which is part of the Lesser Antilles islands of the Caribbean. Soufrière Hills volcano formed because it is located where Earth's plates move together as shown in **Figure 9-4B.** Here, the North and South American plates are forced under the less-dense Caribbean plate.

Figure 9-4 The locations of volcanoes depend on the motion of Earth's plates.

A Volcanic activity occurs where Earth's plates move apart. **Why does Iceland have volcanoes?**

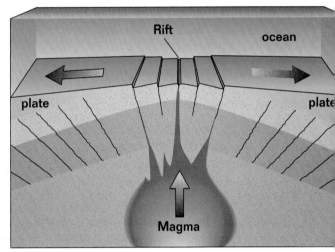

B Volcanoes form where the North and South American plates are forced below the Caribbean plate. **Why does magma form along this type of plate boundary?**

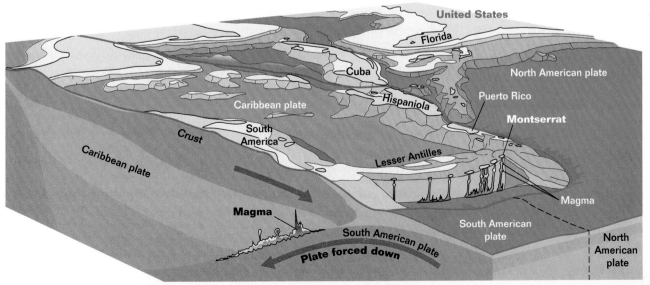

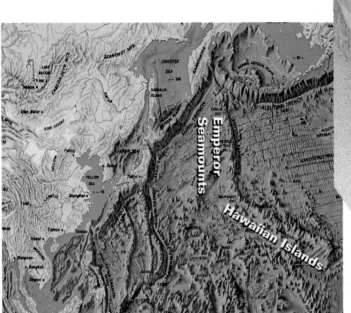

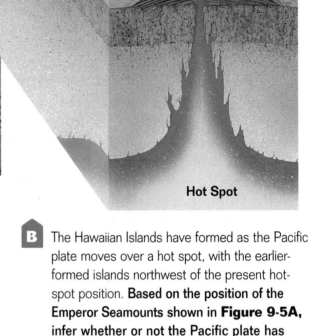

Kauai

Oahu

Molokai

Maui

Hawaii

Direction of plate movement

Hawaiian Islands

Hot Spot

A This map of the ocean floor shows the Hawaiian Islands.

Figure 9-5 Continued movement of the Pacific plate over a hot spot formed the islands of Kauai, Oahu, Molokai, Maui, and Hawaii over a period of about 5 million years. Scientists suggest that the Emperor Seamounts, which are extinct, underwater volcanoes, also formed in this way.

B The Hawaiian Islands have formed as the Pacific plate moves over a hot spot, with the earlier-formed islands northwest of the present hot-spot position. **Based on the position of the Emperor Seamounts shown in Figure 9-5A, infer whether or not the Pacific plate has always moved in the same direction. Explain your answer.**

Magma forms when the plate being forced under the Caribbean plate gets deep enough and hot enough to partially melt. The magma is then forced upward to the surface, forming the volcanoes of the Lesser Antilles. **Figure 9-4B** shows how the North and South American plates are moving below the Caribbean plate.

Hot Spots

Like Iceland, the Hawaiian Islands are volcanic islands. But, unlike Iceland, they haven't formed at a plate boundary. The Hawaiian Islands are in the middle of the Pacific plate, far from its edges. What process could be forming them?

Geologists suggest that some areas in the mantle are hotter than other areas. Some geologists hypothesize that hot-spot magma begins at the boundary between the mantle and the outer core. These **hot spots** melt rock, which is then forced upward toward the crust as magma. The Hawaiian Islands sit on top of a hot spot under the Pacific plate. Magma from

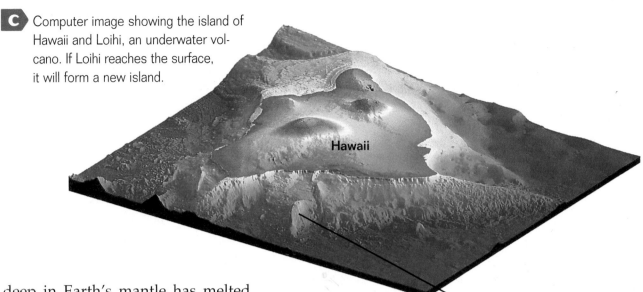

C Computer image showing the island of Hawaii and Loihi, an underwater volcano. If Loihi reaches the surface, it will form a new island.

Hawaii

Loihi
(Underwater volcano)

deep in Earth's mantle has melted through the crust to form several volcanoes. Those that rise above the water form the Hawaiian Islands, as shown in **Figure 9-5C.**

As you can see in **Figures 9-5A** and **9-5B,** the Hawaiian Islands are all in a line. This is because the Pacific plate is moving over the stationary hot spot. The island of Kauai is the oldest Hawaiian island and was once located where the big island of Hawaii is today. As the plate moved, Kauai moved away from the hot spot and became dormant. Continued movement of the Pacific plate formed Oahu, Molokai, Maui, and Hawaii over a period of about 5 million years.

Section Assessment

1. How are volcanoes related to Earth's moving plates?
2. As rock material melts, it becomes less dense. Explain what's happening to the atoms and molecules to cause this.
3. Why does lava cool rapidly along a mid-ocean ridge?
4. **Think Critically:** If the Pacific plate stopped moving, what would happen to the island of Hawaii?
5.  **Skill Builder**
   Concept Mapping Make a concept map that shows how the Hawaiian Islands formed over a hot spot. Use the following terms and phrases: *volcano forms, plate moves, volcano becomes dormant,* and *new volcano forms.* If you need help, refer to Concept Mapping in the **Skill Handbook** on page 714.

Science Journal
Scientists were able to predict approximately when Mount Pinatubo in the Philippines would erupt. Research the changes in Earth's crust that were observed that led to this prediction. In your Science Journal, write a report on equipment used to predict volcanic eruptions.

Materials

- World map
- Tracing paper (2 to 4 pieces)
- Data table on the following page
- **Figure 10-2**
- **Figure 9-3**
- **Figure 12-10**

Locating Active Volcanoes

Have you ever wondered why volcanic eruptions occur in certain regions on Earth? Volcanoes form when hot, melted rock material is forced upward to Earth's surface. As the melted rock moves inside Earth, vibrations occur, which are felt as earthquakes. In this activity, you will see whether the locations of active volcanoes relate to the locations of recent earthquakes.

What You'll Investigate

Is there a correlation between the locations of active volcanoes and the locations of earthquake epicenters?

Goals

- **Plot** the locations of several active volcanoes.
- **Describe** any correlation you see between locations of volcanoes and locations of earthquake epicenters.

Procedure

1. Use tracing paper to outline the continents on a world map. Include the lines of latitude and longitude on your tracing.

2. Use the list of latitudes and longitudes of 21 active volcanoes to plot their locations on your tracing.

3. Compare your tracing with **Figure 8-2** and **Figure 9-3.**

4. In your Science Journal, and on a data table that you make, list the location of each volcano and indicate in a column whether an earthquake epicenter has been plotted close to the volcano. Also include three additional columns in your table to be used in step 5.

5. Using **Figure 10-10,** determine whether each volcano is located near a plate boundary or near a hot spot. Record this information in the extra three columns of your data table.

Volcano Locations		
Volcano	Latitude	Longitude
#1	64° N	19° W
#2	28° N	34° E
#3	43° S	172° E
#4	35° N	136° E
#5	18° S	68° W
#6	25° S	114° W
#7	20° N	155° W
#8	54° N	167° W
#9	16° N	122° E
#10	28° N	17° W
#11	15° N	43° E
#12	6° N	75° W
#13	64° S	158° E
#14	38° S	78° E
#15	21° S	56° E
#16	38° N	26° E
#17	7° S	13° W
#18	2° S	102° E
#19	38° N	30° W
#20	54° N	159° E
#21	17° N	62° W

Conclude and Apply

1. **Describe** any patterns of distribution that active volcanoes form on Earth.

2. **Describe** any patterns of distribution of earthquake epicenters shown in **Figure 8-2.**

3. **Compare and contrast** any patterns that you observe with the locations of Earth's plate boundaries and hot spots shown in **Figures 9-3** and **10-10.**

4. **Write a hypothesis** to explain any patterns you observed for locations of active volcanoes, earthquake epicenters, tectonic plate boundaries, and hot spots. Suggest ways in which geologists might test your hypothesis.

Types of Volcanoes

9•2

What You'll Learn

► How the explosiveness of a volcanic eruption is related to the silica and water vapor content of its magma
► Three forms of volcanoes

Vocabulary
shield volcano
tephra
cinder cone
composite volcano

Why It's Important

► You'll understand what makes a volcano dangerous.

Styles of Eruptions

Some volcanic eruptions are explosive and violent, like those from Soufrière Hills volcano, Mount Pinatubo, and Mount St. Helens. In others, the lava quietly flows from a vent, as in the Kilauea (kihl ah WAY ah) eruptions. What causes these differences?

Two important factors control whether an eruption will be explosive or quiet. One is the amount of water vapor and other gases that are trapped in the magma. The other factor is how much silica is present in the magma. Silica is a compound composed of the elements silicon and oxygen.

Trapped Gases

Have you ever shaken a soft-drink container and then quickly opened it? The pressure from the gas in the drink builds up and is released suddenly when you open the can, spraying the drink. In the same way, gases such as water vapor and carbon dioxide are trapped in magma by the pressure of the surrounding magma and rock. As magma nears

Figure 9-6 A calm day in Washington was suddenly interrupted when Mount St. Helens erupted at 8:32 A.M. on May 18, 1980, as shown in this sequence of photographs. **Why was the eruption so violent compared with eruptions of volcanoes like Kilauea?**

 8:32 A.M.

 38 seconds later

the surface, there is less pressure. This allows the gas to escape from the magma. Gas escapes easily from some magma during quiet eruptions. Gas that builds up to high pressures eventually causes explosive eruptions such as the one shown in **Figure 9-6.**

Magma Composition

The second major factor that affects the type of eruption is the composition of the magma. Magma that is relatively low in silica is fluid and produces quiet, nonexplosive eruptions such as those at Kilauea. This type of lava pours from volcanic vents and runs down the sides of a volcano. These quiet eruptions form volcanoes over hot spots such as Hawaii. They also flow from rift zones, which are long, deep cracks such as those in Iceland. Because the magma is fluid when it is forced upward in a vent, trapped gases can escape easily in a nonexplosive manner.

Silica-rich magma, on the other hand, produces explosive eruptions such as those at Mount St. Helens. This magma sometimes forms where Earth's plates are moving together and one plate is forced under another. When the lower plate gets deep and hot enough, a portion of it is melted. This melting portion is richer in silica than the solid plate. As the melted portion is forced upward, it comes in contact with the crust and becomes more enriched in silica. Silica-rich magma is thick and gas gets trapped, causing pressure to build up. When an explosive eruption occurs, the gases expand rapidly, often carrying pieces of lava in the explosion.

PHYSICS
◄ **INTEGRATION**

LIFE SCIENCE
INTEGRATION

Devastating Eruptions
Whenever a volcano erupts, people who live in its vicinity are affected in many ways. If the eruption is unexpected, lives can be lost. If people know the volcano is about to erupt, they can evacuate. Either way, their lives may never be the same. Research how the continuing eruption of the Soufrière Hills volcano on the Lesser Antilles island of Montserrat has affected life on the island.

C 42 seconds later

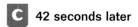

D 53 seconds later

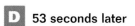

Reading Check

What type of magmas produce violent eruptions?

Magma Water Content

Another factor that causes magma to erupt explosively is its high water content. The magma at some converging zones contains a lot of water vapor. This is because of water in the oceanic crust that is carried by one plate forced below another. The trapped water vapor in the magma causes explosive eruptions. Sometimes, gas causes lava fountains to form from basaltic magmas, as illustrated in **Figure 9-8.** ☑

VISUALIZING
Forms of Volcanoes

Figure 9-7 The form of a volcano is determined by the nature of its eruption.

A When hot, fluid lava flows from one or more vents without erupting violently, it builds a gentle slope when it cools. This creates a shield volcano such as Mauna Loa, in background, in Hawaii.

Magma

Steep sides

Tephra layers

Magma

B Explosive eruptions throw rock and lava high into the air. The lava cools and hardens into tephra. When tephra falls to the ground, it forms a steep-sided, loosely packed cinder cone volcano. Pictured here is a cinder cone in Arizona.

Forms of Volcanoes

A volcano's form depends on whether it is the result of a quiet or an explosive eruption and the type of lava it is made of—silica-poor, silica-rich, or a composition somewhere in between. Volcanoes are of three basic forms— shield volcanoes, cinder cone volcanoes, or composite volcanoes, as shown in **Figure 9-7.**

Shield Volcano

Quiet eruptions spread out silica-poor lava in flat layers. The buildup of these layers forms a broad volcano with gently sloping sides called a **shield volcano.** Examples of shield volcanoes are the Hawaiian Islands.

Cinder Cone Volcano

Explosive eruptions throw lava and rock high into the air. Bits of rock or solidified lava dropped from the air are called **tephra** (TEFF ruh). Tephra varies in size from volcanic ash— the smallest—to cinders, to larger rocks called

Figure 9-8 Usually, the hot, thin lava flows of Kilauea in Hawaii are nonviolent eruptions. **What could be causing the lava fountain shown above?**

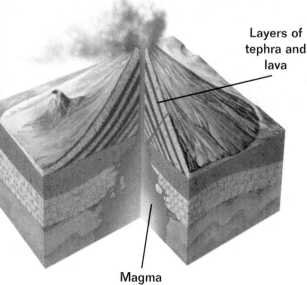

Layers of tephra and lava

Magma

C Whenever volcanic eruptions vary between violent and quieter times, tephra layers alternate with lava layers. A volcano built by this layering of tephra and lava has a composite form, such as Mount Shasta in California, shown here, or Mount St. Helens.

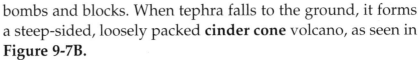
bombs and blocks. When tephra falls to the ground, it forms a steep-sided, loosely packed **cinder cone** volcano, as seen in **Figure 9-7B.**

A Mexican farmer learned about cinder cones one morning when he went to his cornfield. He noticed that a hole in his cornfield that had been there for as long as he could remember was giving off smoke that smelled like sulfur. Throughout the night, hot glowing cinders were thrown high into the air. In just a few days, a cinder cone several hundred meters high covered his cornfield. This is the volcano named Paricutín.

Composite Volcano

Some volcanic eruptions can vary between quiet and violent. An explosive period can release gas and ash, forming a tephra layer. Then, the eruption can switch over to a quiet period, erupting lava over the top of the tephra layer. When this cycle of lava and tephra is repeated over and over in alternating layers, a **composite volcano** is formed. Composite volcanoes are found mostly where Earth's plates come together

Problem Solving

Comparing Volcanic Rocks

During your study of volcanoes and the material that is ejected from volcanoes, you are given four different igneous rocks. Your task is to determine how the rocks formed and what elements they likely contain.

The rocks are fine-grained and some are full of holes. The holes were caused by escaping gases during the cooling of these rocks. The color of volcanic rocks can indicate what minerals each rock contains. Dark-colored rocks tend to contain minerals high in iron and magnesium, whereas light-colored rocks tend to have a higher concentration of silica-rich minerals.

Study the photograph. Based on the overall color of the rocks, what elements do you think each is likely to contain?

Think Critically:
Because some of these rocks are full of holes formed by gases as the rock cooled, it is possible that gases are also trapped inside these rocks. Is there a method to test the possible presence of trapped gas inside the rocks? Explain.

and one plate is forced below the other. Mount St. Helens is an example. As you can see in **Table 9-1,** many things affect volcanic eruptions and the form of a volcano.

Mount St. Helens formed as the Juan de Fuca plate was forced beneath the North American plate. The ocean floor of the Juan de Fuca plate partially melted as it was forced downward. Successive eruptions of lava and tephra were produced. They formed the majestic composite volcano that towers above the surrounding landscape. Before the 1980 eruption, silica-rich magma rose and was trapped beneath the surface. An earthquake-triggered landslide took place that released pressure on the underlying magma. This started a series of explosive eruptions, as seen in **Figure 9-6.**

The action of Earth's plates coming together also caused the 1991 eruption of the composite volcano Mount Pinatubo, in the Philippines, as seen in **Figure 9-9.** Mount Pinatubo erupted violently after lying quiet for more than 600 years. The islands of the Philippines are a volcanic island arc, formed where the Philippine plate meets the Eurasian plate.

Modeling Volcanic Cones

Procedure

1. Pour dry sand or sugar onto one spot on a paper plate, forming a model of a cinder cone volcano. **CAUTION:** *Do not taste, eat, or drink any materials used in the lab.*

2. Mix a batch of plaster of paris and pour it onto one spot on another paper plate, forming a model of a shield volcano.

3. Allow the model of the shield volcano to dry. Use a protractor to measure the slope angles of the sides of the volcanoes.

Analysis

1. Which of your volcano models has steeper sides?

2. What form of volcano is represented by the model with steeper sides?

3. Infer why this is so.

Table 9-1

Thirteen Selected Eruptions in History							
Volcano and Location	Year	Type	Eruptive Force	Magma Content		Ability of Magma to Flow	Products of Eruption
				Silica	H₂O		
Etna, Sicily	1669	composite	moderate	high	low	medium	lava, ash
Tambora, Indonesia	1815	cinder	high	high	high	low	cinders, gas
Krakatoa, Indonesia	1883	cinder	high	high	high	low	cinders, gas
Pelée, Martinique	1902	cinder	high	high	high	low	gas, ash
Vesuvius, Italy	1906	composite	moderate	high	low	medium	lava, ash
Katmai, Alaska	1912	composite	high	high	high	low	lava, ash, gas
Paricutín, Mexico	1943	cinder	moderate	high	low	medium	ash, cinders
Surtsey, Iceland	1963	shield	moderate	low	low	high	lava, ash
St. Helens, WA	1980	composite	high	high	high	low	gas, ash
Kilauea Iki, Hawaii	1989	shield	low	low	low	high	lava
Pinatubo, Philippines	1991	composite	high	high	high	low	gas, ash
Galeras, Colombia	1993	composite	high	high	high	low	gas, ash
Soufrière Hills, Montserrat	1995	composite	high	high	high	low	gas, ash, blocks

Section Assessment

1. Some volcanic eruptions are quiet and others are violent. What causes this difference?

2. Why are silica-rich magmas thicker than silica-poor magmas?

3. **Think Critically:** In 1883, Krakatoa in Indonesia erupted. Infer which kind of lava Krakatoa erupted: silica-rich or silica-poor? Support your inference using data in **Table 9-1.**

4. **Skill Builder**
   Making and Using Graphs Have you ever wondered about how volcanic eruptions compare to one another? To find out more about the sizes of eruptions, do the **Chapter 9 Skill Activity** on page 750.

Using Math

When Mount St. Helens erupted in 1980, about 0.5 km³ of material were ejected from the volcano. Tambora in Indonesia gave off 30 km³ of material in 1815. How many times larger was the volume of material given off by Tambora?

Igneous Rock Features

Intrusive Features

We can observe volcanic eruptions because they are examples of igneous activity on the surface of Earth. But, far more igneous activity occurs underground because most magma never reaches the surface to form volcanoes. Intrusive rock forms when magma cools underground. What forms do intrusive igneous rocks take? You can look at some of these features in **Figure 9-10** and **Figure 9-11**.

Batholiths

The largest intrusive igneous rock bodies are **batholiths.** They can be many hundreds of kilometers wide and long and several kilometers thick. Batholiths form when magma cools underground before reaching the surface. However, not all of

What You'll Learn

► How intrusive igneous rock features form
► How a volcanic neck and a caldera form

Vocabulary
batholith   volcanic neck
dike   caldera
sill

Why It's Important

► Igneous activity formed many features you can observe on Earth's surface.

Figure 9-10 This diagram shows intrusive and other features associated with volcanic activity. **Which features shown are formed above ground? Which are formed by intrusive activities?**

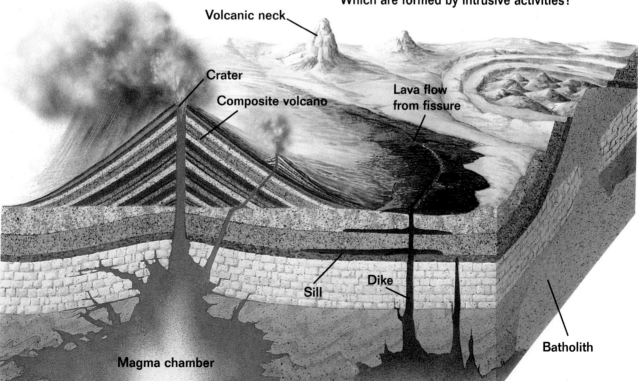

Figure 9-11 Igneous features can form in many different sizes and shapes. Some of the most common are batholiths, dikes, sills, and volcanic necks. **Why are these features often exposed and jutting out at the surface?**

A Most of the bare rock visible in Yosemite National Park in California is a batholith that has been exposed by erosion.

B Ship Rock in New Mexico, seen in the background, is a volcanic neck.

Mini Lab

Modeling Magma Movement

Procedure 🥽 🧴

1. Pour water into a transparent, plastic cup.
2. Pour a small amount of cooking oil in to a separate plastic cup. Use oil that is slightly colored, such as olive oil.
3. Extract a small amount of oil with a dropper.
4. Submerge the dropper tip into the water cup and slowly squeeze oil drops into the water.

Analysis

1. Describe what happened to the oil.
2. How do your observations compare with the movement of magma within Earth's crust?

them are hidden in Earth. Some batholiths have been exposed at Earth's surface by erosion. The granite domes of Yosemite National Park, as seen in **Figure 9-11A,** are the remains of a huge batholith that stretches across much of the length of California.

Dikes and Sills

Magma sometimes squeezes into cracks in rock below the surface. This is like squeezing toothpaste into the spaces between your teeth. Magma that is squeezed into a generally vertical crack

C The horizontal sill shown here is located in Yellowstone National Park. It formed when magma squeezed between rock layers.

D The vertical dikes shown here are located in Nevada. They formed when magma was squeezed into vertical cracks in the surrounding rock layers.

that cuts across rock layers and hardens is called a **dike.** Magma that is squeezed into a horizontal crack between rock layers and hardens is called a **sill.** These features are shown in **Figures 9-11C** and **9-11D.** Most dikes and sills run from a few meters to hundreds of meters long. Some magma that forms a sill may continue to push the rock layers upward.

Other Features

When a volcano stops erupting, the magma hardens inside the vent. Erosion begins to wear away the volcano. The cone is much softer than the solid igneous rock in the vent. Thus, the cone erodes away first, leaving behind the solid igneous core as a **volcanic neck.** Ship Rock, New Mexico, is a volcanic neck. It is just one of many volcanic necks in the southwestern United States.

Sometimes after an eruption, the top of a volcano can collapse. This produces a large opening called a **caldera,** as shown in **Figure 9-12.** Crater Lake in Oregon is a caldera that is now a lake. Crater Lake formed after the violent eruption and destruction of Mount Mazama about 7000 years ago.

PHYSICS
INTEGRATION

Rising Magma
You have learned that large bodies of magma underground are gradually forced upward toward Earth's surface. What forces push the magma upward through solid rock?

Figure 9-12 Crater Lake in Oregon formed when the top of a volcano collapsed, forming a caldera as shown in the sequence below.

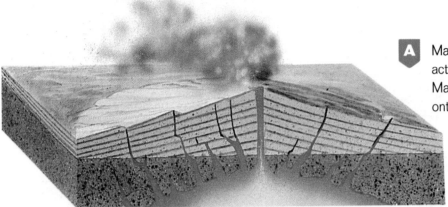

A Magma rises, causing volcanic activity of the former Mount Mazama. Magma is erupted onto the surface as lava.

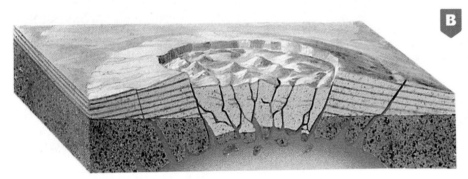

B Magma chamber partially empties, causing rock material to collapse down into the emptied chamber below the surface. This forms a circular-shaped caldera.

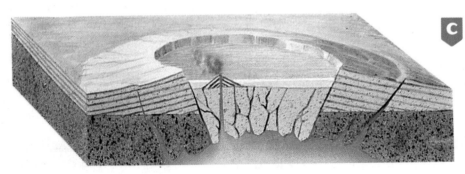

C Crater Lake formed when water collected into the circular space left when surface material collapsed.

Reading Check ✔

What exposes igneous features that formed below the surface?

Igneous Features Exposed

You have learned in this chapter about one way that Earth's surface is continually built up and how it is worn down. The surface of Earth is built up by volcanoes. Also, igneous rock is formed when magma hardens below ground. Eventually, the processes of erosion wear down rock at the surface, exposing features like batholiths, dikes, and sills. ✔

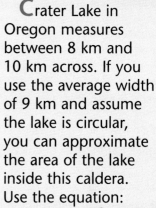

Using Math

Crater Lake in Oregon measures between 8 km and 10 km across. If you use the average width of 9 km and assume the lake is circular, you can approximate the area of the lake inside this caldera. Use the equation:

$$A = \pi r^2$$

where A = the area of a circle and r = the radius of a circle.

D Wizard Island in Crater Lake, in Oregon, is a cinder cone volcano that erupted after the formation of the caldera.

Section Assessment

1. What's the difference between a caldera and a crater?

2. What is a volcanic neck and how does it form?

3. Explain how calderas form.

4. **Think Critically:** Why are the dome features of Yosemite National Park actually intrusive volcanic features when they are exposed at the surface in the park?

5. **Skill Builder**
   Comparing and Contrasting
   Compare and contrast dikes, sills, batholiths, and volcanic necks. If you need help, refer to Comparing and Contrasting in the **Skill Handbook** on page 720.

Using Computers

Graphics Use the graphics software available on your computer to produce an illustration of igneous rock features based on **Figure 9-10.** Be sure to include both intrusive features and features that form above ground. If you need help, refer to page 734.

Materials

- **Table 9-1**
- Paper
- Pencil

Identifying Types of Volcanoes

You have learned that certain properties of magma are related to the type of eruption and the form of the volcano that will develop. Try this activity to see how to make and use a table that relates the properties of magma to the form of volcano that develops.

What You'll Investigate

Are the silica and water content of a volcano related to the form of volcano that develops?

Goals

- **Determine** any relation between the ability of magma to flow and eruptive force.
- **Determine** any relation between magma composition and eruptive force.

Procedure

1. **Copy** the graph shown at right.
2. Using the information from **Table 9-1, plot** the magma content data for each of the volcanoes listed by writing the name of the basic type of volcano in the appropriate spot on the graph.

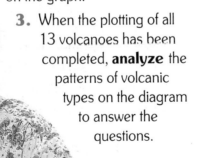

3. When the plotting of all 13 volcanoes has been completed, **analyze** the patterns of volcanic types on the diagram to answer the questions.

Conclude and Apply

1. What relation appears to exist between the ability of the magma to flow and the eruptive force of the volcano?

2. Which would be more liquidlike: a magma that flows easily or one that flows with difficulty?

3. What relation appears to exist between the silica or water content of the magma and the nature of the material ejected from the volcano?

4. How is the ability of a magma to flow related to its silica and water content?

5. **Infer** which of the two variables (silica or water content) appears to have the greater effect on the eruptive force of the volcano.

6. **Describe** the relation that appears to exist between the silica and water content of the magma and the type of volcano that is produced.

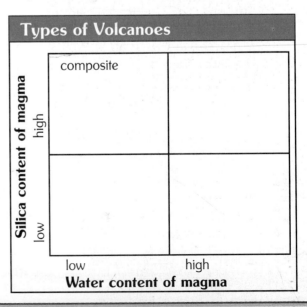

Types of Volcanoes

composite

Silica content of magma — high / low

Water content of magma — low / high

Predicting Volcanic Eruptions

Soufriére Hills volcano on the Caribbean island of Montserrat began erupting in July 1995 and continues to be very active. Although the volcano has killed 20 people in recent years, thousands of lives were saved because of advance warnings. Predicting eruptions doesn't protect buildings or roads, but it can save people and livestock. Scientists are now working on a worldwide volcano warning system.

Predicting Activity on Kilauea

The key to the volcano warning system is another system, the Global Positioning System (GPS), a collection of U.S. satellites orbiting Earth. The GPS makes it possible to take exact measurements of the Earth's surface and to pinpoint any location on the planet with great accuracy. It does this by measuring the distance between a receiver's position on Earth and at least three satellites orbiting Earth. GPS data can show whether the position being measured is moving. If the movement is associated with a volcanic eruption— such as moving magma—the information can be used to warn people about a coming eruption.

Giving Advanced Warning

This is exactly what a team of scientists from Stanford University hypothesized. They placed 13 receivers around a crater on Kilauea (left), a volcano on the island of Hawaii. On January 30, 1997, a new fissure eruption in and around the crater occurred. Eight hours before the eruption, the receivers showed that Kilauea's surface was moving. The volcano's summit was pulling apart, a movement that could have been caused by rising magma inside the volcano. Unfortunately, the volcano erupted before scientists received the information because data were only reported once every 24 hours. Research on this prediction method continues, however, and the Stanford team plans to put in place a better system that will report data continuously. This system will allow scientists to warn people before dangerous eruptions occur.

interNET CONNECTION

To learn more about Kilauea volcanism, use the link on the Glencoe Science Web Site at **www. glencoe.com/sec/science** to visit the Hawaii Center for Volcanology.

For a **preview** of this chapter, study this Reviewing Main Ideas before you read the chapter. After you have studied this chapter, you can use the Reviewing Main Ideas to **review** the chapter.

The Glencoe MindJogger, Audiocassettes, and CD-ROM provide additional opportunities for review.

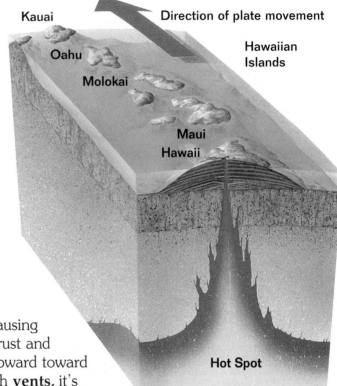

Kauai

Oahu

Molokai

Direction of plate movement

Hawaiian Islands

Maui

Hawaii

Hot Spot

Section

9-1 CAUSES OF VOLCANOES

Volcanoes can be dangerous to people, causing deaths and destroying property. Rocks in the crust and mantle melt to form magma, which is forced upward toward Earth's surface. When the magma flows through **vents,** it's called lava and forms volcanoes. Volcanoes form over hot spots when magma flows onto the seafloor. Sometimes, the lava builds up from the seafloor to form an island. Volcanoes over **hot spots** and rifts sometimes form on land. Volcanoes also form when Earth's plates pull apart or come together. *What happens to the lower plate where two plates come together in order for a volcano to form?*

Section

9-2 TYPES OF VOLCANOES

Some lavas are thin and flow easily, producing quiet eruptions. Other lavas are thick and stiff, and thus produce violent eruptions. Water vapor in magma adds to its explosiveness. **Shield volcanoes** are mountains made of silica-poor lava that have gently sloping sides. **Cinder cones** are steep sided and are made of **tephra. Composite volcanoes,** made of lava and tephra, are steep sided. *Why are eruptions of composite volcanoes so explosive?*

Reading Check ✓

Choose a topic in this chapter that interests you. Look it up in a reference book. Think of a way to share what you learn with others.

Section
9-3 IGNEOUS ROCK FEATURES

Intrusive igneous rock bodies such as batholiths, dikes, and sills form when magma solidifies underground. **Batholiths** are the most massive igneous rock bodies. **Dikes** form when magma squeezes into vertical cracks, cutting across rock layers. **Sills** form when magma squeezes in between rock layers. When a volcano stops erupting, the outer part of it erodes, leaving behind a **volcanic neck.** A **caldera** forms when the top of a volcano collapses, forming a large opening. *What causes a volcano to collapse and form a caldera?*

Career CONNECTION

Robert Ballard, Oceanographer

Not all volcanic activity takes place on land. Robert Ballard, an oceanographer, explores volcanic activity deep in the ocean. He conducted the first manned exploration of the mid-ocean ridge, which is a chain of underwater volcanic rifts that spans the globe. Robert also discovered the hydrothermal vents of the Galápagos Rift. These underwater vents spew out hot, briny water that is heated by magma deep beneath the ocean floor. *Do you think that volcanoes might affect the chemistry of the ocean?*

Chapter 9 Assessment

Using Vocabulary

a. batholith
b. caldera
c. cinder cone
d. composite volcano
e. crater
f. dike
g. hot spot
h. shield volcano
i. sill
j. tephra
k. vent
l. volcanic neck
m. volcano

Each phrase below describes a science term from the list. Write the term that matches the phrase describing it.

1. mountain made of lava and tephra
2. large opening formed by the collapse of a volcano
3. volcano with gently sloping sides
4. steep-sided volcano made of tephra
5. an igneous intrusion formed between rock layers

Checking Concepts

Choose the word or phrase that best answers the question.

6. What type of plate boundary forms composite volcanoes?
   A) plates moving apart
   B) plates sticking and slipping
   C) plates moving together
   D) plates sliding past each other

7. Why is Hawaii made of volcanoes?
   A) Plates are moving apart.
   B) A hot spot exists.
   C) Plates are moving together.
   D) Rift zones exist.

8. What kind of magmas produce violent volcanic eruptions?
   A) those rich in silica
   B) those that are fluid
   C) those forming shield volcanoes
   D) those rich in iron

9. Magma that is low in silica produces what kind of eruptions?
   A) thick
   B) caldera
   C) quiet
   D) explosive

10. What is made entirely of tephra?
    A) shield volcano
    B) caldera
    C) cinder cone
    D) composite volcano

11. What kind of volcano is Kilauea?
    A) shield volcano
    B) composite volcano
    C) cinder cone
    D) caldera cone

12. What is magma that squeezes into a vertical crack and then hardens?
    A) sill
    B) dike
    C) volcanic neck
    D) batholith

13. What is the largest igneous intrusive body?
    A) dike
    B) volcanic neck
    C) sill
    D) batholith

14. Which describes solid material erupted from a volcano?
    A) lava
    B) sand
    C) tephra
    D) sill

15. What is the process that formed Mount St. Helens?
    A) plates sticking and slipping
    B) caldera formation
    C) plates sliding sideways
    D) plates moving together

Thinking Critically

16. Explain how glaciers and volcanoes can exist on Iceland.

17. What kind of eruption is produced when lava that is low in silica flows from a volcano? Explain.

18. How are volcanoes related to earthquakes?

19. A mountain called Misti is a volcano in Peru. Peru is on the western edge of South America. How might this volcano have formed?

20. Describe in detail what a composite volcano is made of. Which parts represent violent eruptions?

Developing Skills

If you need help, refer to the Skill Handbook.

21. Concept Mapping: Make a network tree concept map that compares quiet eruptions with explosive eruptions. Use the following words and phrases: *Hawaii, high-silica, flows easily, quiet, explosive, composite, Mount St. Helens, shield, low-silica,* and *resists flow.*

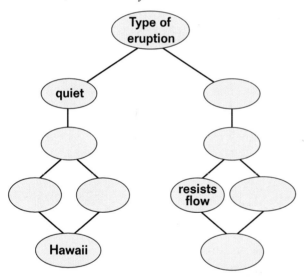

22. Observing and Inferring: A volcano erupted violently in Indonesia in 1883. What can you infer about the magma's composition? If people saw the eruption, what would they observe coming out of the volcano?

23. Classifying: Mount Fuji's steep sides are made of layers of silica-rich lava and ash. Classify Mount Fuji.

24. Measuring in SI: The base of the volcano Mauna Loa is about 5000 m below sea level. The total height of the volcano is 9170 m. What percentage of the volcano is above sea level? Below sea level?

THE PRINCETON REVIEW

Test-Taking Tip

All or None When filling in answer ovals, remember to fill in the entire oval. A computer will be scoring your answers. Don't give the right answer to a problem only to lose points on it because the computer couldn't read your oval.

Test Practice

Use these questions to test your Science Proficiency.

1. Not all volcanoes look or erupt the same. Which of the following statements **BEST** explains why this is true?

A) Volcanoes form at different locations.

B) Magmas of different compositions produce different forms of volcanoes because of the way they erupt.

C) Magma compositions do not vary. Volcanoes form differently because of the latitude at which they form.

D) The form of a volcano is related to the age of the volcano.

2. All Hawaiian Islands have formed in the same way. Which of the following statements **BEST** explains this?

A) The Hawaiian Islands have formed over an area where one plate is forced under another.

B) The Hawaiian Islands have formed over an area where plates are moving apart.

C) Each Hawaiian Island is supplied by its own hot spot of magma.

D) A hot spot provided magma for all islands as the Pacific plate slowly moved over the hot spot's location.

CHAPTER

10 Plate Tectonics

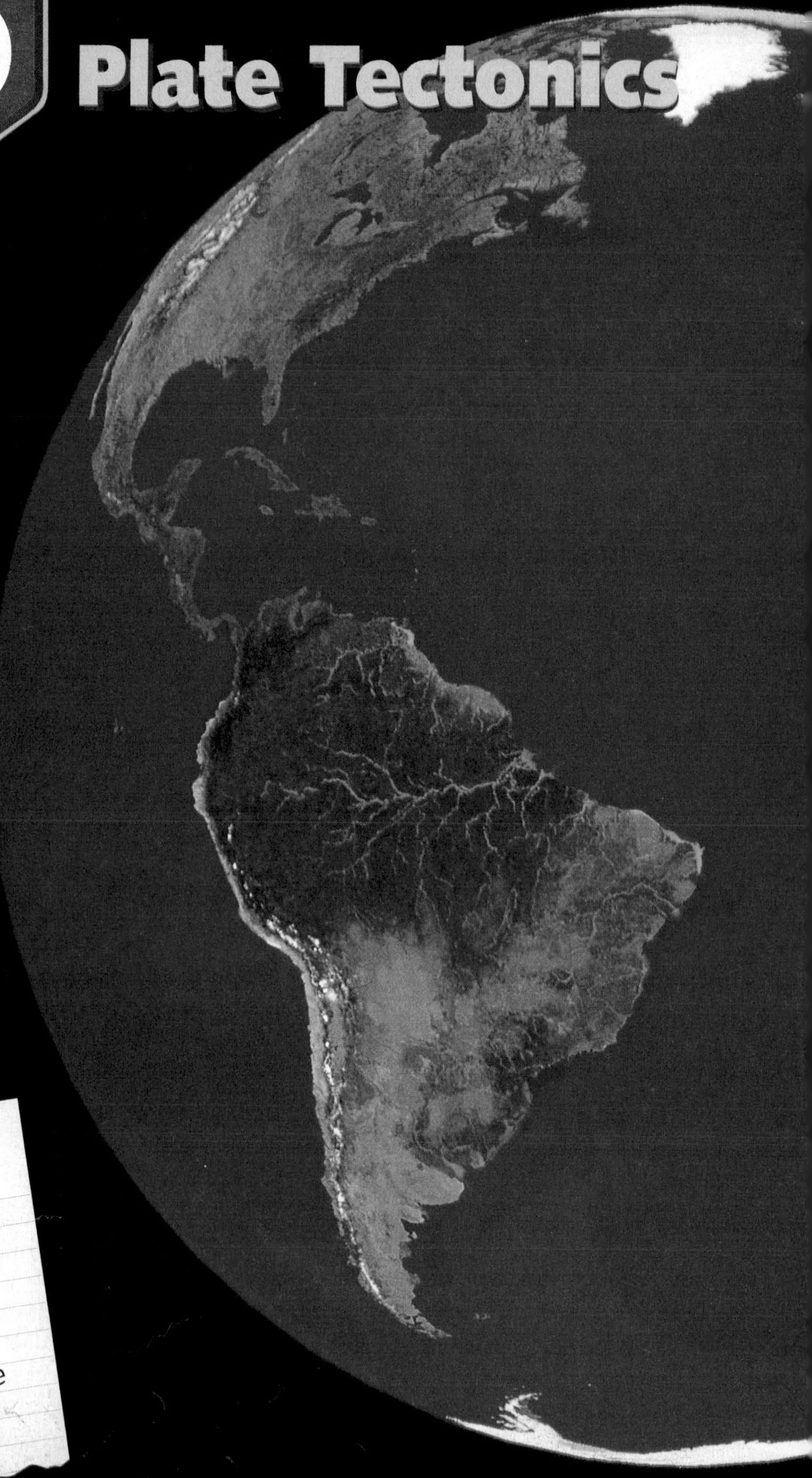

Chapter Preview

Section 10-1
Continental Drift
Section 10-2
Seafloor Spreading
Section 10-3
Plate Tectonics

Skills Preview

Skill Builders
- Compare and Contrast
- Interpret a Scientific Diagram

Activities
- Interpret Data
- Make a Prediction

MiniLabs
- Interpret Data
- Make a Model

Reading Check

As you read, list the prefixes you encounter such as *con-* or *sub-* and look up their meanings. Identify other words that begin with these prefixes.

Explore Activity

This photograph of Earth is unique because the clouds have been removed using a computer. You can see the shapes of the continents just like on a map. Look closely at the general shapes of the continents. Do you see any relationship between continents? If this photograph of Earth were cut into pieces, could you fit the pieces back together? What clues might you use?

Re-Form an Image

1. Working with a partner, obtain photographs that are of interest to you from an old magazine. Do not look at each other's photographs.

2. You and your partner are each to cut one picture into small pieces.

3. Exchange picture pieces with your partner.

4. Using clues on sur-rounding pieces, re-form the image of the photograph your partner has cut into small pieces.

In your Science Journal, describe the characteristics of the cut-up photograph you used to re-form the image. Can you think of other examples in which characteristics of objects are used to match them up with other objects?

10·1 Continental Drift

Evidence for Continental Drift

When you look at a map of Earth's surface, one thing is obvious. In **Figures 10-1** and **10-2,** you can see that the edges of some continents look as if they would fit together like a puzzle. In the early 1800s, as accurate maps of Earth's surface were first being developed, other people also noticed this fact.

Pangaea

Alfred Wegener (VEG nur) thought that the fit of the continents wasn't just a coincidence. He suggested that all the continents were joined together at some point in the past. In a 1912 lecture, he proposed the idea of continental drift. According to the hypothesis of **continental drift,** continents have moved slowly to their current locations. Wegener suggested that all continents were once connected as one large landmass that broke apart about 200 million years ago. He called this large landmass **Pangaea** (pan JEE uh), which means "all land."

What You'll Learn

▶ The hypothesis of continental drift
▶ Four pieces of evidence supporting continental drift

Vocabulary
continental drift
Pangaea

Why It's Important

▶ The hypothesis of continental drift led to plate tectonics, a theory that explains many dynamic processes in Earth.

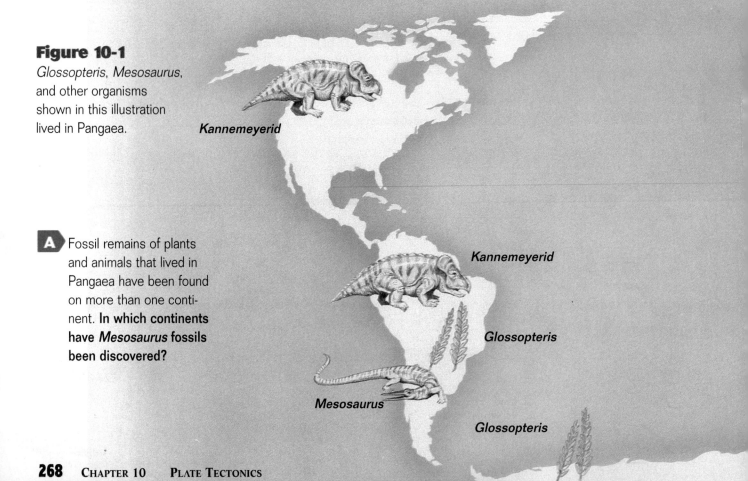

Figure 10-1

Glossopteris, Mesosaurus, and other organisms shown in this illustration lived in Pangaea.

A Fossil remains of plants and animals that lived in Pangaea have been found on more than one continent. **In which continents have *Mesosaurus* fossils been discovered?**

Kannemeyerid

Kannemeyerid

Glossopteris

Mesosaurus

Glossopteris

Long after Wegener's death in 1930, his basic hypothesis, that the continents have moved, was accepted. The evidence Wegener had to support his idea hadn't been enough to convince many people during his lifetime. However, Wegener's early evidence has since been joined by other important observations. Let's explore both Wegener's clues and some newer ones.

Fossil Clues

Besides the puzzlelike fit of the continents, other clues were found from fossils. Fossils of the reptile *Mesosaurus* have been found in South America and Africa, as shown in **Figure 10-1.** This swimming reptile lived in freshwater and on land. How could fossils of *Mesosaurus* be found so far apart? It's unlikely that it could have swum between the continents. Wegener thought this reptile lived on both continents when they were joined as one giant landmass. ☑

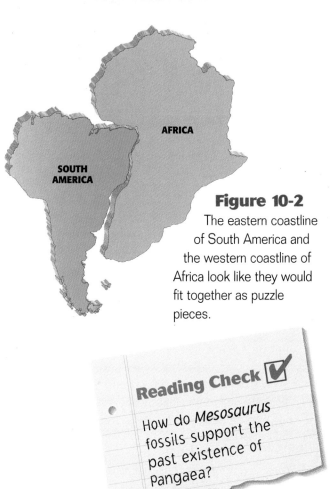

Figure 10-2
The eastern coastline of South America and the western coastline of Africa look like they would fit together as puzzle pieces.

Reading Check ☑

How do *Mesosaurus* fossils support the past existence of Pangaea?

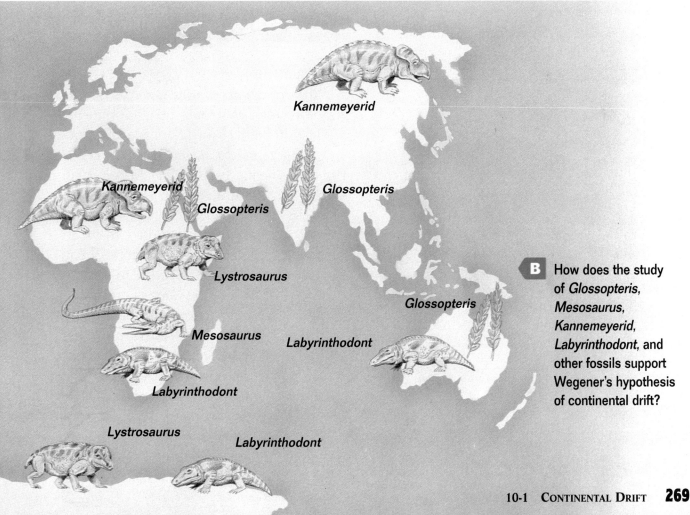

Kannemeyerid

Kannemeyerid

Glossopteris

Glossopteris

Lystrosaurus

Mesosaurus

Glossopteris

Labyrinthodont

Labyrinthodont

Lystrosaurus

Labyrinthodont

B How does the study of *Glossopteris*, *Mesosaurus*, *Kannemeyerid*, *Labyrinthodont*, and other fossils support Wegener's hypothesis of continental drift?

Mini Lab

Interpreting Fossil Data

Procedure

1. Build a three-layer landmass using clay or modeling dough.
2. Mold the clay into mountain ranges.
3. Place similar "fossils" into the clay at various locations around the landmass.
4. Form five continents from the one landmass. Also, form two smaller landmasses out of different clay with different mountain ranges and fossils.
5. Place the five continents and two smaller landmasses around the room.
6. Students who did not make or place the landmasses will locate the drifted continents and reconstruct a model that shows how they were once positioned.

Analysis

1. Were you able to reconstruct all or part of the original clay landmass?
2. What clues, if any, were useful in reconstructing the original landmass?
3. How did you deal with continents that initially didn't seem to fit?

Figure 10-3 This fossil fern, *Glossopteris*, grew in a warm tropical climate.

Another fossil that helps support the hypothesis of continental drift is *Glossopteris*. **Figure 10-3** shows this fossil fern, which has been found in Africa, Australia, India, South America, and most recently in Antarctica. The presence of this fern in so many areas led Wegener to suggest that all of these regions were once connected and had a similar climate.

Climate Clues

Fossils of warm-weather plants were found on the island of Spitzbergen in the Arctic Ocean. Wegener hypothesized that Spitzbergen drifted from the tropic regions. He also used glacial clues to support his theory.

Glacial deposits and grooved bedrock found in South America, Africa, India, and Australia show that these continents were once covered with glaciers. How could you explain why glacial deposits were found in areas where no glaciers exist today? Wegener thought that these continents were all connected and covered with ice near Earth's south pole at one time.

Rock Clues

If the continents were connected at one time, then rocks that make up the continents should be the same. Similar rock structures *are* found on different continents. Parts of the Appalachian Mountains of the eastern United States are similar to those found in Greenland and western Europe. If you were to travel to eastern South America and western Africa, you would find rock structures that are similar. Rock clues like these support the idea that the continents were once connected.

 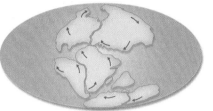 

How could continents drift?

Although Wegener provided evidence to support his hypothesis of continental drift, he couldn't explain how, when, or why these changes, shown in **Figure 10-4,** had taken place. Because other scientists at that time could not provide explanations either, Wegener's idea of continental drift was rejected. The idea was so different that most people closed their minds to it.

Rock, fossil, and climate clues were the main lines of evidence for continental drift. After Wegener's death, more clues were found and new ideas that supported continental drift were discovered. One of these new ideas, seafloor spreading, helped provide an explanation of how the continents could move.

Figure 10-4 These computer models show the probable course that the continents have taken. On the far left is their position 250 million years ago. In the middle is their position 180 million years ago. At right is their current position. **Based on the diagrams, and assuming that the rate of movement will stay the same, what will happen to the Atlantic Ocean during the next 100 million years?**

Section Assessment

1. State one reason why Wegener's ideas about continental drift were not accepted.

2. How did Wegener use climate clues to support his hypothesis about continental drift?

3. **Think Critically:** Why would you expect to see similar rocks and rock structures on two landmasses that were connected at one time?

4. **Skill Builder**
   Comparing and Contrasting Compare and contrast the location of fossils of the tropical plant *Glossopteris,* as shown in **Figure 10-1,** with the climate that exists at each location today. If you need help, refer to Comparing and Contrasting in the **Skill Handbook** on page 720.

Science Journal

Imagine you are Alfred Wegener in the year 1912. In your Science Journal, write a letter to another scientist explaining your idea about continental drift. Try to convince this scientist that your hypothesis is correct.

10·2 Seafloor Spreading

Clues on the Ocean Floor

Up until the early 1950s, little was known about the ocean floor. Scientists didn't have the technology needed to explore the deep oceans. But, the invention of echo-sounding devices allowed the development of accurate maps of the ocean floor. Soon, scientists discovered an ocean floor that had mountains and valleys just like on the continents. They also found a system of ridges and valleys in the Atlantic, the Pacific, and in other oceans around the world. The mid-ocean ridges form an underwater mountain range that stretches along the center of much of Earth's ocean floor. This discovery raised the curiosity of many scientists. What formed these mid-ocean ridges?

What You'll Learn

▶ A description of seafloor spreading
▶ How age and magnetic clues support seafloor spreading

Vocabulary
seafloor spreading

Why It's Important

▶ Seafloor spreading helps explain how continents drift apart.

Age of ocean floor in millions of years

150–200	100–150	50–100	0–50	50–100	100–150	150–200

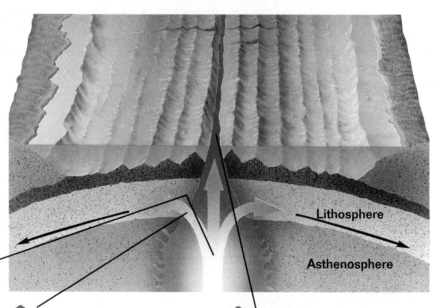

Figure 10-5 As the seafloor spreads apart at a mid-ocean ridge, new seafloor is created. The older seafloor moves away from the ridge in opposite directions. **If seafloor spreading is happening, what evidence should you expect to find by studying rocks taken from the seafloor?**

Lithosphere

Asthenosphere

A Hot, less-dense, partially molten rock material from deep inside Earth is forced upward.

B As this hot material approaches the more rigid upper mantle, it is deflected, and the lithosphere moves along with it.

C Plates of Earth's lithosphere, which are composed of the crust and rigid upper mantle, are forced apart and moved in the direction of the moving hot rock material in the asthenosphere. A rift forms into which molten rock from the upper mantle is forced until it finally flows out onto Earth's surface as lava.

The Seafloor Moves

In the early 1960s, Princeton University scientist Harry Hess suggested an explanation. His now-famous and accepted theory is known as **seafloor spreading.** Hess proposed that hot, less-dense material below Earth's crust is forced upward toward the surface at a mid-ocean ridge. Then, it turns and flows sideways, carrying the seafloor away from the ridge in both directions, as seen in **Figure 10-5.**

As the seafloor spreads apart, magma moves upward and flows from the cracks. It becomes solid as it cools and forms new seafloor. The seafloor that is carried away from the ridge cools, contracts, and becomes more dense than the material below it. Colder seafloor begins to sink downward. The theory of seafloor spreading was later shown to be correct by the following lines of evidence.

Age Evidence

In 1968, scientists aboard the research ship *Glomar Challenger* began gathering information about the rocks on the seafloor. The *Glomar Challenger,* as shown in **Figure 10-6,** was equipped with a drilling rig that allowed scientists to drill into the seafloor to obtain rock samples. The scientists began drilling to study the ages of rocks in the seafloor and made a remarkable discovery. They found no rocks older than 180 million years. In contrast, some continental rocks are almost 4 billion years old. Why are these seafloor rocks so young?

Using Math

Measure the distance between North America and Africa at three locations on a world map. Determine an average distance between the two continents. Assuming the oldest seafloor (180 million years old) formed when Pangaea first broke up, how fast have the two continents been moving apart since then? Use the equation *rate = distance/time.*

Figure 10-6 The research ship *Glomar Challenger* helped in the exploration of the world's oceans and the seafloor.

A Black smokers along mid-ocean ridges give off hot water that is rich in metals.

B Echo-sounding allows scientists to discover seafloor features on a large scale like those shown here on the Atlantic Ocean floor.

Figure 10-7 Many new discoveries have been made on the seafloor.

Scientists also found that the youngest rocks are located at the mid-ocean ridges. The ages of the rocks become increasingly older farther from the ridges on both sides. The evidence for seafloor spreading was getting stronger. New seafloor features and life-forms were also discovered along mid-ocean ridges, as shown in **Figure 10-7**.

Magnetic Clues

Earth's magnetic field has a north and a south pole. Magnetic lines, or directions, of force leave Earth near the south pole and enter Earth near the north pole. During a *magnetic reversal*, the magnetic forces run the opposite way. Scientists have determined that Earth's magnetic field has reversed itself many times in the past. These reversals occur over thousands or even millions of years.

Iron-bearing minerals, such as magnetite, that are found in basalt record Earth's magnetic field direction when they form. If Earth's magnetic field reverses, new iron minerals being formed will reflect that magnetic reversal. ☑

Reading Check ☑

What materials on the seafloor record magnetic field reversals?

Scientists found that rocks on the ocean floor show many magnetic reversals. A magnetometer (mag nuh TAHM ut ur), a sensitive instrument that records magnetic data, is used. The magnetic alignment in the rocks reverses back and forth over time in strips parallel to the mid-ocean ridges, as shown in **Figure 10-8**.

This discovery provided strong support that seafloor spreading was indeed happening. The magnetic reversals showed that new rock was being formed at the mid-ocean ridges.

The ideas of Alfred Wegener and Harry Hess changed the way people think about Earth's crust. Fossil, rock, and climate evidence supporting the hypothesis of continental drift is too strong to be discounted. Seafloor spreading shows that ocean floors change, too. You'll soon see how these two ideas are closely related.

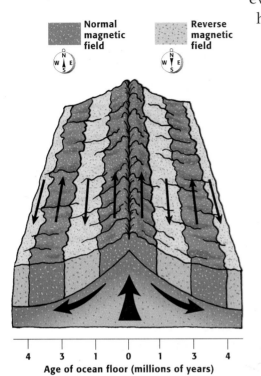

Normal magnetic field

Reverse magnetic field

Age of ocean floor (millions of years)

4 3 1 0 1 3 4

CHEMISTRY
INTEGRATION

Curie Point
Find out what the Curie point is and describe in your Science Journal what happens to iron-bearing minerals when they are heated to the Curie point. Explain how this is important to studies of seafloor spreading.

Figure 10-8 Changes in Earth's magnetic field are preserved in rock that forms on both sides of mid-ocean ridges. The time line on this diagram shows how this happens over millions of years. **Why is this considered evidence for seafloor spreading?**

Section Assessment

1. How does the recording of Earth's magnetic field in iron-bearing minerals help support the theory of seafloor spreading?

2. What eventually happens to seafloor that is carried away from a mid-ocean ridge?

3. **Think Critically:** How is seafloor spreading different from continental drift?

4. **Skill Builder**
   Concept Mapping Make a concept map that discusses the evidence for seafloor spreading using the following terms and phrases: *ages increase away from ridge, pattern of magnetic field reversals, mid-ocean ridge, pattern of ages around ridge,* and *reverses back and forth*. If you need help, refer to Concept Mapping in the **Skill Handbook** on page 714.

Using Math

On average, North America is moving 1.25 cm per year away from the Mid-Atlantic Ridge. Using this rate, determine how much farther apart the continents of North America and Africa will be after 200 million years.

Materials

- Metric ruler
- Pencil

Seafloor Spreading Rates

So far, you've learned a lot about seafloor spreading and magnetic field reversals. How can you use your knowledge to reconstruct Pangaea? Try this activity to see how you can determine where a continent may have been located in the past.

What You'll Investigate

Can magnetic clues, such as magnetic field reversals on Earth, be used to help reconstruct Pangaea?

Goals

- **Interpret** data about magnetic field reversals.
- **Use** these magnetic clues to reconstruct Pangaea.

Procedure

1. **Study** the magnetic field graph below. You will be working only with normal polarity readings, which are the peaks above the baseline in the top half of the graph.

2. **Place** the long edge of a ruler vertically on the graph. Slide the ruler so that it lines up with the center of **peak #1 west** of the Mid-Atlantic ridge.

3. **Determine** and **record** the distance and age that line up with the center of **peak #1 west**. Repeat this process for **peak #1 east** of the ridge.

4. **Calculate** the average age and distance for this pair of peaks: **peaks #1 west** and **east**.

5. **Repeat** steps 1 through 4 for each remaining pair of normal polarity peaks.

6. For the six pairs of peaks, **calculate** the rate of movement in cm/year. Use the formula *rate = distance/time* to **calculate** the rate. You must **convert** kilometers to centimeters.

For example, to calculate a rate using Normal polarity peak #5, West from the ridge:

$$\text{rate} = \frac{125 \text{ km}}{10 \text{ million years}} = \frac{12.5 \text{ km}}{\text{million years}}$$

$$= \frac{1\,250\,000 \text{ cm}}{1\,000\,000 \text{ years}} = 1.25 \text{ cm/year}$$

Conclude and Apply

1. Compare the age of igneous rock found near the mid-ocean ridge with that of igneous rock found farther away from the ridge.

2. If the distance from a point on the coast of Africa to the Mid-Atlantic Ridge is approximately 2400 km, **calculate** how long ago that point in Africa was at or near the Mid-Atlantic Ridge.

3. How could you use this method to reconstruct Pangaea?

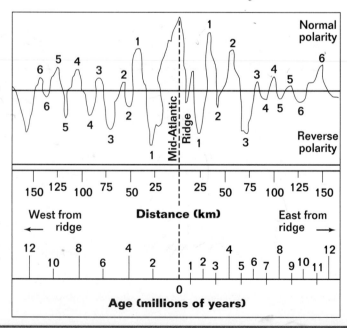

Plate Tectonics

Plate Tectonics

The discovery of seafloor spreading helped scientists understand what was happening to Earth's crust and upper mantle. The idea of seafloor spreading showed that more than just continents were moving, as Wegener had thought. It was now certain to scientists that sections of the seafloor and continents move around in relation to one another.

Plate Movements

In the 1960s scientists developed a new theory that combined the main ideas of continental drift and seafloor spreading. According to the theory of **plate tectonics,** Earth's crust and upper mantle are broken into sections. These sections, called **plates,** move around on a special layer of the mantle. The plates can be thought of as rafts that float and move around on this layer.

Composition of Earth's Plates

Plates are made of the crust and a part of the upper mantle, as seen in **Figure 10-9.** These two parts together are called the **lithosphere** (LIHTH uh sfihr). This rigid layer is about 100 km thick and is less dense than material underneath. The plastic-like layer below the lithosphere is called the **asthenosphere** (as THEN uh sfihr).

What You'll Learn

▶ How to compare and contrast different types of plate boundaries

▶ How convection currents might be the cause of plate tectonics

▶ The effects of plate tectonics found at each type of boundary

Vocabulary

plate tectonics
plate
lithosphere
asthenosphere
convection current

Why It's Important

▶ Plate tectonics explains how many of Earth's features form.

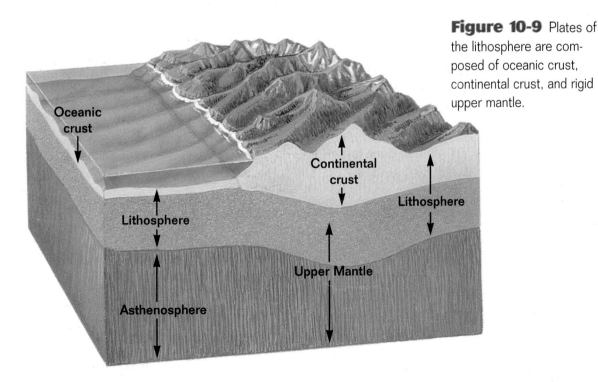

Figure 10-9 Plates of the lithosphere are composed of oceanic crust, continental crust, and rigid upper mantle.

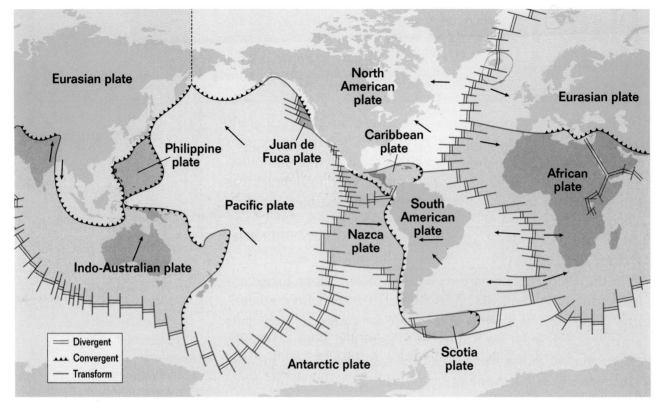

Figure 10-10 This diagram shows the major plates of the lithosphere, their direction of movement, and the type of boundary between them. **Based on what is shown in this figure, what is happening where the Nazca plate meets the Pacific plate?**

The rigid plates of the lithosphere "float" and move around on the asthenosphere. You can think of the plates on the asthenosphere as large, flat stones placed on top of putty. By applying force, you can easily slide the stones around on the putty.

Plate Boundaries

What happens when plates move? They can interact in three ways. They can move toward each other and collide, they can pull apart, or they can simply move past one another. When the plates interact, the result of their movement is seen at the plate boundaries, as in **Figure 10-10.**

Movement along any plate boundary means that changes must happen at other boundaries. What is happening to the Atlantic Ocean between the North American and African plates? Compare this with what is happening along the western margin of South America. ☑

Plates Moving Apart

The boundary between two plates that are moving apart is called a *divergent boundary.* You learned about divergent boundaries when you read about seafloor spreading. In the Atlantic Ocean, the North American plate is moving away from the Eurasian and the African plates, as seen in **Figure 10-10.**

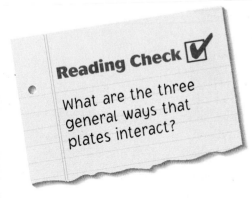

Reading Check ☑

What are the three general ways that plates interact?

That divergent boundary is called the Mid-Atlantic Ridge. The Great Rift Valley in eastern Africa is another example of a divergent plate boundary. Here, a valley has formed where two continental plates are separating. **Figure 10-11B** shows a side view of what a rift valley might look like and the hot material that rises up where plates separate.

Plates Moving Together

If new crust is being added at one location, why doesn't Earth's surface keep expanding? As new crust is added in one place, it disappears at another. The disappearance of crust can occur when seafloor cools, becomes more dense, and sinks. This happens where two plates collide at what is called a *convergent boundary.*

There are three types of convergent boundaries. When an oceanic plate collides with a less-dense continental plate, the oceanic plate is forced under the continental plate. The area where an oceanic plate is pushed down into the upper mantle is called a *subduction zone.* Volcanoes occur above subduction zones.

Figure 10-11C shows how this type of convergent boundary creates a deep-sea trench where one plate is forced beneath the other. High temperatures and pressures cause

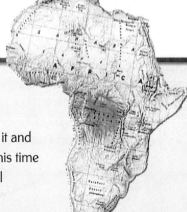

Problem Solving

The Fit Isn't Perfect

Recall the Explore Activity you performed at the beginning of this chapter. While you were trying to fit pieces of a cut-up photograph together, what clues did you use?

Take a copy of a map of the world and cut out each continent. Lay them out on a tabletop and try to fit them together, using techniques you used in the Explore Activity. You will find that the pieces of your Earth puzzle, the continents, do not fit together very well. Yet, several of the areas on some continents fit together extremely well.

Take out another world map—one that shows the continental shelves as well

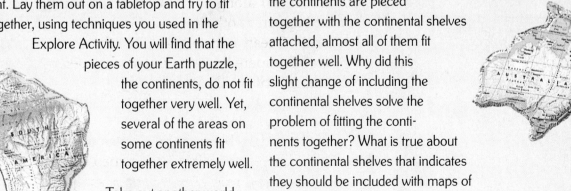

as the continents. Copy it and cut out the continents, this time including the continental shelves.

Think Critically: When the continents are pieced together with the continental shelves attached, almost all of them fit together well. Why did this slight change of including the continental shelves solve the problem of fitting the continents together? What is true about the continental shelves that indicates they should be included with maps of the continents?

the subducted plate to melt as it descends under the other plate. The newly formed magma is forced upward along these plate boundaries, forming volcanic mountains. The Andes mountain system of South America contains many volcanoes. They were formed at the convergent boundary of the Nazca and the South American plates.

✶The second type of convergent boundary occurs when two oceanic plates collide, and when seafloor that has become more dense due to cooling begins to sink. In this type of plate collision, one plate bends and slides under the other, forming a subduction zone as shown in **Figure 10-11E.** A deep-sea trench is formed, and new magma that is produced rises to form an island arc of volcanoes. The islands of Japan are an island arc formed where two oceanic plates collide.

VISUALIZING
Plate Movement

Figure 10-11 Earth's plates pull apart at some boundaries and collide at others, forming mountains and volcanoes.

B Where continental plates pull apart, a rift valley forms. If the rift valley separates further, it may flood and become an ocean.

C As an oceanic plate collides with a less-dense continental plate, the continental plate is forced upward and the oceanic plate is forced under the continental plate. As the oceanic plate descends, it starts to melt. The melted rock is less dense than surrounding rock and is forced upward, forming volcanoes.

A As one continental plate collides with another, lithosphere is pushed up at the boundary and mountains form.

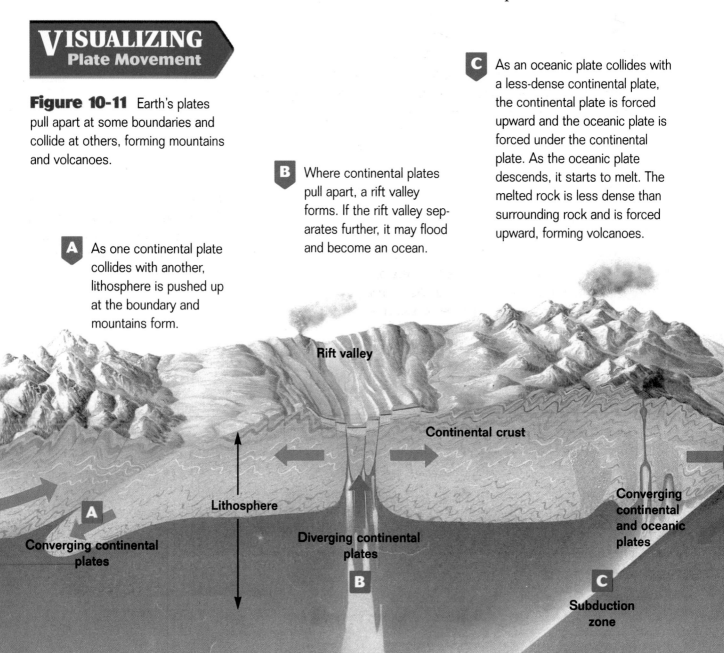

Rift valley

Continental crust

Lithosphere

Converging continental plates

Diverging continental plates

Converging continental and oceanic plates

Subduction zone

The third type of convergent boundary occurs when two continental plates collide as shown in **Figure 10-11A.** Because both of these plates are less dense than the material in the asthenosphere, usually no subduction occurs. The two plates just collide and crumple up, forming mountain ranges. Earthquakes are common at these convergent boundaries. But, volcanoes do not form because there is no subduction. The Himalaya in Asia are forming where the Indo-Australian plate crashes into the Eurasian plate.

Plates Sliding Past Each Other

The third type of plate boundary is called a *transform boundary.* Transform boundaries occur when two plates slide past one another. They move either in opposite directions or in the same direction at different rates. When one plate slips past another suddenly, earthquakes occur. The Pacific plate is sliding past the North American plate, forming the famous San Andreas Fault in California, as seen in **Figure 10-12.** The San Andreas Fault is part of a transform plate boundary. It has been the site of many earthquakes.

E When two oceanic plates collide, one oceanic plate becomes denser due to cooling and begins to sink under the other. Volcanoes form on the surface.

D A mid-ocean ridge forms whenever diverging plates continue to separate, creating a new ocean basin. As the rising magma cools, it forms new ocean crust.

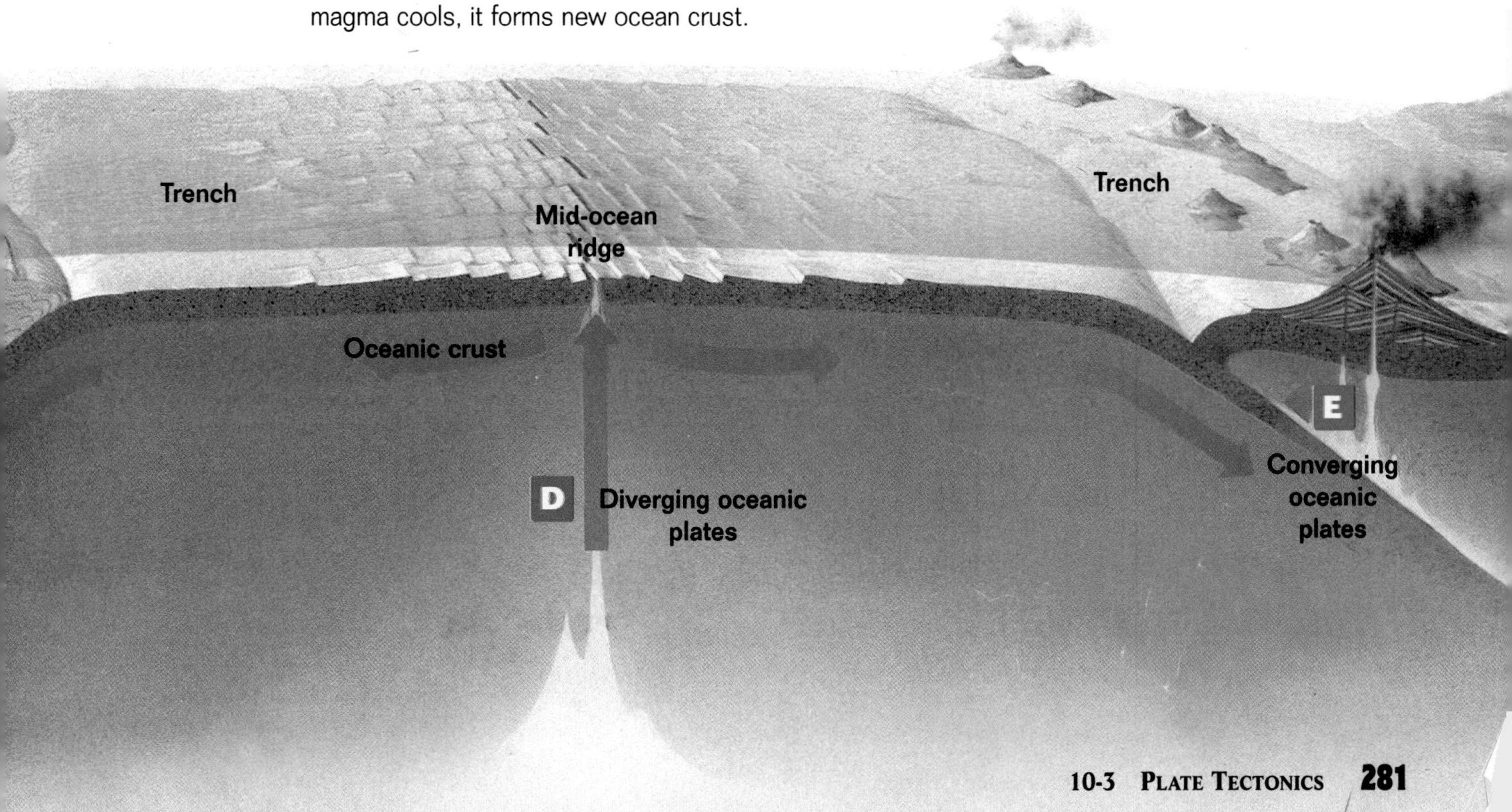

Trench

Mid-ocean ridge

Trench

Oceanic crust

E

D Diverging oceanic plates

Converging oceanic plates

Mini Lab

Modeling Convection Currents

Procedure

1. Fill a clear, colorless casserole dish with water to 5 cm from the top.
2. Center the dish on a hot plate and heat. **CAUTION:** *Wear thermal mitts to protect your hands.*
3. Add a few drops of food coloring to the water directly above the hot plate.
4. Looking from the side of the dish, observe what happens in the water.
5. In your Science Journal, describe what you observe. If possible, make an illustration.

Analysis

1. Determine whether any currents form in the water.
2. If so, infer what causes the currents to form.
3. If not, determine how to change the experiment in order to cause currents to form. Get permission from your teacher before you proceed.

Causes of Plate Tectonics

Many new discoveries have been made about Earth's crust since Wegener's day. But, one question still remains. What causes the plates to move and the seafloor to spread? Scientists now think they have a pretty good idea. They think that plates are moved by the same basic process that is used to heat some buildings.

Convection Currents

In a forced-air heating system, air is warmed in a furnace and a blower forces it into each room of the building. The warm air is forced upward through vents on the floor and heats the surrounding air. Cooler air, which is more dense, sinks to the floor of the room. It returns to the furnace through the cold air return and is reheated. This entire cycle of heating, rising, cooling, and sinking is called a **convection current.** This same process, occurring in the mantle, is thought to be the force behind plate tectonics.

Figure 10-12 The San Andreas Fault in California occurs along the transform plate boundary where the Pacific plate is sliding past the North American plate.

A This photograph shows an aerial view of the San Andreas Fault.

San Andreas Fault

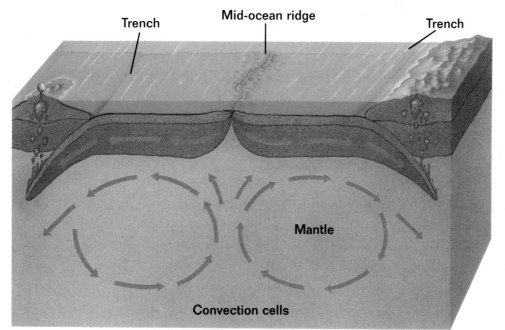

Trench   Mid-ocean ridge   Trench

Mantle

Convection cells

Figure 10-13 Pictured is one hypothesis of how convection currents (see arrows) are the driving force of plate tectonics. In this hypothesis, convection is limited to the upper mantle only. In another hypothesis, convection currents occur throughout the mantle.

Scientists suggest that differences in density cause hot, plasticlike rock to be forced upward toward the surface. When this material reaches Earth's lithosphere, it moves horizontally and carries plates of the lithosphere with it, as described earlier. As it cools, the plasticlike rock becomes more dense. It then sinks into the mantle, taking overlying lithosphere with it.

These huge convection currents provide the energy to move plates as shown in **Figure 10-13.** They are, therefore, the cause of many of Earth's surface features.

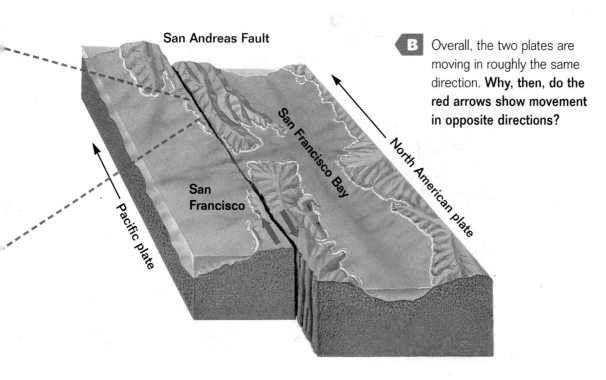

San Andreas Fault

San Francisco Bay

San Francisco

Pacific plate

North American plate

B Overall, the two plates are moving in roughly the same direction. **Why, then, do the red arrows show movement in opposite directions?**

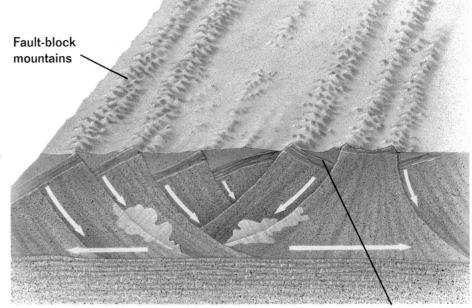

Figure 10-14 Fault-block mountains can form when Earth's crust is stretched by tectonic forces. The arrows indicate the directions that blocks have moved. **What type of force occurs when Earth's crust is pulled in opposite directions?**

Fault-block mountains

Collapse of crust

Figure 10-15 The Great Rift Valley of Africa will probably become an ocean basin as rifting continues.

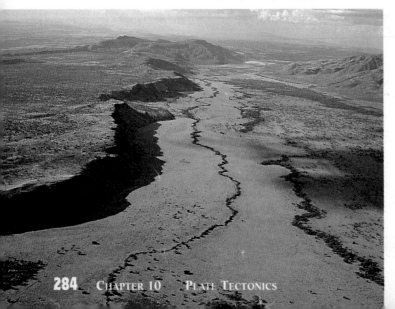

Effects of Plate Tectonics

Earth is a dynamic planet with convection currents inside that power the movement of plates. As the plates move, they interact. The interaction of plates produces forces that build mountains, create ocean basins, and cause volcanoes. Whenever rocks in Earth's crust break and move, a fault forms and energy is released in the form of seismic waves. Humans feel this release as earthquakes. You can see some of the effects of plate tectonics in the **Field Guide to Roadside Geology** at the end of this chapter.

Normal Faults and Rift Valleys

Diverging plates cause tension forces that stretch Earth's crust. This causes large blocks of crust to break and tilt or slide down. Entire mountain ranges may form in the process, called fault-block mountains, as shown in **Figure 10-14.** Generally, the faults that form from tension are normal faults. Once the divergence causes a separation in Earth's crust, rift valleys can form. Examples of rift valleys are the Great Rift Valley in Africa, shown in **Figure 10-15,** and the valleys that occur in the middle of mid-ocean ridges. Examples include the Mid-Atlantic Ridge and the East Pacific Rise.

Strike-Slip Faults

If one plate is sliding past another, the forces are not directly opposite. The plates stick and then slide along large strike-slip faults. One such example is the San Andreas Fault. When plates move suddenly, vibrations are generated inside Earth that are felt as an earthquake. Plate tectonics explains how activity inside Earth can affect Earth's crust differently in different locations. We have seen how plates have moved since Pangaea separated. What was Earth like before that?

Mountains, Arcs, and Volcanoes

Most of Earth's mountain belts, volcanoes, and earthquakes occur at convergent plate boundaries. Compression forces produce several effects where plates move together. When continental plates converge, the forces generated cause massive folding of rock layers into mountain ranges such as the Himalaya, shown in **Figure 10-16,** or the Appalachian Mountains. Reverse faults also may occur if the forces are great enough. If the two converging plates are oceanic plates, one plate slides under the other, melting occurs, and island arcs and volcanoes form.

If an oceanic plate converges with a continental plate, the oceanic plate slides under the continental plate, melting occurs, and volcanoes form. Entire mountain ranges can form at this type of convergent boundary. ☑

Testing for Plate Tectonics

Until recently, the only tests scientists could use to check for plate movement were indirect. They could study the magnetic characteristics of rocks on the seafloor. They could study volcanoes and earthquakes. However, these methods only provided indirect evidence that the plates have moved and are still moving. They did not provide proof—only support of the idea.

PHYSICS
INTEGRATION

Tectonic Forces
In what directions are forces applied at convergent, divergent, and transform boundaries? Demonstrate these forces using wooden blocks or your hands.

Reading Check

What features occur where plates converge?

Figure 10-16 The Himalaya are still forming today as the Indo-Australian plate collides with the Eurasian plate.

Figure 10-17 When using the Satellite Laser Ranging System, scientists on the ground shoot laser pulses at a satellite, shown here. The pulses reflect off the satellite and are used to determine an exact location on the ground.

Now, scientists can measure exact movements of Earth's plates of as little as 1 cm/year. New methods had to be discovered to be able to measure the small amounts of movement of Earth's plates. One method uses lasers and a satellite, as shown in **Figure 10-17.**

Current data from these methods show that Hawaii is moving toward Japan at a rate of about 8.3 cm/year. Also, Maryland is moving away from England at a rate of about 1.7 cm/year. The total range of data from the methods taken all over the world shows that lithospheric plates move between 1 to 12 cm/year relative to the positions of other plates.

Section Assessment

1. What happens to plates at a transform plate boundary?

2. What occurs at plate boundaries associated with seafloor spreading?

3. Describe three types of plate boundaries where volcanic eruptions can occur.

4. **Think Critically:** Using **Figure 10-10** and a world map, determine what natural disasters might be likely to occur in Iceland.

5. **Skill Builder**
   Interpreting Scientific Illustrations Plate tectonic activity causes many events that can be dangerous to humans. One of these events is an earthquake that occurs on the seafloor. This can form a seismic sea wave, or tsunami. Learn how scientists predict the arrival time of a tsunami in a coastal area. Do the **Chapter 10 Skill Activity** on page 751.

Using Computers

Graphics Research ten recent earthquakes of magnitude 3.0 or greater. Make a bar graph that plots the number of earthquakes on the y-axis and their Richter magnitudes on the x-axis. Make the first bar on the x-axis have a Richter range of 3–4, the second a range of 4–5, etc. If you need help, refer to page 734.

Finding and Using Rates

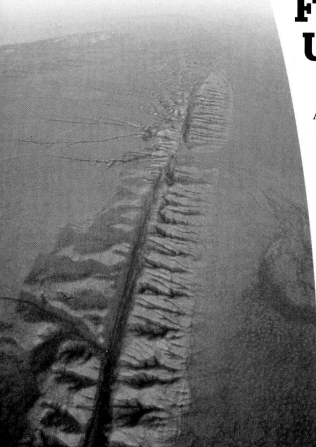

A rate is a ratio of two measurements with different units. You are familiar with some rates, such as kilometers per hour. Kilometers per hour is also a unit rate because the denominator of the rate is one unit. Finding unit rates can help you solve problems about the movement of geologic features in Earth's crust, such as strike-slip faults.

Problem

A well-known strike-slip fault is the San Andreas Fault in California (see aerial view at left). The fault has moved about 600 km in 150 million years. Follow the steps below to answer two questions. What is the rate of movement per year of the San Andreas Fault? At this rate, how far will the fault move in 1000 years?

Solution

1. Think: 150 million is a large number, and 600 is a much smaller number. You will be dividing to find the rate, so convert 600 km to millimeters. Since 1 km = 1000 m and 1 m = 1000 mm, multiply 600 by 1000 to get meters and again by 1000 to get millimeters. $600 \times 1000 \times 1000 = 600\,000\,000$; 600 km is 600 000 000 mm.

2. Find the unit rate: Write the rate as a fraction. Then, simplify the fraction to have a denominator of 1.

$$\frac{mm}{years} = \frac{600\,000\,000 \div 150\,000\,000}{150\,000\,000 \div 150\,000\,000} = \frac{4\ mm}{1\ year} = 4\ mm/year$$

The unit rate is 4 mm per year.

3. To find the movement of the fault over 1000 years: Multiply the unit rate by 1000. $4 \times 1000 = 4000$. The movement in 1000 years is 4000 mm, or 4 m.

Practice PROBLEMS

1. The Great Glen Fault in Scotland moved 8 km in 220 million years. What is the rate of movement per year of this fault?

2. How many times faster than the Great Glen Fault is the San Andreas Fault moving?

3. During the last 90 years, the San Andreas Fault has been moving much faster than in previous years. During this time period, the rate has been about 4 cm per year. About how much has the fault moved in the last 90 years?

Activity 10•2

Predicting Tectonic Activity

Earthquakes occur every day on Earth. Many of them are too small to be felt by humans, but all of them can tell us something about our planet. Active volcanoes can do the same. Active volcanoes often form at plate boundaries. The movement of plates on Earth causes forces that build energy in rocks. The release of this energy can produce vibrations in Earth (earthquakes).

Recognize the Problem

Can tectonically active areas be predicted by plotting locations of earthquake epicenters and volcanic eruptions?

Form a Hypothesis

Think about where earthquakes and volcanoes have occurred in the past. **Make a Hypothesis** about whether the locations of earthquake epicenters and active volcanoes can be used to predict tectonically active areas.

Goals

- **Plot** earthquake epicenters and the locations of volcanic eruptions obtained from the Glencoe Science Web Site.

- **Predict** tectonically active locations based on a plot of the locations of earthquake epicenters and active volcanoes.

Data Sources

Visit the Glencoe Science Web Site at **www.glencoe.com/sec/science** for more information about earthquake and volcano sites. If you do not have access to the Internet, you can obtain the locations of earthquake epicenters and active volcanoes from the U.S. Geologic Survey or local newspapers.

Locations of Epicenters and Eruptions		
Earthquake Epicenter/ Volcanic Eruption	Longitude	Latitude

Test Your Hypothesis

Plan

1. **Make a data table** like the one shown on the opposite page.

2. **Collect data** for earthquake epicenters and volcanic eruptions for at least the past two weeks. Your data should include the longitude and latitude for each location. For help, refer to the **data sources** given on the opposite page.

3. **Plot the locations** of earthquake epicenters and volcanic eruptions on a map of the world. Use an overlay of tissue paper or plastic.

Do

1. Make sure your teacher approves your plan and your data table before you proceed.

2. After you have collected and plotted the locations of earthquake epicenters and volcanic eruptions from at least the past two weeks, it's time to predict tectonically active areas on Earth.

3. Using your data, **predict** what areas of the world are tectonically active.

4. **Compare** and **contrast** the areas that you predicted to be tectonically active with the plate boundary map shown in **Figure 10-10.**

Analyze Your Data

1. What areas on Earth do you **predict** to be the locations of tectonic activity?

2. How close did your prediction come to the actual location of tectonically active areas?

Draw Conclusions

1. How could you make your predictions closer to the locations of actual tectonic activity?

2. Would data from a longer period of time help? **Explain.**

3. What types of plate boundaries were close to your locations of earthquake epicenters? Volcanic eruptions?

4. **Explain** which types of plate boundaries produce volcanic eruptions. Be specific.

Roadside Geology

FIELD *ACTIVITY*

Geologic forces slowly push and pull on Earth's crust, creating the surface features we can see around us. As you travel, look around you. The next time you drive along the road, whether on a personal journey or a field trip with your school, use this field guide to help you identify Earth structures you observe along the way. What forces are at work to form the structures you see? Record your observations and inferences about forces in your Science Journal.

Earthquakes! Landslides! Volcanic eruptions! These are some of the ways that Earth's surface can change quickly. However, most of the changes in Earth's crust are less spectacular and occur much more slowly. Because of the life span of humans, Earth's surface appears to change little. Features like mountains and rivers will not appear or disappear during a person's lifetime, but these features do change over much longer periods of time. In this field guide, you'll see some examples of how Earth's crust changes over time

Faults

- A fault is created when rocks move along a break or fracture.
- Faults can be small, with only centimeters of movement, or they can be large, stretching for hundreds of kilometers.
- There are three basic types of faults: normal faults, reverse faults, and strike-slip faults.

- Normal faults can form when tectonic forces pull on Earth's crust in opposite directions.

Tension

Fault

Tension

A

Layers of rock have dropped downward along a normal fault.

B This normal fault located in Death Valley, California, shows a large amount of movement.

- When a section of Earth's crust is squeezed from both sides, a reverse fault can form.

Compression

Fault

Reverse fault

Compression

A Layers of rock have been displaced upward along a reverse fault.

B This reverse fault has shifted layers of sedimentary rock.

- Sometimes roads, sidewalks, and buildings are constructed across strike-slip faults. When the two sides along a fault move, human-made structures are often broken and shifted.

- Strike-slip faults form when tectonic forces cause slabs of Earth's crust to slide past one another.

Shear forces

Fault

Shear forces

B

A

A The ground has been broken and shifted by movements along a strike-slip fault.

B In this strike-slip fault, side A of the block is being pushed away from you and side B is being pushed toward you.

Folds

- When rocks are subjected to stress, they do not always break and form faults. Under some conditions, rocks will bend and fold instead of breaking.
- Upward-arching folds are known as anticlines.
- Downward-sagging folds are called synclines.
- Folds can be large enough to form mountains or small enough to hold in your hand.

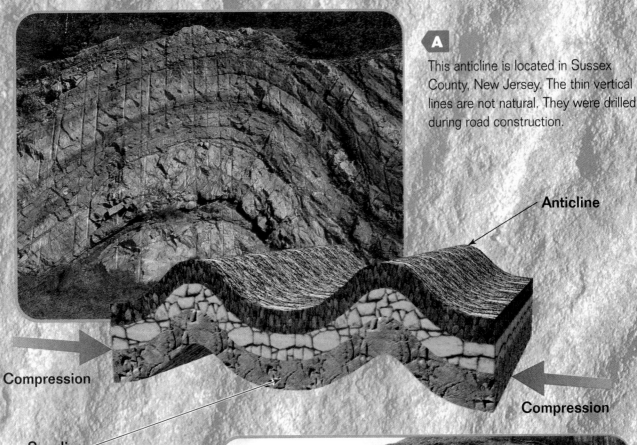

A

This anticline is located in Sussex County, New Jersey. The thin vertical lines are not natural. They were drilled during road construction.

Anticline

Compression

Compression

Syncline

B

This syncline is part of the Sideling Hill road-cut on Interstate 68 in Maryland.

Limestone Features

- Layers of limestone are common rock formations in Earth's crust.
- Water in nature is usually slightly acidic. When acidic water comes in contact with limestone, it reacts with the rock. Over time, the acidic water changes the rock into material that can then be washed away.
- Caves and sinkholes form when acidic water below Earth's surface slowly destroys the limestone.

A This cave in Luray Caverns, Virginia, is a hole left over after some limestone was removed by groundwater.

B This sinkhole in Winter Park, Florida, formed when limestone at Earth's surface collapsed into caves below.

Landslides

- A landslide happens when a mass of earth and rock moves downhill in response to gravity.
- Landslides often are triggered by heavy rains or sometimes by earthquakes.
- A landslide generally can be recognized by two surface features. A large curved depression, or scar, is left behind where the landslide started. A bumpy region of mixed-up rock and soil is formed where the landslide stops.

A

This landslide in the Madison Range, in Montana, was triggered by an earthquake on August 17, 1959.

B

This slump is a type of landslide that is common in oversteepened areas that are eroded by streams, lakes, and oceans. This slump is located in central California. The scar shows the area where the slump broke away from the slope.

Scar

Jumbled rock and soil

Sedimentary Features

- Sediments are deposited in many different environments such as beaches, rivers, swamps, and mudflats. Leaf imprints, animal tracks, mud cracks, fossils, and even raindrop patterns have been preserved in sedimentary rocks.

- One type of sedimentary feature that is often observed in sandstone is ripple marks. When water flows over a sandy area, the sand forms a series of small ridges, or ripples.

A This region of ripples was formed by flowing water at a beach in St. Johns County, Florida.

- If a rippled layer is gently buried by more sediments, the ripples can be preserved in the rock. Careful observation of sandstone layers often reveals ripple marks.

B These ripple marks are preserved in a sandstone formation in Utah.

For a **preview** of this chapter, study this Reviewing Main Ideas before you read the chapter. After you have studied this chapter, you can use the Reviewing Main Ideas to **review** the chapter.

The Glencoe MindJogger, Audiocassettes, and CD-ROM provide additional opportunities for review.

Section

10-1 CONTINENTAL DRIFT

The hypothesis of **continental drift** states that continents have moved to their present positions on Earth. Wegener believed that all continents were once connected into one large landmass he called **Pangaea.** The puzzlelike fit of the continents, fossils, climatic evidence, and similar rock structures supports Wegener's idea of continental drift. One problem with Wegener's idea was that he could not explain what process could be responsible for moving continents through the oceans. *What is true of the fossils of Mesosaurus that Wegener felt supported the hypothesis of continental drift?*

Section

10-2 SEAFLOOR SPREADING

Echo-sounding devices used to construct maps of the ocean floor showed underwater mountains and rift valleys. **Seafloor spreading** is the spreading apart of the seafloor at the mid-ocean ridges. The theory of seafloor spreading is supported by magnetic evidence in rocks and in the age of rocks on the ocean floor. The oldest rocks found on the ocean floor are 180 million years old. The youngest rocks are near the mid-ocean ridges, and the rocks become progressively older farther from the ridges. *What type of magnetic evidence in rocks supports the theory of seafloor spreading?*

Reading Check ☑

Suggest one or two additional illustrations for this chapter and explain why they would be valuable.

Section
10-3 PLATE TECTONICS

Plates move away from each other at divergent boundaries. Plates collide at convergent boundaries. At a transform boundary, two plates move horizontally past each other. Hot, plasticlike material from the mantle is forced upward to the **lithosphere,** moves horizontally, cools, and then sinks back into the mantle, causing **convection currents,** which are the driving force of **plate tectonics.** Most mountain belts, volcanoes, and earthquakes occur at convergent boundaries. Mid-ocean ridges and rift valleys occur at divergent boundaries. Major earthquakes occur at transform boundaries. *At which type of plate boundary does subduction occur?*

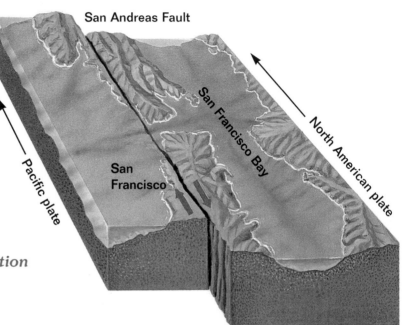

San Andreas Fault

San Francisco Bay

North American plate

Pacific plate

San Francisco

Career
CONNECTION

Dr. Samuel B. Mukasa, Isotope Geochemist

As an isotope geochemist, Dr. Samuel Mukasa studies the elements that make up rocks. By comparing the concentrations of certain elements, he can figure out the date when a rock was actually formed. Dr. Mukasa then uses this information to understand the timing of the breakup and movement of continents in Earth's past. *What information does a scientist need to figure out the rate at which continents have moved in the past?*

Chapter 10 Assessment

Using Vocabulary

a. asthenosphere   **e.** Pangaea
b. continental drift   **f.** plate
c. convection   **g.** plate tectonics
  current   **h.** seafloor
d. lithosphere   spreading

Each phrase below describes a vocabulary term from the list. Write the term that matches the phrase describing it.

1. plastic-like layer below the lithosphere
2. idea that continents move on Earth's surface
3. large landmass made of all continents
4. process that forms new seafloor
5. driving force for plate movement

Checking Concepts

Choose the word or phrase that best answers the question.

6. Where is Earth's asthenosphere located?
   A) crust   C) outer core
   B) mantle   D) inner core

7. What type of plate boundary is the San Andreas Fault a part of?
   A) divergent boundary
   B) subduction boundary
   C) convergent boundary
   D) transform boundary

8. What hypothesis states that continents moved to their present positions?
   A) subduction
   B) seafloor spreading
   C) continental drift
   D) erosion

9. Which plate is subducting beneath the South American plate to form the Andes mountain system?
   A) North American C) Indo-Australian
   B) African   D) Nazca

10. Evidence of which of the following features indicates that many continents were once near Earth's south pole?
    A) glaciers
    B) mid-ocean ridges
    C) volcanoes
    D) convection currents

11. What evidence in rocks supports the theory of seafloor spreading?
    A) plate movement
    B) subduction
    C) reversals of Earth's magnetic field
    D) convergence

12. Which type of plate boundary is the Great Rift Valley a part of?
    A) convergent   C) transform
    B) divergent   D) lithosphere

13. What theory states that plates move around on the asthenosphere?
    A) continental drift
    B) seafloor spreading
    C) subduction
    D) plate tectonics

14. What forms when one plate is forced under another plate?
    A) transform boundary
    B) divergent boundary
    C) subduction zone
    D) mid-ocean ridge

15. When oceanic plates collide, what volcanic landforms are made?
    A) folded mountains
    B) island arcs
    C) strike-slip faults
    D) mid-ocean ridges

Thinking Critically

16. Why are there few volcanoes in the Himalaya range but many earthquakes?
17. Glacial deposits often form at high latitudes near the poles. Explain why glacial deposits have been found in Africa.

18. How is magnetism used to support the theory of seafloor spreading?
19. Explain why volcanoes do not form along the San Andreas Fault.
20. Why wouldn't the fossil of an ocean fish found on two different continents be good evidence of continental drift?

Developing Skills

If you need help, refer to the **Skill Handbook**.

21. **Hypothesizing:** Mount St. Helens in the Cascade Mountain Range is a volcano. Use **Figure 10-10** and a U.S. map to hypothesize how it may have formed.
22. **Measuring in SI:** Movement along the African Rift Valley is about 2.1 cm per year. If plates continue to move apart at this rate, how much larger will the rift be (in meters) in 1000 years? In 15 500 years?
23. **Concept Mapping:** Make an events chain concept map that describes seafloor spreading along a divergent plate boundary. Choose from the following phrases: *magma cools to form new seafloor, magma rises, convection currents circulate hot material along boundary,* and *older seafloor is forced apart.*

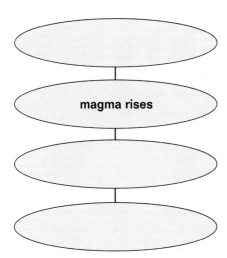

magma rises

THE PRINCETON REVIEW

Test-Taking Tip

The "Best" Answer Is Often the "Least Incorrect" If none of your answer choices look right, use the process of elimination to eliminate the *worst* ones. The one you've got left is the best choice.

Test Practice

Use these questions to test your Science Proficiency.

1. Alfred Wegener's original hypothesis of continental drift was not accepted by other scientists of his time. Which of the following statements **BEST** explains why this was true?
   A) Wegener had very little evidence to support his hypothesis.
   B) Wegener could not explain how continents move.
   C) Wegener was not a geologist.
   D) Wegener based his hypothesis only on the fossil record.
2. Island arcs form at convergent plate boundaries. Which of the following statements **BEST** explains this process?
   A) When two continental plates converge, subduction stops and mountains are built.
   B) When an oceanic plate converges on a continental plate, subduction leads to the formation of volcanoes.
   C) When two ocean plates diverge, magma is forced to Earth's surface, forming volcanoes.
   D) When two oceanic plates converge, subduction leads to the formation of volcanoes.

4

Change
Through
Time

What's Happening Here?

What traces of your existence will you leave for future generations to interpret? Long ago, someone painted these magnificent beasts on the walls of Lascaux (left), a cave in southern France. Archaeologists hypothesize that these drawings were created by Stone Age artists about 17 000 years ago. From the walls of this cave and others like it, scientists are piecing together the story of the ancestors of modern humans. While such drawings can help us interpret the human past, how can we figure out what happened before humans appeared on Earth? Even if you had been around and lived a long life, you could not have witnessed much of what happened. Why? Because like this glacier flowing into Prince William Sound, Alaska (below), many important changes happened too gradually to be seen. In this unit, you will learn about some of these slow changes and how to read the record these changes have left in the layers of Earth's crust.

interNET CONNECTION

Explore the Glencoe Science Web Site at **www.glencoe. com/sec/science** to find out more about topics found in this unit.

CHAPTER

11 Clues to Earth's Past

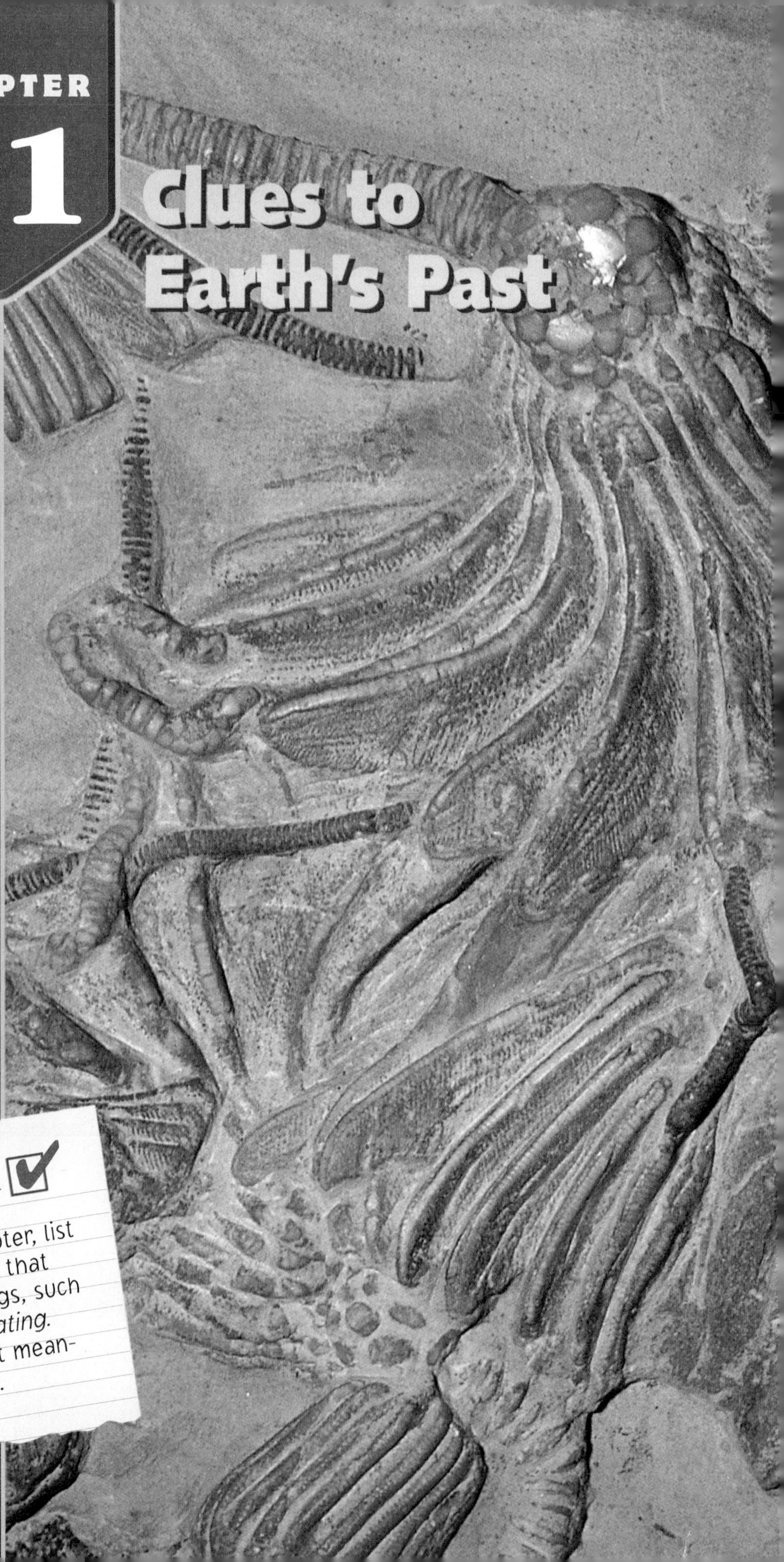

Chapter Preview

Section 11-1
Fossils

Section 11-2
Relative Ages of Rocks

Section 11-3
Absolute Ages of Rocks

Skills Preview

Skill Builders

- Interpret Data
- Make and Use a Table

Activities

- Interpret Data
- Analyze and Conclude

MiniLabs

- Observe
- Infer

Reading Check

As you read this chapter, list words you encounter that have several meanings, such as *mold, cast,* and *dating.* Explain the different meanings of these terms.

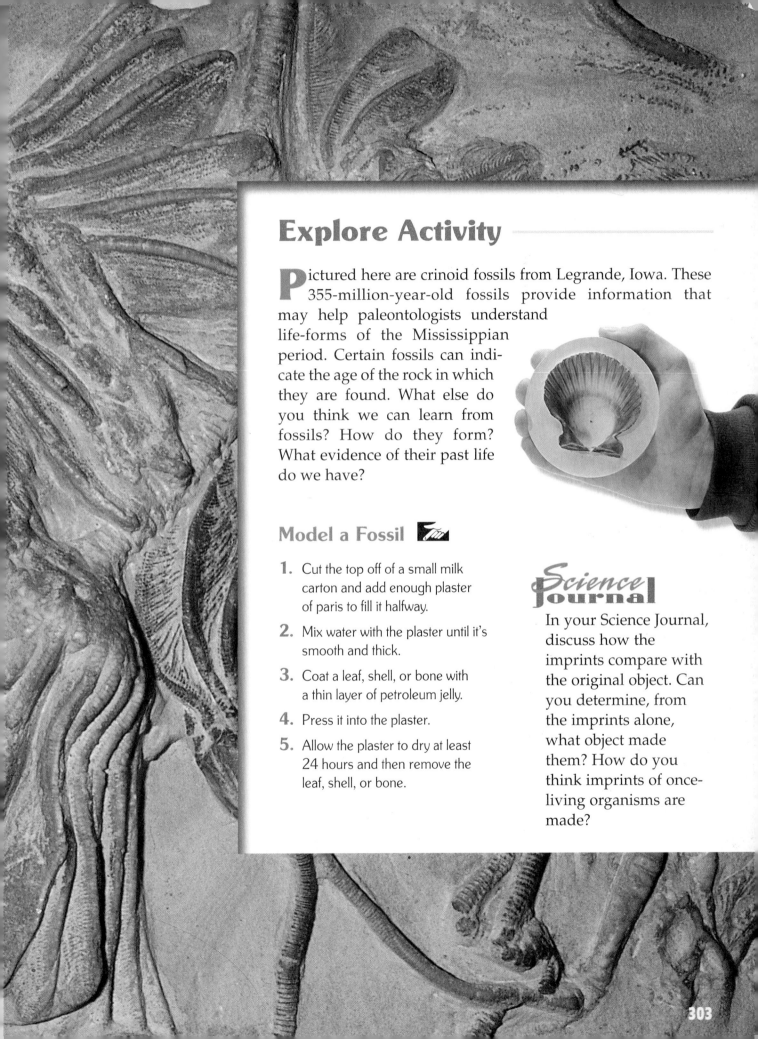

Explore Activity

Pictured here are crinoid fossils from Legrande, Iowa. These 355-million-year-old fossils provide information that may help paleontologists understand life-forms of the Mississippian period. Certain fossils can indicate the age of the rock in which they are found. What else do you think we can learn from fossils? How do they form? What evidence of their past life do we have?

Model a Fossil

1. Cut the top off of a small milk carton and add enough plaster of paris to fill it halfway.

2. Mix water with the plaster until it's smooth and thick.

3. Coat a leaf, shell, or bone with a thin layer of petroleum jelly.

4. Press it into the plaster.

5. Allow the plaster to dry at least 24 hours and then remove the leaf, shell, or bone.

Science Journal

In your Science Journal, discuss how the imprints compare with the original object. Can you determine, from the imprints alone, what object made them? How do you think imprints of once-living organisms are made?

11·1 Fossils

Traces from Our Past

The thick forest shakes as an *Allosaurus* charges forward in search of an evening meal. On the other side of the swamp, a herd of apatosaurs moves slowly and cautiously. The adults surround the young to protect them from predators. Soon, night will fall on this prehistoric day, 160 million years ago.

Does this story sound familiar to you? It's likely that you've read about dinosaurs and other past inhabitants of Earth. But, how do you know they really lived? What evidence do we have of past life on Earth? Scientists reconstruct what an animal looked like from its fossil remains, as in **Figure 11-1**.

Fossil Formation

In the Explore Activity, you made imprints of parts of organisms. Imprints are records, or evidence, of life. Evidence such as the remains, imprints, or traces of once-living organisms preserved in rocks are **fossils.** By studying fossils, geologists help solve mysteries of Earth's past.

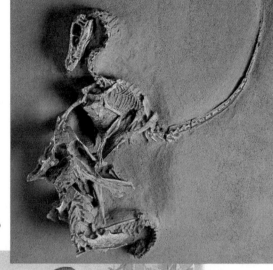

What You'll Learn

► Conditions necessary for fossils to form
► Processes of fossil formation
► How fossil correlation is used to determine rock ages

Vocabulary
fossil
petrified remains
carbonaceous film
mold
cast
index fossil

Why It's Important

► Fossils can help you interpret how life on Earth has changed through time.

Figure 11-1 Scientists and artists can reconstruct what dinosaurs looked like using fossil remains. Two dinosaur fossils (A) were found in this position. Artists used the fossils to reconstruct a *Velociraptor* attacking a *Protoceratops* (B).

Fossils have helped geologists and biologists find out exactly when life began, when plants and animals first lived on land, and when certain types of organisms, such as the dinosaurs, disappeared. Fossils tell us not only *when* and *where* organisms once lived, but also *how* they lived.

Usually, the remains of dead plants and animals are quickly destroyed. Scavengers eat the dead organisms, or fungi and microorganisms cause them to decay. If you've ever left a banana on the shelf too long, you've seen this process begin. Compounds in the banana cause it to become soft and brown, and microorganisms move in and cause it to decay quickly. What keeps some plants and animals from decaying so that they become fossils?

Necessary Conditions

First of all, to become a fossil, the body of a dead organism must be protected from scavengers and microorganisms. One way this can occur is to have the body buried quickly by sediments. If a fish dies and sinks to the bottom of a pond, sediments carried into the pond by a stream will rapidly cover the fish. As a result, no animals or microorganisms can get to it. However, quick burial alone isn't enough to make a fossil.

Organisms have a better chance of being preserved if they have hard parts such as bones, shells, or teeth. As you may know, these hard parts are less likely to be eaten by other organisms, they decay more slowly, and they are less likely to weather away. Most fossils, such as the fossil leaf in **Figure 11-2,** are made of the hard parts of organisms. Fossils are most often found in sedimentary rocks. The heat and pressure involved in forming igneous and metamorphic rocks most often destroy fossil material.

Figure 11-2 The hard parts in plants, such as the cellulose in cell walls, made preservation of this fossil leaf possible.

Try at Home
Mini Lab

Predicting Fossil Preservation

Procedure

1. Take a brief walk outside and observe the area near your school or home.

2. Look around and notice what type of litter has been discarded on the school grounds. Note whether there is a paved road near your school. Note anything else that was made by humans.

Analysis

1. Predict what human-made or natural objects from our time might be preserved far into the future.

2. Explain what conditions would need to exist for these objects to be preserved as fossils.

Figure 11-3 This pile of petrified wood is in the Petrified Forest National Monument in Arizona. Much of the original matter in these petrified plant remains has been replaced by quartz and other minerals. **Why have the fossils retained the shape of the original plant?**

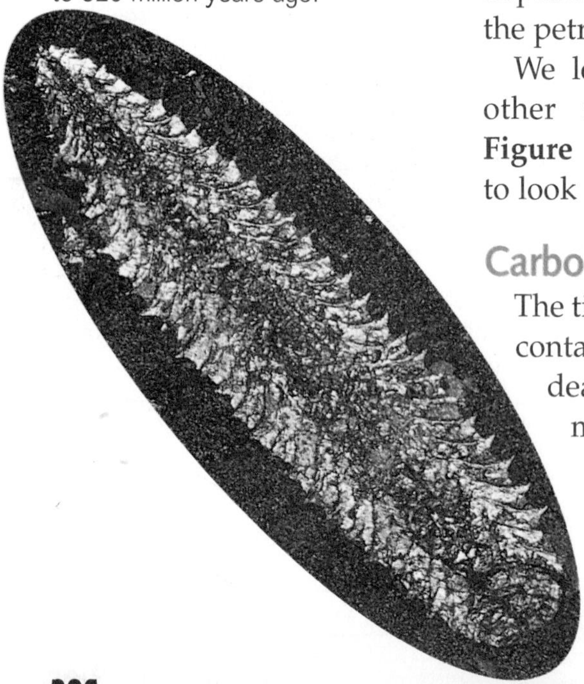

Figure 11-4 This fossil graptolite has been preserved as a carbonaceous film. Graptolites are extinct colonial animals that lived in the oceans from about 530 million to 320 million years ago.

Petrified Remains

You have some idea of what *Tyrannosaurus rex* looked like because you've seen drawings of this dinosaur. Perhaps you've also seen the skeletons of other dinosaurs in museums. Artists who draw *Tyrannosaurus rex* and other dinosaurs base their drawings on fossil bones. These bones are usually petrified.

Petrified (PEH truh fide) **remains** are hard and rocklike. Some or all of the original materials in the remains have been replaced by minerals. For example, a solution of water and dissolved quartz may flow through the bones of a dead organism. The water dissolves the calcium in the bone and deposits quartz in its place. Quartz is harder than calcium, so the petrified bone is rocklike.

We learn about past life-forms from bones, wood, and other remains that become petrified, like those in **Figure 11-3**. But, there are many other types of fossils to look at, too.

Carbonaceous Films

The tissues of most organisms are made of compounds that contain carbon. Sometimes, the only fossil remains of a dead plant or animal is this carbon. As you know, fossils most often form when a dead organism is buried in sediments. As more and more sediments pile up, the organism is exposed to pressure and heat. These conditions force gases and liquids from the organism. A thin film of carbon is left, forming an outline of the original organism. This type of fossil is called a **carbonaceous** (kar boh NAY shus) **film.** The process of chemically changing organic material is called carbonization. An example is shown in **Figure 11-4.**

In swamps and deltas, large amounts of plant matter accumulate. Over millions of years, these deposits become completely carbonized, forming the sedimentary rock coal. Coal is more important as a fuel than as a fossil because the makeup of the plant is most often lost when the coal forms.

Molds and Casts

Think again about the imprints in the plaster of paris you made earlier. In nature, such imprints are made when seashells or other hard parts of organisms fall into soft sediments such as mud. The object and sediments are then buried by more sediments. The sediments are squeezed and cemented together into rock. Holes in the rock let water and air reach the shell or hard part, causing it to dissolve, and leaving behind a hollow place in the rock called a **mold.** Later, other sediments may fill in the hollow place, harden into rock, and make a **cast** of the original organism, as shown in **Figure 11-5.**

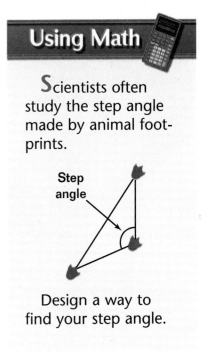

Using Math

Scientists often study the step angle made by animal footprints.

Step angle

Design a way to find your step angle.

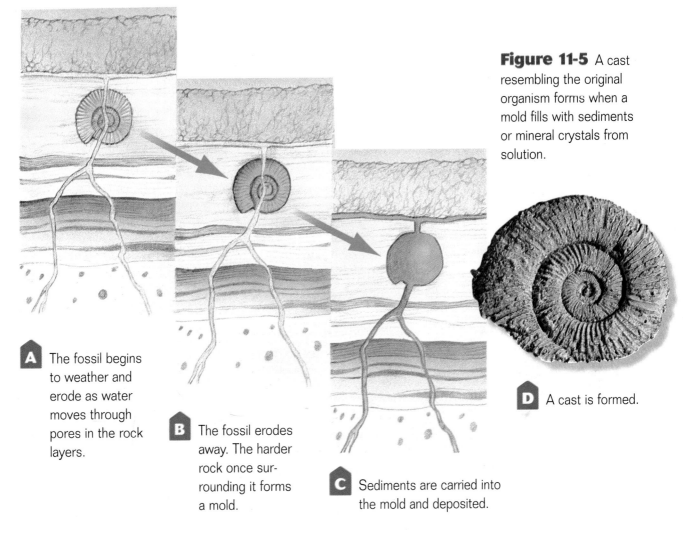

Figure 11-5 A cast resembling the original organism forms when a mold fills with sediments or mineral crystals from solution.

A The fossil begins to weather and erode as water moves through pores in the rock layers.

B The fossil erodes away. The harder rock once surrounding it forms a mold.

C Sediments are carried into the mold and deposited.

D A cast is formed.

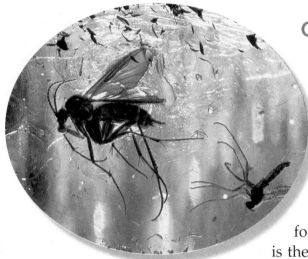

Figure 11-6 This 40-million-year-old insect was trapped in the sticky resin produced by a plant. Over time, the resin crystallized into amber, preserving the insect inside.

Original Remains

Sometimes the actual organism or parts of the organism are found. **Figure 11-6** shows an insect trapped in amber, a hard form of the sticky resin produced by some trees. The amber protects the insect's body from decay and petrification. Other organisms, such as woolly mammoths, have been found preserved in frozen ground. In 1991, the entire body of a man who lived 5300 years ago was found frozen in glacial ice in the southern Alps. It is the oldest complete human body ever discovered. Original remains have also been found in tar seeps such as the La Brea (BRAY ah) tar pits in California.

Trace Fossils

Fossilized tracks and other evidence of animal activity are called *trace fossils*. Perhaps your parents made your handprint or footprint in plaster of paris when you were born. If so, it's a record that tells something about you. From it, you can guess your size and maybe your weight at that age. Animals walking on Earth long ago have left similar tracks, such as those in **Figure 11-7**. In some cases, tracks can tell us more about how an organism lived than any other type of fossil. For example, the story described at the beginning of this chapter really took place.

A

Figure 11-7 Tracks made in soft mud, and now preserved in solid rock, can provide information about animal size, speed, and other behavior patterns. These tracks are located on the Navajo Reservation in Arizona (A) and in the Glenrose Rock Formation in Texas (B).

B

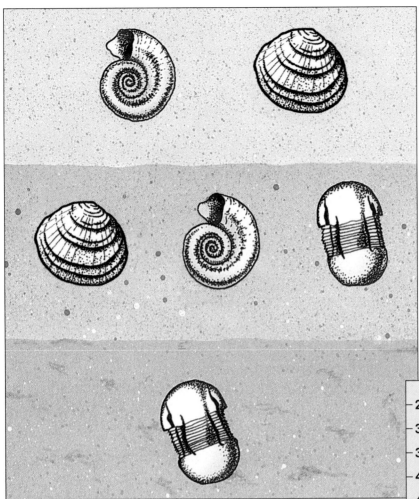

Figure 11-8 The sequence of sedimentary rock and the fossils each contains (A) can be used to date the rocks. The chart (B) shows when each organism inhabited Earth. **Why is it possible to say that the middle layer of rock had to be deposited between 438 and 408 million years ago?**

A Illustration of a sequence of rocks and the fossils they contain.

B Fossil Range Chart

Millions of years ago	*Euomphalus*	*Illaenus*	*Rhipidomella*
286			
320			
360			
408			
438			
505			

From a set of tracks at Davenport Ranch, Texas, we have learned something about the social life of *Apatosaurus,* one of the largest known dinosaurs. The largest tracks of the herd are on the outer edges and the smallest are on the inside. This suggests that the adult apatosaurs surrounded the young as they traveled—probably to protect them from enemies. In fact, a nearby set of allosaur tracks shows that one was stalking the herd.

Other trace fossils include worm holes and burrows made by marine animals. As you can see, a group of fossils can tell us a great deal about the individuals that lived on Earth before us. ☑

Index Fossils

The study of fossils tells that species are constantly changing, or evolving. Evidence shows that species live on Earth for a certain period of time before they evolve into new species or they die out completely. Some species of organisms inhabit Earth for long periods of time without changing much. Other species remain unchanged for only a short time. It is these organisms that make index fossils.

Reading Check ☑

How do fossil footprints provide information about social behavior?

Index fossils are species that lived on Earth for short periods of time, were abundant, and were widespread geographically. Scientists use index fossils to tell the age of rock layers. Because few fossils meet all the conditions to be an index fossil, groups of fossils are usually used to date rocks. This is how the rock layer in **Figure 11-8** was dated. Which fossil is the index fossil?

Fossils and Ancient Environments

Fossils also can be used to tell what the environment of an area was like long ago. For example, rocks in Antarctica contain fossils of tropical plants. As shown in **Figure 11-9**, the environment of Antarctica today isn't tropical, but we hypothesize that it was at the time these fossilized plants were living.

How would you explain the presence of fossilized brachiopods, animals that lived in shallow seas, in the rocks of the midwestern United States? **Figure 11-10** shows an example of

Figure 11-9 The position and environment of Antarctica, shown in red, have changed through time. Fossils found in its rocks indicate that Antarctica once had a tropical environment. **What caused the continents to change position?**

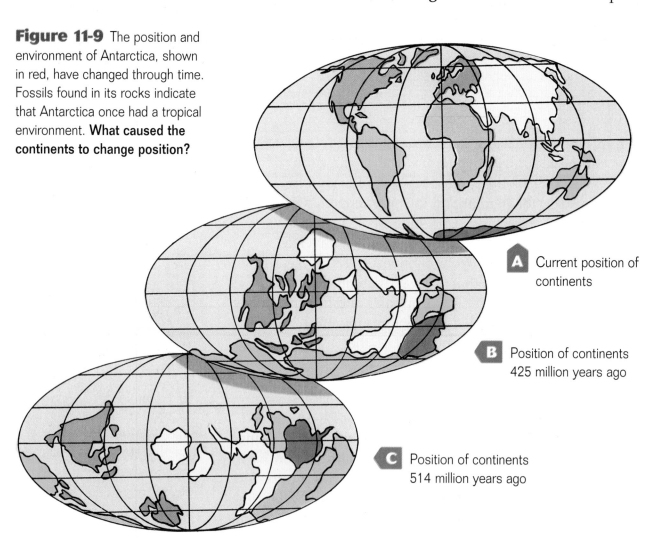

A Current position of continents

B Position of continents 425 million years ago

C Position of continents 514 million years ago

A

B

a modern brachiopod (BRACH kee uh pahd) and a fossil bra-chiopod. As shown in **Figure 11-9B** and **C,** North America was once found at the equator. The shallow seas that covered the central part of North America during some of this time were warm and hospitable to organisms such as brachiopods.

Fossils tell us not only about past life on Earth, but also about the history of the rock layers that contain them. Fossils can give information about environment, climate, and animal behavior, as well as dating the rocks.

Figure 11-10
(A) This Paleozoic-aged brachiopod lived in the warm shallow seas that once covered portions of North America.
(B) *Terebratulina septentrionalis* is a modern brachiopod. It lives off the coast of York, Maine. **How do the habitats of these brachiopods compare?**

Section Assessment

1. What conditions are needed for most fossils to form?
2. Describe how a mold-and-cast fossil might form.
3. Explain how index fossils are used.
4. **Think Critically:** What can be said about the ages of two geographically separated layers of rock that contain the same type of fossil?
5.  **Skill Builder**
   Concept Mapping Make a concept map that compares and contrasts petrified remains and original remains. Use the following terms and phrases: *types of fossils, original remains, evidence of former life, petrified remains, materials replaced by minerals,* and *actual parts of organisms.* If you need help, refer to Concept Mapping in the **Skill Handbook** on page 714.

Science Journal
Collect samples of fossils or visit a museum that has fossils on display. In your Science Journal, make an illustration of each fossil. Write a brief description, noting key facts about each. Also, write about how each fossil might have been formed.

11·2 Relative Ages of Rocks

The Principle of Superposition

It's a hot summer day in July, and you're getting ready to meet your friends at the park. You put on your helmet and pads and grab your skateboard. But, the bearings in one of the wheels are worn, and the wheel isn't spinning freely. You remember reading an article in a skateboarding magazine about how to replace wheels, and you decide to look it up. In your room is a stack of magazines from the past year, as seen in **Figure 11-11.** You know that the article came out in the January edition, so it must be near the bottom of the pile. As you dig downward, you find the magazine from March, then February. You know that January must be next.

How did you know that the January issue of the magazine would be on the bottom? To find the older issue under newer ones, you used the principle of superposition.

Youngest Rocks on Top

The **principle of superposition** states that for undisturbed layers of rock, the oldest rocks are on the bottom and the rocks become younger and younger toward the top. Why is this the case? Is it always true?

As you know, sediments are often deposited in horizontal beds, forming layers of sedimentary rock. The first layer to form is usually on the bottom. Each additional layer forms on top of the previous one. Unless forces such as those made

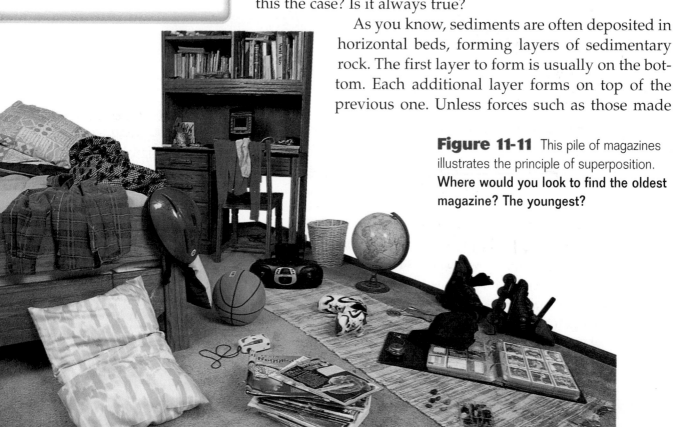

Figure 11-11 This pile of magazines illustrates the principle of superposition. **Where would you look to find the oldest magazine? The youngest?**

Figure 11-12 This illustration and photograph show a large-scale dome in sedimentary rocks with exposed rock layers in Wyoming. The oldest layers are folded up and exposed in the center. **Does the principle of superposition still apply here?**

by tectonic activity turn the layers upside down, the oldest rocks are found at the bottom. When layers have been turned upside down, geologists use other clues in the rock layers to tell their original positions.

Relative Dating

Suppose you now want to look for another issue of a magazine. You're not sure exactly how old it is—all you know is that it arrived after the January issue. You can find it in the stack by using relative dating.

Relative dating is used in geology to determine the order of events and the relative age of rocks by examining the position of rocks in a sequence. For example, if layers of sedimentary rock are offset by a fault, you know that the layers had to be there first before a fault could cut through them. The relative age of the rocks is older than the relative age of the fault. So, using the magazine example, how do you find the issue by relative dating?

Relative dating doesn't tell you anything about the exact age of rock layers. You don't know if a layer is 100 million or 10 000 years old—only that it's younger than the layers below it and older than the fault cutting through it.

Other Clues Help

Relative dating works well if rocks haven't been folded or overturned by tectonic processes. For example, look at **Figure 11-12.** Which layer is the oldest? In cases where rock layers have been disturbed, you may have to look for fossils and other clues to date the rocks. If you find a fossil in the top layer that's older than a fossil in a lower layer, you can hypothesize that layers have been turned upside down or faulted.

*inter*NET
CONNECTION

Visit the Glencoe Science Web Site at **www.glencoe.com/ sec/science** to learn more about how the relative dating of rocks is done.

Another clue you can use is the way the fossils are arranged in the layers. Most attached marine organisms grow upward, toward the sunlight. If you find a limestone formation with corals that are upright, you can infer that the rocks have not been tilted or overturned. Even something as simple as a hole in the rock can help. Sediments are always deposited horizontally at the bottom of a hole. If a hole looks like it is half filled from the top, the sample is upside down.

VISUALIZING
Unconformity Formation

Figure 11-13 An angular unconformity results when horizontal layers overlie tilted layers.

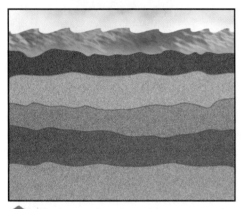

 A Rocks are originally deposited as horizontal layers.

B The horizontal rock layers are tilted as they are deformed by forces inside Earth.

C The tilted layers are eroded.

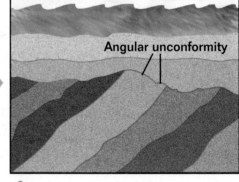

Angular unconformity

D An angular unconformity results when new horizontal layers form on the tilted layers as deposition is resumed.

Unconformities

As you have seen, a layer of rock is a record of past events. But, most rock records are not complete—layers are missing. These gaps in rock layers are called **unconformities** (un kun FOR mihteez).

Unconformities develop when agents of erosion remove existing rock layers. They also form when a period of time passes without any new deposition occurring to form new layers of rock. ✔

Reading Check

What is an unconformity?

Angular Unconformities

Figure 11-13 illustrates one way an unconformity can form. Horizontal layers of sedimentary rock are tilted and uplifted, so that erosion and weathering wear them down. Eventually, younger sediment layers are deposited horizontally on top of the eroded and tilted layers. Such an unconformity is called an angular unconformity.

Disconformity

Suppose you're looking at a sequence of sedimentary rocks. They look complete, but layers are missing. If you look closely, you may find an old erosional surface. This records a time when the rocks were exposed and eroded. Later, younger rocks formed above the erosional surface when sediment deposition began again. Even though all the layers are horizontal, a gap still exists in the record. This type of unconformity, called a disconformity, is shown in **Figure 11-14.**

Figure 11-14 The buried erosional surface in the far right illustration is a disconformity. **How could you determine how much time and rock is missing?**

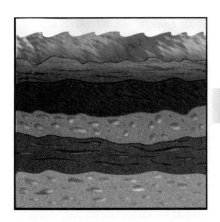

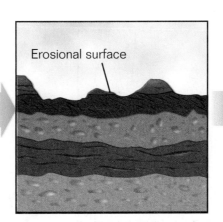

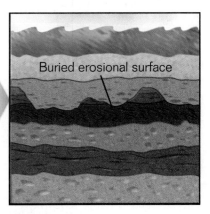

A Sedimentary rock layers are deposited horizontally.

B The layers are uplifted, exposed, and eroded.

C When deposition resumes, younger horizontal sediments are deposited on the buried erosional surface.

Nonconformity

Another type of unconformity, called a nonconformity, occurs when metamorphic or igneous rocks are uplifted and eroded. Sedimentary rocks are then deposited on top of this erosional surface. The surface between the two rock types is a nonconformity.

Correlating Rock Layers

Suppose you're studying a layer of sandstone in Bryce Canyon in Utah. Later, when you visit Canyonlands National Park, you notice that a layer of sandstone there looks just like the sandstone in Bryce Canyon, 250 km away. Above the sandstone in Canyonlands is a layer of limestone and then another sandstone layer. You return to Bryce Canyon and find the same sequence—sandstone, limestone, and sandstone. What do you infer? It's likely that you're actually looking at the same layer of rocks in two different locations. These rocks are parts of huge deposits that covered this whole area of the western United States, as seen in **Figure 11-15.** The sandstone and limestone you found at the two parks are the exposed surfaces of the same rock layers.

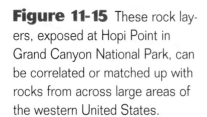

Figure 11-15 These rock layers, exposed at Hopi Point in Grand Canyon National Park, can be correlated or matched up with rocks from across large areas of the western United States.

Evidence Used for Correlation

Geologists match up, or correlate, layers of rocks over great distances, as seen in **Figure 11-16.** It's not always easy to say that a rock layer exposed in one area is the same as a rock layer exposed in another area. Sometimes it's possible to walk along the layer for kilometers and prove that it's a continuous layer. In other cases, such as at Canyonlands and Bryce Canyon, the rock layers are exposed only where rivers have cut through overlying layers of rock and sediment. How can you prove that the limestone sandwiched between the two layers of sandstone in Canyonlands is the same limestone as at Bryce Canyon? One way is to use fossil evidence. If the same types of fossils are found in both outcrops of limestone, it's likely that the limestone at each place is the same age, and therefore, one continuous deposit. ☑

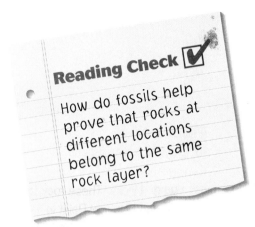

Reading Check ☑

How do fossils help prove that rocks at different locations belong to the same rock layer?

Problem Solving

Interpreting Scientific Illustrations

When geologists study the rock outcrops in an area, they obtain rock samples from, measure the thickness of, and record a description of each rock layer. For example, one report might describe a 1-m-thick, massive sandstone of medium-brown color.

Once the descriptions are recorded for each layer of rock that is observed in one location, geologists draw a column that shows each of the rock layers. They then try to correlate or match up a rock column from one location to rock columns from other locations. A geologist can tell much about the geologic history of an area from a study of rock column correlations.

The rock column shown on the left is from Green River, Utah. The rock column on the right is from Westwater, Colorado. Using the rock columns, recon-

struct the geologic history of the area. Correlate similar rock layers between the two locations. An example of how to correlate the rock columns is shown for rock layer 1. How many unconformities, and what types, can you recognize in each column?

Think Critically: Explain the geologic history of the Green River area in terms of erosion and deposition. Why are some layers missing from the Westwater column?

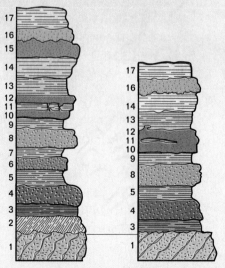

Green River, Utah   Westwater, Colorado

Are there other ways to correlate layers of rock? Sometimes relative dating isn't enough, and other dating methods must be used. In the next section, you'll see how the actual age of rocks can be determined and how geologists have used this information to determine the age of Earth.

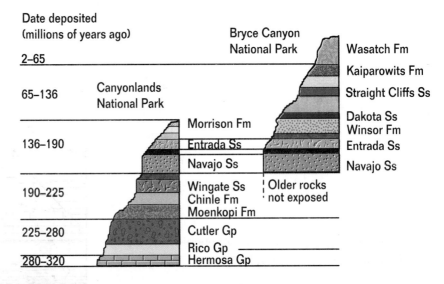

Figure 11-16 The many rock layers, or formations, in Canyonlands and Bryce Canyon have been dated and named. Some formations have been correlated between the two canyons. (NOTE: Fm = formation, Ss = sandstone, Gp = group.) **Which layers are present at both canyons?**

Date deposited (millions of years ago)

Bryce Canyon National Park

2–65

65–136   Canyonlands National Park

136–190

190–225

225–280

280–320

Wasatch Fm
Kaiparowits Fm
Straight Cliffs Ss
Dakota Ss
Winsor Fm
Entrada Ss
Navajo Ss

Morrison Fm
Entrada Ss
Navajo Ss
Wingate Ss   Older rocks not exposed
Chinle Fm
Moenkopi Fm
Cutler Gp
Rico Gp
Hermosa Gp

Section Assessment

1. Suppose you haven't cleaned out your locker all year. Where would you expect to find papers from the beginning of the year? What principle in geology would you use to find these old papers?

2. Why is it more difficult to recognize a disconformity than an angular unconformity?

3. A geologist finds a series of rocks. The sandstone contains a fossil that is 400 million years old. The shale contains fossils that are between 500 million and 550 million years old. The limestone, which lies under the sandstone, contains fossils that are between 400 million and 500 million years old. Which rock bed is oldest? Explain.

4. **Think Critically:** What are the relative ages of an igneous intrusion and overlying sedimentary rock layers that dome upward? Explain.

5. **Skill Builder**
   Observing and Inferring Do the **Chapter 11 Skill Activity** on page 752 to find out how fossils are used to interpret environments.

Using Computers

Spreadsheet Use the information about unconformities in Section 11-2 to prepare an electronic spreadsheet listing the types of unconformities, their differences, and their similarities. Use graphics software to generate illustrations of each type of unconformity. If you need help, refer to page 738.

Relative Age Dating

Can you tell which of two rock layers is older? You don't need to know the exact ages of the layers to tell. Geologists can learn a lot about rock layers simply by studying their arrangement.

What You'll Investigate

Can the relative ages of rocks be determined by studying the rock layers and structures?

Goals

- **Determine** the relative order of events by interpreting illustrations of rock layers.

Procedure

1. Study **Figures A** and **B**. The legend will help you interpret the figures.
2. Determine the relative ages of the rock layers, unconformities, igneous dikes, and fault in each figure.

Conclude and Apply

Figure A

1. Were any layers of rock deposited after the igneous dike formed? Explain.
2. What type of unconformity is shown? Is it possible that there were originally more layers of rock than are shown here? Explain.
3. What type of fault is shown?
4. Explain how to determine whether the igneous dike formed before or after the fault occurred?

Figure B

5. What type of fault is shown?
6. Is the igneous dike on the left older or younger than the unconformity near the top? Explain.
7. Are the two igneous dikes shown the same age? How do you know?
8. Which two layers of rock may have been much thicker at one time than they are now?

Materials

- Paper
- Pencil

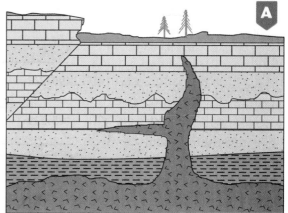

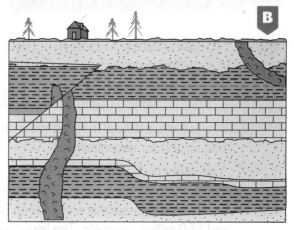

Granite	Limestone
Sandstone	Shale

Interpreting Scientific Illustrations

1. Make a sketch of Figure A. On it, **identify** the relative age of each rock layer, igneous dike, fault, and unconformity. For example, the shale layer is the oldest, so mark it with a *1*. Mark the next-oldest feature with a *2,* and so on.
2. Repeat the procedure in question 1 for Figure B.

Extinction of Dinosaurs

What killed the dinosaurs?

The fossil record indicates that dinosaurs appeared between 230 and 220 million years ago. As time passed, dinosaurs multiplied, diversified, and came to inhabit every continent on Earth. Then quite abruptly, in geologic terms, the dinosaurs disappeared. This happened about 66 million years ago. Left behind were only fossilized tracks, teeth, and bones (right) as proof of their existence. What caused this dramatic extinction? No one really knows yet, but scientists have proposed several hypotheses to explain the disappearance of the dinosaurs.

One early hypothesis suggested that egg-eating mammals interfered with dinosaur reproduction, so that the dinosaurs eventually died out. However, this hypothesis did not explain why many other animals also became extinct when dinosaurs did.

In the early 1980s, several scientists proposed that a large asteroid collided with Earth some 66 million years ago. According to this hypothesis, the asteroid vaporized rocks and seawater on impact and sent clouds of dust and acidic gases into the atmosphere. The dust clouds would have blocked out so much sunlight that plants were unable to carry out photosynthesis. As vegetation withered, plant-eating dinosaurs died, leaving their meat-eating relatives to starve as well. Other researchers suggest that the asteroid impact led to widespread wildfires, acid rain, or global warming that caused the dinosaur extinction.

Other Hypotheses

Another hypothesis proposes that intense volcanic activity spewed enormous quantities of dust and gases into the ancient atmosphere and led to global cooling. Animals unable to adapt died out, including the dinosaurs. Any hypothesis regarding dinosaur extinction must take into account that many other species perished when the dinosaurs did, and yet many mammals survived. Scientists continue to search for evidence that will determine what event, or combination of events, ended the age of dinosaurs.

Science JOURNAL

How the dinosaurs became extinct remains an intensely debated topic. In your Science Journal, write an essay that discusses how one of the hypotheses could be supported and why.

Absolute Ages of Rocks

Absolute Dating

Remember the stack of magazines? As you continue to shuffle through them, looking for articles about wheels and bearings, you decide you need to restack them into a neat pile. By now, they're a mess and no longer in the order of their relative ages, as shown in **Figure 11-17.** How can you stack them so the oldest are on the bottom and the newest on top? Fortunately, magazines have their dates printed on their covers. Thus, stacking magazines in order is a simple process. Unfortunately for geologists, rocks don't have their ages stamped on them. Or do they?

Absolute dating is a method used to determine the age, in years, of a rock or other object. Absolute dating is a process that uses the properties of atoms in rocks and other objects to find their ages.

Radioactive Decay

An element can have atoms with different numbers of neutrons in their nuclei. These are called isotopes. Some of these isotopes undergo a process called **radioactive decay.** When an atom of some isotopes decays, one of its neutrons breaks down into a proton and an electron. The electron leaves the atom as a beta particle. The nucleus loses a neutron but gains a proton. Other isotopes give off two protons and two neutrons in the form of an alpha particle, as seen in **Figure 11-18.** As you know, when the number of protons in an atom is changed, as it is in radioactive decay, a new element is formed. For example, when an atom of the radioactive isotope uranium-238 decays, it eventually forms an atom of lead-206. Lead-206 isn't radioactive, so it does not decay any further.

What You'll Learn

► How absolute dating differs from relative dating
► How the half-lives of isotopes are used to determine a rock's age

Vocabulary
absolute dating
radioactive decay
half–life
radiometric dating
uniformitarianism

Why It's Important

► Determining the absolute age of rocks and minerals allows scientists to calculate the age of Earth.

PHYSICS ◄**INTEGRATION**

Figure 11-17 The magazines that have been shuffled through no longer illustrate the principle of superposition.

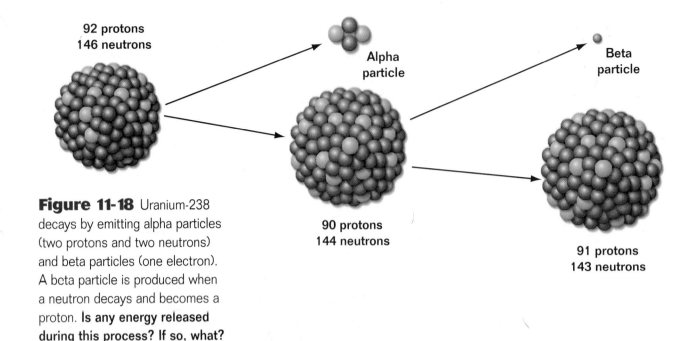

Figure 11-18 Uranium-238 decays by emitting alpha particles (two protons and two neutrons) and beta particles (one electron). A beta particle is produced when a neutron decays and becomes a proton. **Is any energy released during this process? If so, what?**

92 protons
146 neutrons

Alpha particle

Beta particle

90 protons
144 neutrons

91 protons
143 neutrons

In the case of uranium decaying to lead, uranium-238 is known as the parent material and lead-206 as the daughter product. Another example of a parent material is carbon-14, which decays to its daughter, nitrogen-14. Each radioactive parent material has a certain rate at which it decays to its daughter product. This rate is known as its half-life.

Half-Life

The **half-life** of an isotope is the time it takes for half of the atoms in an isotope to decay. For example, the half-life of carbon-14 is 5730 years. So it will take 5730 years for half of the carbon-14 atoms in an object to decay to nitrogen-14.

You might guess that in another 5730 years, all of the remaining carbon-14 atoms will have decayed to nitrogen-14. However, this is not the case. Only half of the atoms of carbon-14 remaining after the first 5730 years will decay during the second 5730 years. So, after two half-lives, one-fourth of the original carbon-14 atoms still remain. Half of the remaining carbon-14 will decay during another 5730 years. After many half-lives, such a small amount of the parent material remains that it may not be measurable.

Radiometric Dating

To a geologist, the decay of radioactive isotopes is like a clock ticking away. The clock is keeping track of time that's passed since rocks have formed. As time passes, the amount of parent material in a mineral decreases as the amount of daughter product increases, as seen in **Figure 11-19.** By measuring the ratio of daughter product to parent isotope in a mineral and by knowing the half-life of the parent, a geologist can calculate the absolute age of the mineral. This process is called **radiometric dating.** ☑

A scientist must decide which parent and daughter materials to measure when dating a mineral or a fossil. If the object to be dated is very old, then a parent isotope with a long half-life must be used. For example, carbon-14 dating would be useful to date a fossil shell that is 10 000 years old but could not be used to date a fossil that is 100 million years old. However, the half-life of uranium-238 is 4.5 billion years. This isotope has been used to date minerals that are billions of years old.

Radiocarbon Dating

Carbon-14 is useful for dating fossils, bones, and wood up to 75 000 years old. Organisms take in carbon from the environment to build tissues in their bodies. The amount remains constant throughout their lives. After the organism dies, the carbon-14 slowly decays and escapes as nitrogen-14 gas. The amount of carbon-14 remaining can be measured to determine the age of the fossil or when humans used a fire site, as in **Figure 11-20.**

Reading Check ☑

What happens to the amount of parent material as an isotope decays?

Figure 11-19 After each half-life, one-half the amount of parent material remains. Eventually, such a small amount of the parent material is left that it may not be measurable. **How much parent material is left after a fifth half-life?**

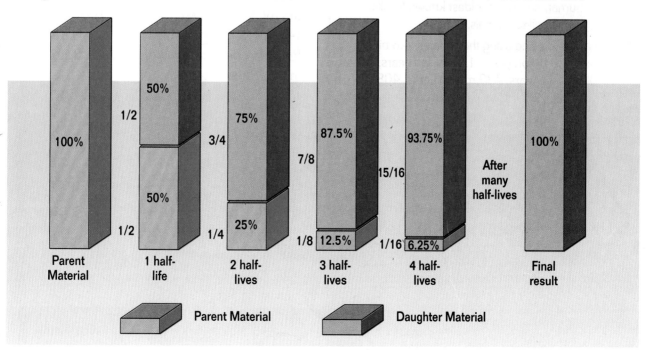

Parent Material   Daughter Material

Figure 11-20 Human activity, like this campfire, also can be dated with carbon-14. **What other events could leave charcoal behind and provide radiocarbon dates?**

Rocks that can be radiometrically dated are mostly igneous although some metamorphic rocks can be used too. Sedimentary rocks cannot be dated by this method because only the absolute age of the sediment grains in the rock can be determined, not the rock itself. Radiometric dating has been used to date the oldest rocks found on Earth. These rocks are 3.96 billion years old. In western Australia sandstones, zircon mineral grains have been dated to about 4.1 to 4.2 billion years. Scientists have estimated the age of Earth at 4.6 billion years.

Source for Error

How sure can scientists be that the dates they calculate are accurate? First, they must make sure that no parent material is added to the mineral after decay has begun and no daughter product is removed after forming. This can be difficult when elements such as potassium (K) and argon (Ar) are being analyzed, as shown in **Figure 11-21.** Second, care must be taken if the rocks have been metamorphosed. Remember that metamorphism changes minerals. This resets the decay

Figure 11-21 Over time, the potassium in the mineral decays to argon. The argon escapes, making the ratiio of potassium to argon decrease. **Why does Argon (Ar) escape so easily?**

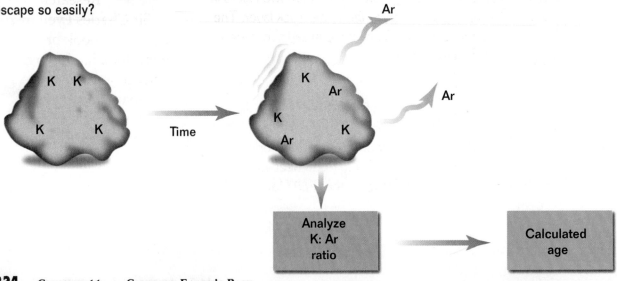

clock. What effect would this have on the calculated age? Scientists avoid wrong ages by using more than one radioactive isotope, by running more than one check, and by using fresh, unweathered samples.

Uniformitarianism

Before radiometric dating was known, many people had estimated the age of Earth to be only a few thousand years old. But in the 1700s, Scottish scientist James Hutton estimated that Earth was much older. He used the principle of **uniformitarianism** (yew nih for mih TAHR ee ah nizm). This principle states that Earth processes taking place today are similar to those that took place in the past. Observing that the processes that changed the rocks and land around him were slow, he inferred that these processes had been just as slow throughout Earth's history. Hutton hypothesized that it took much longer than a few thousand years to form the rock layers around him and to erode mountain peaks to hills. John Playfair advanced Hutton's theories, but an English geologist, Sir Charles Lyell, is given the most credit for advancing uniformitarianism. What processes operating on Earth today also operated in the distant past?

Visit the Glencoe Science Web Site at **www.glencoe.com/ sec/science** for more information about the ages of rocks.

Section Assessment

1. You discover three undisturbed rock layers. The absolute age of the middle layer is 120 million years. What can you say about the ages of the layers above and below it?

2. How old would a fossil be if it had only one-eighth of its original carbon-14 content remaining?

3. **Think Critically:** Suppose you radiometrically date an igneous dike running through only the bottom two layers in question 1. The dike is cut off by the upper rock layer. The dike is 70 million years old. What can you say about the absolute age of the upper layer?

4. **Skill Builder**
   Making and Using Tables Make a table that shows the amounts of parent and daughter materials left of a radioactive element after four half-lives if the original parent material had a mass of 100 g. If you need help, refer to Making and Using Tables in the **Skill Handbook** on page 716.

Science Journal Research Sir Charles Lyell in a geology book or encyclopedia. In your Science Journal, write a one-page report about his contribution to uniformitarianism.

Materials

- Shoe box with lid
- Brass fasteners (100)
- Paper clips (100)
- Graph paper
- Pennies (100)
- Colored pencils (2)

Radioactive Decay

Radioactive isotopes, elements that contain atoms with different numbers of neutrons, decay into their daughter elements in a specific amount of time. The rate of decay varies for each individual isotope. This rate can be used to determine the age of rocks that contain the isotopes under study. In this activity, you will develop a model that demonstrates how the half-life of certain radioactive isotopes can be used to determine absolute ages.

What You'll Investigate

What materials can be used to model age determination using radioactive half-lives?

Goals

- **Model** radioactive half-lives using listed materials.
- **Model** absolute age determination using the half-lives of radioactive isotopes.

Safety Precautions

Hold the lid of the box on tight to avoid having objects flying out of the box.

Procedure

1. Place 100 pennies into the shoe box with all heads up.
2. Place the lid on the box and shake it one time.
3. Remove the lid. Replace the pennies that are now tails up with paper clips. Record the number of pennies remaining in the box in a data table similar to the one shown on the next page.
4. Repeat steps 2 and 3 until all the pennies have been removed.

5. Remove the paper clips from the box. Put an "X" on one of the shorter sides of the box. Place 100 fasteners in the box, all pointed away from the "X".

6. Repeat step 2.

7. Remove the lid. Replace the fasteners that point toward the "X" with paper clips. Record the number of fasteners remaining in the box in a data table similar to the one shown at right.

8. Repeat steps 2 and 7 until all the fasteners have been removed.

9. Plot both sets of data on the same graph. Graph the "shake number" on the horizontal axis and the "number of pennies or fasteners remaining" on the vertical axis. Be sure to use a different colored pencil for each set of data.

Half-life Data

Shake Number	Number Remaining	
	Pennies	Fasteners

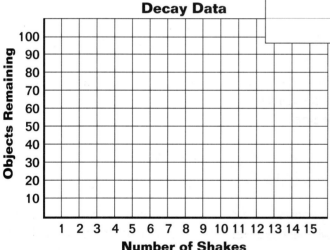

Decay Data

Objects Remaining (100, 90, 80, 70, 60, 50, 40, 30, 20, 10)

Number of Shakes (1 2 3 4 5 6 7 8 9 10 11 12 13 14 15)

Conclude and Apply

1. In this model of radioactive decay, what do the coins and fasteners represent? The paper clips? The box? Each shake?

2. What was the half-life of the pennies? The fasteners?

3. How does the difference between the two objects affect the half-life? Compare the objects to the differences among radioactive elements.

4. Suppose you could make only one shake in 100 years. How many years would it take to have 25 coins and 75 paper clips remaining? To have 25 fasteners and 75 paper clips remaining?

5. How can absolute age of rocks be determined?

Chapter **11** Reviewing Main Ideas

For a **preview** of this chapter, study this Reviewing Main Ideas before you read the chapter. After you have studied this chapter, you can use the Reviewing Main Ideas to **review** the chapter.

The Glencoe MindJogger, Audiocassettes, and CD-ROM provide additional opportunities for review.

Section
11-1 FOSSILS

Fossils are more likely to form if hard parts of the dead organisms are buried quickly. Some fossils form when original materials that made up the organisms are replaced with minerals. Other fossils form when remains are subjected to heat and pressure, leaving only a **carbonaceous film** behind. When an organism is buried, decays, and leaves a cavity in the rock that is later filled with sediment, a **mold** and **cast** fossil forms. Some fossils are merely the tracks or traces left by former organisms. As a rule, a rock layer can be no older than the age of the fossils embedded in it. *What type of fossil forms when original remains have been replaced with minerals?*

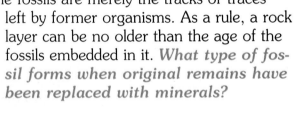

Reading Check ☑️

List any questions you still have about the chapter content. Review the chapter and try to answer them.

Section
11-2 RELATIVE AGES OF ROCKS

The **principle of superposition** states that older rocks lie underneath younger rocks in areas where the rocks haven't been disturbed. Faults are always younger than the rocks they cut across. Relative ages indicate if one layer of rock is younger or older than another. They do not indicate the layer's exact age in years. **Unconformities,** or gaps in the rock record, are due to erosion, nondeposition, or both. Three different types of unconformities can occur: angular unconformities, disconformities, and nonconformities. Fossils and rock types are often helpful when correlating similar rock bodies. *What process or processes occur to form a disconformity?*

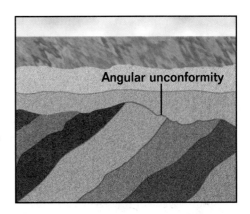

Angular unconformity

Section
11-3 ABSOLUTE AGES OF ROCKS

Unlike relative dating of rocks, **absolute dating** gives geologists a method by which they can determine the age in years of a rock or other object. The **half-life** of a radioactive isotope is the time it takes for half of the atoms in the isotope to decay. One half of the carbon-14 present in an object will decay to nitrogen-14 over a period of 5730 years. Because half-lives are constant, absolute ages of rocks containing radioactive elements can be determined. *How are geologists able to determine a rock layer's age due to radiometric dating?*

92 protons
146 neutrons

Alpha particle

90 protons
144 neutrons

Chapter 11 Assessment

Using Vocabulary

a. absolute dating
b. carbonaceous film
c. cast
d. fossil
e. half-life
f. index fossil
g. mold
h. petrified remains
i. principle of superposition
j. radioactive decay
k. radiometric dating
l. relative dating
m. unconformity
n. uniformitarianism

The sentences below include terms that have been used incorrectly. Change the incorrect terms so that the sentence reads correctly.

1. Rocklike fossils made of minerals are called *petrified remains.*

2. *Correlation fossils* are fossils of species that existed for a short time and were abundant and widespread.

3. The *principle of uniformitarianism* explains the fact that younger rock layers overlie older rock layers.

4. *Relative dating* allows geologists to determine the exact age of rocks and fossils.

5. *Radiometric dating* is the time it takes for half of the atoms of a radioactive isotope to decay.

Checking Concepts

Choose the word or phrase that completes the sentence.

6. What are remains of organisms in rocks called?
   A) half-lives
   B) fossils
   C) unconformities
   D) extinctions

7. What conditions allow dead organisms to change into fossils?
   A) slow burial
   B) exposure to microorganisms
   C) soft parts present
   D) hard parts present

8. What are cavities left in rocks called when a shell or bone decays?
   A) casts
   B) petrified remains
   C) molds
   D) carbon films

9. Which of the following is evidence of animal activity, such as fossilized tracks?
   A) a trace fossil
   B) petrified remains
   C) original remains
   D) carbonaceous film

10. "The present is the key to the past" is an explanation of which principle?
    A) superposition
    B) succession
    C) radioactivity
    D) uniformitarianism

11. A fault can be used to find what kind of age of a group of rocks?
    A) relative
    B) radiometric
    C) index
    D) absolute

12. What is an unconformity between horizontal rock layers called?
    A) fault
    B) angular unconformity
    C) disconformity
    D) nonconformity

13. During which process are new elements formed?
    A) superposition
    B) radioactive decay
    C) evolution
    D) uniformitarianism

14. In one type of radioactive decay, what breaks down, releasing an electron?
    A) alpha particle
    B) proton
    C) beta particle
    D) neutron

15. According to radiometric dating, how many years old is Earth?
    A) 2000
    B) 5000
    C) 3.5 billion
    D) 4.6 billion

Thinking Critically

16. We don't have a complete fossil record of life on Earth. Give some reasons why.

17. Suppose a lava flow were found between two sedimentary rock layers. How could the lava flow be used to date the rocks? (Hint: Most lava contains radioactive isotopes.)

18. A set of dinosaur tracks, as in **Figure 11-7,** is found. How might the tracks be used to determine how tall the dinosaur was or how fast it was moving?

19. Suppose you're correlating rock layers in the western United States. You find a layer of shale that contains volcanic dust deposits. How can this layer help you in your correlation over a large area?

20. Why is carbon-14 not suitable for dating fossils formed about 2 million years ago?

Developing Skills

If you need help, refer to the Skill Handbook.

21. **Concept Mapping:** Make a concept map listing the following possible steps in the process of making a cast of a fossil: *replacement by minerals, organism dies, mineral crystals form from solution, burial, fossil erodes away, protection from scavengers,* and *bacteria.*

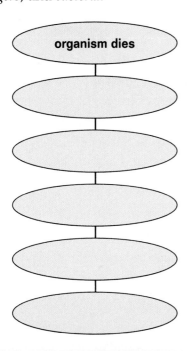

THE PRINCETON REVIEW

Test-Taking Tip

Make Yourself Comfortable When you take a test, try to make yourself as comfortable as possible. You will then be able to focus all your attention on the test.

Test Practice

Use these questions to test your Science Proficiency.

1. Many small fossil tracks of one type of animal are found surrounded by larger tracks of the same type of animal. What might this indicate about their social structure?
   A) Larger animals were attacking the smaller ones.
   B) Animals of different sizes were playing in a group.
   C) Large animals were surrounding the smaller ones for protection.
   D) Large animals run faster and therefore move to the outside of the herd.

2. An object was radiometrically dated and determined to be 90 000 years old. The half-life of the parent isotope is 30 000 years. Which statement **BEST** explains how this date was determined?
   A) In the object, 87.5 percent of the parent isotope and 12.5 percent of the daughter isotope are present.
   B) In the object, 50 percent of the parent isotope and 50 percent of the daughter isotope are present.
   C) In the object, 25 percent of the parent isotope and 75 percent of the daughter isotope are present.
   D) In the object, 12.5 percent of the parent isotope and 87.5 percent of the daughter isotope are present.

Change Through Time

Chapter Preview

Skills Preview

Skill Builders
- Make a Table
- Map Concepts

Activities
- Collect and Organize
  Data
- Formulate a Model

MiniLabs
- Make a Model
- Infer

Reading Check ✔

Before reading this chapter,
list the kinds of images you
expect to see. Compare this
list with the images you find
as you read.

Explore Activity

The Central Indian Tiger is a fierce hunter. It preys mostly on large mammals, including lions and other tigers. If injured or unable to get food, tigers have even been known to eat humans. Because tigers can run swiftly only for a short distance, they must conceal themselves so they can spring on their prey and kill it before it gets away. Tigers are camouflaged according to their natural environment. The tiger on the opposite page is colored perfectly for its surroundings. Its stripes blend in with the tall grass, making it almost invisible as it stalks its prey.

Model Camouflage

1. Spread a sheet of classified ads from a newspaper on the floor.

2. Using a hole punch, punch out 100 circles each from sheets of white paper, black paper, and classified ads.

3. Scatter the paper circles on the spread-out sheets of classified ads. Pick up as many paper circles as possible for 10 s. Have a partner time you.

4. Count each kind of paper circle that you picked up. Then, pour the circles back on the newspaper pages.

5. Repeat steps 3 and 4 three times. Graph your data.

In your Science Journal, describe which paper circles were most difficult to find. What can you infer from this activity?

Mechanisms of Evolution

What You'll Learn

► Lamarck's explanation of evolution and Darwin's theory of evolution
► The importance of variations in organisms
► How gradualism and punctuated equilibrium describe the rate of evolution

Vocabulary

species
evolution
natural selection
variation
gradualism
punctuated equilibrium

Why It's Important

► The theory of evolution explains why living things are different and predicts changes that will occur.

Early Thoughts About Evolution

On Earth today, there are millions of different types of organisms. Among these organisms are different species of plants, animals, bacteria, fungi, and protists. A **species** is a group of organisms with members that reproduce among themselves in their natural environment. Have any of these species of organisms changed since they first appeared on Earth? Are they still changing today? Evidence from observation of fossils indicates that living things have changed through time and are still changing. Change in the hereditary features of a species over time is **evolution.** For example, **Figure 12-2** shows how the camel has changed over time.

In 1809, Jean Baptiste de Lamarck, a French scientist, proposed one of the first explanations as to how species evolve or change. Lamarck hypothesized that species evolve by keeping traits that their parents develop during their lives. Characteristics that are not used are lost from the species. According to Lamarck's theory of evolution, if the parents lift weights, their children will be born with muscles stronger or larger than children of nonweight lifters. Lamarck's explanation of evolution is often called the theory of acquired characteristics.

Figure 12-1 Lamarck's explanation can be tested by experimentation. Weight lifters do not produce offspring with muscles that are larger or stronger than those of children produced by nonweight lifters.

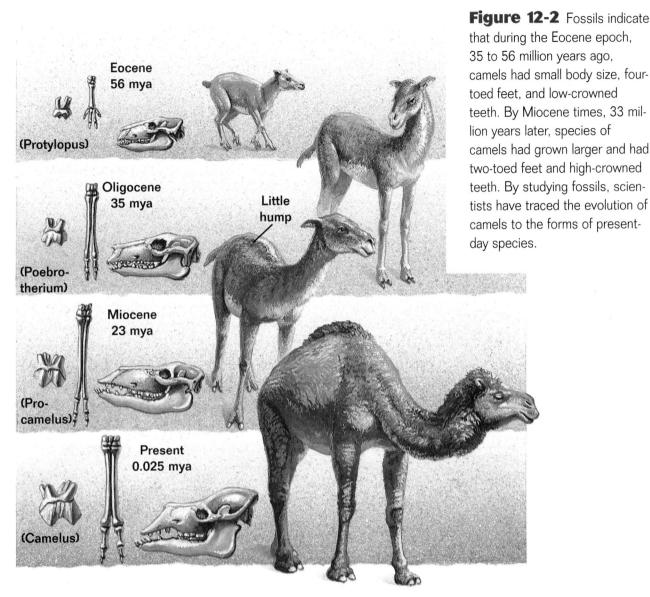

Eocene
56 mya

(Protylopus)

Oligocene
35 mya

(Poebro-
therium)

Little
hump

Miocene
23 mya

(Pro-
camelus)

Present
0.025 mya

(Camelus)

Figure 12-2 Fossils indicate that during the Eocene epoch, 35 to 56 million years ago, camels had small body size, four-toed feet, and low-crowned teeth. By Miocene times, 33 million years later, species of camels had grown larger and had two-toed feet and high-crowned teeth. By studying fossils, scientists have traced the evolution of camels to the forms of present-day species.

Genes on chromosomes control the inheritance of traits. The traits that develop during an organism's life, such as large muscles, as shown in **Figure 12-1,** are not inherited. After scientists collected large amounts of information on the inheritance of characteristics, Lamarck's explanation was rejected. The data showed that characteristics an organism develops or acquires during its lifetime aren't passed on to its offspring. ☑

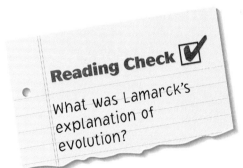

Reading Check ☑

What was Lamarck's explanation of evolution?

Evolution by Natural Selection

In the mid-1800s, Charles Darwin came up with the theory of evolution that is still accepted today. At the age of 22, Darwin became the ship's naturalist aboard HMS *Beagle.* The *Beagle* was on a trip to survey the east and west coasts of South America. The ship sailed from England in December 1831. Darwin's work was to record facts about all the plants and animals he observed during the journey.

Darwin's Observations

Darwin collected many plants, animals, and fossils from stops all along his route, which is shown in **Figure 12-3.** He was amazed by the variety of plants and animals he found in the Galápagos Islands. The Galápagos Islands are off the coast of Ecuador. The plants and animals Darwin saw in these islands must have come from Central and South America, yet on these 19 small islands, he found many species that he had not seen before. He observed giant cactus trees, 13 species of finches, and huge land tortoises, but he saw few other reptiles, only nine mammal species, and no amphibians at all. Darwin became particularly interested in the finches. He wondered how so many different, but closely related, species of finches could live on islands just a few miles apart.

For 20 years after the voyage, Darwin continued studying his collections. He thought about his observations and made further studies. He collected evidence of variations among species by breeding pigeons for racing. He also studied breeds of dogs and varieties of flowers. Darwin knew that people selected traits they wanted in plant and animal offspring by breeding parents that had those traits.

Figure 12-3 A map of Darwin's voyage is illustrated below. Some of the unique organisms he found in the Galápagos Islands included a cactus tree, a land iguana, a finch, and a giant tortoise.

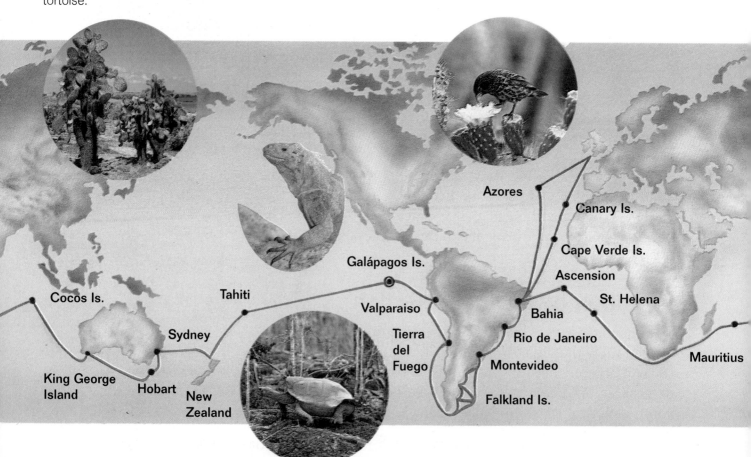

Azores

Canary Is.

Cape Verde Is.

Ascension

St. Helena

Galápagos Is.

Cocos Is.

Tahiti

Valparaiso

Bahia

Rio de Janeiro

Sydney

Tierra del Fuego

Montevideo

Mauritius

King George Island

Hobart

New Zealand

Falkland Is.

Principles of Natural Selection

Darwin's observations suggested that organisms with traits most favorable for their environment survived and passed these traits on to their offspring. After many experiments, Darwin's hypothesis became the theory of evolution by natural selection. **Natural selection** means that organisms with traits best suited to their environment are more likely to survive and reproduce. The factors identified in natural selection are as follows.

1. Organisms produce more offspring than can survive.
2. Variations are found among individuals of a species.
3. Variations are passed on to offspring.
4. Some variations allow members of a population to survive and reproduce better than others.
5. Over time, offspring of individuals with helpful variations make up more and more of a population.

Darwin wrote a book describing his theory of evolution by natural selection. His book, *On the Origin of Species by Means of Natural Selection,* was published in 1859. Some changes have been made to Darwin's theory as new information has been gathered. However, his theory remains one of the most important ideas in the study of life science.

*inter***NET**
CONNECTION

Visit the Glencoe Science Web Site at **www.glencoe.com/ sec/science** for more information about the finches Darwin observed.

Problem Solving

When can some fish be sold?

Alejandro has decided to raise tropical fish as a hobby and to sell his extra fish to a local store to make some spending money. In his research, Alejandro learned that each tropical fish requires one gallon of water. Eventually, they will produce more young than can be kept in his 30-gallon aquarium. He knew that he wanted to keep his most beautiful fish and sell the others. Alejandro realized that selecting fish in this way would be similar to Charles Darwin's theory of evolution by natural selection.

Solve the Problem

1. Assume Alejandro buys one pair of adult fish that just produced young. The species of fish Alejandro bought produce equal numbers of males and females. Each adult pair of fish begins to breed when they are two months old and produce ten young every subsequent two months. Also assume that all of the young survive to reproduce. How many fish will Alejandro have after two months?

2. If Alejandro continues to raise fish, how long will it be before he must sell some fish or get another aquarium?

Think Critically: How does Alejandro's problem relate to the first factor that governs natural selection as listed at the top of this page?

Adaptation and Variation

One of the points in Darwin's theory is that differences are found among individuals of a species. These differences are called variations. A **variation** is an inherited trait that makes an individual different from other members of the same species. Variations can be small, such as differences in the shape of human hairlines, or large, such as an albino squirrel in a population of gray squirrels, or fruit without seeds. Variations are important in populations of organisms. A population is a group of organisms of one species that live in an area. If enough variations occur in a population as it produces new offspring, a new species may evolve from the existing species. It may take hundreds, thousands, or even millions of generations for a new species to evolve.

The Sources of Variations

Some variations are more helpful than others. An adaptation is any variation that makes an organism better suited to its environment. The variations that result in adaptation can be in an organism's color, shape, behavior, or chemical makeup. Camouflage is an adaptation that lets an organism blend into its environment, as shown in **Figure 12-4A.** An organism that can camouflage itself is more likely to survive and reproduce. These types of variations result from mutations, which are changes in an organism's DNA.

What other factors bring about evolution? The movement of individuals of the same species into or out of an area brings in or removes new genes and variations. Have you ever had an exchange student come to your school? The student

Using Math

Use the data from the Explore Activity. The experimental probability of picking up a white circle is as follows.

Probability = white circles ÷ total circles

Find the probability of picking up white, black, and classified ad circles. Are these events equally likely? Is that what actually happened?

Figure 12-4 Variations may be beneficial, harmful, or neutral in a population.

A Camouflage causes some organisms to blend into their environment. **How does camouflage coloration give this spider an advantage in survival?**

B Variations that result in a disadvantage, such as albinism, tend to decrease in a population over time. **What would likely happen to an albino squirrel in its natural environment?**

probably brought new ideas, maybe a new style of dress, and even a new language. When new individuals come into an existing population, they can bring in new genes and variations in much the same way. Some organisms are separated from others by geography and changes in climate. This isolation can result in evolutionary change, as you can see in **Figure 12-5.** Each of these factors affects how fast evolution occurs.

How fast does evolution occur?

Scientists do not agree on the answer to this question. Many scientists hypothesize that evolution occurs slowly, perhaps taking tens or hundreds of millions of years. Other scientists hypothesize that evolution may occur quickly. As you study evolution, you will see that evidence supports both of these models.

Mini Lab

Relating Evolution to Species

Procedure

1. On a piece of paper, print the alphabet in lowercase letters.
2. Order the letters into three groups. Put all of the vowels in the first group. Place all of the consonants that do not drop below the line into the second group and all of the consonants that do drop below the line in the third group.

Analysis

1. How are the three groups of letters similar to each other?
2. If the letters were organisms, how would scientists know how closely related the letters were to each other?

Figure 12-5 The Tana river in Kenya separates two populations of giraffes. Over time, these two populations have become distinct. **Do these giraffes have different appearances? What does this tell you about their genetic makeup?**

A The common giraffe is known as Rothchild's giraffe, *Giraffa camelopardalis rothschildi.*

B This is the reticulated giraffe, *Giraffa camelopardalis reticulata.* The word *reticulated* means "having lines or veins."

Gradualism

Darwin hypothesized that the rate of evolution was steady, slow, and ongoing. The model that describes evolution as a slow change of one species to another, new species is known as **gradualism.** According to the gradualism model, continued mutations and variations will result in a new species over time. According to this model, there should be intermediate forms of all species. Evolution involves a change in the phenotype, or appearance, of a species as its hereditary features change. Look back at **Figure 12-1,** showing evolution of the camel. Fossil evidence shows gradual changes between the camel as it first appeared and how it looks today. Camels appear to have evolved gradually over millions of years. Fossil evidence shows the gradual evolution of many present-day species.

Punctuated Equilibrium

But gradualism doesn't explain the evolution of some species, especially those in which there is a gap in the fossil record because few intermediate forms have been discovered. The **punctuated equilibrium** model, as seen in **Figure 12-6,** shows that rapid evolution can come about by the mutation of just a few genes, resulting in the appearance of a new species. How fast is evolution by this model? New species could appear as quickly as every few million years and sometimes even more rapidly than that. For example, bacteria that cause illness in humans can sometimes be killed by antibiotics such as penicillin. Penicillin has been available only since 1940, yet some species of bacteria are now resistant to this drug. How did this happen so quickly? As in any population, some of the bacteria had variations that allowed them to keep from being

Figure 12-6 Evolution can occur slowly, as in gradualism, or rapidly, as in punctuated equilibrium. In the diagrams below, branches of different colors represent different species. Branches that do not continue to the top of the graph represent species that are extinct and, therefore, are no longer evolving. A change in the phenotype of a species is a change in its appearance.

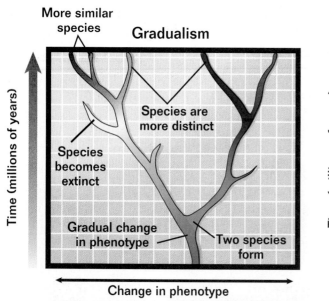

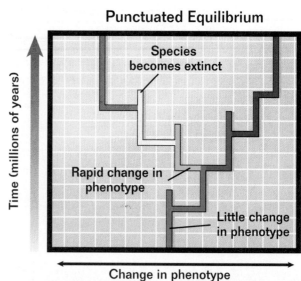

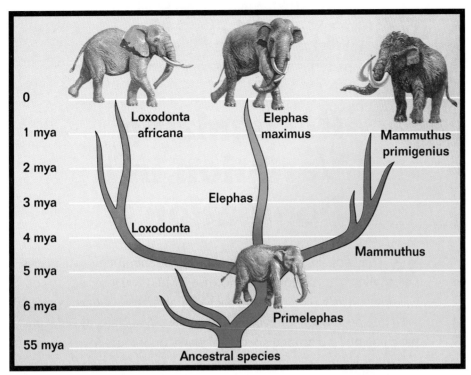

Figure 12-7 The evolution of the elephant illustrates how punctuated equilibrium usually occurs. Notice that three distinct species evolved over 1 million years—a relatively short amount of time. This same change would have taken several million years to occur in gradualism.

Labels in figure:
0
1 mya
2 mya
3 mya
4 mya
5 mya
6 mya
55 mya

Loxodonta africana
Elephas maximus
Mammuthus primigenius
Elephas
Loxodonta
Mammuthus
Primelephas
Ancestral species

killed by penicillin. When the drug was used to kill bacteria, the few individuals with this variation lived to reproduce. Over a short period of time, the entire population of bacteria became resistant to penicillin. The bacteria had evolved quickly—an example of punctuated equilibrium. In this step-like pattern, large changes take place in a short period of time. The fossil record also gives examples of this type of evolution, as you can see in **Figure 12-7.** Punctuated equilibrium and gradualism are compared in **Figure 12-6.**

Section Assessment

1. Compare Lamarck's and Darwin's ideas of evolution.

2. How are variations important in a population?

3. Define what an adaptation is and give an example.

4. **Think Critically:** Explain how the gradualism model of evolution differs from the punctuated equilibrium model.

5. **Skill Builder**
   Making and Using Graphs
   Do the **Chapter 12 Skill Activity** on page 753 to learn how to make and use a graph.

Using Math

Figure 12-2 states that the evolution of the camel can be traced for at least 56 million years. Use the information in **Figure 12-2** to determine the approximate percent of this time that the modern camel has existed.

Recognizing Variation in a Population

Possible Materials

- Leaves, flowers, and seeds from one species of plant
- Metric ruler
- Magnifying glass
- Graph paper

When you first see a group of plants or animals of one species, they may all look alike. However, when you look closer, you will notice minor differences in each characteristic. Variations must exist in a population for evolution to occur. What kinds of variations have you noticed among species of plants or animals?

Recognize the Problem

How can you measure variation in a plant or animal population?

Form a Hypothesis

Make a hypothesis about the amount of variation in seeds, leaves, or flowers of one species of plant.

Goals

- **Design an experiment** that will allow you to collect data about variation in a population.
- **Observe, measure,** and **analyze** variations in a population.

Safety Precautions

Do not put any seeds, flowers, or plant parts in your mouth. Wash your hands after handling plant parts.

Test Your Hypothesis

Plan

1. As a group, agree upon and write out the hypothesis statement.

2. List the steps you need to take to **test your hypothesis.** Be specific. Describe exactly what you will do at each step. List your materials.

3. Decide what characteristic of seeds, leaves, or flowers you will study. For example, you could **measure** the length of seeds, the width of leaves, or the number of petals on the flowers of plants.

4. **Design a data table** in your Science Journal to collect data about one variation. Use the table to record the data your group collects as you complete the experiment.

5. **Identify** any constants, variables, and controls of the experiment.

6. How many seeds, leaves, or flowers will you examine? Will your data be more accurate if you examine larger numbers?

7. **Summarize** the data in a graph or chart.

Do

1. Make sure your teacher approves your plan before you proceed.

2. Carry out the experiment as planned.

3. While the experiment is going on, write down any observations that you make and complete the data table in your Science Journal.

Analyze Your Data

1. **Compare** your results with those of other groups.

2. How did you determine the amount of variation present?

Draw Conclusions

1. **Graph** your results, placing the *range* of variation on the *x*-axis and the number of organisms that had that measurement on the *y*-axis.

2. **Calculate** the *mean* and *range* of variation in your experiment.

The *range* of a set of data is the difference between the greatest measurement and the smallest measurement. The *mean* is the sum of all the data divided by the sample size.

What You'll Learn

▶ The importance of fossils as evidence of evolution

▶ How relative and radiometric dating are used to date fossils

▶ Examples of five types of evidence for evolution

Vocabulary

sedimentary rock
radioactive element
homologous
vestigial structure
embryology

Why It's Important

▶ Valid scientific theories must be backed up by observable or testable evidence.

Fossil Evidence

On a hot day in July 1975, in northern Texas, two people were walking along the shores of Lake Lavon. They came across some odd-looking rocks sticking up from the muddy shore. They noticed that the rocks seemed different from the surrounding limestone rocks. They took a few of the rocks to a scientist who studies reptiles and amphibians. The rocks were skull pieces of a fossil mosasaur, an extinct lizard that had lived in salt water.

A group of scientists returned to the site and carefully dug up the rest of the fossil mosasaur. This find indicates that about 120 million years ago, the northern Texas area—now more than 500 km from the Gulf of Mexico—was covered by a shallow sea. Fossils such as those found on the shores of Lake Lavon are studied by scientists called paleontologists (pay lee ahn TAHL uh justs), shown in **Figure 12-8.**

Figure 12-8 Digging for fossils requires careful work. Paleontologists, scientists who study the past by examining fossils, sift tons of earth and rock to find tiny bones. They may use dental equipment such as dental picks and toothbrushes to remove dirt as they work to uncover larger bones, such as these dinosaur bones found in Thailand.

Figure 12-9 Three examples of fossils are shown. **Which of these would most likely be found in a layer of sedimentary rock?**

A This is an imprint fossil made by a leaf.

B An insect caught in amber that hardened over time is also a fossil.

C This is the cast fossil of an ammonite, an extinct marine organism.

Kinds of Fossils

The most evidence for evolution comes from fossils like those found on the shore of Lake Lavon in Texas. A fossil is any evidence of life from an earlier geological time, such as those illustrated in **Figure 12-9.** Examples of fossils include the following.

1. the imprint of a leaf, feather, or organism in rock
2. a cast made of minerals that filled in the hollows of an animal track, mollusk shell, or other parts of an organism
3. a piece of wood or bone replaced by minerals
4. an organism frozen in ice
5. an insect or other organism trapped in amber

Sedimentary rock contains the most fossils. **Sedimentary rock** is a rock type formed from particles of preexisting rocks. These particles can be deposited by water, wind, gravity, or ice. Limestone, sandstone, and shale are all examples of sedimentary rock. Fossils are found more often in limestone than in any other kind of sedimentary rock.

*inter*NET
CONNECTION

Visit the Glencoe Science Web Site at **www.glencoe.com/ sec/science** for more information on fossils.

Table 12-1

Geologic Time Scale							
Era	Cenozoic		Mesozoic			Paleozoic	
Period	Quaternary	Tertiary	Cretaceous	Jurassic	Triassic	Permian	Pennsylvanian
Millions of years ago	1.6	66	146	208	245	290	

EARTH SCIENCE INTEGRATION➤

The Fossil Record

You learned that the mosasaur fossil found in Texas was 120 million years old. How did scientists come up with this date? Scientists have divided Earth's history into eras and periods. These divisions make up the geologic time scale as shown in **Table 12-1.** Unique rock layers and fossils give information about the geology, weather, and life-forms of each time period. There are two basic methods for reading the record of past life. When these methods are used together, estimates of the ages of certain rocks and fossils can be made.

Relative Dating

One way to find the approximate age of a rock layer, or fossils within the layer, is relative dating. Relative dating is based on the idea that in undisturbed areas, older rock layers lie below younger rock layers, as shown in **Figure 12-10.** Therefore, fossils found in lower layers of rock are older than those in upper layers. Relative dating cannot give the exact age of a fossil. It can give only an estimate of how old the fossil might be.

Radiometric Dating

Scientists can give a more accurate age to a rock layer using radioactive elements. A **radioactive element** gives off radiation due to an unstable nucleus. As radioactive elements give off radiation, they eventually change to more stable products. The radiation is given off at a steady rate

Paleozoic					Precambrian
Mississippian	Devonian	Silurian	Ordovician	Cambrian	
					4600
323	362	408	439	510	543

Reading Check ✔

Which is more accurate, relative dating or radiometric dating?

that is different for each element. Scientists can estimate the age of the rock by comparing the amount of radioactive element with the amount of nonradioactive element in the rock. However, many times this method of dating gives inconsistent dates because the original amount of radioactive element in the rock is never completely certain. ✔

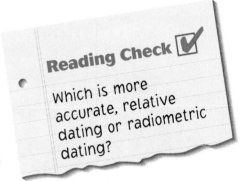

Figure 12-10 Fossils found in lower layers of sedimentary rock are usually older than the fossils found in upper layers.

A In the Grand Canyon, the Colorado River has cut through the sedimentary rock, exposing the layers.

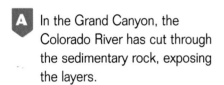

B Paleontologists can date fossils by the age of the rock layer in which they occur.

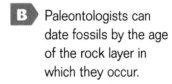

Figure 12-11 In the Pennsylvanian period, 300 million years ago, amphibians and land plants were the dominant life-forms on Earth. Many of the plants of this period eventually became peat and coal. **Why do we call these fossil fuels?**

Fossils Show Evolution Occurred

Fossils are a record of organisms that lived in the past. But, the fossil record has gaps, much like a book with pages missing. Because every living thing doesn't or can't become fossilized, the record will never be complete. By looking at fossils, scientists conclude that many simpler forms of life existed earlier in Earth's history, and more complex forms of life appeared later. The oldest fossil bacteria appeared about 3.5 billion years ago. Invertebrates with hard shells appeared in the Cambrian period, about 540 million years ago. The first land plants did not appear until the Silurian period, about 439 million years ago. Dinosaurs were common on Earth during the Jurassic and Cretaceous periods, from about 208 to 66 million years ago. The first mammals and birds did not appear until the Jurassic period, about 200 million years ago. **Figure 12-11** shows an artist's drawing of a scene of 300 million years ago. The fossil record gives scientists direct evidence that living things evolved. There are also other types of ideas that support the theory of evolution.

Other Evidence for Evolution

Besides fossils, what other evidence is there for evolution? Scientists have found more evidence by looking at similarities in chemical makeup such as DNA, development, and embryological structure among organisms. You know that the functions of a dolphin's flipper, a bat's wing, and a bird's wing are different. Yet, as you can see in **Figure 12-12,** each of these structures is made up of the same kind of bones. Each has about the same number of muscles and blood vessels. Each of these limbs developed from similar tissues. Body parts that are similar in origin and structure are called **homologous** (huh MAHL uh gus). Homologous structures indicate that two or more species might share common ancestors.

Figure 12-12 A bird wing, a bat wing, and dolphin flipper are homologous. Each has about the same number of bones, muscles, and blood vessels.

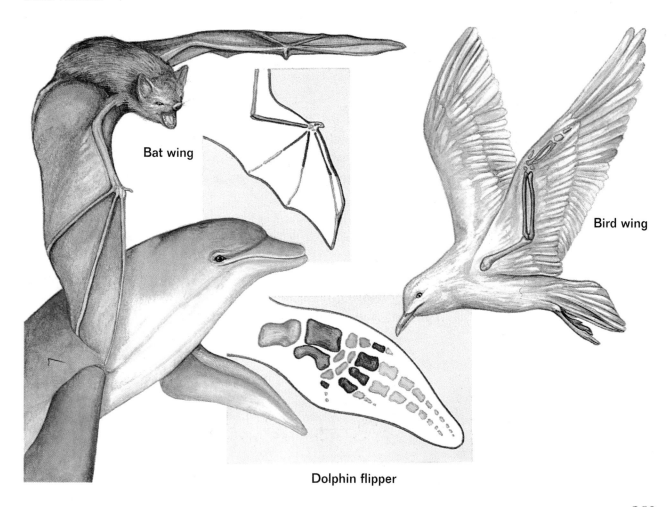

Bat wing

Bird wing

Dolphin flipper

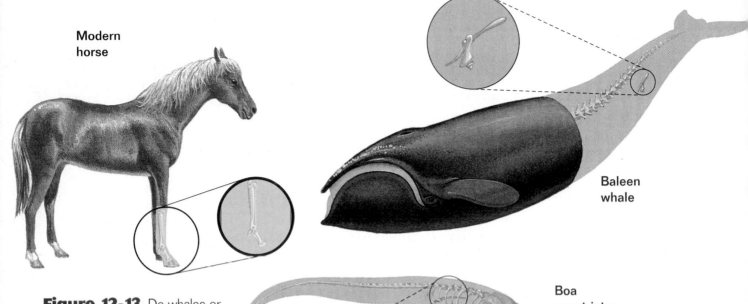

Modern
horse

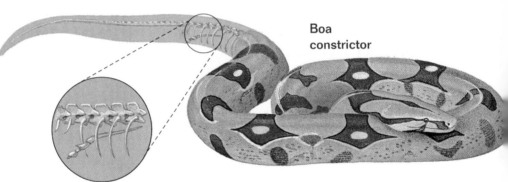

Baleen
whale

Figure 12-13 Do whales or snakes have back legs? You can see that they don't, yet both animals have vestigial hipbones and leg bones where legs may once have existed. Horses once had four functional toes. Now, they walk on just one toe. The others are no longer functional.

Boa
constrictor

Vestigial Structures

Vestigial structures also give evidence for evolution. A **vestigial** (veh STIHJ ee ul) **structure** is a body part that doesn't seem to have a function. For example, manatees no longer have back legs, but they still have pelvic bones. Scientists hypothesize that vestigial structures are parts that once functioned in an ancestor, as seen in **Figure 12-13.**

Embryology

The study of development in organisms is called **embryology** (em bree AHL uh jee). An embryo is an organism in its earliest stages of development. Compare the embryos of the organisms in **Figure 12-14.** In the early stages of development, the embryos of fish, reptiles, birds, and mammals

Figure 12-14 Similarities in the embryos of fish, reptiles, birds, and mammals suggest evolution. Many of the same features are found in all of these organisms. **How can you tell which organism's embryo is which?**

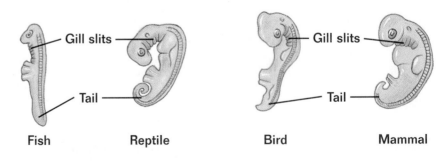

Gill slits

Tail

Gill slits

Tail

Fish   Reptile   Bird   Mammal

have a tail and gills or gill slits. The gill slits of fish continue to develop into gills, which are kept throughout life. The gill slits of other organisms are lost during development. Fish, birds, and reptiles keep their tails, but mammals may lose theirs. These similarities suggest an evolutionary relationship among all vertebrate species.

DNA

DNA is the molecule that controls heredity. It is contained on chromosomes and directs the development of every organism. Scientists can determine whether or not organisms are closely related by looking at their DNA. Organisms that are close relatives have similar DNA. By studying DNA, scientists have determined that dogs are the closest relatives of bears. You would not be surprised to learn that primates, such as gorillas, bonobos, and chimpanzees, like the one shown in **Figure 12-15,** also have DNA that is similar.

Genetic evidence also supports the view that primates all evolved from a common ancestor. Primates share many of the same proteins, including hemoglobin. Hemoglobin is a protein in red blood cells that carries oxygen. Many primates have hemoglobin that is nearly the same.

Figure 12-15 The DNA of humans and chimpanzees is similar in many ways.

Section Assessment

1. How are relative and radiometric dating used to interpret the fossil record?

2. How are fossils important evidence of evolution? List the different kinds of fossils.

3. How can DNA provide evidence of evolution?

4. **Think Critically:** Compare and contrast the five types of evidence for evolution.

5. **Skill Builder**
   Making and Using Tables
   Use **Table 12-1,** the geologic time scale, to answer the following questions. Which was the longest period of the Paleozoic era? Which was the shortest? What period began 1.6 million years ago? If you need help, refer to Making and Using Tables in the **Skill Handbook** on page 716.

Using Computers

Spreadsheet Prepare a spreadsheet that contains the name of each era and its corresponding length expressed in millions of years. Use the spreadsheet to make a chart that shows the information graphically. What information becomes more evident from a graphical presentation? If you need help, refer to page 738.

Footprints in Geologic Time

In 1978, a team led by renowned archaeologist Mary Leakey (shown in inset) made an astounding discovery in the Laetoli area of northern Tanzania in Africa. Amid the ancient tracks left by prehistoric giraffes, elephants, and rhinoceros were the fossilized footprints of three hominids—thought to be early ancestors of *Homo sapiens*. Preserved in volcanic ash, the Laetoli footprints (right) are estimated to be some 3.4 million years old.

Settling the Debate

In the minds of many, Leakey's discovery laid to rest the debate as to when our ancestors began to walk upright. The depth and spacing of the footprints indicated that these early hominids, nearly 3.4 million years ago, had erect posture and walked like modern humans. Leakey, who spent more than six decades conducting research in East Africa, considered the find her greatest achievement.

Preserving the Past

After studying the footprints, Leakey's team buried the fossils in sand for preservation. Unknown to them, the sand contained seeds of acacia trees, which soon sprouted. Scientists expressed concern that eventually the tree roots would damage the footprints. In 1994, scientists working with the Tanzanian government began a two-year project to uncover, repair, and then re-cover the footprints. They buried the site in sand, soil, and materials to prevent root growth. The scientists also photographed the footprints again to create more detailed diagrams of each imprint. The diagrams, accurate to within half a millimeter, may help answer lingering questions about the hominids who made the footprints, such as whether they were male or female.

In 1996, Mary Leakey attended an event held at Laetoli by the Masai, a local tribe. Knowing the significance of the site, the Masai have agreed to help protect it.

Science JOURNAL

Many fossils are dug up, then stored in museums for further study and safekeeping. Research why scientists decided not to dig up the Laetoli footprints. Write your findings in your Science Journal.

A Model of Natural Selection

Materials
- Red beans and white beans (10 each)
- Paper bag
- Pencil and paper

Natural selection has been observed in a variety of organisms in nature. Studying natural selection takes a long time because natural selection occurs in populations that may take years to produce a new generation. However, the process occurs in a way that can be explained by a simple model.

What You'll Investigate
What is the result of natural selection?

Safety Precautions

CAUTION: *Do not taste or eat any material used in the lab.*

Procedure
1. Take a paper bag and write "Rabbit Gene Pool" on it.
2. Place ten red beans and ten white beans in the bag.
3. **Make a table** that you can use to record the genetics in the population. **Assume** that the pairs of beans are rabbits. A pair of red beans make a brown rabbit. A red bean and a white bean make a gray rabbit, and a pair of white beans make a white rabbit.
4. Without looking into the bag, take out two beans to represent an offspring. Write the colors of beans in the table.
5. Continue taking beans out of the bag two at a time and writing the results.
6. To model selection, predators eat all of the white rabbits and half of the gray rabbits. For each brown rabbit, place six baby rabbits (two red beans for each rabbit) in the bag along with its parents. For each remaining gray rabbit, do the same thing (one red bean and one white bean for each rabbit).
7. Repeat steps 4 and 5 two more times.

Conclude and Apply
1. How did the rabbit gene pool change during the activity?
2. What eventually happens to the white rabbits?
3. Describe how this model is similar to the way natural selection occurs in nature.
4. How is this model unlike the way natural selection occurs in nature?

Rabbit Offspring	
Rabbit #	**Bean Colors**
1	
2	
3	
4	
5	
6	
7	
8	
9	
10	
11	
12	
13	
14	
15	

What You'll Learn

► The differences in living primates
► The adaptations of primates
► The evolutionary history of modern primates

Vocabulary
primates
hominids
Homo sapiens

Why It's Important

► Studying primate evolution will help you appreciate the differences between humans and other primates.

Primates

Monkeys, apes, and humans belong to the group of mammals called **primates.** The primates share several characteristics that lead scientists to think that all primates may have evolved from a common ancestor. All primates have opposable thumbs that allow them to reach out and grasp things, as shown in **Figure 12-16.** Having an opposable thumb allows you to cross your thumb over your palm and touch your fingers. Think of the problems you might have if you didn't have this type of thumb.

Primates also have binocular vision. Binocular vision permits a primate to judge depth or distance with its eyes. All primates have flexible shoulders and rotating forelimbs. These allow tree-dwelling primates to swing easily from branch to branch and allow you to swing on a jungle gym. Each of these characteristics suggests that all primates may share common ancestry.

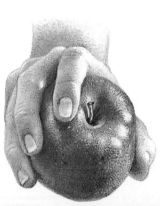

Figure 12-16 An opposable thumb allows tree-dwelling primates to hold onto branches. It also allows you to use your hand in many ways.

Primate Classification

Primates are divided into two major groups. The first group includes organisms such as lemurs and tarsiers, the prosimians, as shown in **Figure 12-17.** These animals are active at night and have large eyes and excellent hearing. The second group of primates includes monkeys, apes, and humans.

Hominids

About 4 to 6 million years ago, our earliest ancestors branched off from the other primates. These ancestors, called **hominids,** were humanlike primates that ate both meat and vegetables and walked upright on two feet. Hominids shared some common characteristics with gorillas, orangutans, and chimpanzees, but a larger brain size separated them from these other great apes.

African Origins

In the early 1920s, Raymond Dart, a South African scientist, discovered a fossil skull in a quarry in South Africa. The skull had a small space for the brain, but humanlike jaw and teeth. Dart named his discovery *Australopithecus*. He chose the name *Australopithecus* for one of the earliest hominid

EARTH SCIENCE
INTEGRATION

African Rift Valley
Many fossils from hominids and early humans have been found in the African Rift Valley. This area of Africa is where two tectonic plates of Earth's crust are moving past one another. Do research on this area and draw a map of it in your Science Journal. Write a paragraph that explains why you might expect to find many fossils there.

Figure 12-17 Tarsiers belong to a subgroup of primates called the prosimians, which means "before apes." They are commonly found in the rain forests of Southeast Asia.

Try at Home
Mini Lab

Living Without Thumbs

Procedure

1. Tape your thumb securely to your hand. Do this for both hands.

2. Leave your thumbs taped down for at least two hours. During this time, do the following activities: eat a meal, change clothes, and brush your teeth. Be careful not to try anything that could be dangerous.

3. Write about your experiences in your Science Journal.

Analysis

1. Did not having usable thumbs significantly affect the way you did things? Explain.

2. Infer how having opposable thumbs may have influenced primate evolution.

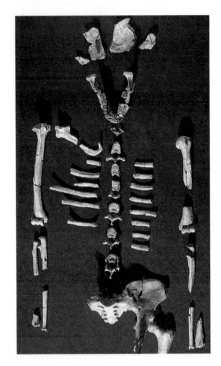

Figure 12-18 The fossil remains of Lucy, a hominid, are estimated to be 2.9 to 3.4 million years old.

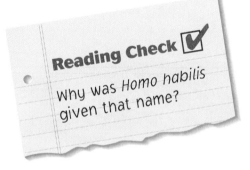

Reading Check

Why was *Homo habilis* given that name?

Figure 12-19 In this photograph, the skull of a Neanderthal, right, can be compared with the skull of a Cro-Magnon, left. **What differences can you see between these two skulls?**

groups discovered because it means "southern ape." In 1974, an almost-complete skeleton of *Australopithecus,* as shown in **Figure 12-18,** was discovered by American scientist Donald Johanson and his coworkers. They named the fossil Lucy. Lucy had a small brain but is thought to have walked upright. This fossil is important because it indicates how modern hominids may have evolved.

About 40 years after the discovery of *Australopithecus,* a discovery was made in East Africa by Louis, Mary, and Richard Leakey. The Leakeys discovered a fossil more like present-day humans than *Australopithecus.* They named this hominid *Homo habilis,* the "handy man," because they found simple stone tools near him. Scientists estimate *Homo habilis* to be 1.5 to 2 million years old. ☑

Based upon many fossil comparisons, anthropologists have suggested that *Homo habilis* gave rise to another species about 1.6 million years ago, *Homo erectus. Homo erectus* had a larger brain than *Homo habilis.* This hominid moved out of Africa about 1 million years ago. *Homo habilis* and *Homo erectus* both are thought to be ancestors of humans because they had larger brains and were more like humans than *Australopithecus.*

Modern Humans

Our species is named ***Homo sapiens,*** meaning "wise human." The fossil record indicates that the human species evolved about 400 000 years ago. By about 125 000 years ago, two early groups of *Homo sapiens,* Neanderthals and Cro-Magnon humans, probably lived at the same time in parts of Africa and Europe.

Neanderthals had short, heavy bodies with thick bones; small chins; and heavy browridges, as you can see in **Figure 12-19.** The Neanderthals lived in family groups in caves and

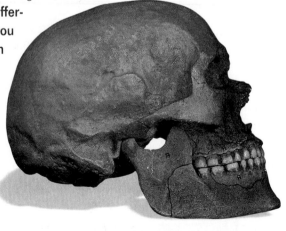

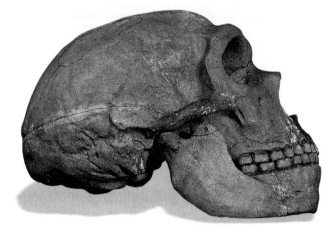

hunted mammoths, deer, and other large animals, with well-made stone tools. For reasons that are not clear, Neanderthals disappeared from the fossil record about 35 000 years ago. Most scientists think Neanderthals were a side branch of human evolution but are not direct ancestors of modern humans.

Cro-Magnon fossils have been found in Europe, Asia, and Australia. These fossils are dated from 40 000 to about 10 000 years old. The oldest recorded art dates from the caves of France where Cro-Magnon humans first painted bison, horses, and spear-carrying people. Cro-Magnon humans lived in caves, made stone carvings, and buried their dead, as seen in **Figure 12-20.** Standing about 1.6 m to 1.7 m tall, the physical appearance of Cro-Magnon people was almost the same as that of modern humans. Cro-Magnon humans are thought to be direct ancestors of modern humans.

Figure 12-20 This grave contained objects thought to be placed there by Cro-Magnon humans. In addition to graves such as this, tools and paintings on cave walls have led scientists to hypothesize that Cro-Magnon humans had a well-developed culture.

Section Assessment

1. Describe at least three kinds of evidence that suggest all primates may have shared a common ancestor.

2. What is the importance of *Australopithecus?*

3. Describe the differences among Neanderthals, Cro-Magnon humans, and modern humans.

4. **Think Critically:** Propose a hypothesis about why teeth represent the most abundant available fossils of hominids.

5. 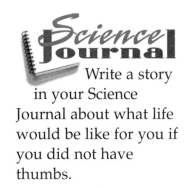 **Skill Builder**
   Concept Mapping Using information in this section, make a concept map to show the sequence of hominids. Use the following terms: Neanderthal, *Homo habilis, Australopithecus,* modern *Homo sapiens,* and Cro-Magnon human. If you need help, refer to Concept Mapping in the **Skill Handbook** on page 714.

Science Journal Write a story in your Science Journal about what life would be like for you if you did not have thumbs.

For a **preview** of this chapter, study this Reviewing Main Ideas before you read the chapter. After you have studied this chapter, you can use the Reviewing Main Ideas to **review** the chapter.

GLENCOE TECHNOLOGY

The Glencoe MindJogger, Audiocassettes, and CD-ROM provide additional opportunities for review.

12-1 MECHANISMS OF EVOLUTION

Evolution is one of the central ideas of biology. It explains how living things changed in the past and provides predictions for how they may change in the future. Charles Darwin developed the theory of evolution by **natural selection** to explain how these changes account for the diversity of organisms. The factors that control natural selection are as follows.

1. Organisms produce more offspring than can survive.
2. **Variations** are found among individuals of a **species.**
3. Variations are passed on to offspring.
4. Some variations allow members of a population to survive and reproduce better than others.
5. Over time, offspring of individuals with helpful variations make up more and more of a population.

How did Darwin's theory differ from Lamarck's theory?

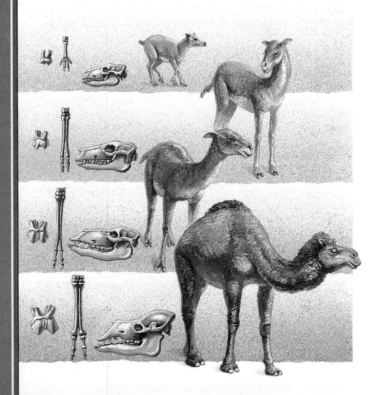

Section 12-2 EVIDENCE FOR EVOLUTION

Fossils are one of the main sources of evidence for evolution. They are tested using relative dating and radiometric dating to estimate how old they are. Other evidence includes comparative **embryology**, **homologous** structures, **vestigial structures**, and chemical similarities. *How are chemical similarities evidence of evolution?*

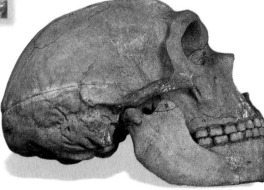

Section 12-3 PRIMATE EVOLUTION

Primates include monkeys, apes, and humans. **Hominids** are humanlike primates. The earliest known hominid is *Australopithecus*. Modern humans are thought to have evolved at least 400 000 years ago. *What are the common characteristics of primates?*

Using Vocabulary

a. embryology
b. evolution
c. gradualism
d. hominids
e. homologous
f. *Homo sapiens*
g. natural selection
h. primates
i. punctuated equilibrium
j. radioactive element
k. sedimentary rock
l. species
m. variation
n. vestigial structure

Each phrase below describes a science term from the list. Write the term that matches the phrase describing it.

1. model of evolution showing slow change
2. structure with no obvious use
3. similar organisms that successfully reproduce
4. body structures that are similar in origin
5. group containing monkeys, apes, and humans

Checking Concepts

Choose the word or phrase that best answers the question.

6. What is an example of adaptation?
   A) a fossil
   B) a homologous structure
   C) camouflage
   D) gradualism

7. How can the most accurate age of a fossil be estimated?
   A) natural selection
   B) radiometric dating
   C) relative dating
   D) camouflage

8. What do homologous structures, vestigial structures, and fossils all provide evidence of?
   A) gradualism
   B) food choice
   C) species populations
   D) evolution

9. What is a factor that controls natural selection?
   A) inheritance of acquired traits
   B) unused traits become smaller
   C) organisms produce more offspring than can survive
   D) the size of an organism

10. What may a series of helpful variations in a species result in?
    A) adaptation
    B) fossils
    C) embryology
    D) climate change

11. What describes organisms that are adapted to their environment?
    A) homologous
    B) not reproducing
    C) forming fossils
    D) surviving and reproducing

12. Which model of evolution shows rapid change?
    A) embryology
    B) punctuated equilibrium
    C) gradualism
    D) adaptation

13. What are opposable thumbs and binocular vision characteristics of?
    A) all primates
    B) hominids
    C) humans only
    D) monkeys and apes

14. What is the study of an organism's early development?
    A) adaptation
    B) relative dating
    C) natural selection
    D) embryology

15. A fossil has the same number of bones in its hand as a gorilla. What type of evidence for evolution does this represent?
    A) DNA
    B) homologous structures
    C) vestigial structures
    D) embryology

Thinking Critically

16. How would Lamarck and Darwin have explained the webbed feet of a duck?

17. Using an example, explain how a new species of organism could evolve.

18. How is the color-changing ability of chameleons an adaptation to their environment?

19. Describe the processes a scientist would use to figure out the age of a fossil.

20. Explain how a species could adapt to its environment. Give an example.

Developing skills

If you need help, refer to the **Skill Handbook.**

21. **Observing and Inferring:** Observe the birds' beaks pictured below. Describe each. Infer the types of food each would eat and explain why.

22. **Interpreting Data:** The chemicals present in certain bacteria were studied. Each letter below represents a different chemical found in the bacteria. Use this information to determine which of the bacteria are closely related.

Chemicals Present	
Bacteria 1	A, G, T, C, L, E, S, H
Bacteria 2	A, G, T, C, L, D, H
Bacteria 3	A, G, T, C, L, D, P, U, S, R, I, V
Bacteria 4	A, G, T, C, L, D, H

THE PRINCETON REVIEW

Test-Taking Tip

Make Yourself Comfortable When you take a test, try to make yourself as comfortable as possible. You will then be able to focus all your attention on the test.

Test Practice

Use these questions to test your Science Proficiency.

1. Which of the following statements **BEST** describes how evolution happens?
   A) An insect with an adaptation for surviving insecticide lives to reproduce after being sprayed. Its offspring inherit the trait.
   B) Two Great Danes have their ears cropped. They have a litter of puppies that also need to have their ears cropped.
   C) Two excellent musicians have a baby. After years of practice, the child learns to play instruments as well as the parents.
   D) After generations of stretching their necks to get leaves, all giraffes now have long necks.

2. Which of the following would **BEST** explain the punctuated equilibrium model of evolution?
   A) A mountain range is built up over millions of years due to tectonic plates colliding.
   B) During 54 million years of evolution, the camel evolved to its present form.
   C) Many species become extinct after a meteor strikes Earth, causing darkness for many months.
   D) Two populations become separated because of a flood, each evolving to look very different from the other.

CHAPTER

13 Geologic Time

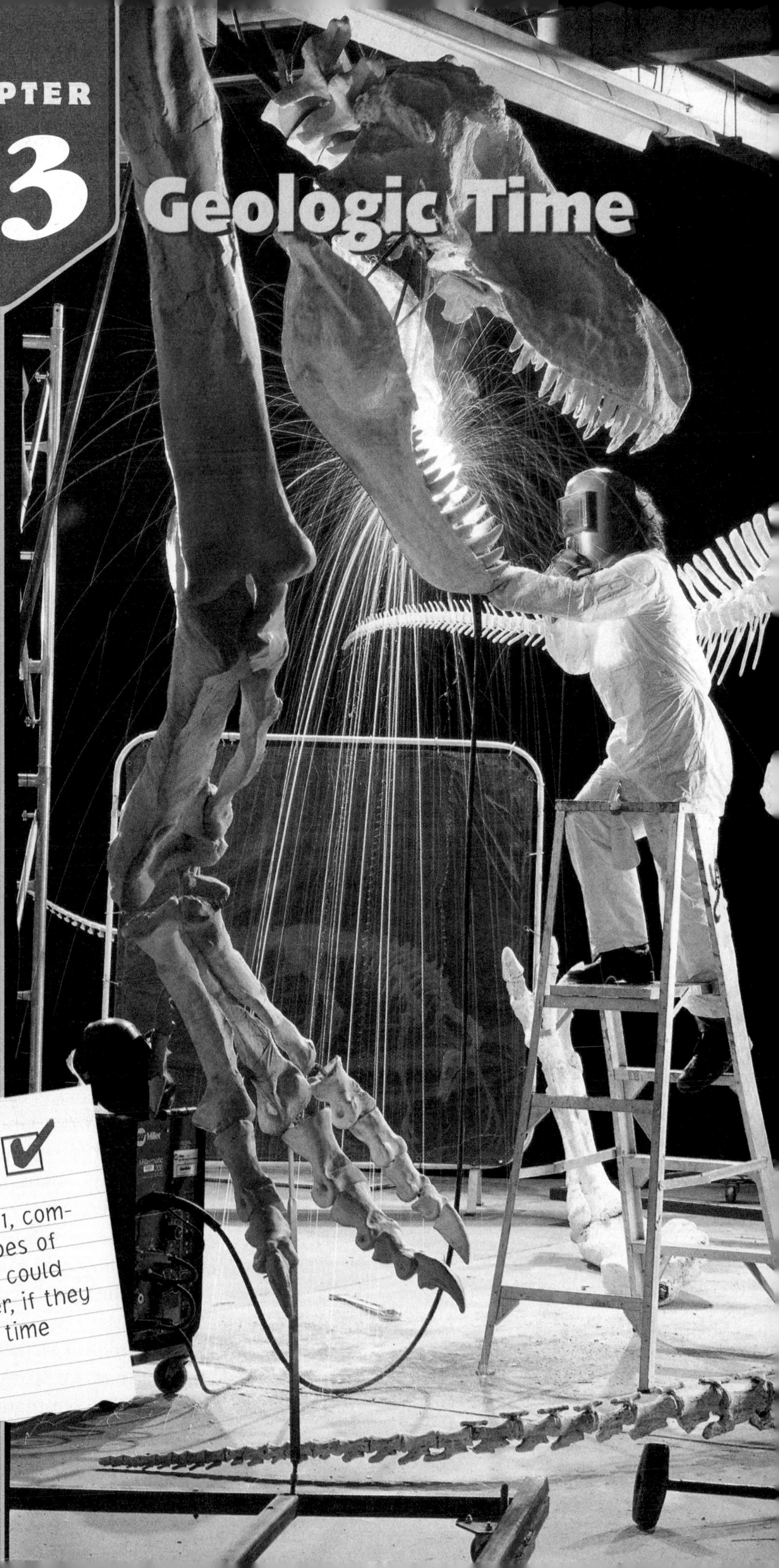

Chapter Preview

Skills Preview

Skill Builders
- Make and Use a Table

Activities
- Make a Model

MiniLabs
- Measure in SI

Reading Check ✓

After reading Section 1, compare the different types of trilobites shown. How could you put them in order, if they were not labeled by time period?

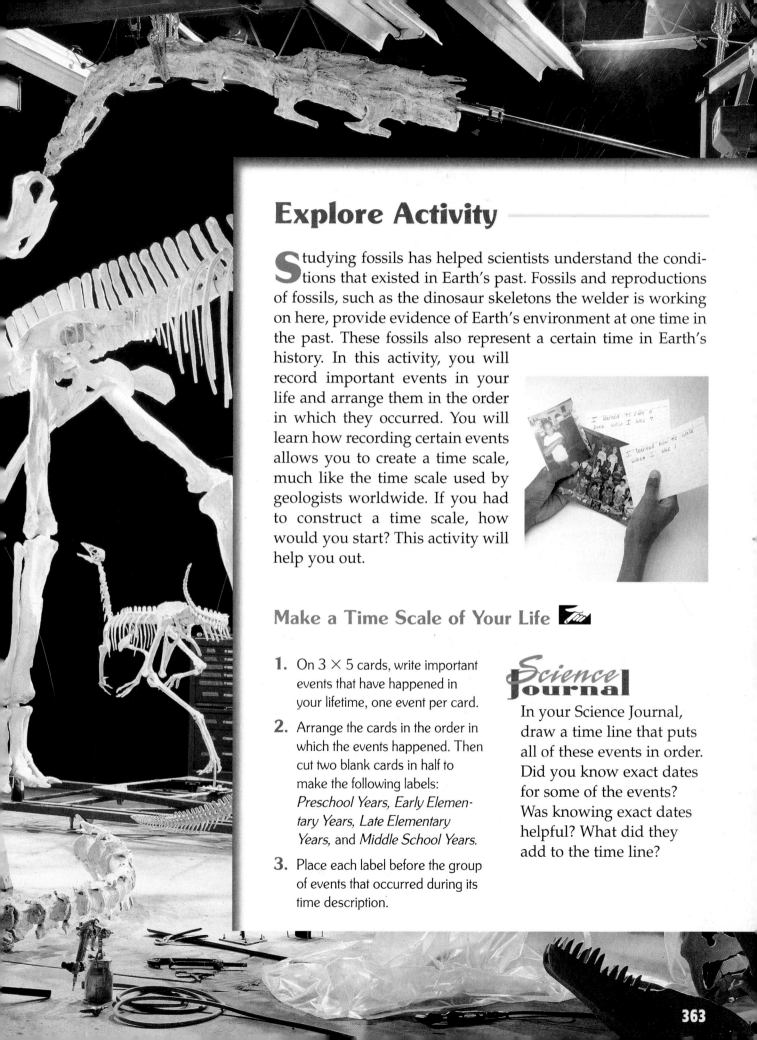

Explore Activity

Studying fossils has helped scientists understand the conditions that existed in Earth's past. Fossils and reproductions of fossils, such as the dinosaur skeletons the welder is working on here, provide evidence of Earth's environment at one time in the past. These fossils also represent a certain time in Earth's history. In this activity, you will record important events in your life and arrange them in the order in which they occurred. You will learn how recording certain events allows you to create a time scale, much like the time scale used by geologists worldwide. If you had to construct a time scale, how would you start? This activity will help you out.

Make a Time Scale of Your Life

1. On 3 × 5 cards, write important events that have happened in your lifetime, one event per card.

2. Arrange the cards in the order in which the events happened. Then cut two blank cards in half to make the following labels: *Preschool Years, Early Elementary Years, Late Elementary Years,* and *Middle School Years.*

3. Place each label before the group of events that occurred during its time description.

Science Journal

In your Science Journal, draw a time line that puts all of these events in order. Did you know exact dates for some of the events? Was knowing exact dates helpful? What did they add to the time line?

13·1 Life and Geologic Time

What You'll Learn

► How geologic time is divided into units
► How trilobites from different periods of the Paleozoic era may have evolved through geologic time
► How plate tectonics affects changes in species

Vocabulary
geologic time scale
era
period
epoch
trilobite

Why It's Important

► Because organisms change through time, scientists can describe Earth history using the Geologic Time Scale.

Figure 13-1 The physical appearance of many types of organisms, such as the trilobites shown here, has changed throughout geologic time.

Geologic Time

A group of students went digging for fossils with their teacher. They knew that paleontologists study geologic history by collecting and studying fossils of organisms that lived long ago. The students were hoping to find some fossils from the Paleozoic era and, in particular, trilobites (TRI luh bites). They were told that they would be looking in rocks that are about 510 million years old.

Some examples of what they found are shown in **Figure 13-1.** The fossils are small and appear to have segments over much of their bodies. Some of them seem to be curled into a ball. What are they? Are these the trilobites their teacher told them about? Finding out about Earth's history will help you determine if these fossils are trilobites.

The Geologic Time Scale

The appearance and disappearance of types of organisms throughout Earth's history give scientists data to mark important changes or geologic occurrences in time. We can divide Earth's history into smaller units based on the types of lifeforms living during certain periods. The division of Earth's history into smaller units makes up the **geologic time scale.** All the divisions in the geologic time scale are based on changes in fossil organisms. Changes in the fossils can be caused by geologic events such as changes in sea level or mountain building.

A *Modocia typicales* is from Cambrian rocks in Utah.

B *Isotelus maximus* is from Ordovician rocks in Ohio.

The geologic time scale is a record of Earth's history, starting with Earth's formation about 4.6 billion years ago. Each period of time is named. When the ages of fossils and rock layers are determined, scientists can assign them to a specific place on the geologic time scale.

Subdivisions of Geologic Time

Geologic time is divided into three subdivisions: eras, periods, and epochs. **Eras** are major subdivisions of the geologic time scale based on differences in life-forms. There are three named eras—the Paleozoic, which means ancient life, the Mesozoic, or middle life, and the Cenozoic, or recent life. As you can see in **Figure 13-2** on the next page, the Mesozoic era began about 245 million years ago. Its end is marked by the extinction of the dinosaurs and many other organisms about 66 million years ago. When did trilobites first appear? Were the students looking in rocks of the correct age to find trilobites?

Eras are subdivided into **periods.** Periods are based on the types of life that existed at the time. Periods are divided into smaller units of time called **epochs.** Generally, only the Cenozoic era is shown subdivided further into epochs as seen in **Figure 13-2.** The epochs of the other periods are usually called early, middle, and late. Why is this so? The fossil record is more complete in these recent rock layers. As a result, geologists have more data with which to divide the time scale.

Visit the Glencoe Science Web Site at **www.glencoe.com/ sec/science** to find out more about fossils.

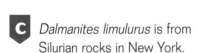
Dalmanites limulurus is from Silurian rocks in New York.

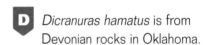
Dicranuras hamatus is from Devonian rocks in Oklahoma.

Figure 13-2 The geologic time scale is divided into subunits based on the appearance and disappearance of types of organisms. The numbers listed show the beginning of each subunit. **Beginning at the bottom, which events do you think were most important in Earth history?**

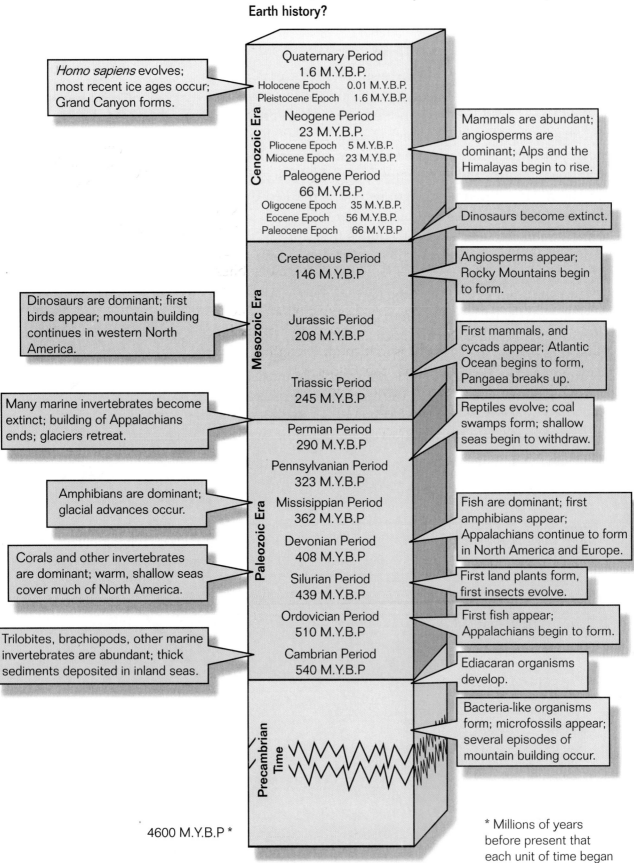

Homo sapiens evolves; most recent ice ages occur; Grand Canyon forms.

Mammals are abundant; angiosperms are dominant; Alps and the Himalayas begin to rise.

Dinosaurs become extinct.

Angiosperms appear; Rocky Mountains begin to form.

Dinosaurs are dominant; first birds appear; mountain building continues in western North America.

First mammals, and cycads appear; Atlantic Ocean begins to form, Pangaea breaks up.

Many marine invertebrates become extinct; building of Appalachians ends; glaciers retreat.

Reptiles evolve; coal swamps form; shallow seas begin to withdraw.

Amphibians are dominant; glacial advances occur.

Fish are dominant; first amphibians appear; Appalachians continue to form in North America and Europe.

Corals and other invertebrates are dominant; warm, shallow seas cover much of North America.

First land plants form, first insects evolve.

First fish appear; Appalachians begin to form.

Trilobites, brachiopods, other marine invertebrates are abundant; thick sediments deposited in inland seas.

Ediacaran organisms develop.

Bacteria-like organisms form; microfossils appear; several episodes of mountain building occur.

Cenozoic Era

Quaternary Period
1.6 M.Y.B.P.
Holocene Epoch   0.01 M.Y.B.P.
Pleistocene Epoch   1.6 M.Y.B.P.

Neogene Period
23 M.Y.B.P.
Pliocene Epoch   5 M.Y.B.P.
Miocene Epoch   23 M.Y.B.P.

Paleogene Period
66 M.Y.B.P.
Oligocene Epoch   35 M.Y.B.P.
Eocene Epoch   56 M.Y.B.P.
Paleocene Epoch   66 M.Y.B.P

Mesozoic Era

Cretaceous Period
146 M.Y.B.P

Jurassic Period
208 M.Y.B.P

Triassic Period
245 M.Y.B.P

Paleozoic Era

Permian Period
290 M.Y.B.P

Pennsylvanian Period
323 M.Y.B.P

Missisippian Period
362 M.Y.B.P

Devonian Period
408 M.Y.B.P

Silurian Period
439 M.Y.B.P

Ordovician Period
510 M.Y.B.P

Cambrian Period
540 M.Y.B.P

Precambrian Time

4600 M.Y.B.P *

* Millions of years before present that each unit of time began

Geologic Time and Fossils

Geologists study fossils to help describe Earth's past environments, to interpret how extinct organisms lived, and to document changes in organisms through time. A brief study of trilobites illustrates how this is done.

When people look for fossils, they like to find trilobites. **Trilobites** (TRI luh bites) were organisms that lived hundreds of millions of years ago. They crawled on the seafloor and occasionally swam through the water. They ranged in size from 6 mm to 75 cm in length, with most between 2 cm and 7 cm in length and between 1 cm and 3 cm in width.

Trilobites first appeared during the Cambrian period and existed on Earth throughout the Paleozoic era. They became extinct at the end of the Permian period. Numerous species of trilobites lived on Earth for more than 300 million years. Although trilobites existed throughout Paleozoic time, they did not all look the same. The characteristics of trilobites changed with time.

The name *trilobite* is derived from an interesting fact about the structure of its exoskeleton. The exoskeleton of each trilobite is divided into three lobes that run the length of the body. Just as with insects, the trilobite's body was divided into three sections: the head (cephalon), the body (thorax), and the tail (pygidium). These are shown in **Figure 13-3.** ☑

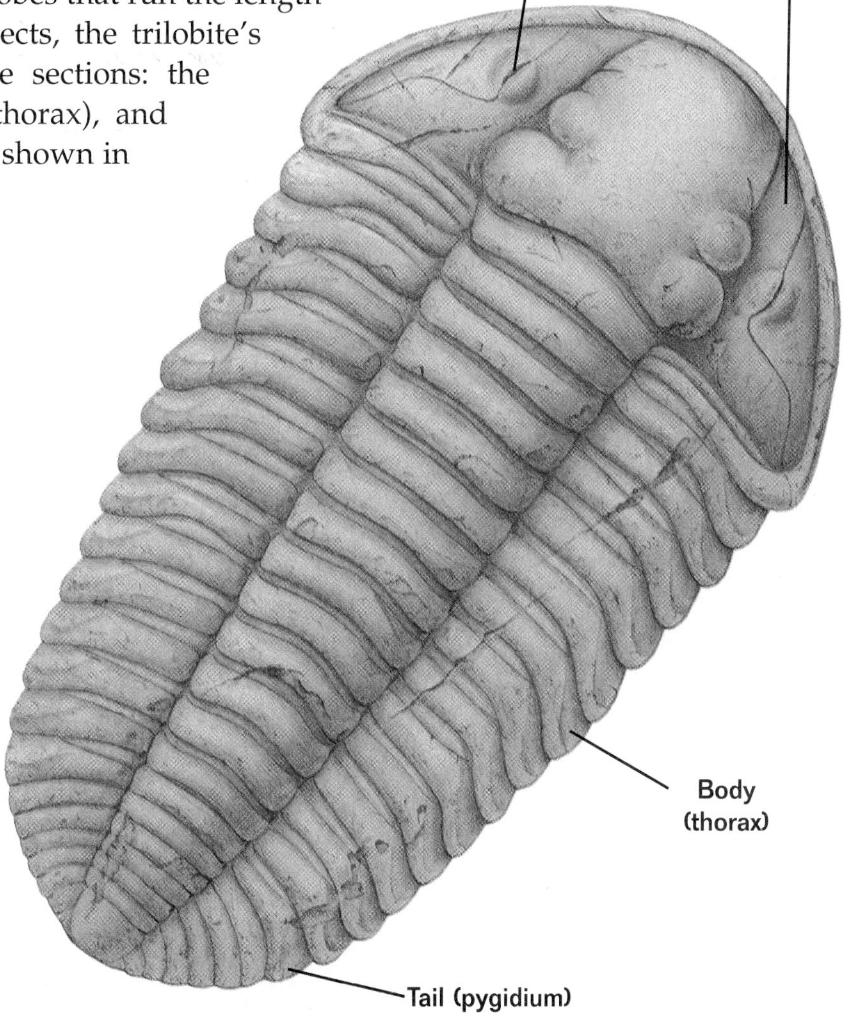

Reading Check ☑

From what characteristic did trilobites get their name?

Eye Head (cephalon) Body (thorax) Tail (pygidium)

Figure 13-3 This illustration shows the parts of a typical trilobite.

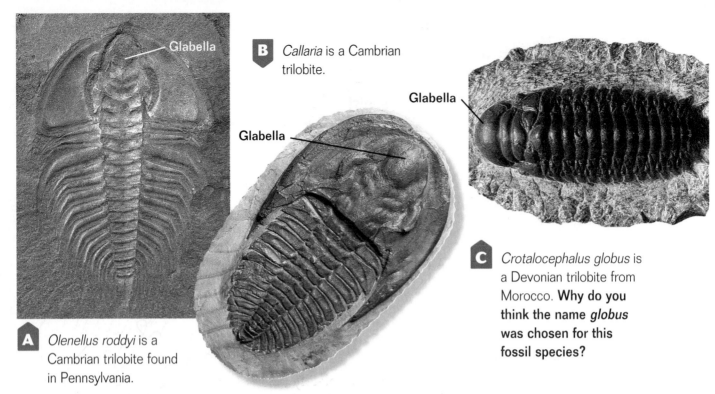

B *Callaria* is a Cambrian trilobite.

Glabella

Glabella

C *Crotalocephalus globus* is a Devonian trilobite from Morocco. **Why do you think the name *globus* was chosen for this fossil species?**

Glabella

A *Olenellus roddyi* is a Cambrian trilobite found in Pennsylvania.

Figure 13-4 The *glabella* is a part of the trilobite's head. **Describe how the glabella changed through time.**

LIFE SCIENCE
INTEGRATION ►

Using Math

Make a circle graph comparing the periods of the Paleozoic era. Sections of the circle graph should represent the lengths of the various periods of the Paleozoic era. Based on the circle graph, which period is the longest? Which period is the shortest?

Changing Characteristics of Trilobites

Trilobites were common during the Cambrian period. Some species of trilobites became extinct at the close of the Cambrian period, others at the close of the Devonian period. Some species, however, survived until the end of the Permian period. Species of trilobites that lived during one period of the Paleozoic era show characteristics different from species of other periods. The different characteristics are used to show a gradual change of trilobites through geologic time as shown in **Figures 13-1** and **13-4.** Additionally, trilobites lived over large areas of the world during the Paleozoic era. They are considered an index fossil of the Paleozoic era. Index fossils are fossils that pinpoint a particular time in geologic history. In order to be an index fossil, the organism must have been geographically widespread, have lived for a relatively short period of time, and have distinct characteristics that help it stand out from other fossils. Because of physical changes through time, many species can be used as index fossils for specific geologic periods, such as the Cambrian period.

Trilobite Eyes

Trilobites may have been the first organisms with true eyes and the capability to look out on their world. The position of the eyes on a trilobite fossil tells much about where the organism lived. If the eyes are located toward the front of the head, the organism was probably an active swimmer. If the eyes are located toward the back of the head, the organism might have been an ocean bottom dweller. In most species,

Figure 13-5 Changes in trilobite eyes allowed species to adapt to their environment. (A) *Modocia typicalis* had long, crescent-shaped eyes; (B) *Calymene granulosa's* eyes were reduced in size; (C) *Peronopsis interstrictus* had no eyes and was blind; (D) The eyes of *Phacops rana* were compound like many modern-day insects.

the eyes were located midway on the head—ideal for an organism that both crawled on the seafloor and swam in the water.

Trilobite eyes changed in one of two ways. In many trilobite species, the eyes became progressively smaller until they completely disappeared, as shown in **Figure 13-5.** The blind trilobites might have burrowed into the sediments on the seafloor or lived deeper than light could penetrate. In other species, the eyes became more complex. One genus, *Aeglina*, developed large compound eyes composed of numerous individual lenses. Some eyes developed stalks that held the eyes upward. Where do you think this would be useful?

The trilobite body and tail also underwent major changes in form through time as shown in **Figure 13-6.** Of special note is *Olenellus*, as shown in **Figure 13-7A.** This genus of trilobite from the Lower Cambrian period has pronounced spines. Although the exact use of the spines is not understood, the appearance of them is limited to earlier species. No spines are found in fossils between the Mississippian to the Permian periods. These differences also help identify different species and can be used to infer how and where they lived.

Figure 13-6 The physical features of trilobites changed throughout the Paleozoic era. **Which environments do you think each of these trilobites was adapted for?**

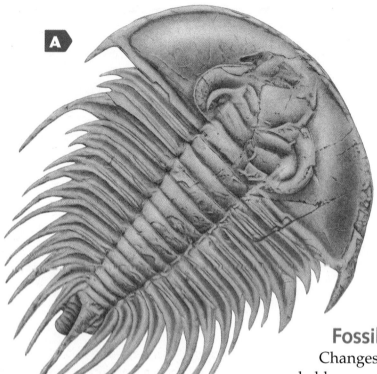

Figure 13-7 (A) This illustration shows an Olenellus trilobite. Trilobite spines can help determine a fossil's age. (B) *Kettneraspis williamsmi* is a spiny trilobite from the Devonian of Oklahoma.

Fossils Show Changes

Changes in the exoskeleton of trilobites probably occurred at least in part because they were adapting to changing environments, geographic isolation, how they lived, and the competition for survival. You have learned how paleontologists use the physical features of individual fossil species to interpret their life modes and environments. As you read through the rest of this chapter, you will see how studies such as the trilobite example helped enable geologists to interpret Earth history and create the geologic time scale.

The Effect of Plate Tectonics

Plate tectonics is one process that causes changing environments on Earth. As plates on Earth's surface moved over time, continents collided with and separated from each other many times. Continental collisions caused mountain building and the draining of seas. Continental separations caused deeper seas to develop between continents. This rearranging of land and sea still causes changes in climates today.

If species adapt to the changes, or evolve, they survive. If a species doesn't have individuals with characteristics needed to survive in the changing environment, the species becomes extinct. Trilobites lived in the oceans. As the supercontinent Pangaea came together at the end of the Paleozoic era, much of the ocean environment where trilobites lived was either changed or destroyed. What effect might these changes have had on the trilobite population? **Figure 13-8** illustrates the effect plate tectonics had on another ocean organism, coral.

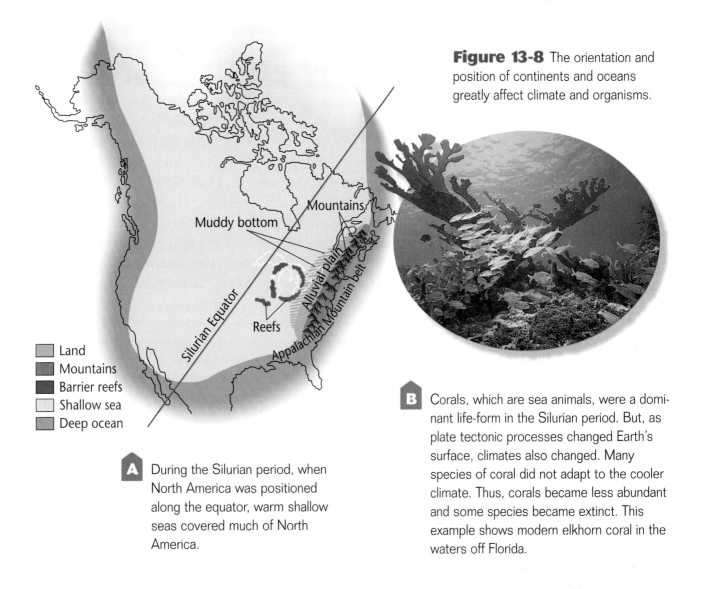

Figure 13-8 The orientation and position of continents and oceans greatly affect climate and organisms.

Land
Mountains
Barrier reefs
Shallow sea
Deep ocean

A During the Silurian period, when North America was positioned along the equator, warm shallow seas covered much of North America.

B Corals, which are sea animals, were a dominant life-form in the Silurian period. But, as plate tectonic processes changed Earth's surface, climates also changed. Many species of coral did not adapt to the cooler climate. Thus, corals became less abundant and some species became extinct. This example shows modern elkhorn coral in the waters off Florida.

Section Assessment

1. What are the major subdivisions of the geologic time scale based on?

2. Compare and contrast trilobite eyes and the type of environment they might have been adapted to.

3. How might plate tectonics affect all life on Earth?

4. **Think Critically:** How might movement of the continents have affected trilobite survival?

5. 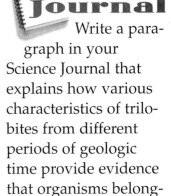 **Skill Activity**
   Interpreting Data Do the **Chapter 13 Skill Activity** on page 754 to interpret data about the age relationships between different dinosaurs.

Science Journal
Write a paragraph in your Science Journal that explains how various characteristics of trilobites from different periods of geologic time provide evidence that organisms belonging to the same genus or family change physically through time.

Precambrian Time

Look again at the geologic time scale in **Figure 13-2.** **Precambrian** (pree KAM bree un) **time** represents the longest geologic time unit of Earth's history. This time lasted from 4.6 billion to about 540 million years ago. Although the Precambrian was the longest unit of geologic time, relatively little is known about Earth and the organisms that lived during this time. Why is the fossil record from Precambrian time so sparse?

Precambrian rocks have been buried deeply and changed by heat and pressure. They also have been eroded more than younger rocks. These changes affect not only the rocks, but the fossil record, as well. Most fossils can't withstand the metamorphic and erosional processes that most Precambrian rocks have undergone.

Figure 13-9 In some conditions, cyanobacteria produce mound-shaped layers of calcium carbonate called stromatolites. Stromatolites were common about 2.8 billion years ago and are still being formed today. **What does this imply about the life-form cyanobacteria?**

A Stromatolites have changed little throughout geologic time. These modern ones in Australia look much like ancient stromatolites.

Early Life

It wasn't until fossilized cyanobacteria forming layered mats, called stromatolites, were found that scientists could begin to unravel Earth's complex history. Stromatolites are shown in **Figure 13-9.** Cyanobacteria first appeared on Earth about 3.5 billion years ago. **Cyanobacteria** are thought to be one of the earliest forms of life on Earth. They contain chlorophyll and as they photosynthesize, they give off oxygen. As these organisms evolved, they contributed to changes in Earth's atmosphere. During the few billion years following the appearance of cyanobacteria, oxygen became a major gas in Earth's atmosphere. The ozone layer in the stratosphere also began to develop, shielding Earth from ultraviolet rays. These major changes in the air allowed species of single-celled organisms to evolve into more complex organisms.

Animals without backbones, called invertebrates, developed near the end of Precambrian time. Imprints of jellyfish and marine worms have been found in late Precambrian rocks. However, because these early invertebrates were soft-bodied, they weren't easily preserved as fossils. This is another reason the Precambrian fossil record is so sparse.

CHEMISTRY
INTEGRATION

Bacteria and Air
Cyanobacteria are thought to have been one of the mechanisms by which Earth's early atmosphere became richer in oxygen. Research the composition of Earth's early atmosphere. Describe where these gases originated.

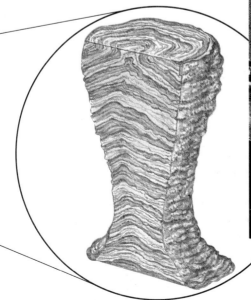

B A cross section of an individual stromatolite head shows the dark layers of bacteria that formed this fossil. The lighter brown layers are sediment trapped by the sticky bacteria layers.

Figure 13-10 These fossils are some of the first soft-bodied organisms preserved. They were first found in the Ediacara Hills in Australia.

A Some Ediacaran life-forms were attached to the ocean bottom, while others were able to freely move.

B *Dickinsonia* was a worm-like organism.

Unusual Life-Forms

Also developing at this time was a group of soft-bodied animals, first found in the Ediacara Hills of southern Australia. This group of organisms has become known as the *Ediacaran fauna*. Examples of these organisms are shown in **Figure 13-10.** Some paleontologists hypothesize that these organisms are the soft-bodied ancestors of many of the life-forms that developed during the Cambrian period. Other paleontologists hypothesize that these organisms were a completely different, now-extinct life-form. Some consider that the Ediacaran fossils are of organisms that were neither animal nor plant.

The Paleozoic Era

Fossils are more likely to form if organisms have hard parts. The beginning of the **Paleozoic** (pay lee uh ZOH ihk) **era** is marked by the presence of the first organisms with hard parts. Organisms were then more easily preserved.

The Paleozoic era, or era of ancient life, began about 544 million years ago. Warm, shallow seas covered much of Earth's surface during early Paleozoic time. Because of this, most of the life-forms were marine, meaning they lived in the ocean. Trilobites were common. Brachiopods (BRAH kee uh pahdz) and crinoids (KRI noyds), which still exist today, were also common. Although these animals may not be familiar to you, one type of animal you are familiar with—fish—evolved during this era, as well.

The Paleozoic era is broken into seven periods. The Cambrian period marks the appearance of marine animals with hard parts or skeletons. The most conspicuous and well known of these are trilobites. The start of the Ordovician period is marked by the beginning of the Appalachian Mountain–building process. This was probably caused by the collision of the Eurasian or African continental plate with the North American plate.

The first vertebrates, animals with backbones, developed during the Ordovician period. Plant life evolved on land during the Silurian period. Fish became dominant in the Devonian period, as seen in **Figure 13-11.** By this time, animals began to move onto land with the plants.

Try at Home
Mini Lab

Interpreting Rock Layers

Procedure

1. Draw a sequence of three sedimentary rock layers.
2. Number the rock layers 1 through 3, bottom to top.
3. Identify the fossils in each layer as follows: Layer 1, contains fossils B and A; layer 2 contains fossils A, B, and C; layer 3 contains only fossil C.
4. Assign each of the fossils to one or more geologic periods. For example, fossil A lived from the Cambrian through the Devonian periods. Fossil C lived from the Devonian through the Permian periods, and so on.
5. Analyze the fossils' occurrence in each layer to help you determine the ages of each rock layer.

Analysis

1. Which layer or layers were you able to date to a specific period?
2. Why isn't it possible to determine during which specific period the other layers formed?
3. What is the age or possible age of each layer?

Figure 13-11 The giant fish, *Dunkleosteus,* which grew to more than 9 m long, lived during the Devonian period. This fossilized skull was found in Ohio. **What can you infer about the environment in Ohio during the Devonian?**

Life on Land

One type of aquatic animal evolved a lung that enabled it to survive on land. This animal used its fins to move across the ground. Other aquatic animals evolved into amphibians. **Amphibians** live on land and breathe air, but they must return to water to reproduce. Their eggs must be kept moist in water. They first appeared during the Devonian period and became the dominant form of vertebrate life on land by the Mississippian period.

Over time, amphibians evolved an egg with a strong outer shell that protected it from drying out. The egg also contained a nutritious yolk for the embryo. Because of this, they no longer needed to return to water to reproduce. By the Pennsylvanian period, reptiles had evolved, probably from the same ancestor as amphibians. **Reptiles** do not need to return to water to reproduce, as shown in **Figure 13-12.** Reptiles have skin with hard scales that prevent loss of body fluids. This adaptation enables them to survive farther from water. They can survive in relatively dry climates, whereas amphibians with their thin, moist skins, cannot. ☑

Reading Check ☑

What developed that allowed amphibians to reproduce away from water?

Problem Solving

Skull Structures

Scientists study the structure of bones and other pre-served fossil parts in an attempt to determine which organisms are related. Bones, or the way bones are connected at joints, in related organisms show similar structures or connections. For example, if the skull from a modern organism shows similar eye openings and a similar structure of the nasal passages to the fossil skull of an animal from Earth's past, the two organisms may be related. Some scientists might even hypothesize that the modern animal evolved from the earlier animal.

The photographs show the shape and structure of four different organisms. One of the skulls is a fossil of an ancient, now-extinct life-form. The other three skulls are from modern-day organisms: an iguana, a bird, and a muskrat. Compare and contrast the shape and structure of the four skulls.

Think Critically: Which of the modern skulls looks most like the fossil skull? Hypothesize about which of the modern animals evolved from the ancient life-form.

Sinosauropteryx   **Bird**

Muskrat   **Iguana**

Figure 13-12 Unlike frogs, salamanders, and other amphibians, reptiles such as these snakes can lay their eggs on land. This allows them to survive in relatively dry environments. **What characteristic of reptile eggs prevents the developing embryos from drying out?**

Many of the coal deposits mined today began forming during the Pennsylvanian period. Inland seas were cut off from the oceans. These freshwater seas covered much of the land. Swamps similar to those found in the Florida Everglades formed. When the swamp vegetation died, it was deposited in layers and quickly buried. This material later changed to today's coal beds. **Figure 13-13** shows what a forest might have looked like in the Pennsylvanian period.

Figure 13-13 The plants that make up the coal layers in the United States once lived in swampy areas.

A This illustration reconstructs what a Pennsylvanian-period forest might have looked like 300 million years ago.

B The plants end up as layers, or seams, of coal, as seen in this strip mine in southeastern Montana.

End of an Era

Mass extinctions of many land and sea animals have occurred. One mass extinction occurred at the end of the Paleozoic era. The cause of mass extinctions may have been changes in the environment following movement of continents through plate tectonics. Near the end of the Permian period, all continental plates came together to form the single landmass Pangaea, and major glaciers formed.

The slow, gradual collision of continental plates caused mountain building. Mountain-building processes caused seas to drain away, and interior deserts spread over parts of the United States and Europe. Climates changed from mild and warm to cold and dry. Many species, especially marine organisms, weren't able to adapt to these and other changes and became extinct.

interNET
CONNECTION

Visit the Glencoe Science Web Site at **www.glencoe.com/ sec/science** for more information on mass extinctions.

Section Assessment

1. What geologic events occurred at the end of the Paleozoic era?

2. How might geologic events at the end of the Paleozoic era have caused the mass extinctions that occurred?

3. Why is the Precambrian fossil record so sparse?

4. What major change occurred in the atmosphere during the Precambrian?

5. **Think Critically:** What adaptations were needed for life to move onto the land?

6. **Skill Builder**
   Recognizing Cause and Effect
   Describe the cause-and-effect relationship between amphibians, reptiles, and the eggs they use in reproduction. If you need help, refer to Recognizing Cause and Effect in the **Skill Handbook** on page 721.

Using Computers

Using a Database
Research trilobites, brachiopods, and crinoids in a computer database of historical geology. Write a paragraph in your Science Journal describing each of these organisms and its habitat. Include hand-drawn illustrations, and compare them with the illustrations in the computer database of historical geology. If you need help, refer to page 733.

Changing Species

Materials
• Deck of playing cards

In this activity, you will observe how adaptation within a species might cause the evolution of a particular trait, leading to the development of a new species.

What You'll Investigate

How might adaptation within a species cause the evolution of a particular trait?

Goals

• **Model** adaptation within a species.

Procedure

1. **Remove** all of the kings, queens, jacks, and aces from a deck of playing cards.

2. Each remaining card represents an individual in a population of animals called "varimals." The number on each card represents the height of the individual. For example, the 5 of diamonds is a varimal that's 5 units tall.

3. **Calculate** the average height of the population of varimals represented by your cards.

4. Suppose varimals eat grass, shrubs, and leaves from trees. A drought causes many of these plants to die. All that's left are a few tall trees. Only varimals at least 6 units tall can reach the leaves on these trees.

5. All the varimals under 6 units leave the area to seek food elsewhere or die from starvation. **Discard** all of the cards with a number value less than 6.

Calculate the new average height of the population of varimals.

6. Shuffle the deck of remaining cards.

7. **Draw** two cards at a time. Each pair represents a pair of varimals that will mate and produce offspring.

8. The offspring of each pair reaches a height equal to the average height of his or her parents. **Calculate** and **record** the height of each offspring.

9. Repeat by discarding all parents and offspring under 8 units tall. Now **calculate** the new average height of varimals. Include both the parents and offspring in your calculation.

Conclude and Apply

1. How did the average height of the population change over time?

2. If you hadn't discarded the shortest varimals, would the average height of the population have changed as much? **Explain.**

3. What trait was selected for?

4. Why didn't every member of the original population reproduce?

5. If there had been no varimals over 6 units tall in step 5, what would have happened to the population?

6. If there had been no variation in height in the population before the droughts occurred, would the species have been able to evolve into a taller species? **Explain.**

7. How does this activity **demonstrate** that traits evolve in species?

Fast Track to Extinction

Human Impact

Extinctions—the loss of all members of a species—have occurred throughout Earth's history. In past millennia, extinctions were due to changes in the environment or competition for resources. Some extinctions may have been caused by early humans. Today, humans are causing extinctions at a much higher rate. See the chart below.

When members of a species die out faster than they reproduce, so that only few of its members are living, a species is considered endangered. If the population continues to decline, the species will become extinct.

Humans contribute to extinction directly by overhunting and overcollecting and indirectly by changing a species' habitat—where the species lives. If that habitat is altered or destroyed and the species cannot adapt, that species will die.

Time	Rates of Extinction
70 000 000 years ago (disappearance of the dinosaurs)	1 species/1000 years
1 A.D. to 1650	1 species (mammal or bird)/82 years
1650 to 1850	1 species (mammal or bird)/5 years
1850 to 1900	1 species (mammal or bird)/9.5 months
1900 to 1950	1 species (mammal or bird)/8 months
1992	All plant & animal life, 1 to 6 species/day
2000	All plant & animal life, 1 species/hour

Rain Forests

In the past decade, people cleared tropical rain forests for farming, logging, and other industries at an unprecedented rate. At right, a charred tree still burns as a farmer clears more land. Destroying rain forest eliminates habitats for many plants and animals. It is estimated that the destruction of all rain forests could result in a 90 percent loss of Earth's biodiversity, the variety of species on Earth.

Development with Habitat Protection

To slow or prevent loss of habitat, governments can restrict construction to allow both development and preservation. Development can include plans for preserving habitats or disturbing them as little as possible. Ecotourism (tourism that minimizes ecological impact), replanting efforts, and cultivating renewable crops are all ways to protect the world's rain forests.

interNET CONNECTION

Many organizations are working to slow the rate of extinction of animals and plants. Visit the Glencoe Science Web Site at **www.glencoe.com/sec/ science** to learn more about the preservation of wildlife. What is being done to help endangered species? Do you think this type of effort is effective? Why or why not?

Middle and Recent Earth History

The Mesozoic Era

Some of the most fascinating life-forms ever to live on Earth evolved during the Mesozoic era. One group of organisms you're probably familiar with—the dinosaurs—appeared during this geologic era.

The Breakup of Pangaea

The **Mesozoic** (mez uh ZOH ihk) **era,** or era of middle life, began about 245 million years ago. At the beginning of the Mesozoic era, all continents were joined as a single land-mass. This landmass was called Pangaea, as shown in **Figure 13-14.** Pangaea separated into two large landmasses during the Triassic period. The northern mass was *Laurasia,* and *Gondwana* was in the south. As the Mesozoic era continued, *Laurasia* and *Gondwana* broke up and formed the present-day continents.

Species that survived the mass extinctions of the Paleozoic era adapted to new environments. Recall that the hard scales of a reptile's skin help to retain body fluids. This trait, along with the hard shell of their eggs, enabled them to adapt to the drier climate of the Mesozoic era. They became the dominant animal life-form in the Jurassic period. Some of the reptiles evolved into archosaurs, suggested as being the common ancestor of crocodiles, dinosaurs, and birds.

What You'll Learn

► How dominant life-forms in the Mesozoic and Cenozoic eras compare and contrast
► How changes caused by plate tectonics affected the evolution of life during the Mesozoic era
► When humans probably first appeared on Earth

Vocabulary
Mesozoic era
gastrolith
Cenozoic era

Why It's Important

► As Earth's environments, plants, and animals changed through time, Earth became suitable for human life.

300 million years ago

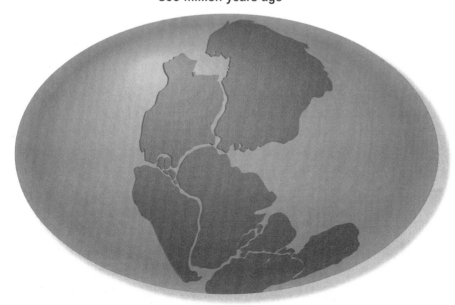

Figure 13-14 The supercontinent Pangaea formed at the end of the Paleozoic era. It began to break up at the end of the Triassic period. **Based on the position of the equator, describe the climate as tropical, temperate, or cold on each major landmass.**

Figure 13-15 Fossil evidence suggests that some dinosaurs, such as *Maiasaura*, may have nurtured their young. Fossil nests contain newly hatched and juvenile young. **What type of evidence might support this idea?**

Dinosaurs

What were dinosaurs like? Dinosaurs ranged in height from less than 1 m to enormous creatures such as *Apatosaurus*, which grew to 30 m in length, and *Tyrannosaurus*, which grew to 6 m in height. Some dinosaurs ate meat, whereas others ate only plants.

The first dinosaurs were small, and they appeared during the Triassic period. Larger species appeared during the Jurassic and Cretaceous periods. Throughout the Mesozoic era, new species of dinosaurs evolved as other species became extinct.

Good Mother Dinosaurs

The fossil record indicates that some dinosaurs nurtured their young and traveled in herds in which the adults surrounded their young. One such dinosaur is *Maiasaura*, shown in **Figure 13-15.** This dinosaur built nests in which it laid its eggs and raised its offspring. Nests have been found in clusters, indicating that more than one family of dinosaurs built in the same area. Some fossils of hatchlings have been found close to the adult animal. This has led some scientists to hypothesize that some dinosaurs nurtured their young. In fact, *Maiasaura* hatchlings may have stayed in the nest while they grew in length from about 35 cm to more than 1 m.

Reptile or Mammal?

Dinosaurs were reptiles. Recent studies indicate that dinosaurs may not have been cold blooded, as are present-day reptiles. Tracks left in the mud by individual reptiles are usually close together. Tracks close together indicate that an animal moves slowly. Some dinosaur tracks that have been found indicate that they were much faster than most reptiles. This faster speed would be expected of warm-blooded animals, which need speed to be successful in hunting. *Gallimimus* was 4 m long and from its tracks, it is known that it could reach speeds of 80 km/h—as fast as a modern racehorse.

Other evidence that leads scientists to hypothesize that dinosaurs may have been warmblooded has to do with their bone structure. Cross sections of the bones of cold-blooded animals exhibit rings similar to growth rings in trees. The bones of some dinosaurs don't show this ring structure. Instead, they are similar to bones found in birds and mammals. These observations indicate that dinosaurs may have been warm-blooded, fast-moving, nurturing animals somewhat like present-day mammals and birds. They may have been quite different from present-day reptiles.

Birds

Many scientists hypothesize that birds evolved from dinosaurs. Some scientists have even suggested that birds may have evolved from the advanced theropod called *Troodon*, shown in **Figure 13-16.** Theropods form a group of meat-eating dinosaurs that walked mainly on their hind legs.

Figure 13-16 A highly evolved dinosaur called *Troodon* had a birdlike stance, much like a modern ostrich.

Figure 13-17 Fossils of *Archaeopteryx* that are about 150 million years old show both birdlike features and dinosaurlike features. **What birdlike and dinosaurlike features can you recognize?**

A A reconstruction of what *Caudipteryx* may have looked like.

B Considered the world's most priceless fossil, *Archaeopteryx* was found in a limestone quarry in Germany in 1861.

C This *Caudipteryx* fossil shows tail feathers and gastroliths.

D This reconstruction shows what *Archaeopteryx* may have looked like.

Evidence for this is found in fossils of the first birds. They appeared during the Jurassic period of the Mesozoic era, as seen in **Figure 13-17.** The animal *Archaeopteryx* had wings and feathers like a bird but teeth and claws like a meat-eating dinosaur. *Archaeopteryx* may not have been a direct ancestor of today's birds. But, modern birds and *Archaeopteryx* probably share a common ancestor. ☑

A new discovery in China is a fossil of an earlier birdlike organism with dinosaurlike characteristics. It has been named *Caudipteryx*. Imprints of feathers were found on the fossil, shown in **Figure 13-17C.** *Caudipteryx* shows different teeth from those shown by *Archaeopteryx*. The teeth point outward toward the front of the organism. The teeth were positioned such that they could fit easily into a beak, similar to that of a bird's. Also, the shape of the organism's body was more like a theropod, a meat-eating dinosaur, than like *Archaeopteryx*.

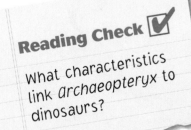

Reading Check ☑

What characteristics link *archaeopteryx* to dinosaurs?

Also found associated with the fossil were **gastroliths,** stones swallowed to help with digestion. These can be found in the gizzards of modern birds. Fossils of *Caudipteryx* demonstrate strong evidence that this animal is related to the earliest birds, yet it looks more like a small, meat-eating dinosaur from that age.

Gymnosperms

During the Cretaceous period, seas expanded inland and species of plants, animals, and other organisms continued to adapt to new environments. Gymnosperms (JIHM nuh spurmz), which first appeared in the Paleozoic era, continued to adapt to their changing environment. The seeds of gymnosperms are not produced inside a fruit, as are the seeds of flowering plants. Pines, sequoias, and firs are gymnosperms.

Angiosperms

A new type of plant, called angiosperms (AN jee uh spurmz), evolved in the early Cretaceous period. Angiosperms, or flowering plants, produce seeds inside a fruit. Common angiosperms are magnolias and willows.

Many angiosperms survived while non-seed plants did not because their seeds were enclosed and protected in a fruit, allowing them to develop in varied environments. Angiosperms are so adaptive that they remain the dominant land plant today. A flower from an angiosperm is shown in **Figure 13-18.** Present-day angiosperms that evolved during the Mesozoic era include maple and oak trees.

Figure 13-18 Angiosperms and pollinating insects evolved together to become dependent upon each other. The sweet nectar produced by many flowers attracts insects in search of food. The pollen of the flower sticks to the insect, which carries it to another flower. Some angiosperms wouldn't be able to reproduce without a particular species of insect.

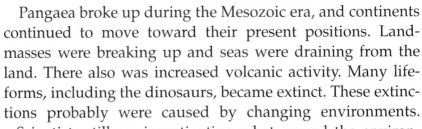
Figure 13-19 Many prehistoric North American animals became extinct during the ice ages in the Pleistocene epoch.

Pangaea broke up during the Mesozoic era, and continents continued to move toward their present positions. Landmasses were breaking up and seas were draining from the land. There also was increased volcanic activity. Many life-forms, including the dinosaurs, became extinct. These extinctions probably were caused by changing environments. Scientists still are investigating what caused the environments to change.

The Cenozoic Era

The **Cenozoic** (sen uh ZOH ihk) **era,** or era of recent life, began about 66 million years ago when dinosaurs and many other life-forms became extinct. Many of the mountain ranges throughout North and South America began to form at this time.

During the Cenozoic era, the climate became cooler and ice ages occurred. The Cenozoic era is subdivided into three periods. The present-day period is the Quaternary. We live in the Holocene epoch, which began after the last ice age. Many changes on Earth, its climate, and its life-forms, shown in **Figure 13-19,** occurred in the Cenozoic era. The two other periods (Neogene and Paleogene) were previously listed together as the Tertiary period.

Times of Mountain Building

The Alps formed when the African plate collided with the Eurasian plate. The Himalayas started to form when the Indo-Australian plate collided with the Eurasian plate.

As the number of flowering plants increased, their pollen and fruit provided food for the many insects and small, plant-eating mammals. The plant-eating mammals provided food for meat-eating mammals.

Woolly mammoth

Horses

Camels

Dire wolves

Irish elk   **Saber-toothed tiger**

Further Evolution of Mammals

Many kinds of mammals evolved into larger life-forms. The first mammals were most likely small insect eaters that developed about the same time as the dinosaurs. Not all mammals remained on land. Fossil evidence shows that ancestors of the present-day whales and dolphins once lived on land.

As Australia and South America separated from Antarctica in the continuing breakup of Pangaea, many life-forms became isolated. They evolved separately from life-forms in other parts of the world. Evidence of this can be seen today with the dominance of marsupials in Australia. Marsupials are mammals that carry their young in a pouch, as seen in **Figure 13-20.**

Our species, *Homo sapiens,* probably appeared about 500 000 years ago but became a dominant animal only about 10 000 years ago. As the climate remained cool and dry, many of the larger mammals became extinct. Some scientists hypothesize that the appearance of early humans may have led to the extinction of these mammals. Fossil records indicate that early humans were hunters. As their numbers grew, humans competed for food that other animals relied upon. They may have contributed to extinctions by overkill.

Figure 13-20 Kangaroos are marsupials that live in Australia and carry their young (a joey) in a pouch.

Section Assessment

1. In which era, period, and epoch did *Homo sapiens* first appear?

2. How did the development of hard seeds enable angiosperms to survive in a wide variety of climates?

3. What evidence indicates that dinosaurs were warm-blooded?

4. **Think Critically:** What is the connection between plate tectonics and the occurrence of marsupials?

5. **Skill Builder**
   Sequencing Arrange these organisms in sequence according to when they first appeared on Earth: *mammals, reptiles, dinosaurs, fish, ediacaran fauna, angiosperms, birds, insects, amphibians, first land plants,* and *bacteria.* If you need help, refer to Sequencing in the **Skill Handbook** on page 714.

Using Math

Make a graph comparing the periods of time that make up the Mesozoic and Cenozoic eras. Express how long dinosaurs were dominant compared with the time humans have been dominant.

Activity 13•2

Discovering the Past

I magine how the world looked millions of years ago. What animals might have been roaming around the spot where you are now sitting? You might be having trouble picturing the prehistoric world. Fortunately, the animals and plants of the past left a record of their existence—fossils. Scientists use fossils to find out what Earth looked like in the past. Fossils can help determine whether an area used to be dry land or an ocean. They also can help scientists determine what the climate in the past was like. Using the resources of the Internet and sharing data with your peers, you can start to discover how North America has changed through time.

Recognize the Problem

How has your area changed over geologic time?

Form a Hypothesis

How might the area where you are now living have looked thousands or millions of years ago? Do you think the types of animals and plants have changed much over time? **Form a hypothesis** concerning the change in organisms and geography from long ago to the present day in your area.

Goals

- **Gather and communicate** details about fossils found in your areas.

- **Synthesize** information from various sources to make conclusions about the fossil record and the changes in your area over time.

- **Form conclusions** about the fossil record and changes in your area over time based on

information from various sources.

Data Sources

Go to the Glencoe Science Web Site at **www.glencoe. com/sec/science** to find links to data on the Internet and hints on how to locate information. You also can visit a local natural history museum or library to gather information on fossils.

Test Your Hypothesis

Plan

1. **Choose** one of the following geologic time periods to research: the Pleistocene epoch, the Cretaceous period, the Pennsylvanian period, or the Ordovician period.

2. **Gather information** from the links on the Glencoe Science Web Site or the library about the fossil plants and animals found in your area during one of these geologic time periods. Find information on where and how the fossil organisms lived.

Do

1. Obtain descriptions of other fossils in your area from the sites listed on the Glencoe Science Web Site.

2. Complete a data table in your Science Journal like the one below. Add any additional information that you think is important. One example has been given.

3. Post the information on the data table for this activity on the Glencoe Science Web Site.

Analyze Your Data

1. Is there a present-day relative of your prehistoric animals or plants?

2. How have the organisms in your area changed over time? Is your hypothesis supported?

Draw Conclusions

1. **Infer** from the fossil organisms found in your area what the geography and climate were like during the geologic time period you chose.

2. Using information posted on the Glencoe Science Web Site, write a report about what North America looked like during one of the geologic time periods listed.

Fossil Data				
Fossil Name	**Location**	**Period or Epoch**	**How or Where Fossil Lived**	**Additional Information**
snail or gastropod	Kansas City, Kansas	Cretaceous period	lived in a shallow ocean, climate was tropical	had thick shell and spines to protect it from predators

For a **preview** of this chapter, study this Reviewing Main Ideas before you read the chapter. After you have studied this chapter, you can use the Reviewing Main Ideas to **review** the chapter.

The Glencoe MindJogger, Audiocassettes, and CD-ROM provide additional opportunities for review.

Section

13-1 LIFE AND GEOLOGIC TIME

Geologic time is divided into **eras, periods,** and **epochs.** Divisions within the geologic time scale are based on major evolutionary changes in organisms. The fossil record indicates that life-forms have changed over time. These changes include the physical appearance of organisms. Plate movements cause changes in Earth's climate that affect changes in organisms. *Why is the Cenozoic era the only one in which periods are separated into named epochs on the geologic time scale?*

Homo sapiens evolves; most recent ice ages; Grand Canyon forms.

Cenozoic Era

Quaternary Period
1.6 M.Y.B.P.
Holocene Epoch   0.01 M.Y.B.P.
Pleistocene Epoch   1.6 M.Y.B.P.

Neogene Period
23 M.Y.B.P.
Pliocene Epoch   5 M.Y.B.P.
Miocene Epoch   23 M.Y.B.P.

Paleogene Period
66 M.Y.B.P.
Oligocene Epoch   35 M.Y.B.P.
Eocene Epoch   56 M.Y.B.P.
Paleocene Epoch   66 M.Y.B.P

Mammals are abundant; angiosperms are dominant; Alps and the Himalayas begin to rise.

Dinosaurs become extinct.

Section

13-2 EARLY EARTH HISTORY

Cyanobacteria were an early form of life that evolved during **Precambrian time. Trilobites,** brachiopods, fish, and corals were abundant during the **Paleozoic era.** Through time, bacteria evolved into higher life-forms, which evolved into many marine invertebrates during the early Paleozoic era. Plants and animals began to move onto land once a protective ozone layer had been established. During the Paleozoic era, glaciers advanced and seas withdrew from the continents. Many marine invertebrates became extinct. *What was different between life-forms of Precambrian time and life-forms of the Cambrian period that allowed a better fossil record to be preserved?*

Reading Check ✔

After you read this Reviewing Main Ideas, choose a sentence in each section that you feel best represents the main idea of that section.

Section 13-3 MIDDLE AND RECENT EARTH HISTORY

Reptiles and gymnosperms were dominant land life-forms in the **Mesozoic era.** All continents were together as one landmass called Pangaea at the beginning of the Mesozoic era. Pangaea separated into two landmasses during the Triassic period. While animals and birds evolved during the Jurassic period, dinosaurs continued to dominate throughout the Jurassic and Cretaceous. Angiosperms evolved in the early Cretaceous. They were dominant throughout the Cretaceous and continue to be dominant today. Mammals also began to dominate the land in the Cenozoic era. Plate tectonic changes in the Mesozoic era caused climates to become drier and seas to expand. *Homo sapiens* evolved during the Pleistocene epoch. *What caused a change in Earth's climate during the Mesozoic era?*

Chapter 13 Assessment

Using Vocabulary

a. amphibian
b. Cenozoic era
c. cyanobacteria
d. epoch
e. era
f. gastrolith
g. geologic time scale

h. Mesozoic era
i. Paleozoic era
j. period
k. Precambrian time
l. reptile
m. trilobite

Each phrase below describes a science term from the list. Write the term that matches the phrase describing it.

1. record of events in Earth history
2. geologic time with poorest fossil record
3. probably evolved from the same ancestor as amphibians
4. the geologic era in which we live
5. used by dinosaurs and birds to help digest food

Checking Concepts

Choose the word or phrase that best answers the question.

6. How many millions of years ago did the era in which you live begin?
   A) 650   C) 1.6
   B) 245   D) 66

7. What is one of the most important fossils for determining age from the Paleozoic era?
   A) dinosaur   C) fish
   B) angiosperm   D) trilobite

8. Which is the longest division of geologic time?
   A) the Paleozoic era
   B) the Cenozoic era
   C) Precambrian time
   D) the Mesozoic era

9. What is the next-smaller division of geologic time after the era?
   A) period   C) epoch
   B) stage   D) eon

10. During which period was the most recent ice age?
    A) Pennsylvanian   C) Paleogene
    B) Triassic   D) Quaternary

11. What was one of the earliest forms of life on Earth?
    A) gymnosperm   C) angiosperm
    B) cyanobacterium D) dinosaur

12. Which had the same ancestors as amphibians?
    A) trilobites   C) angiosperms
    B) lungfish   D) gymnosperms

13. In which era did the dinosaurs live?
    A) Mesozoic   C) Miocene
    B) Paleozoic   D) Cenozoic

14. What has seeds without protective coverings?
    A) angiosperms   C) gymnosperms
    B) flowering plants D) magnolias

15. What evolved to become the dominant land plant during the Cenozoic era?
    A) gymnosperms   C) ginkgoes
    B) angiosperms   D) algae

Thinking Critically

16. Why couldn't plants move onto land prior to the establishment of an ozone layer?

17. Why are some trilobites classified as index fossils?

18. What is the most significant difference between Precambrian and Paleozoic life-forms?

19. How might the extinction of plant species from a tropical rain forest affect animals that live in the forest?

20. Explain why the discovery of gastroliths supports the theory that dinosaurs are ancestors of birds.

Developing Skills

If you need help, refer to the Skill Handbook.

21. Observing and Inferring: Use the outlines of the present-day continents to make a sketch of the Mesozoic supercontinent Pangaea.

22. Hypothesizing: Why did trilobites become extinct at the end of the Paleozoic era?

23. Interpreting Data: Fernando found what he thought was a piece of coral in a chunk of coal. Was he right? Explain.

24. Interpreting Scientific Illustrations: The circle graph below represents geologic time. Determine which era of geologic time is represented by each portion of the graph.

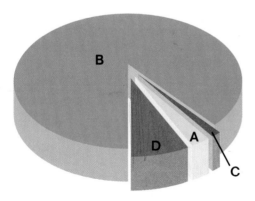

25. Interpreting Scientific Illustrations: The Cenozoic era has lasted 66 million years. What percentage of Earth's 4.6-billion-year history is that? How many degrees on the pie graph represent the Cenozoic era?

THE PRINCETON REVIEW

Test-Taking Tip

Use the Buddy System Study in a group. A small gathering of people works well because it allows you to draw from a broader base of skills and expertise. Keep it small and keep on target.

Test Practice

Use these questions to test your Science Proficiency.

1. The fossil record increased greatly around 544 million years ago. What one fact about organisms alive at that time **BEST** explains the change in the fossil record?
A) Organisms became more mobile.
B) Organisms had developed hard parts.
C) Organisms were composed mostly of soft parts.
D) Organisms moved onto land.

2. The fossil record is limited for Precambrian time. What does this tell you about the life-forms from that age?
A) Organisms from Precambrian time did not have hard parts and were not preserved well.
B) Few life-forms existed then.
C) Precambrian life-forms were too small for fossilization.
D) Precambrian time is too long for fossils to remain.

5

Foundations of Life

NATIONAL GEOGRAPHIC

What's Happening Here?

It's a morning like any other. You gulp down some orange juice, grab your notebook, and catch the bus to school. What do all these activities have in common? They all depend on plants and on the carbon-containing molecules that plants produce. Without plants and certain other organisms, life's foundations would crumble. That's because plants, like the sunflowers at left, have the ability to manufacture carbon-containing molecules using only three simple ingredients: water, energy, and the gas carbon dioxide. When you pop a handful of sunflower seeds into your mouth or eat fruits and vegetables, you are eating plant-manufactured carbon compounds essential for life. Those contained in foods like milk, cheese, and meat come to you from animals that eat plants. Some of those carbon-containing molecules provide energy to move, breathe, and think. Others are the stuff of cells and enzymes and of the spiraling molecules of DNA (inset) which contain the "blueprints" needed to make you.

interNET CONNECTION

Explore the Glencoe Science Web Site at **www.glencoe. com/sec/science** to find out more about topics found in this unit.

Chapter Preview

Skills Preview

Skill Builders
- Sequence
- Make and Use a Graph

Activities
- Form a Hypothesis

MiniLabs
- Make a Model

Reading Check ✔

Review or find out the meanings of these word parts so you will better understand this chapter: *carbo-*, *hydro-*, *iso-*, *poly-*, *-mer*, *-ane*, *-ene*.

Explore Activity

T his family is going on a picnic, and they're taking along a lot of stuff. Besides the picnic basket full of food, there are the baseball gloves, tennis rackets, towels and blankets, and the beach chairs. Different as they are, these items all share one thing in common—they contain the element carbon. Even many parts of the minivan are made of compounds that contain carbon. What is special about carbon that allows it to form so many different compounds?

Infer Carbon's Bonding

CAUTION: *Do not eat foods used in your activity.*

1. Insert four toothpicks into a small clay or plastic foam ball so that the toothpicks are evenly spaced around the sphere. The ball represents a carbon atom. The toothpicks represent chemical bonds.

2. Use raisins to represent hydrogen atoms, grapes to represent chlorine atoms, and gumdrops to represent fluorine atoms. Make models of molecules by adding any combination of raisins, grapes, and gumdrops to the toothpicks.

3. Compare your models with those of other class members.

Science **Journal**

Draw each model and write the formula for it. Did you make all the models that were possible with the materials you had? Did the class make all that were possible? What can you infer about the number of compounds a single carbon atom can form with only three kinds of atoms?

14·1 Simple Organic Compounds

What You'll Learn

▶ Why carbon is able to form many compounds
▶ How saturated and unsaturated hydrocarbons differ
▶ How to identify isomers of organic compounds

Vocabulary
organic compound
hydrocarbon
saturated hydrocarbon
unsaturated hydrocarbon
isomer

Why It's Important

▶ Plants, animals, and most of the things that are part of your life are made of organic compounds.

Figure 14-1 Organic substances contain carbon.

Organic Compounds

One way to classify the substances that are a part of your life is shown in **Figure 14-1.** Some substances are made by living organisms, for example, leaves and wood. Other substances, such as most rocks and minerals, are not and have never been alive. Most of the substances associated with living things contain the element carbon. Scientists used to think that this group of substances could be produced only by living plants and animals, so these carbon-containing substances were called organic compounds. The word *organic* means "derived from a living organism." But, in 1828, a German scientist formed the organic compound urea from substances that were not organic compounds. Scientists then realized that living organisms are not necessary to form organic compounds. Now, most compounds that contain carbon are called **organic compounds.**

Atoms form chemical bonds and thus obtain the stability of a noble gas with eight electrons in their outer energy level. A carbon atom has four electrons in its outer energy level, so it forms four covalent bonds with as many as four other atoms. A single covalent bond is a pair of electrons that is shared between two atoms. One of carbon's most frequent partners in covalent bonds is hydrogen.

A Most of the substances in the photo are organic. Although some are, or were, alive, others were manufactured.

B The substances in this photo are mostly composed of elements other than carbon.

Hydrocarbons

Many compounds are made of carbon and hydrogen alone. A compound in which the only elements are carbon and hydrogen is called a **hydrocarbon.** The simplest hydrocarbon is methane, sometimes called natural gas. If you have a gas stove or gas furnace in your home, the fuel that may be burned in these appliances is methane. It consists of a single carbon atom covalently bonded to four hydrogen atoms. Methane's formula is CH_4. **Figure 14-2** shows a model of the methane molecule and its structural formula. In a structural formula, the lines between one atom and another atom represent pairs of electrons shared between the atoms. A single line represents one pair of electrons.

Now, visualize one of the hydrogen atoms being plucked from a methane molecule, as in **Figure 14-3A.** A fragment of the molecule called a methyl group, $-CH_3$, would remain. The methyl group can then form a single bond with another methyl group. If two methyl groups bond with each other, the result is the two-carbon hydrocarbon ethane, C_2H_6, which is shown with its structural formula in **Figure 14-3B.**

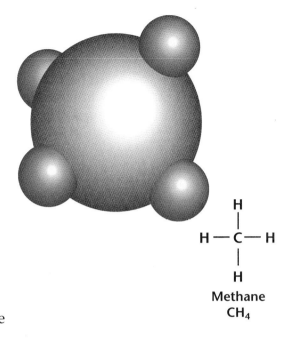

Methane
CH_4

Figure 14-2 This simple molecule is the first of a long list of hydrocarbon molecules.

Figure 14-3 Here's a way to visualize the building up of larger hydrocarbons. **Would it matter which hydrogen atom was plucked off?**

VISUALIZING Hydrocarbon Formation

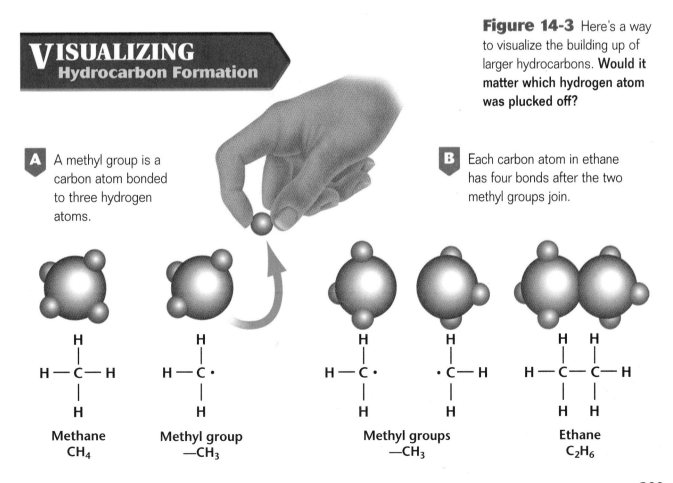

A A methyl group is a carbon atom bonded to three hydrogen atoms.

B Each carbon atom in ethane has four bonds after the two methyl groups join.

Methane
CH_4

Methyl group
$-CH_3$

Methyl groups
$-CH_3$

Ethane
C_2H_6

Figure 14-4 Propane and butane are two useful fuels.

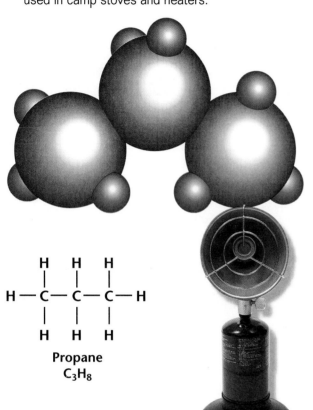

A When propane burns, it releases energy for cooking food and warmth. It's the fuel used in camp stoves and heaters.

Propane
C₃H₈

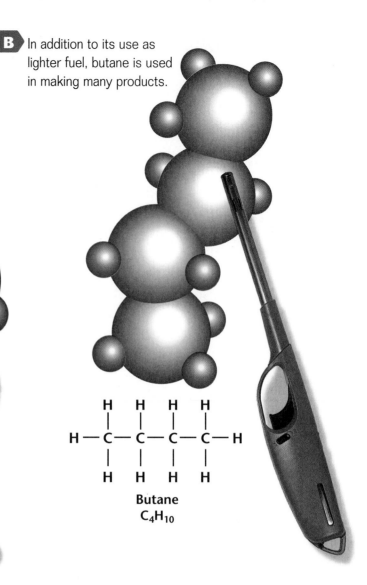

B In addition to its use as lighter fuel, butane is used in making many products.

Butane
C₄H₁₀

![EARTH SCIENCE INTEGRATION]

Petroleum from Dinosaurs
Petroleum is a mixture of hydrocarbons that was formed from aquatic plants and animals—perhaps even dinosaurs—that lived hundreds of millions of years ago. With the right temperature and pressure, dead plant and animal matter, buried deep under Earth's surface, is decomposed to form petroleum. Why is petroleum a nonrenewable resource?

Saturated Hydrocarbons

Methane and ethane are the first two members of a family of molecules in which carbon and hydrogen atoms are joined by single covalent bonds. When all the bonds in a hydrocarbon are single bonds, the molecule is called a **saturated hydrocarbon.** You can visualize the formation of larger hydrocarbons in the same way you visualized the formation of ethane. A hydrogen atom is removed from ethane and replaced by a –CH₃ group. Propane is the third member of the series. Butane, with four carbon atoms, is the fourth.

These short hydrocarbon chains have low boiling points, so they evaporate and burn easily. That makes methane a good fuel for your stove or furnace. Propane is used in gas grills and in hot-air balloons. Butane is a fuel for camp stoves and lighters. You can see the structures of these hydrocarbons in **Figure 14-4.** Some long-chain hydrocarbons have more than 50 carbon atoms. Longer hydrocarbons are used as oils, waxes, or in asphalt. **Table 14-1** lists the names and the chemical formulas of a few of the smaller saturated hydrocarbons.

Unsaturated Hydrocarbons

Carbon also forms hydrocarbons with double and triple bonds. In a double bond, two pairs of electrons are shared between two atoms, and in a triple bond, three pairs of electrons are shared. Hydrocarbons with double or triple bonds are called **unsaturated hydrocarbons.** Ethene, or ethylene, the simplest unsaturated hydrocarbon, has two carbon atoms joined by a double bond. Propene, or propylene, is an unsaturated hydrocarbon with three carbons. Some unsaturated hydrocarbons have more than one double bond. Butadiene has four carbon atoms and two double bonds. The structures of ethylene, propylene, and butadiene are shown in **Figure 14-5.**

Table 14-1

The Structures of Hydrocarbons

Name	Structural Formula	Chemical Formula
Methane		CH_4
Ethane		C_2H_6
Propane		C_3H_8
Butane		C_4H_{10}
Hexane		C_6H_{14}

Figure 14-5 You'll find unsaturated hydrocarbons in many of the products you use every day.

Ethylene
C_2H_4

Propylene
C_3H_6

Butadiene
C_4H_6

A Ethylene helps ripen fruits and vegetables. It's also used to make milk and soft-drink bottles.

B This detergent bottle contains the tough plastic polypropylene made from propylene.

C Butadiene made it possible to replace natural rubber with synthetic rubber.

Figure 14-6 In the welder's torch, ethyne (acetylene) is combined with oxygen to form a mixture that burns, releasing intense light and heat. The

$$H—C \equiv C—H$$

Ethyne or Acetylene
C_2H_2

two carbon atoms in ethyne are joined by a triple bond. **Why is the oxygen important?**

Unsaturated hydrocarbons also may have triple bonds, as you can see in the structure of ethyne (ETH ine) shown in **Figure 14-6.** Ethyne, commonly called acetylene, is a gas used for welding because it produces high heat as it burns in a mixture with oxygen in the welding torch.

Hydrocarbon Isomers

Suppose you want to redecorate your room but you can't get new furniture or posters for the walls. One thing you can do is rearrange all of the things that you already have. Even though your room contains the same items, it is different from before. The atoms in an organic molecule also can have different arrangements but still have the same formula. Compounds that have the same chemical formula but different structures are called **isomers** (I suh murz). Two isomers, butane and isobutane, are shown in **Figure 14-7.** Notice that their formulas are the same. But, because of their different structures, they

Try at Home

Mini Lab

Modeling Isomers

Procedure

1. Construct a model of pentane, C_5H_{12}. Use toothpicks for covalent bonds and small balls of different colored clay for carbon atoms and hydrogen atoms.
2. Using the same collection of atoms, build a molecule with a different arrangement of the atoms. Are there any other possibilities?
3. Make a model of hexane, C_6H_{14}.
4. Arrange the atoms of hexane in different ways.

Analysis

1. How many isomers of pentane did you build? How many isomers of hexane?
2. Do you think there are more isomers of heptane, C_7H_{16}, than hexane? Why or why not?

Figure 14-7 Butane and isobutane have the same formula, C_4H_{10}, but they are different in their structure and properties.

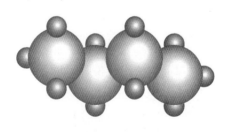

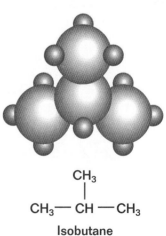

$$CH_3—CH_2—CH_2—CH_3$$

Butane
C_4H_{10}

$$CH_3—CH—CH_3$$

with CH_3 above the central CH

Isobutane
C_4H_{10}

have different chemical and physical properties. As the size of a hydrocarbon molecule increases, the possibilities for isomers also increase. ✔️

Hydrocarbons in Rings

You may be thinking that all hydrocarbons are chains of carbon atoms with two ends. But, no rule states that a molecule must have two ends. Just as a rope can be tied together to form a loop, some molecules can occur in rings. You can see the structures of two different molecules in **Figure 14-8.** The carbon atoms bond together to form closed rings containing five and six carbons. The prefix *cyclo-* in their names tells you that the molecules are cyclic or ring shaped.

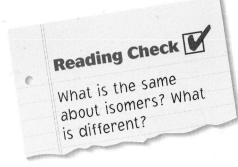

Reading Check ✔️

What is the same about isomers? What is different?

Cyclopentane
C_5H_{10}

Cyclohexane
C_6H_{12}

Figure 14-8 Visualize a hydrogen plucked from the carbon atoms on both ends of a pentane or hexane chain. Then, the two end carbons form a bond with each other. **How does the formula for cyclohexane differ from the formula for hexane?**

Section Assessment

1. Explain the difference between a saturated hydrocarbon and an unsaturated hydrocarbon, and give an example of each.

2. From the structure of the carbon atom, explain the large number of compounds that can be formed by carbon.

3. **Think Critically:** Are propane and cyclopropane isomers? Use diagrams and formulas to explain your answer.

4. **Skill Builder**
Making and Using Graphs Make a graph using the information in **Table 14-1.** For each compound, plot the number of carbon atoms on the x-axis and the number of hydrogen atoms on the y-axis. Use your graph to predict the formula for the saturated hydrocarbon that has 11 carbon atoms. If you need help, refer to Making and Using Graphs in the **Skill Handbook** on page 717.

Using Math

The general formula for saturated hydrocarbons is C_nH_{2n+2} where *n* can be any whole number except zero. Use the general formula to determine the formula for a saturated hydrocarbon with 25 carbon atoms.

Other Organic Compounds

What You'll Learn

▶ How new compounds are formed by substituting hydrocarbons
▶ The classes of compounds that result from substitution

Vocabulary
hydroxyl group
carboxyl group
amino group
amino acid

Why It's Important

▶ Many organic compounds that you use every day have been made by chemists.

Substituted Hydrocarbons

Suppose you pack an apple in your lunch every day. One day, you have no apples, so you substitute a pear. When you eat your lunch, you'll notice a difference in the taste and texture of your fruit. Chemists make substitutions, too. They change hydrocarbons to make compounds called substituted hydrocarbons. To make a substituted hydrocarbon, one or more hydrogen atoms are taken off and replaced by atoms such as the halogens, or by groups of atoms. Such changes result in compounds with chemical properties different from the original hydrocarbon. When one or more chlorine or fluorine atoms are added to methane in place of hydrogens, new compounds are formed like the ones in **Figure 14-9.**

Figure 14-9 Chlorine can replace from one to four of methane's hydrogen atoms.

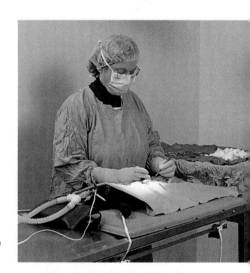

C The trichloromethane, or chloroform, molecule has three chlorine atoms that replace hydrogen atoms in methane. Chloroform is used as a veterinary anesthetic

Trichloromethane or chloroform CHCl₃

A In chloromethane, a single chlorine atom replaces a hydrogen atom in methane. Chloromethane is a gas used to cool refrigerators.

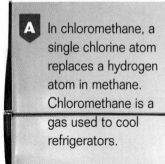

Chloromethane CH₃Cl

B Dichloromethane forms when two hydrogen atoms are replaced by chlorine atoms. Dichloromethane is a liquid used in manufacturing decaffeinated coffee.

Dichloromethane CH₂Cl₂

D Carbon tetrachloride is a fully substituted methane molecule. It is a poisonous substance that was formerly used as a dry-cleaning solvent.

Carbon tetrachloride CCl₄

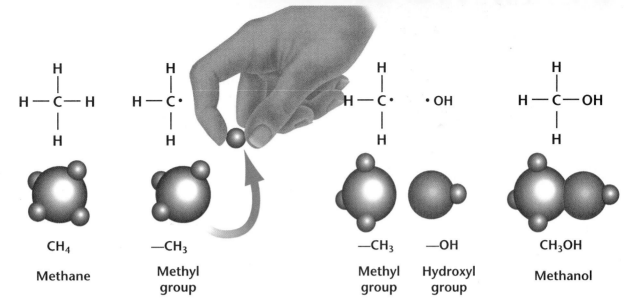

CH₄	—CH₃	—CH₃	—OH	CH₃OH
Methane	Methyl group	Methyl group	Hydroxyl group	Methanol

Alcohols

Groups of atoms also can be added to hydrocarbons to make different compounds. The **hydroxyl group** (hi DROX ul) is made up of an oxygen atom and a hydrogen atom joined by a covalent bond. It is represented by the formula –OH. When a hydroxyl group replaces a hydrogen atom in a hydrocarbon, an alcohol forms. **Figure 14-10** shows the formation of the alcohol methanol as a hydrogen in the methane molecule is replaced by a hydroxyl group.

Larger alcohol molecules are formed by adding more carbon atoms to the chain. Ethanol is an alcohol produced naturally when sugar in corn, grains, and fruit ferments. It is a combination of ethane and an –OH group. Isopropyl alcohol forms when the hydroxyl group is substituted for a hydrogen on the middle carbon of propane rather than one of the end carbons. You've probably used isopropyl alcohol to disinfect injuries. **Table 14-2** lists several alcohols with their structures and uses.

Figure 14-10 After the methane molecule loses one of its hydrogens, it has an extra electron to share, as does the hydroxyl group. **What kind of bond do they form?**

*inter*NET
CONNECTION

Visit the Glencoe Science Web Site at **www.glencoe.com/ sec/science** for more information about substituted hydrocarbons.

Table 14-2

Three Common Alcohols			
	Methanol	**Ethanol**	**Isopropyl Alcohol**
	H—C—OH (with H above and below C)	H—C—C—OH (with H's)	H—C—C—C—H (with H, OH, H)
Uses			
Fuel	yes	yes	no
Cleaner	yes	yes	yes
Disinfectant	no	yes	yes
Manufacturing chemical	yes	yes	yes

Carboxylic Acids

Remember the reaction between vinegar and baking soda? The reactant in vinegar is acetic acid. You can think of acetic acid as the hydrocarbon methane with a carboxyl group substituted for a hydrogen. A **carboxyl group** (car BOX ul) consists of a carbon atom, two oxygen atoms, and a hydrogen atom. Its formula is –COOH. When a carboxyl group is substituted in a hydrocarbon, the substance formed is called a carboxylic acid. The simplest carboxylic acid is methanoic acid, commonly called formic acid. Formic acid consists of a single hydrogen atom and a carboxyl group. You can see the structures of formic acid and acetic acid in **Figure 14-11.** Some ants produce formic acid naturally. When they sting you, they inject formic acid into your skin.

Methanoic or formic acid
$HCOOH$

Ethanoic or acetic acid
CH_3COOH

Figure 14-11 Ants make the simplest carboxylic acid, formic (methanoic) acid. **How do the structures of formic acid and acetic acid differ?**

You can probably guess that many other carboxylic acids are formed from longer hydrocarbons. Many carboxylic acids occur in foods. Citric acid is found in citrus fruits such as oranges and grapefruit. Lactic acid is present in milk.

Amines

Amines are a group of substituted hydrocarbons formed when an amino group replaces a hydrogen atom. An **amino group** (uh ME no) is a nitrogen atom joined by covalent bonds to two hydrogen atoms. It has the formula $-NH_2$. Methylamine, shown in **Figure 14-12,** is formed when one of the hydrogens in methane is replaced with an amino group. A more complex amine that you may have experienced is the novocaine your dentist uses to numb the pain of dental work.

Figure 14-12 Complex amines account for the strong smells of cheeses such as these, as well as the odor of other decaying organic matter.

Methylamine
CH_3NH_2

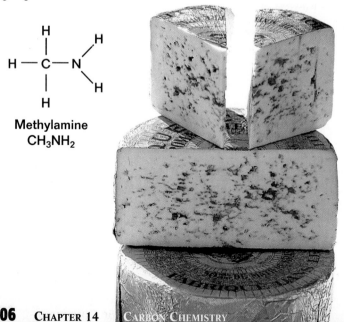

Amino groups are important because they are a part of many biological compounds.

Amino Acids

You have seen that a group can be substituted onto one end of a chain to change the molecule. It's also possible to substitute groups on both ends of the chain, and even to replace hydrogen atoms bonded to carbon atoms in the middle of the chain. When both an amino group ($-NH_2$) and a carboxyl group ($-COOH$) replace hydrogens on the same carbon atom in a molecule, a special type of compound known as an amino acid is formed. **Amino acids** are the building blocks of proteins, which are an important class of biological molecules needed by living cells. Twenty different amino acids bond together in different combinations to form the variety of proteins that are needed in the human body. Glycine and alanine are shown in **Figure 14-13**. Glycine is the simplest amino acid. It is a methane molecule in which one hydrogen atom has been replaced by an amino group and another has been replaced by a carboxyl group. The other 19 amino acids are formed by replacing the highlighted hydrogen atom with different groups. For example, in alanine, the hydrogen atom is replaced by a methyl (–CH_3) group.

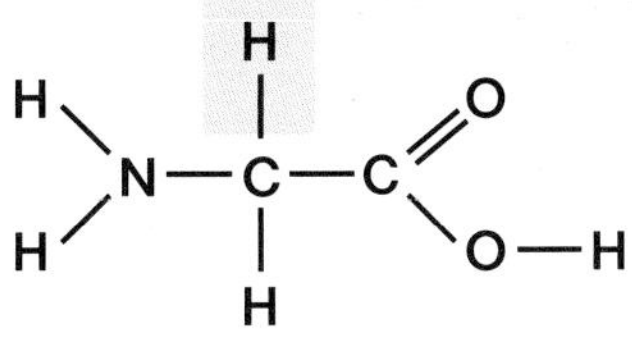

Glycine

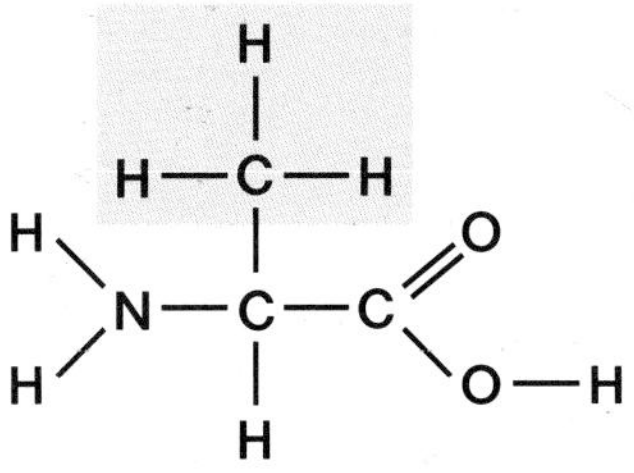

Alanine

Figure 14-13 The amino acids glycine and alanine are the simplest building blocks of proteins.

Section Assessment

1. The nonstick coating found on some pots and pans is made from tetrafluoroethylene, a substituted hydrocarbon in which all four of the hydrogen atoms of ethylene are replaced by fluorine. Draw the structural formula for this molecule.

2. In what way is an amino acid different from a carboxylic acid?

3. How do the 20 amino acids differ from each other?

4. **Think Critically:** Both of the substituted hydrocarbons, chloromethane and dichloromethane, result from the replacement of hydrogen atoms with chlorine atoms. Predict which of these compounds will have the lower boiling point. Explain.

5. **Skill Builder**
   Making Models A substituted hydrocarbon can be made by removing a hydrogen atom from a carbon and putting another atom or group in its place. Do the **Chapter 14 Skill Activity** on page 755 to make models of substituted hydrocarbons.

Using Computers

Word Processing Use the table function in a word processing program to make a table listing the classes of substituted hydrocarbons in this section: halogen-substituted hydrocarbons, alcohols, carboxylic acids, amines, and amino acids. List the substituted group(s) for each class and give the name and formula of a molecule that belongs in each class. If you need help, refer to page 732.

Conversion of Alcohols

Materials

- Test tube and stopper
- Test-tube rack
- Potassium permanganate solution (1 mL)
- Sodium hydroxide solution (1 mL)
- Ethanol (3 drops)
- pH test paper
- Graduated cylinder

Wine will spoil when the ethanol it contains is exposed to air and the bacteria *Acetabactor*. Is this spoilage a chemical change?

What You'll Investigate

What changes occur when ethanol is exposed to conditions like those produced by exposure to air and bacteria?

Goals

- **Observe** a chemical change in an alcohol.
- **Infer** the product of the chemical change.

Procedure

Wash your hands after completing the experiment.

1. Measure 1 mL of potassium permanganate solution and pour it into a test tube. Measure 1 mL of sodium hydroxide solution and add it to the test tube. **CAUTION:** *Handle these chemicals with care. Immediately flush any spills with water and call your teacher.*

2. **Dip** a piece of pH paper into the mixture in the test tube. **Record** the result in your Science Journal.

3. **Add** three drops of ethanol to the test tube. Put a stopper on the test tube and gently **shake** it for one minute.

4. Place the test tube in a test-tube rack and **observe** what happens. Record any changes you notice during the next five minutes.

5. **Test** the sample with pH paper again. **Record** what you observe.

6. **Dispose** of the solutions as directed by your teacher.

Conclude and Apply

1. Did a chemical reaction take place? What leads you to **infer** this?

2. Alcohols may undergo a chemical reaction to form carboxylic acids in the presence of potassium permanganate. If the alcohol used is ethanol, what would you **predict** to be the chemical formula of the acid produced?

Alcohol Conversion	
Procedure Step	**Observations**
Step 2	
Step 4	
Step 5	

Nature's Medicines and the Organic Chemist

Nature's Medicine Chest

Plants have long been used as sources of medicine. Ancient Egyptian, Chinese, and Indian writings describe many plant-based treatments for diseases of the eyes, skin, and internal organs. In the inset, a thirteenth-century Arabic manuscript shows six healing herbs. Sap of both the piñon pine (left) and ponderosa pine tree was used by Native Americans to prevent infection in wounds.

Tree Bark to Drugstore

A chemical compound called quinine is found in the bark of the Cinchona tree. Long before Europeans arrived in the New World, native people in the Andes mountain region of South America used Cinchona bark to treat malaria, a disease that still afflicts millions of people worldwide. Around 1630, Jesuit priests in Peru learned from their native neighbors how to grind the bark and mix it with water to make an effective malaria remedy. For centuries, Cinchona bark was the world's only weapon against malaria.

Advances in organic chemistry have made it possible to synthesize, or put together, many medicinal compounds obtained from plants. In 1908, chemists identified the chemical formula of quinine as $C_{20}H_{24}N_2O_2$, but it wasn't until 1944 that quinine was synthesized in the laboratory.

The Search Continues

Today, the search goes on for new medicines derived from plants. When a plant compound shows promise in treating a disease, chemists often use computer models to help figure out its structure. Then, they try to synthesize that compound in the laboratory. The new medicine must then be tested for safety and effectiveness—a process that can take many years before the medicine reaches your local drugstore.

interNET CONNECTION

Visit the Glencoe Science Web Site at **www.glencoe.com/sec/science** to find more information about taxol, aspirin, and codeine. Prepare a presentation that includes the identity of the natural remedy and the medicine's uses.

Biological Compounds

What You'll Learn

► How large organic molecules are made
► The roles of organic molecules in the body
► Why eating the recommended amounts of certain foods is important for maintaining health

Vocabulary

polymer   carbohydrate
protein   lipid

Why It's Important

► Your diet may affect how you feel.

What's a polymer?

Now that you know about some simple organic molecules, you can begin to learn about more complex biological molecules. These are organic substances found in milk, muscle, and blood, and some common materials such as the nonstick coating on a frying pan or the nylon in your jacket. All of these substances contain large molecules called polymers. A **polymer** is a molecule made up of many small organic molecules that link up with each other to form a long chain. The name polymer comes from the Greek words *poly,* which means "many," and *meros,* which means "part."

In **Figure 14-14,** you can see what happens in the polymerization of ethylene. Polymerization (pah lih mer i ZAY shun) is a chemical reaction that occurs between many small molecules when they link to form long chains. The ethylene molecule, C_2H_4, is an unsaturated hydrocarbon, so there is a double bond between the carbon atoms. One of the bonds in the double bond breaks in each ethylene molecule. The two carbon atoms then form new bonds with carbon atoms in other ethylene molecules. This process goes on as a chain reaction that results in the formation of a much larger molecule called polyethylene. It is a polymer that is used to make many products, such as plastic bottles. Polyethylene is an example of a synthetic polymer, but many polymers occur naturally. Some of them play important roles in keeping your body healthy.

Figure 14-14 Small molecules link into long chains to form polymers.

A The carbon atoms that were joined by the double bond each have an electron to share with another carbon in another molecule of ethylene.

B The process goes on until a huge molecule is formed.

Ethylene   Ethylene   Polyethylene

Proteins Are Polymers

You've probably heard about proteins when you've been urged to eat healthy foods. A **protein** is a polymer that consists of a chain of individual amino acids linked together. Your body cannot function properly without them. Proteins serve as catalysts and speed up chemical reactions in cells. Some proteins make up the structural materials in ligaments, tendons, muscles, cartilage, hair, and fingernails. Hemoglobin, which carries substances through the blood, is a protein.

The different functions in your body are performed by different proteins. Your body makes many of these proteins by assembling 20 amino acids in different ways. Eight of the amino acids that are needed to make proteins cannot be produced by your body. These amino acids, which are called essential amino acids, must come from the food you eat. That's why you need to eat a diet containing protein-rich foods, like those in **Figure 14-15.**

LIFE SCIENCE
◀ **INTEGRATION**

Try at Home

Mini Lab

Summing Up Protein

Procedure

1. Make a list of the foods you ate during the last 24 hours.

2. Use the data your teacher gives you to find the total number of grams of protein in your diet for the day. Multiply the grams of protein in one unit of food by the number of units of food you ate.

Analysis

1. The recommended daily allowance (RDA) of protein for girls, 11 to 14 years old, is 46 g per day. For boys, 11 to 14 years old, the RDA is 48 g per day. Was your total greater or less than the RDA?

2. Which of the foods you ate supplied the largest amount of protein? What percent of the total did that food supply?

Figure 14-15 Your body can't make eight of the amino acids needed for making proteins. **How can you be sure that you aren't missing any proteins?**

Glycine   Alanine

Figure 14-16 Both ends of an amino acid can link with another amino acid. **What molecule is released in the process?**

The process by which your body converts amino acids to proteins is shown in **Figure 14-16.** In this reaction, the amino group of the amino acid alanine forms a bond with the carboxyl group of the amino acid glycine, and a molecule of water is released. Each end of this new molecule can go on to form similar bonds with another amino acid. The process continues in this way until the amino acid chain, or protein, is complete. ☑

Reading Check ☑

Describe how proteins are formed from amino acids.

Carbohydrates

The day before a race, marathon runners like the ones in **Figure 14-17** often eat large amounts of pasta. What's in pasta and other foods like bread and fruit that makes them good choices for prerace eating? These foods contain sugars and starches, which are members of the family of organic compounds called carbohydrates. A **carbohydrate** is an organic compound that contains only carbon, hydrogen, and oxygen in a ratio of two hydrogen atoms to one oxygen atom and one carbon atom. In the body, carbohydrates are broken down into simple sugars that the body can use for energy. In effect, the marathon runners are storing energy for the next day's race.

Figure 14-17 These athletes are eating a meal high in carbohydrates. **How will this help them in the next day's race?**

Sugars

If you like chocolate-chip cookies or ice cream, then you're familiar with sugars. They are the substances that make both fresh fruit and candy sweet. Simple sugars are carbohydrates containing five, six, or seven carbon atoms arranged in a ring. The structures of glucose and fructose, two common simple sugars, are shown in **Figure 14-18.** Glucose forms a six-carbon ring. It is found in many naturally sweet foods, such as grapes.

Glucose

Fructose

Figure 14-18 Glucose and fructose are simple six-carbon carbohydrates found in many fresh foods and in packaged foods.
Name some products that contain these sugars.

Problem Solving

Comparing Sweetness

There are natural sugars, and there are artificial sweeteners. Natural sugars include sucrose, glucose, fructose, maltose, and lactose. Artificial sweeteners are compounds unrelated to sugars. They include saccharin, aspartame, and acesulfame. They are not all equally sweet. If you taste equal amounts of aspartame and sucrose, the aspartame will taste 200 times sweeter than sucrose. Assume sucrose has a sweetness index of 100. A sweetness index is a measure of how sweet a compound is. Compared with sucrose, other sweeteners have the following sweetness indices: glucose, 70; fructose, 170; maltose, 30; lactose, 16; saccharin, 40 000; aspartame, 20 000; acesulfame, 20 000.

Solve the Problem

1. Determine how many times sweeter than sucrose each sweetener is. You can figure this out by taking the ratio of the sweetness index of any sweetener to the sweetness index of sucrose. For example, aspartame's sweetness index is 20 000. The ratio of 20 000/100 = 200, so aspartame is 200 times sweeter than sucrose. For a sweetener with a

sweetness index of 50, the ratio would be 50/100 = 1/2. This sweetener is one half as sweet as sucrose. Present your results in a table with three columns. List the eight sweeteners in the first column. List their sweetness indices in the second column. In the third column, show how many times sweeter each sweetener is than sucrose.

2. Make a bar graph that compares the sweetness indices of the sweeteners.

3. Which sugar is the sweetest? Which artificial sweetener is the sweetest?

4. How much maltose would match the sweetness of one teaspoon of sucrose?

Think Critically: Why might a person choose to use an artificial sweetener rather than a natural sugar?

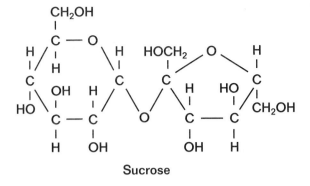

Sucrose

Figure 14-19 Sucrose is a molecule of glucose combined with a molecule of fructose. **What small molecule must be added to sucrose when it separates to form the two six-carbon sugars?**

Fructose is the sweet substance found in ripe fruit and honey. It is often made into corn syrup and added to many foods as a sweetener. The sugar you probably have in your sugar bowl or use in baking a cake is sucrose. Sucrose, shown in **Figure 14-19,** is a combination of the two simple sugars glucose and fructose. In the body, sucrose cannot move through cell membranes. It must be broken down into glucose and fructose to enter cells. Inside the cell, these simple sugars are broken down further to provide energy for cell functions.

Starches

Starches are large carbohydrates that exist naturally in grains such as rice, wheat, and corn. Starches are polymers of glucose molecules in which hundreds or thousands of sugar molecules may be joined together. Because each sugar molecule releases energy when it is broken down, starches are sources of large amounts of energy.

Other Glucose Polymers

Two other important polymers that are made up of glucose molecules are cellulose and glycogen. Cellulose is a polymer that consists of long chains of glucose units linked together. This structure results in long, stiff fibers that make up the walls of plant cells, like the strands that pull off the celery stalk in **Figure 14-20.** Glycogen is a polymer that also contains chains of glucose units, but the chains are highly branched. Glycogen molecules are found in animal tissue where their function is to store energy. Although starch, cellulose, and glycogen are all polymers of glucose, humans can't use all of them as sources of energy. The human digestive system can't convert cellulose into sugars. Grazing animals, such as cows, have special digestive systems that allow them to break down cellulose polymer into sugars.

Figure 14-20 Your body cannot break down long cellulose fibers on celery, but your health can benefit from eating a certain amount of fiber.

Lipids

Many of the foods you eat contain lipids, for example, butter, salad dressings, ice cream, cheese, meat, and potato chips. A **lipid** is an organic compound that contains the same elements as carbohydrates—carbon, hydrogen, and oxygen—but in different proportions. They are composed of three long-chain carboxylic acids bonded to an alcohol called glycerol that has three –OH groups. Lipids are commonly called fats and oils, but they also are found in greases and waxes like the beeswax in **Figure 14-21.**

Lipids Store Energy

Lipids store energy in their bonds, just as carbohydrates do, but they are a more concentrated source of energy than carbohydrates. If you eat more food than your body needs to supply the energy for your usual activities, the excess energy from the food is stored by producing lipids.

How can energy be stored in a molecule? The chemical reaction that produces lipids is endothermic. An endothermic reaction is one in which energy is absorbed. That means that energy is stored in the chemical bonds of lipids. When your body needs energy, the bonds are broken and energy is released. This process protects your body in times when you need extra energy or in times when you may not be able to eat. If you regularly eat more food than you need, large amounts of lipids will be produced and stored as permanent fat on your body.

*inter*NET
CONNECTION

Visit the Glencoe Science Web Site at **www.glencoe.com/ sec/science** for more information about lipids.

Using Math

One gram of carbohydrates releases 4 Calories of energy and 1 g of lipids releases 9 Calories. If your daily diet provides 400 g of carbohydrates and 100 g of lipids, how many Calories of energy will be available to you?

Figure 14-21 Fats and oils are not the only kinds of lipids. Wax is a lipid that is harder than fat. Bees secrete wax from a gland in the abdomen to form beeswax, which is part of the honeycomb.

Saturated and Unsaturated Lipids

Not all lipids are the same. Remember the difference between saturated and unsaturated hydrocarbons? Unsaturated molecules have one or more double or triple bonds between carbon atoms. Lipid molecules may be saturated or unsaturated. As you can see in **Figure 14-22A,** when a lipid is saturated, the acid chains are straight because all the bonds are single bonds. They are able to pack together closely. A compact arrangement of the molecules is typical of a solid. These solid lipids are called saturated fats.

When a lipid is unsaturated, as in **Figure 14-22B,** the molecule bends wherever there is a double bond. This prevents the chains from packing close together, so these lipids tend to be liquid oils. They are called unsaturated fats.

Scientists and doctors have observed that people who eat a diet high in saturated fats have a high rate of cardiovascular problems such as heart disease. Fortunately, many foods containing both saturated and unsaturated fats are available so that you can choose the foods you want to include in your diet.

Figure 14-22 Whether a lipid is a liquid or a solid depends on the type of bonds.

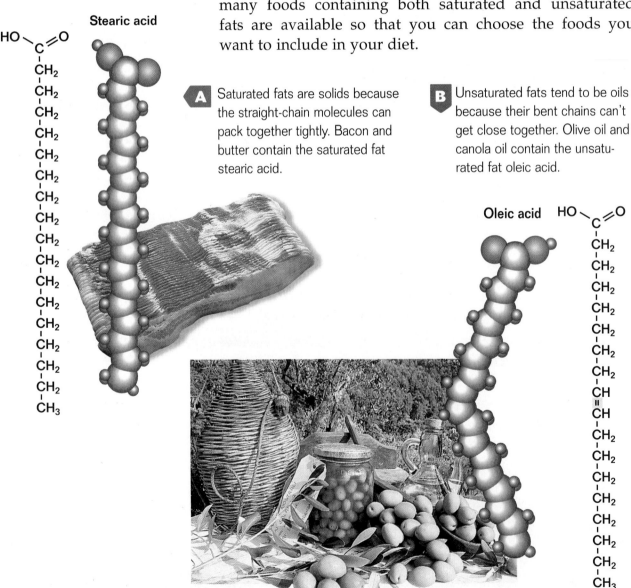

A Saturated fats are solids because the straight-chain molecules can pack together tightly. Bacon and butter contain the saturated fat stearic acid.

B Unsaturated fats tend to be oils because their bent chains can't get close together. Olive oil and canola oil contain the unsaturated fat oleic acid.

Cholesterol

Cholesterol is a complex lipid present in foods that come from animals, such as fatty meat, butter, eggs, and cheese. Even if you don't eat foods containing cholesterol, your body makes its own supply. Your body needs cholesterol for building cell membranes. Cholesterol is not found in plants, so oils derived from plants are free of cholesterol. However, the body can convert fats in these oils to cholesterol.

High cholesterol levels in the blood can lead to the buildup of deposits of cholesterol on the inside walls of arteries. This condition, known as atherosclerosis, is shown in **Figure 14-23**. When arteries become clogged, the flow of blood is restricted, which results in high blood pressure. This, in turn, can lead to heart disease. Eating less saturated fat and cholesterol can help to lower cholesterol levels in the blood and reduce the risk of heart problems.

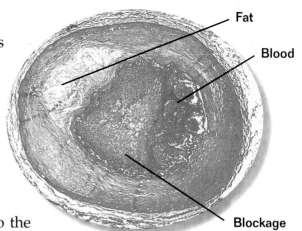

Fat

Blood

Blockage

Figure 14-23 This view of an artery shows atherosclerosis, a dangerous condition in which arteries in the body become clogged. Deposits build up on the walls of the artery leaving less room for blood to flow.

Section Assessment

1. Describe the process by which large organic molecules such as proteins are made. What other product is formed along with a protein molecule?

2. Identify some of the roles of carbohydrates, proteins, and lipids in the functioning of your body.

3. How are cellulose and glycogen different from sugars and starches?

4. **Think Critically:** Explain why even people who eat a healthy diet may gain weight if they don't get enough exercise.

5.  **Skill Builder**
   Forming a Hypothesis A chemist who planned to do experiments on refrigerants opened a valve on a tank that was supposed to contain the gas tetrafluoroethylene. He was surprised to find that no gas was released. When he opened the tank, he found a waxy, white solid. Form a hypothesis about how this white solid came to be inside the tank and what happened to the gas. If you need help, refer to Forming a Hypothesis in the **Skill Handbook** on page 722.

Science Journal
In your Science Journal, make a record of all the foods you eat during one day. Write a paragraph identifying the foods that contain proteins, carbohydrates (identify both starches and sugars), and lipids.

Design Your Own Experiment

Detecting Fats and Starches

Possible Materials

- Paper grocery bag
- Iodine solution in dropper bottle
- Marker
- Scissors
- Liquid cooking oil
- Bread
- Raw potato slice
- Cooked bacon
- Cheese
- Cracker
- Cooked egg white
- Potato chip

It's important to know what's in the foods you eat. Simple tests can show which foods contain carbohydrates and which contain fats. When rubbed on brown paper, foods that contain fats leave a grease spot, just as they make your hands feel greasy. When a drop of iodine solution is placed on foods containing starches, they turn dark blue.

Recognize the Problem

How will you find out which foods contain starch? Which contain fat?

Form a Hypothesis

How will you and your group use procedures that you know to test foods to determine which foods contain starch, fat, or both?

Goals

- **Predict** which foods contain starch and which contain fat.

- **Observe** the tests on each food to determine the presence of starch and fat.

Safety Precautions

CAUTION: *Iodine is poisonous.* Do NOT eat food used in a laboratory experiment. Dispose of all food after your experiment.

Test Your Hypothesis

Plan

1. **Predict** which foods contain starch and which contain fat.

2. Reread the opening paragraph of the experiment. How can you use that information to plan your experiment? You know that cooking oil is a fat and bread contains starch. Testing these foods will result in a positive test. Can you use these positive tests as a comparison to other tests?

3. **Write** the procedure you will use to test your hypothesis.

4. **Copy** the data table in your Science Journal.

Do

1. Make sure your teacher approves your plan and your data table before you begin your experiment.

2. Make your predictions and then carry out your plan.

3. Immediately **record** all your observations and results in your data table.

Analyze Your Data

1. **Describe** the evidence that allowed you to **infer** that fat was present in the food.

2. **Describe** the evidence that showed that starch was present.

Draw Conclusions

1. Which of the foods you tested contain carbohydrates? Which contain fat?

2. Did any foods contain both carbohydrates and fat?

3. Were your predictions correct?

Predictions and Tests for Fat and Starch			
Food	Prediction	Paper Bag	Iodine
oil			
bread			
potato			
bacon			

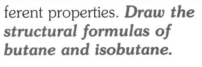

Section
14-1 COMPOUNDS OF CARBON AND HYDROGEN

Hydrocarbons are compounds containing only carbon and hydrogen. If a hydrocarbon has only single bonds, it is called a **saturated hydrocarbon.** A hydrocarbon chain can be lengthened by substituting a methyl group for a hydrogen. **Isomers** are compounds with the same chemical formula but different structures, and so they have different properties. ***Draw the structural formulas of butane and isobutane.***

UNSATURATED HYDROCARBONS

Unsaturated hydrocarbons have one or more double or triple bonds. The simplest unsaturated hydrocarbons are ethylene and propylene. Each has one double bond and is used to form useful polymers. Butadiene has two double bonds and is used to make synthetic rubber. ***Draw the structural formula for an unsaturated hydrocarbon with five carbon atoms and two double bonds.***

Propane
C_3H_8

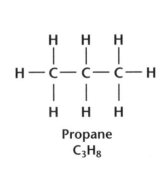

Ethyne or Acetylene
C_2H_2

Reading Check ✓

Choose a major illustration, such as Figure 14-4, and explain three things you learned from it.

Section
14-2 SUBSTITUTED HYDROCARBONS

Hydrocarbons may be substituted with other atoms such as the halogens, or with groups of atoms. An alcohol is formed when a **hydroxyl group** is substituted for a hydrogen in a hydrocarbon. A carboxylic acid is made when a **carboxyl group** is substituted. An amine is formed when an **amino group** is substituted. An **amino acid** contains both an amino group and a carboxyl group substituted on the same carbon atom. Substituted hydrocarbons have different physical and chemical properties from the unsubstituted hydrocarbons. *List three functional groups and give their chemical formulas.*

Section
14-3 MOLECULES OF LIFE

Biological compounds are complex, substituted hydrocarbons that make up living things. Many biological compounds are large molecules called **polymers,** which are made up of small repeating units. **Proteins** serve a variety of functions, including catalyzing many cell reactions and providing the structural material for many parts of the body. **Carbohydrates** and **lipids** are both energy sources and the means of storing energy. Eating a healthy diet is important. *List different types of carbohydrates.*

Chapter 14 Assessment

Using Vocabulary

a. amino acid
b. amino group
c. carbohydrate
d. carboxyl group
e. hydrocarbon
f. hydroxyl group
g. isomer
h. lipid
i. organic compound
j. polymer
k. protein
l. saturated hydrocarbon
m. unsaturated hydrocarbon

Answer the following questions about the Vocabulary words.

1. Explain the difference between an amino group and an amino acid.
2. How does a hydroxyl group differ from a carboxyl group?
3. How can an organic compound be an isomer?
4. What is the connection between a polymer and a protein?
5. What do carbohydrates and lipids have in common?

Checking Concepts

Choose the word or phrase that best answers the question.

6. A certain carbohydrate molecule has ten oxygen atoms. How many hydrogen atoms does it contain?
   A) five   C) ten
   B) 20   D) 16
7. Which is **NOT** a group that can be substituted in a hydrocarbon?
   A) amino   C) hydroxyl
   B) carboxyl   D) lipid
8. Which chemical formula represents an alcohol?
   A) CH_3COOH C) CH_3OH
   B) CH_3NH_2 D) CH_4

9. Which can build up in arteries and lead to heart disease?
   A) cholesterol   C) glucose
   B) fructose   D) starch
10. What is an organic molecule that contains a triple bond called?
    A) polymer
    B) saturated hydrocarbon
    C) isomer
    D) unsaturated hydrocarbon
11. What is the name of the substituted hydrocarbon with the chemical formula CH_2F_2?
    A) methane   C) difluoromethane
    B) fluoromethane D) trifluoromethane
12. Excess energy is stored in your body as which of the following?
    A) proteins   C) lipids
    B) isomers   D) saturated hydro-carbons
13. What are produced by reactions between carboxylic acids and glycerol?
    A) lipids   C) sugars
    B) proteins   D) carbohydrates
14. Which is a chemical formula that represents an amino acid?
    A) CH_3COOH C) NH_2CH_2COOH
    B) CH_3NH_2 D) CH_4
15. Which is a ring-shaped molecule?
    A) acetone   C) cyclopentane
    B) Freon   D) dichloroethane

Thinking Critically

16. Some drugs that were obtained from trees and plants are now manufactured. Do you think these manufactured drugs can be the same as the natural products? Explain.
17. Ethanol is used as a fuel for cars. Would you have predicted that ethanol would burn and produce energy? Explain.

Assessment

18. Candle wax is one of the longer hydrocarbons. What do you think are the products of the burning of candle wax?

19. In the polymerization of proteins, water molecules are produced as part of the reaction. But, in the polymerization of ethylene, no water is produced. Explain.

Developing Skills

If you need help, refer to the **Skill Handbook.**

20. Recognizing Cause and Effect Marathon runners go through a process known as hitting the wall. They have used up all their stored glucose and start using stored lipids as fuel. What is the advantage of eating lots of complex carbohydrates the day before a race?

21. Using a Graph The graph shows the boiling points of some saturated hydrocarbons with from one to five carbon atoms. How does boiling point depend upon the number of carbon atoms? What would you predict would be the approximate boiling point of hexane, a hydrocarbon with six carbon atoms?

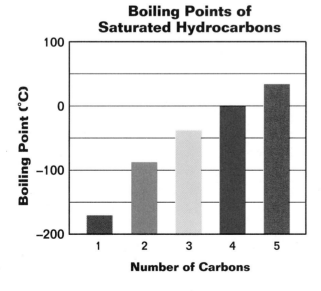

Boiling Points of Saturated Hydrocarbons

Test-Taking Tip

Study in Quiet It's best to study in an environment similar to the one in which you'll be tested. Blaring stereos, video game machines, chatty friends, and beepers are not allowed in the classroom during test time. So, why get used to them when you study?

Test Practice

Use these questions to test your Science Proficiency.

1. Which of the following is an unsaturated hydrocarbon?
A) propane
B) hexane
C) ethene
D) methane

2. When biological compounds are digested by the human body, which of the following processes does **NOT** occur?
A) Carbohydrates are broken down into simple sugars.
B) Excess energy released from food is stored as lipids.
C) Proteins are broken down into lipids.
D) Sugars are broken down to provide energy to cells.

3. Which of the following describes isomers?
A) They contain a hydroxyl group.
B) They occur in rings.
C) They have the same formula but different structures.
D) They have different formulas but the same structures.

Plant Processes

Chapter Preview

Skills Preview

Skill Builders
- Compare and Contrast
- Observe and Infer

Activities
- Predict
- Design an Experiment

MiniLabs
- Observe and Infer
- Measure in SI

Reading Check ✔

Before you read the chapter, make a list of all the vocabulary words. Next to each word, write what you think it means. Then, as you read, change your definitions if necessary.

Explore Activity

Plants are similar to other living things. They are made of cells, reproduce, make and use substances, and need water. If someone forgot to water the petunias shown in the photograph, what do you think would happen? From your own experience, you probably know they would wilt. Do the following activity to discover the relationship between plants and water. Find out how water goes in and out of a plant. In this chapter, you will learn about other plant processes.

Observe Plants

1. Obtain a resealable plastic bag and a small potted plant from your teacher.

2. Place the potted plant in the plastic bag.

3. Seal the bag and place it in a sunny window.

4. Look at the plant at the same time every day for a few days.

Science Journal

In your Science Journal, describe what happens in the bag. If enough water is lost by a plant and not replaced, predict what will happen to the plant.

15·1 Photosynthesis and Respiration

What You'll Learn

► How plants take in and give off gases
► Why photosynthesis and respiration are important
► Why photosynthesis and respiration are related

Vocabulary
stomata
transpiration
photosynthesis
respiration

Why It's Important

► Understanding photosynthesis and respiration in plants will help you understand their importance to life on Earth.

Gas Exchange in Plants

When you breathe, you take in and release mixtures of gases. You inhale air, a mixture of nitrogen, oxygen, carbon dioxide, and other gases. The mixture of gases that you exhale is mostly nitrogen, carbon dioxide, and water vapor. Gas exchange is one of the ways living cells obtain raw materials and get rid of waste products. For most organisms, carbon dioxide and water vapor are waste products of cell processes.

In plants, water and carbon dioxide are two of the raw materials needed for survival. Plant roots or rootlike structures absorb most of the water and it moves up through the plant to where it is needed. Water leaves a plant as water vapor. It may leave cells by diffusion and then be released through openings called **stomata** (sing., *stoma*). Stomata are on the surface(s) of a leaf or leaflike structure.

Stomata

How does carbon dioxide enter a leaf? Each stoma is surrounded by two guard cells that control the size of the opening. Water moves into and out of guard cells by osmosis. As water moves into guard cells, they swell and change shape,

Figure 15-1 Stomata open when guard cells absorb water (A). They close when water is lost (B). **Would a buildup of salt in the soil around a plant make the stomata open or close?**

Magnification: 300✕

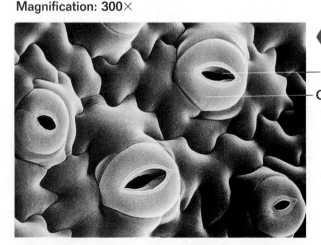

Magnification: 300✕

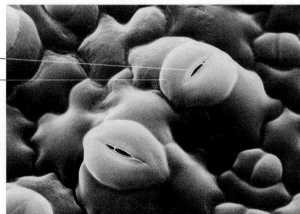

— Stoma
— Guard cell

Ⓐ

Ⓑ

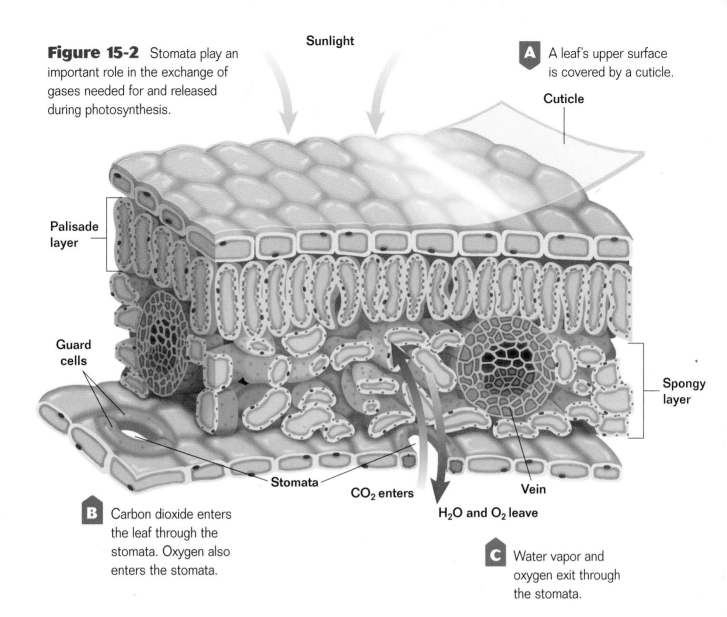

Figure 15-2 Stomata play an important role in the exchange of gases needed for and released during photosynthesis.

Sunlight

A A leaf's upper surface is covered by a cuticle.

Cuticle

Palisade layer

Guard cells

Spongy layer

Stomata

CO_2 enters

H_2O and O_2 leave

Vein

B Carbon dioxide enters the leaf through the stomata. Oxygen also enters the stomata.

C Water vapor and oxygen exit through the stomata.

creating a stoma. Carbon dioxide enters the leaf through the stoma and water vapor may escape during this process. When guard cells lose water, they deflate and change shape again. This action closes the stoma. **Figure 15-1** shows open and closed stomata.

Light, water, and carbon dioxide all affect the opening and closing of stomata. Stomata usually are open during the day and closed at night. Less carbon dioxide enters and less water vapor escapes from the leaf when stomata are closed. Because leaves usually have more stomata on the lower surface, more carbon dioxide reaches the spaces around the spongy layer, as shown in **Figure 15-2.** Water vapor also is found in the air spaces of the spongy layer.

If you did the Explore Activity for this chapter, you saw that water vapor condensed on the inside of the plastic bag. Loss of water vapor through stomata of a leaf is called **transpiration.** Far more water is lost by transpiration than is used during the food-making process of photosynthesis.

Using Math

A corn plant transpires about 15 L of water per week. How much water will it transpire in a 100-day growing season?

Figure 15-3 Light and chlorophyll are both essential parts of photosynthesis.

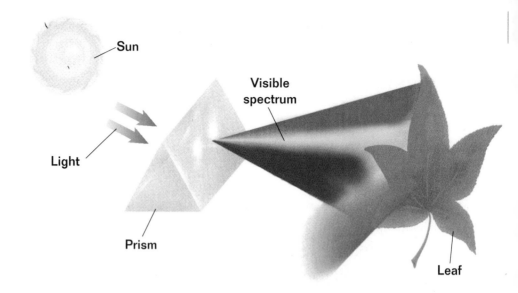

Sun

Visible spectrum

Light

Prism

Leaf

A As light from the sun passes through a prism, it separates into the colors of the visible spectrum. When light strikes a green leaf, most of the colors are absorbed. Green is reflected by the leaf and is seen by the viewer.

B Leaves of some trees, such as those on this sweet gum, change color in the autumn.

Spring

Summer

Fall

Photosynthesis

Why aren't all the leaves of the trees in **Figure 15-3B** green? If you live in a place that has changing seasons, you may see trees in the fall like in the photograph on the far right. In some places, many trees and bushes change color as the days get shorter and the weather grows colder. Leaves may change from green to red, brown, yellow, or orange. Some plants may even have leaves of different colors at the same time. These colors are the result of pigments in leaves. A pigment is a substance that reflects a particular part of the visible spectrum and absorbs the rest. In the spring and summer, there is so much green pigment chlorophyll in most leaves that it hides all other pigments. In the fall, chlorophyll breaks down and the other pigments become visible.

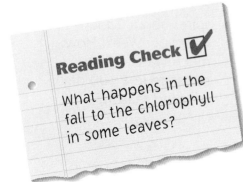

Reading Check ☑

What happens in the fall to the chlorophyll in some leaves?

As shown in **Figure 15-3A,** light from the sun contains all colors. When you see a green leaf, orange carrot, or red rose, you are seeing the reflected color. In plant cells, pigments absorb the other colors and trap light energy.

The Food-Making Process

Chlorophyll is a pigment in plants that traps light energy. Plants use this energy to make food. **Photosynthesis,** illustrated in **Figure 15-4,** is the process in which plants use light energy to produce food.

What do plants use besides light to make food? Carbon dioxide and water are the raw materials for photosynthesis. Some of the light energy trapped in the chlorophyll is used to split water molecules. Light energy is then used to join hydrogen from the water to carbon dioxide molecules. The new molecule formed is a simple sugar called glucose. The chemical bonds of glucose contain the energy a plant uses for growth and maintenance.

Mini Lab

Observing Plant Use of Carbon Dioxide

Procedure

1. Pour 5 mL of tap water into a clean test tube.
2. Add 10 drops carbonated water and 20 drops of bromothymol blue indicator to the tap water. Place the test tube in a holder.
3. Write the color of the solution in your Science Journal.
4. Repeat steps 1 and 2. Then, add a sprig of *Elodea* to this test tube.
5. Write the color of this test tube's solution in your Science Journal.
6. Place the two test tubes in sunlight for 30 minutes. Observe the test tubes every five minutes. If using artificial lights, increase the time to one hour.

Analysis

1. In your Science Journal, describe and compare the two test tubes of solution before and after the 15 minutes.
2. What gas did you add to the solution?
3. Relate your observations to photosynthesis.

VISUALIZING
Photosynthesis

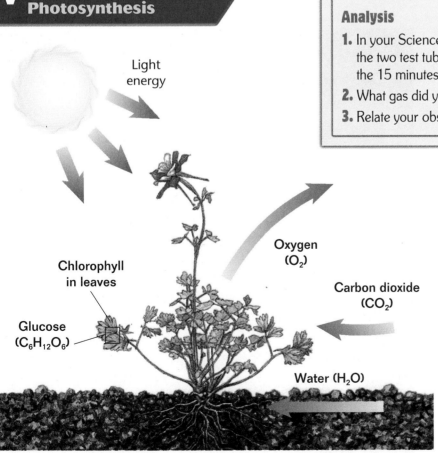

Light energy

Oxygen (O$_2$)

Chlorophyll in leaves

Carbon dioxide (CO$_2$)

Glucose (C$_6$H$_{12}$O$_6$)

Water (H$_2$O)

Figure 15-4 During photosynthesis, carbon dioxide from the air, water from the soil, and light energy react to form glucose and oxygen.

Photosynthesis is illustrated in the following equation:

$$6CO_2 + 6H_2O + \text{light energy} \longrightarrow C_6H_{12}O_6 + 6O_2$$

carbon dioxide   water   chlorophyll   glucose   oxygen

A plant needs six molecules of carbon dioxide (CO_2) and six molecules of water (H_2O) to make one molecule of glucose ($C_6H_{12}O_6$). Six molecules of oxygen gas (O_2) are also produced during photosynthesis. Light energy is used in photosynthesis, then stored in the chemical bonds that hold the glucose molecule together.

What happens to the products of photosynthesis? Most of the oxygen from photosynthesis is released through stomata. But some of it is used to break down food molecules and release the energy stored in the chemical bonds of the food molecules. This energy is used for all of the plant's life processes such as growth and reproduction. Glucose is the main form of food for plant cells. A plant usually produces more glucose than it can use. Excess glucose is stored in plants as other sugars and starches. When you eat beets, carrots, potatoes, or onions, you are eating stored food. Glucose is also the basis of a plant's structure. The cellulose in plant cell walls is made from glucose.

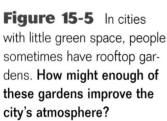

interNET
CONNECTION

Besides glucose, what other sugars do plants produce? Visit the Glencoe Science Web Site at **www.glencoe. com/sec/science** for more information about plant sugars.

Figure 15-5 In cities with little green space, people sometimes have rooftop gardens. **How might enough of these gardens improve the city's atmosphere?**

Importance of Photosynthesis

Why is photosynthesis important to living things? First, photosynthesis is food production. Organisms that carry on photosynthesis provide food for nearly all the other organisms on Earth. Second, photosynthetic organisms, like the plants in **Figure 15-5,** use carbon dioxide and release oxygen. This removes carbon dioxide from the atmosphere and replaces the oxygen most organisms, including humans, need to stay alive. As much as 90 percent of the oxygen entering our atmosphere today is a result of photosynthesis.

In most algae and photosynthetic bacteria, photosynthesis occurs in every cell. However, in green plants, only cells with chloroplasts carry on photosynthesis.

Respiration

Look at the photographs in **Figure 15-6.** Do these organisms have anything in common? Both of these organisms are similar in that they break down food to release energy.

Photosynthesis and Earth's Air

Earth's atmosphere had no oxygen before the evolution of organisms that carry on photosynthesis. In the last 2 billion years, the relative amount of oxygen in Earth's atmosphere has increased more than 50 times. What might happen if photosynthesis suddenly stopped?

Figure 15-6 Respiration, the release of energy from food, occurs in all living cells. You may know that animals such as the cheetah respire, but so do all plants such as the oak tree.

Mini Lab

Demonstrating Respiration in Yeast

Procedure 🖐 🥽 🧤 🚱

1. Pour 10 mL of bromothymol blue into a clean test tube.
2. Add 20 drops of yeast suspension and 10 drops of sugar solution.

Analysis

1. Record in your Science Journal any color change observed after five minutes, ten minutes, and 15 minutes.
2. What caused the color change you observed?
3. Compare the results of this MiniLab with those from the one earlier in the chapter.

Respiration is a series of chemical reactions by which all organisms break down food to release energy. The breakdown of food may or may not require oxygen. For organisms that are only one prokaryotic cell—a cell without a nucleus or other organelles—respiration takes place in the cytoplasm of the cell. For organisms made of one or more eukaryotic cells—cells that have a nucleus and other organelles—respiration involves organelles called mitochondria (sing., *mitochodrion*), as shown in **Figure 15-7.** Respiration that uses oxygen to chemically break down food is called aerobic respiration. The overall chemical equation for aerobic respiration is as follows.

$$C_6H_{12}O_6 \; + \; 6O_2 \longrightarrow 6CO_2 \; + \; 6H_2O \; + \; energy$$

glucose   oxygen   carbon dioxide   water

Is the equation for aerobic respiration familiar? How does it relate to the chemical equation for photosynthesis? If you look closely, you can see that aerobic respiration is the reverse of photosynthesis. Photosynthesis combines carbon dioxide and water by using light energy. The end products are glucose (food) and oxygen. During photosynthesis, energy is stored in food. Photosynthesis occurs only in cells that contain chlorophyll, such as those in the leaves of plants. Aerobic respiration

Table 15-1

Comparing Photosynthesis and Aerobic Respiration				
	Energy	**Raw materials**	**End products**	**Where**
Photosynthesis	stored	water and carbon dioxide, plus energy	glucose, oxygen	cells with chlorophyll
Aerobic respiration	released	glucose, oxygen	water and carbon dioxide, plus energy	all eukaryotic cells

combines oxygen and food to release the energy in the chemical bonds of the food. The end products of aerobic respiration are energy, carbon dioxide, and water. Aerobic respiration occurs in cells with mitochondria. It provides the energy needed by the cell and the entire organism. **Table 15-1** compares the processes of photosynthesis and aerobic respiration.

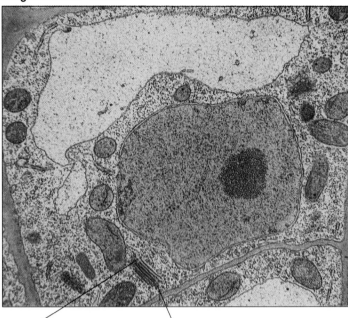

Magnification: 4000×

VISUALIZING
Respiration

Figure 15-7 Respiration takes place in the mitochondria of eukaryotic cells.

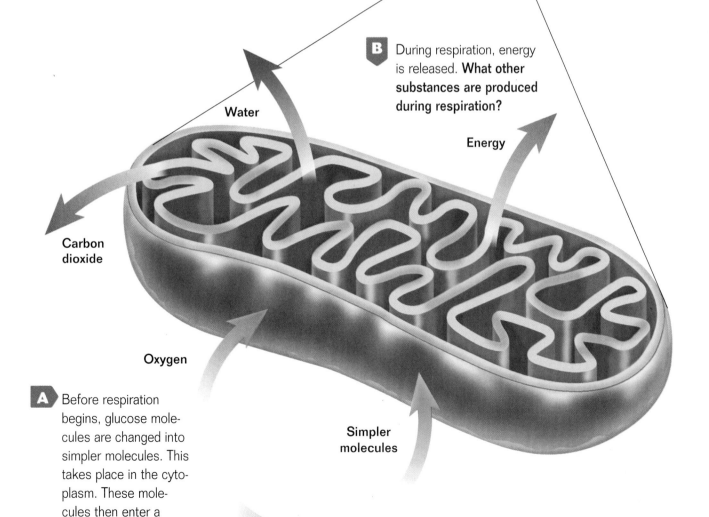

Water

B During respiration, energy is released. **What other substances are produced during respiration?**

Energy

Carbon dioxide

Oxygen

Simpler molecules

A Before respiration begins, glucose molecules are changed into simpler molecules. This takes place in the cytoplasm. These molecules then enter a mitochondrion, where they react with oxygen.

Glucose

Importance of Respiration

If food, like the items in **Figure 15-8,** contains energy, why do cells carry out the process of respiration? The energy in food molecules is in a form that cannot be used by cells. During respiration, the food energy is changed into a form all cells can use. This energy drives the life processes used by almost all organisms on Earth. Even the process of photosynthesis uses some of this energy. Aerobic respiration returns carbon dioxide to the atmosphere, where it may again be used by photosynthetic organisms.

Figure 15-8 Humans and other animals depend on the glucose produced by plants during photosynthesis. Animals use the glucose to produce energy through respiration.

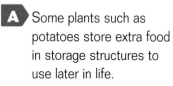 Some plants such as potatoes store extra food in storage structures to use later in life.

B Wheat and rice are important sources of food for much of the world's population.

Section Assessment

1. Explain how carbon dioxide and water vapor are exchanged by a leaf.

2. Why are photosynthesis and respiration important?

3. What must happen to food molecules before respiration begins?

4. **Think Critically:** Humidity is water vapor in the air. How do plants contribute to humidity?

5. **Skill Builder**
   Observing and Inferring To learn how observation is a good scientific tool, do the **Chapter 15 Skill Activity** on page 756.

Using Math

How many carbon dioxide molecules (CO_2) result from the aerobic respiration of one glucose molecule ($C_6H_{12}O_6$)? Refer to the equation in the section about respiration.

Activity
15•1

Stomata in Leaves

One of the interesting things about leaves is how stomata open and close to allow gases into and out of a leaf. Stomata are usually invisible without the use of a microscope. Try this activity to see some stomata for yourself.

What You'll Investigate

Where are stomata in lettuce leaves?

Goals

- **Describe** guard cells and stomata.
- **Infer** the conditions that make them open and close.

Procedure

1. Copy the Stomata Data table into your Science Journal.

2. From a head of lettuce, tear off a piece of an outer, crisp, green leaf.

3. Bend the piece of leaf in half to remove the epidermis, the transparent tissue that covers a leaf. Carefully use a pair of forceps to peel off some of the epidermis. Prepare a wet mount of this tissue.

4. Examine your wet mount slide under low and high power on the microscope. Using **Figure 15-2** as a guide, draw and label this tissue in your Science Journal.

5. Count the total number of stomata in your field of view and then count the number of open stomata. Enter these numbers in the data table.

6. Make a second slide of the lettuce leaf epidermis. This time, place a few drops of salt solution on the leaf instead of water.

7. Repeat steps 4 and 5 with the second wet mount of tissue.

Materials

- Lettuce in dish of water
- Coverslip
- Microscope
- Microscope slide
- Salt solution
- Forceps

8. Using the following equation, calculate the percent of open stomata.

(number of stomata open ÷ total number of stomata) × 100 = percent open

Stomata Data		
	Wet mount	**Salt solution mount**
Total number of stomata		
Number of open stomata		
Percent open		

Conclude and Apply

1. How are guard cells different from the other cells of the leaf epidermis?

2. **Infer** why fewer stomata were open in the salt solution mount.

3. Which slide preparation had a greater percent of open stomata?

4. What can you **infer** about the function of stomata in a leaf?

Plant Responses

What are plant responses?

What You'll Learn

► The relationship between stimuli and tropisms in plants
► Differences between long-day and short-day plants
► How plant hormones and responses are related

Vocabulary
tropism
auxin
photoperiodism
long-day plant
short-day plant
day–neutral plant

Why It's Important

► You will be a better gardener if you understand how plants respond to certain stimuli.

It's dark. You're alone in a room watching a horror film on television. Suddenly, the telephone near you rings. You jump, and your heart begins to beat faster. Did you know that you've just responded to a stimulus? A stimulus is anything in the environment that causes a change in the behavior of an organism. The organism's change in behavior is called a response. A stimulus may come from outside or inside the organism. The ringing telephone is an example of an outside stimulus. It caused you to jump, a response. Inside stimuli include chemical reactions and hormones. Hormones are substances made by cells for use somewhere else in the organism. Your beating heart is a response to inside stimuli. All living organisms, including plants, respond to stimuli. Plants respond to outside and inside stimuli. The response of a plant to an outside stimulus is a **tropism.** A tropism may be seen as movement or a change in growth. Tropisms can be positive or negative. For example, plants might grow toward or away from a stimulus.

Tropisms

Touch is one stimulus that results in a change in a plant's behavior. The pea plants in **Figure 15-9** show a response to touch. The response to touch is thigmotropism, from the Greek

Figure 15-9
The pea plant's tendrils respond to touch by coiling around things. The response to touch is called *thigmotropism.*

Figure 15-10 Plants also show phototropism. This plant is obviously growing toward the light, an example of positive phototropism. **What do you think would happen if the plant were turned halfway around?**

word *thigma*, meaning "touch." Plants also respond to the stimuli of light, gravity, temperature, and amount of water.

Did you ever see a plant leaning toward a window? Light is an important stimulus to plants. When a plant responds to sunlight, the cells on the side of the plant opposite the light get longer than those facing the light. This causes the plant to bend toward the light. The response of a plant to light is called phototropism. A plant growing toward light is called a positive phototropism, as shown in **Figure 15-10.**

The response of an organism to gravity is called gravitropism. The downward growth of plant roots is a positive gravitropism. A stem growing upward is a negative gravitropism.

Plant Hormones

When you visit a supermarket or fruit stand, have you ever noticed that oranges are all about the same size and color? In nature, orange trees flower and produce fruit over a period of time. How do growers get fruits to respond so that most of it is ripe when it reaches the market? One way that growers do this is by using plant hormones.

Auxin and Ethylene

Plant hormones are chemical substances that affect growth. An **auxin** is a type of plant hormone. One of the ways auxin affects plants is that it causes plant stems and leaves to exhibit positive phototropism. When light shines on a plant from one side, the auxin moves to the shaded side of the stem. The auxin causes cells on the shaded side of the stem to increase in length. This causes the stem to curve toward the light.

*inter*NET
CONNECTION

Auxin and ethylene are just two of the hormones found in plants. Visit the Glencoe Science Web Site at **www.glencoe. com/sec/science** for more information about other plant hormones.

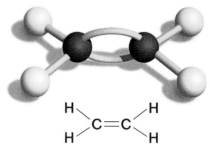

Figure 15-11 Ethylene, C_2H_4, is the plant hormone responsible for fruit ripening, such as these grapes.

Many plants produce the hormone ethylene, a chemical of carbon and hydrogen, as illustrated in **Figure 15-11.** Ethylene causes different plant responses. One response is that it causes fruit to ripen.

Today, fruit growers and shippers use this knowledge to get ripe fruit to market. Fruits such as oranges, grapes, and bananas are picked when they are still green. Green fruit is easier to handle because it does not bruise like ripe fruit does. During shipping, green fruit is exposed to ethylene gas. When the fruit arrives at the store, most of it has ripened.

Problem Solving

Predicting Plant Responses

Jason and his family returned from their two-week vacation and found that several potted plants on the patio were on their sides. After unpacking the car, Jason began to set up the potted plants. To his surprise, the plants looked like they were growing sideways. Later that day, Jason's grandmother telephoned. Jason told her about the plants. She told him not to worry because the plants would soon start to grow upright again.

Solve the Problem

1. Explain why the plants grew as they did.

2. What hormone may have played a part in this plant response?

Think Critically: Predict what Jason might find if he removed a plant's pot and looked at its roots. Explain.

Photoperiods

Sunflowers bloom in the summer, and cherry trees flower in the spring. Some plant species produce flowers at specific times during the year. **Photoperiodism** is a plant's response to the number of hours of daylight and darkness it receives daily.

Earth makes one revolution around the sun every year. As it moves in its orbit about the sun, Earth also rotates. One rotation takes 24 hours. Because Earth is tilted about 23.5° from a line perpendicular to its orbit, the hours of daylight and darkness vary with the seasons. You may have noticed that the sun sets later in summer than in winter. These changes in lengths of daylight and darkness affect plant growth.

Most plants require a specific length of darkness to begin the flowering process. Generally, plants that require less than ten to 12 hours of darkness are called **long-day plants.** You may be familiar with long-day plants such as spinach, lettuce, and beets. Those plants that need 12 or more hours of darkness are called **short-day plants.** Some short-day plants are poinsettias, strawberries, and ragweed. **Figure 15-12** shows both long-day plants and short-day plants. ✔

Reading Check ✔

What is needed to begin the flowering process?

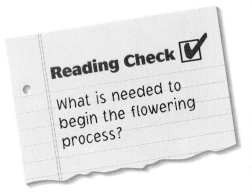

Figure 15-12 Long-day plants such as zinnias (A) and short-day plants such as primroses (B) flower in response to specific periods of darkness.

Figure 15-13 Day-neutral plants, as seen in this garden, produce flowers all summer long.

Other plants like the marigolds shown in **Figure 15-13** are day-neutral. **Day-neutral plants** have no specific photoperiod, and the flowering process can begin within a range of hours of darkness.

In nature, photoperiodism is one factor that affects where flowering plants can grow and produce fruit. Even if the proper temperature and other growing conditions for a plant are in a particular environment, the plant will not flower and produce fruit without the correct photoperiod. Sometimes, the photoperiod of a plant has a narrow range. For example, some soybeans will flower with 14.5 hours of daylight but will not flower with only 14 hours of daylight. Farmers must choose the variety of soybeans with a photoperiod that matches the hours of daylight where they plant their crop.

Today, greenhouse growers can provide any length of artificial daylight or darkness. This means that all types of flowers are available year-round. You can buy short-day plants during the summer and long-day plants during the winter.

Section Assessment

1. Describe the difference between a response and a tropism.
2. Compare photoperiodism and phototropism.
3. Some red raspberries produce fruit in late spring, then again in the fall. What term describes their photoperiod?
4. **Think Critically:** What is the relationship between plant hormones and tropisms?
5. **Skill Builder**
   Comparing and Contrasting Different plant parts exhibit positive and negative tropisms. Compare and contrast the responses of roots, stems, and leaves to light. If you need help, refer to Comparing and Contrasting in the **Skill Handbook** on page 720.

Science Journal
For three years, a farmer in Costa Rica grew healthy strawberry plants. But, each year he was disappointed because the plants never produced any fruit. In your Science Journal, explain why this happened.

1

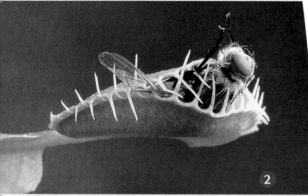

2

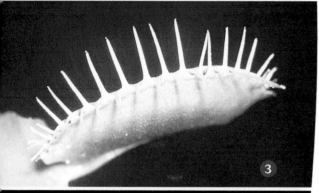

3

Carnivorous Plants

Carnivorous plants grow in soils that lack or are low in certain nutrients, particularly nitrogen. Over time, these plants have evolved ways to secure the nutrients they need. A Venus's-flytrap is one kind of carnivorous plant. It is currently on the list of endangered species. The ones available in stores are grown in nurseries because collecting Venus's-flytraps in the wild is illegal.

EATING HABITS OF A VENUS'S-FLYTRAP

1 The leaves form a hinged trap. Each half of the trap has three trigger hairs (see arrow) in a triangular arrangement.

2 When an insect or other small animal touches two of these hairs in quick succession, it causes a series of reactions that snap the trap shut within 0.4 s.

3 Stiff hairs along the outer edges of the leaf interlock, preventing the animal's escape.

4 Glands on the leaf secrete enzymes that help digest the prey. The glands are stimulated as the prey struggles to get free.

5 Digestion takes about ten days. During this time, the plant absorbs the digested nutrients. The leaf opens again when digestion and absorption are complete. The insect remains are then blown away.

Think Critically

1. Insects and other small animals provide carnivorous plants with nitrogen compounds. From what other sources do these plants get nutrients?

2. A pitcher plant is another carnivorous plant. Look again at the name of this plant. How do you think this plant traps its prey?

Plant Tropisms

Possible Materials

- Petri dish
- Tape
- String
- Corn seeds
- Bean seeds
- Paper towels
- Water

Have you ever seen a Venus's-flytrap's leaves close around an insect? Its movement was a response to a stimulus. In this case, the stimulus was the movement of the insect against sensitive, hairlike structures on the leaves. Tropisms are specific plant responses to stimuli outside of the plant. They can be positive or negative. What stimuli will cause responses by plants?

Recognize the Problem

How do plants respond to stimuli?

Form a Hypothesis

Based on your knowledge of tropisms, state a hypothesis about how the plant will respond to a stimulus.

Goals

- **Design** an experiment that tests the effects of a variable.
- **Observe** and analyze a plant response to a stimulus.

Safety Precautions

Some kinds of seeds are poisonous. Do not put any seed in your mouth.

Test Your Hypothesis

Plan

1. As a group, agree upon and write out a hypothesis statement.

2. As a group, **list** the steps needed to test your hypothesis. Be specific, describing exactly what you will do at each step. **List** your materials.

3. It is important to keep the seeds moist during the experiment. **Devise a method** to keep your seeds moist.

4. **Read** over your entire experiment to make sure that all your steps are in a logical order.

5. **Identify** any constants, variables, and controls of the experiment.

6. Is it necessary to run any tests more than one time?

7. If you need a data table, design one in your Science Journal so that it is ready to use as your group collects data.

8. Will the data be summarized in a graph? If yes, what kind of graph would be most useful?

Do

1. Make sure your teacher approves your plan before you proceed.

2. Carry out the experiment as planned.

3. While you are conducting the experiment, write down any observations that you make and complete the data table in your Science Journal.

Analyze Your Data

1. **Compare** your results with those of other groups.

2. **Identify** how the plants responded to the stimulus.

Draw Conclusions

1. What name would you give to the response you observed?

2. **Classify** the responses as positive or negative.

3. Infer why many plant growers sprout seeds under artificial light from lamps that are placed just a short distance above the soil.

Chapter 15 Reviewing Main Ideas

For a **preview** of this chapter, study this Reviewing Main Ideas before you read the chapter. After you have studied this chapter, you can use the Reviewing Main Ideas to **review** the chapter.

GLENCOE TECHNOLOGY The Glencoe MindJogger, Audiocassettes, and CD-ROM provide additional opportunities for review.

Section

15-1 PHOTOSYNTHESIS AND RESPIRATION

Gases like carbon dioxide and water vapor enter and leave a plant through openings called **stomata.** Stomata are usually found in the epidermis covering a leaf. Two guard cells surround each stoma. Water diffusing into and out of the guard cells causes stomata to open and close. ***What role do stomata play in transpiration?***

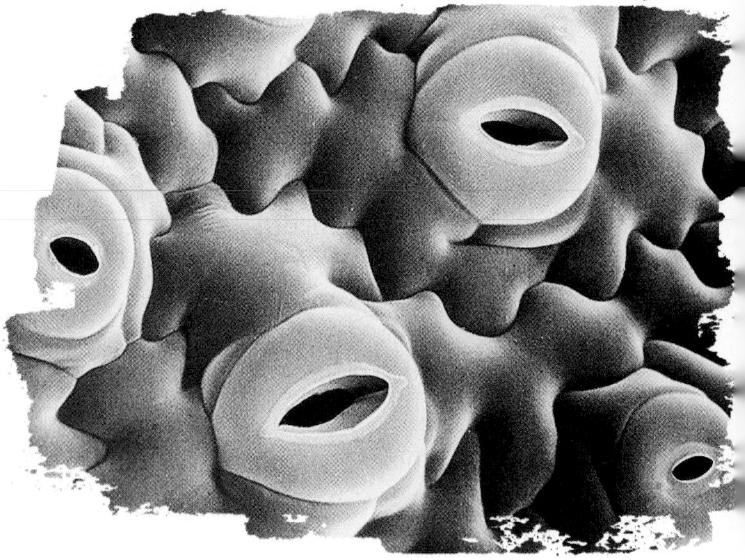

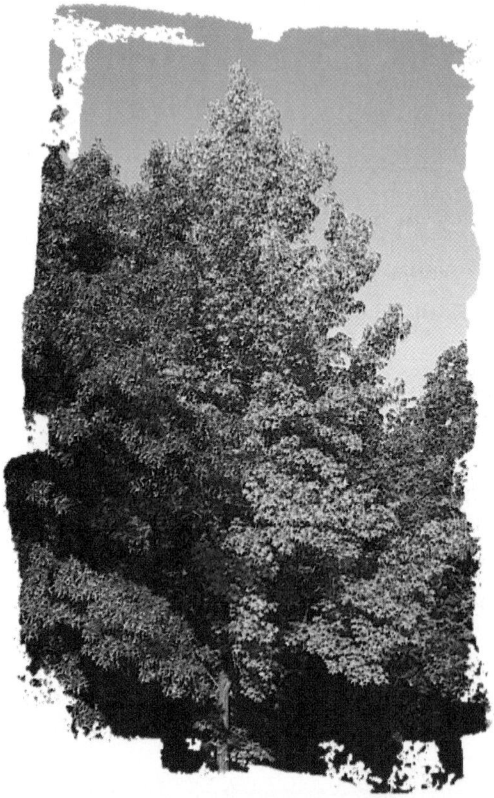

PHOTOSYNTHESIS

In plants, food is produced during the process of **photosynthesis.** Photosynthesis takes place in the chloroplasts of plant cells. Light energy is trapped by chlorophyll, the green pigment in chloroplasts. This energy is used to produce glucose and oxygen from carbon dioxide and water. The energy is stored in the chemical bonds of glucose. Photosynthesis provides the food for most organisms on Earth. ***Why are plants called producers?***

Reading Check ✓

What approach to reading is most helpful to you? Is it asking yourself questions, outlining, or something else? Share your approach with another student.

RESPIRATION

All organisms use **respiration** to release the energy stored in food molecules. The process begins in the cytoplasm of cells. First, food molecules are broken down into simpler forms. In prokaryotic cells, the process continues in the cytoplasm and some energy is released. Eukaryotic cells generally use oxygen to complete respiration. The release of energy occurs in the mitochondria. Carbon dioxide and water vapor are also products of respiration in eukaryotic cells. *What are the three products of respiration for most eukaryotic cells?*

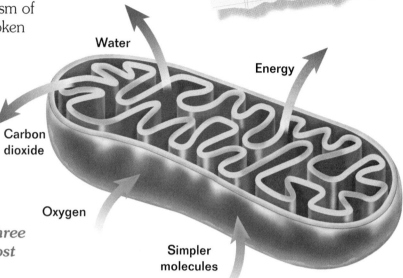

Water

Energy

Carbon dioxide

Oxygen

Simpler molecules

Glucose

Section

15-2 PLANT RESPONSES

Plants respond to stimuli. The response may be a movement, change in growth, or the beginning of some process, such as flowering. A stimulus from outside the plant is called a **tropism.** Outside stimuli include such things as light, gravity, and touch. The lengths of daylight and darkness each day may affect flowering times of plants. Hormones are stimuli from inside plants. These chemicals affect plants in many ways. **Auxin** and ethylene are two plant hormones. *What things may act as outside stimuli for plants?*

Chapter 15 Assessment

Using Vocabulary

a. auxin
b. day-neutral plant
c. long-day plant
d. photoperiodism
e. photosynthesis
f. respiration
g. short-day plant
h. stomata
i. transpiration
j. tropism

Match each phrase with the correct term from the list of Vocabulary words.

1. a plant hormone
2. using light to make glucose and oxygen
3. loss of water through stomata
4. plant that requires long nights to flower
5. releases energy from food

Checking Concepts

Choose the word or phrase that best answers the question.

6. What enters a plant when stomata open?
   A) sugar
   B) water
   C) carbon dioxide
   D) light

7. Which of these is a product of respiration?
   A) CO_2
   B) O_2
   C) C_2H_4
   D) H_2

8. Water, carbon dioxide, and energy are all products of what plant process?
   A) cell division
   B) photosynthesis
   C) growth
   D) respiration

9. What type of plant needs short nights to flower?
   A) day-neutral
   B) short-day
   C) long-day
   D) nonvascular

10. What do you call such things as light, touch, and gravity that cause plant responses?
    A) tropisms
    B) growth behaviors
    C) responses
    D) stimuli

11. What is a plant's response to gravity called?
    A) phototropism
    B) gravitropism
    C) thigmotropism
    D) hydrotropism

12. What are plant substances that affect plant growth called?
    A) tropisms
    B) glucose
    C) germination
    D) hormones

13. Leaves change colors because what substance breaks down?
    A) hormone
    B) carotenoid
    C) chlorophyll
    D) cytoplasm

14. What is a function of stomata?
    A) photosynthesis
    B) to guard the interior cells
    C) to allow sugar to escape
    D) to permit the release of oxygen

15. What are the products of photosynthesis?
    A) glucose and oxygen
    B) carbon dioxide and water
    C) chlorophyll and glucose
    D) carbon dioxide and oxygen

Thinking Critically

16. Growers of bananas pick green bananas, then treat them with ethylene during shipping. Why?

17. Identify each response as a positive or negative tropism.
    a. stem grows up
    b. roots grow down
    c. plant grows toward light
    d. a vine grows around a pole

18. Scientists who study sedimentary rocks and fossils suggest that oxygen did not occur on Earth until plantlike protists appeared. Why?

19. Explain why crab apple trees bloom in the spring but not in the summer.

20. Why do day-neutral and long-day plants grow best in countries near the equator?

Developing Skills

If you need help, refer to the **Skill Handbook.**

21. **Hypothesizing:** Make a hypothesis about when guard cells open and close in desert plants.

22. **Designing an Experiment to Test a Hypothesis:** Design an experiment to test your hypothesis from question 21.

23. **Observing and Inferring:** Based on your knowledge of plants, infer how the number and location of stomata differ in land and water plants.

24. **Classifying:** Make a chart that classifies these plants according to their photoperiod: flower year-round—corn, dandelion, tomato; flower in the spring, fall, or winter—chrysanthemum, rice, poinsettia; flower in summer—spinach, lettuce, petunias.

25. **Comparing and Contrasting:** Compare and contrast the action of auxin and the action of ethylene on a plant.

26. **Concept Mapping:** Complete the following concept map using the terms and plants in question 24.

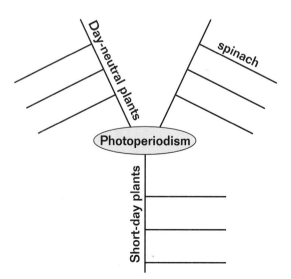

Test-Taking Tip

You Are Smarter Than You Think
Nothing on the science tests you will take this year is too difficult for you to understand. You can learn to master any of it. Be self-confident, and just keep practicing.

Test Practice

Use these questions to test your Science Proficiency.

1. What diffuses into and out of guard cells, causing them to open and close?
   A) carbon dioxide
   B) ethylene
   C) water
   D) glucose

2. What does respiration provide for every cell?
   A) energy
   B) food
   C) oxygen
   D) water

3. What is a plant's change in behavior to an outside stimulus called?
   A) hormone
   B) tropism
   C) transpiration
   D) reactant

4. What term is used for a plant's response to the number of hours of daylight and darkness it receives daily?
   A) gravitropism
   B) thigmotropism
   C) transpiration
   D) photoperiodism

CHAPTER

16 Plant Reproduction

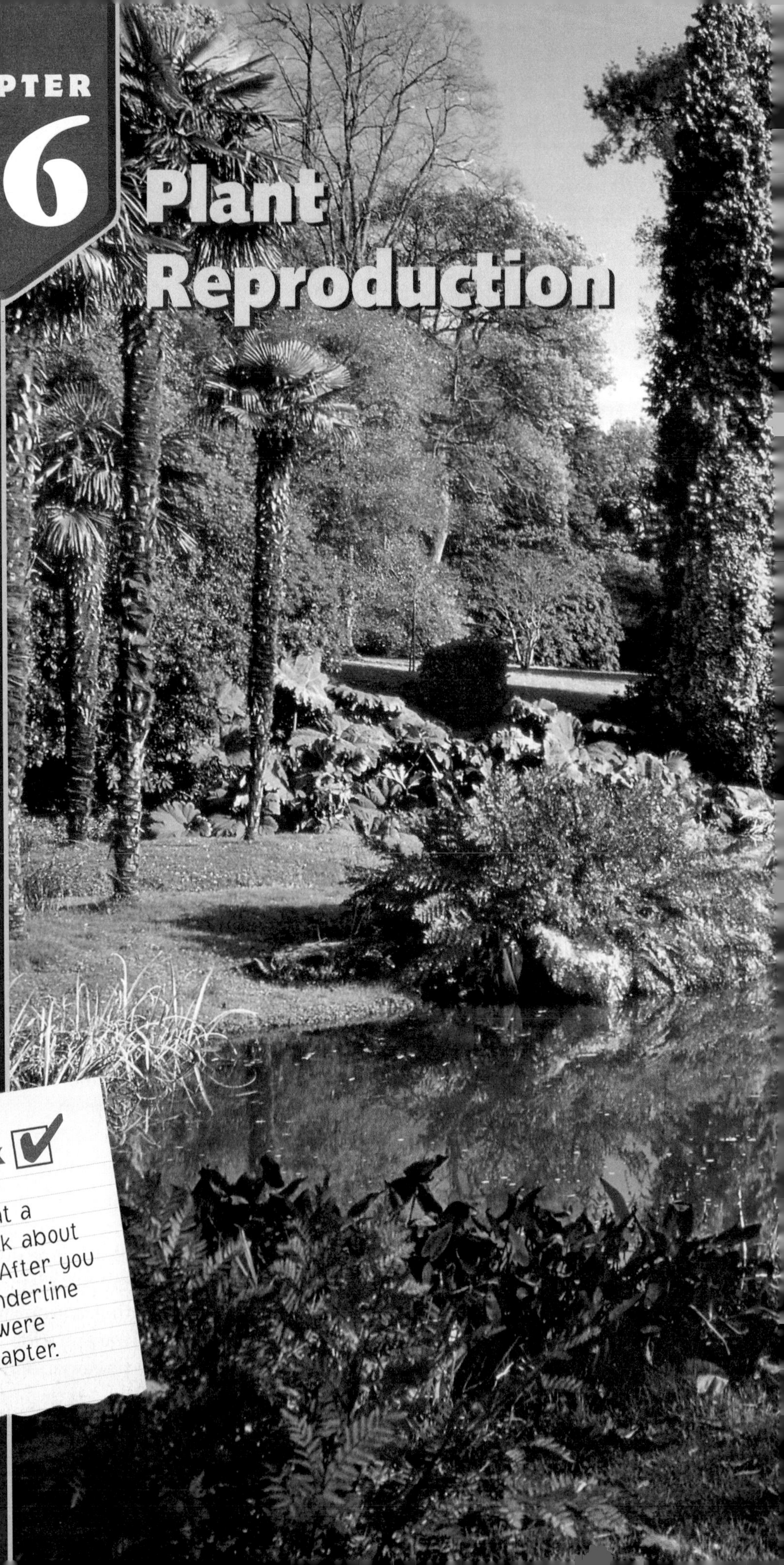

Chapter Preview

Skills Preview

Skill Builders

- Classify
- Hypothesize

Activities

- Compare and Contrast
- Design an Experiment to Test a Hypothesis

MiniLabs

- Observe
- Identify

Reading Check

List ten questions that a young child might ask about plant reproduction. After you read the chapter, underline the questions that were answered in the chapter.

Explore Activity

It's almost spring! The shelves in the garden center are over-flowing with seed packets. Many familiar plants, like some of the plants you see here, grow from seeds. Some seeds come from flowers and others from cones. Seeds are just one way plants reproduce. To find out more about seeds, try the activity below. Then, in the chapter that follows, learn about the different ways plants reproduce.

Observe the Inside of a Seed

1. Obtain a lima bean or other large seed.

2. If the seed is hard and dry, place it in water overnight.

3. Observe the seed and describe it in your Science Journal.

4. Remove the paperlike covering from the seed and carefully pull apart the seed halves.

5. Look for the parts of the immature plant on one side of the seed.

Science Journal

In your Science Journal, identify the different parts of the immature plant.

Why It's Important

► You'll be aware that you
can grow new plants without
using seeds.

Figure 16-1 Plants are living
organisms that have all the characteristics of life.

Types of Reproduction

You and the garden plants shown in **Figure 16-1** are living
organisms. But, you don't have leaves or roots, and a plant
doesn't have a heart or a brain. Despite your differences, you
are alike in many ways. You both can make similar copies
of yourselves. This process is called reproduction. In this
chapter, you'll learn how plants reproduce.

Sexual Reproduction

Plant sexual reproduction is similar to animal sexual reproduction. Both require fertilization, which is the combining of
an egg and a sperm. Like animals, the plant's egg is produced
in the female reproductive organs, and sperm are produced
in male reproductive organs. The process of meiosis forms
these sex cells. Meiosis is two divisions of a reproductive
cell's nucleus. Meiosis results in four sex cells. Sex cells
are haploid cells. That means that each sex cell has half the
chromosomes of the original cell.

Male and female reproductive organs of plants may be on
the same plant or on separate plants. For example, holly
plants are referred to as male or female. A female holly, as
shown in **Figure 16-2,** has flowers that have only female
reproductive structures. Most plants have both sexes on one

Figure 16-2 Holly berries develop after the egg is fertilized.

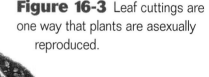

interNET
CONNECTION

Visit the Glencoe
Science Web Site at
**www.glencoe.com/
sec/science** for more
information on plants that
are male and female like
holly.

plant and can reproduce by themselves. Plants, such as apples and pears, have flowers with both sexes, but it takes another plant for fertilization to happen.

Many plants depend on animals or environmental factors to help get the egg and sperm together. For most plants, a seed develops following fertilization. A spore develops in some plants, such as mosses and ferns.

Asexual Reproduction

Have you ever eaten seedless oranges and grapes? If these plants do not produce seeds, how do growers get new plants? Growers can produce new plants by asexual reproduction. Because most plant cells have the ability to grow into other cell types, a new plant can be produced from just part of a plant. For example, roots and leaves can grow from just a portion of the stem. The begonia shown in **Figure 16-3** is being asexually reproduced. A plant produced by asexual reproduction is genetically identical to the original plant. The plant part(s) used for asexual reproduction varies from species to species. People have used these methods of reproducing plants for centuries. You or someone you know may grow plants this way.

Figure 16-3 Leaf cuttings are one way that plants are asexually reproduced.

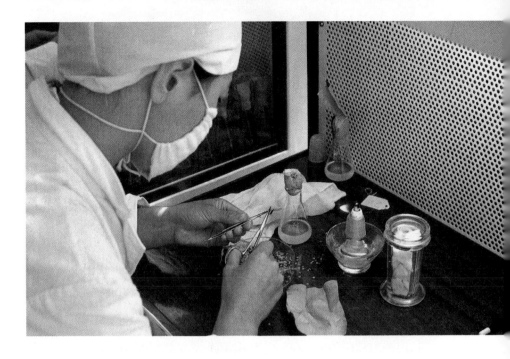

Figure 16-4 Many plants can be produced from just a few plant cells when grown using tissue culture techniques. Many orchids are reproduced by tissue culture.

Tissue culture is a form of asexual reproduction that uses a cluster of young cells to produce plants. This technology allows many identical plants to be produced from just a small portion of one plant. However, tissue culture requires special laboratory equipment and procedures, as in **Figure 16-4.**

Haploid and Diploid Stages

Every plant has a life cycle that contains two stages. The gametophyte (guh MEET uh fite) stage begins when cells in reproductive organs undergo meiosis. The cells formed are haploid (n). This means they contain half the number of chromosomes of a reproductive diploid cell. These haploid cells undergo mitosis to form plant structures. When all plant structures are made of haploid cells, it is called the **gametophyte stage.** Fertilization is the beginning of the sporophyte (SPOR uh fite) stage. Because cells in this stage are formed after fertilization, they have pairs of chromosomes, or are diploid. In the **sporophyte stage,** plant structures are made of cells with the diploid number ($2n$) of chromosomes. As you will learn in this chapter, these stages are different for different plant groups.

Seedless Plants

Have you ever walked in a cool, damp, shaded forest or woods and noticed that only leafy plants like ferns were growing near the ground? Sometimes, mosses cover the ground or grow on logs. Ferns and mosses are two types of seedless plants. They reproduce sexually by spores, not by seeds.

Using Math

A diploid apple has 34 chromosomes. How many chromosomes do cells in the gametophyte stage and cells in the sporophyte stage have?

The Moss Life Cycle

The life cycle of a moss is shown in **Figure 16-5.** You may know mosses as green, low-growing masses of plants. This is the gametophyte stage that produces the sex cells. Sometimes, a gametophyte moss plant has just male or female reproductive structures. Usually, both are on the same plant. For mosses, water is needed for fertilization. During a heavy dew or rain, water carries the sperm from the male reproductive structure to the female reproductive structure. Sperm swim to the eggs and fertilization occurs. A diploid cell forms, called a zygote. This is the beginning of the sporophyte stage. The zygote undergoes mitosis and develops into an embryo. The embryo grows into the mature sporophyte. ☑

A moss sporophyte usually grows from the tip of the gametophyte. The sporophyte is not green and cannot carry on photosynthesis. It depends on the gametophyte for water and nutrients. The sporophyte consists of a stalk and a capsule. Inside the capsule, many cells undergo meiosis and form hundreds of haploid spores. When environmental conditions are just right, the capsule opens and releases the spores. If a spore lands on wet soil or rocks, it may grow into a green, threadlike structure. New moss gametophytes grow from this structure and the cycle begins again. When a plant's life cycle alternates between a sex-cell producing stage and a spore-producing stage, it is called **alternation of generations.** Liverworts have similar life cycles.

Reading Check
What event comes before the sporophyte stage of a moss's life cycle?

Figure 16-5 The life cycle of a moss alternates between gametophyte and sporophyte stages. **What is produced by the gametophyte stage?**

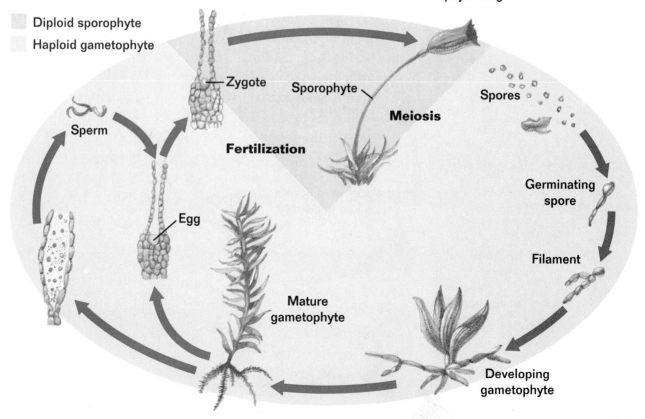

Diploid sporophyte
Haploid gametophyte

Zygote   Sporophyte   Spores

Sperm   Meiosis

Fertilization

Egg   Germinating
                                             spore

                                           Filament

              Mature
              gametophyte

                                    Developing
                                    gametophyte

Mosses and liverworts may reproduce asexually. If a piece of a moss gametophyte plant breaks off, it may grow into a new plant. Liverworts reproduce asexually by forming small balls of cells on the surface of the gametophyte plant. These are carried away by water and may grow into new gametophyte plants.

The Fern Life Cycle

Like mosses, ferns have alternation of generations. The life cycle of a fern is illustrated in **Figure 16-6.** The fern plants that you see in nature or as houseplants are fern sporophyte plants. The leaves, called **fronds,** grow from an underground stem called a **rhizome.** Roots grow from the rhizome, anchor the plant, and absorb water and nutrients. Fern sporophytes make their own food.

Spores are produced in structures called **sori** (sing., *sorus*) on the underside of the fronds. Sori usually look like crusty rust-, brown-, or blackish-colored bumps. When a sorus opens, it exposes the spore cases. Inside each spore case, cells have undergone meiosis to form spores. Thousands of fern spores are ejected when spore cases open.

If fern spores land on damp soil or rocks, they can grow into small, green, heart-shaped gametophyte plants. The fern gametophyte is called a **prothallus** (proh THAL us). It can

Figure 16-6 A fern's life cycle is similar in many ways to the life cycle of a moss. However, the sporophyte and gametophyte are both photosynthetic and can survive and grow without the other.

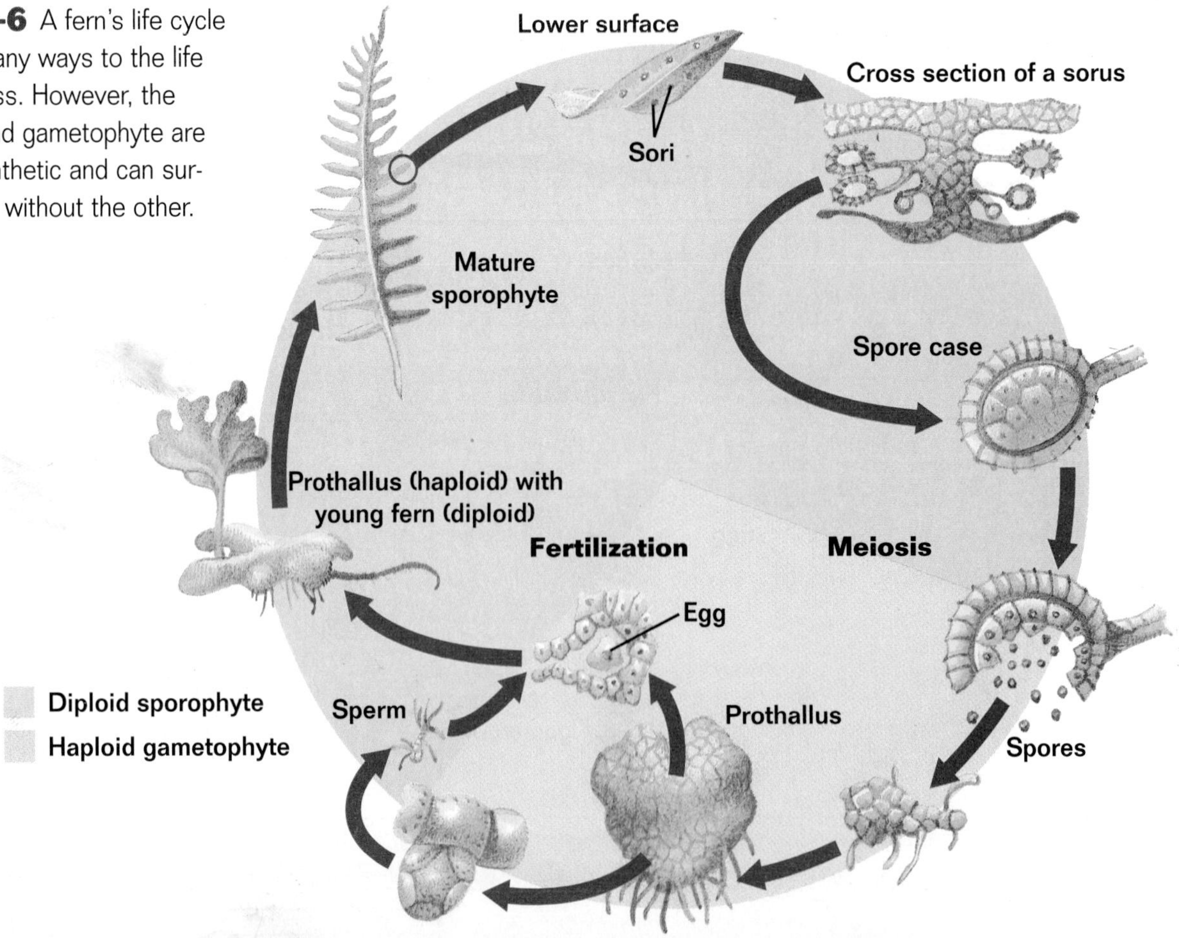

Lower surface

Cross section of a sorus

Sori

Spore case

Mature sporophyte

Meiosis

Prothallus (haploid) with young fern (diploid)

Fertilization

Egg

Sperm

Prothallus

Spores

Diploid sporophyte

Haploid gametophyte

make its own food and absorb water and nutrients from the soil. The prothallus has both male and female reproductive structures. Sex cells form, and water is needed to bring them together. The zygote forms by fertilization. It grows into the familiar fern plant.

Ferns may reproduce asexually, also. Fern rhizomes grow and form branches. New fronds develop from each branch as shown in **Figure 16-7**. The new rhizome branch and fronds can be separated from the main plant. It can grow on its own and form more fern plants.

Figure 16-7 New plants grow from the rhizome of a fern.

Section Assessment

1. Describe the life cycle of mosses.
2. Explain the stages in the life cycle of a fern.
3. **Think Critically:** You see a plant that you like and want to grow an identical one. What type of plant reproduction would you use? Why?

4. **Skill Builder**
   Sequencing The life cycle of a plant is a sequence of events. Do the **Chapter 16 Skill Activity** on page 757 to learn about the events in the life cycle of a fern and those in the life cycle of a pine.

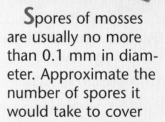

Using Math

Spores of mosses are usually no more than 0.1 mm in diameter. Approximate the number of spores it would take to cover one side of a penny.

Materials

- Live mosses, liverworts, and ferns with gameto- phytes and sporophytes
- Hand lens
- Forceps
- Dropper
- Microscope slide and coverslip
- Microscope
- Dissecting needle
- Pencil with eraser

Comparing Mosses, Liverworts, and Ferns

Mosses and liverworts make up the division of plants called Bryophyta. Ferns make up the division Pterophyta and are called pteridophytes (tuh RIH duh fites). Try this activity to observe the similarities and differences in these groups of plants.

What You'll Investigate

How are the gametophyte and sporophyte stages of liver- worts, mosses, and ferns similar and different?

Goals

- **Describe** the sporophyte and gametophyte forms of liverworts, mosses, and ferns.
- **Identify** the spore-producing structures of liverworts, mosses, and ferns.

Procedure

1. Obtain a gametophyte of each plant. With a hand lens, **observe** the rhizoids, leafy parts, and stemlike parts, if any are present.

2. Obtain a sporophyte of each plant and use a hand lens to **observe** it.

3. Locate the spore structure on the moss plant. **Remove** it and place it in a drop of water on the slide. Place a coverslip over it. Use the eraser of a pencil to gently push on the cover- slip to release the spores. **CAUTION:** *Do not break the coverslip.* **Observe** the spores under low and high power.

4. Make labeled drawings of all observations in your Science Journal.

Conclude and Apply

1. For each plant, **compare** the gametophyte's appearance to the sporophyte's appearance.

2. List the structure(s) common to all three plants.

3. **Form a hypothesis** about why each plant produces a large number of spores.

Using Similar Triangles to Solve Problems

Trees, Trees, Trees

Prairie Creek, California, is home to the largest known coastal redwood in the United States. If you stood next to this towering tree on a sunny day, you could calculate its height. Remember that two similar triangles have the same shape but are different sizes. The sides of similar triangles are proportional. Using this relationship, you can follow these steps to find the tree's height.

Calculating Tree Height

At a certain time of day, the redwood's shadow measures 187.8 m. At the same time, a person 1.5 m tall stands near the tree and casts a shadow 3 m long. Both the tree and the person form 90° angles with the ground. The sun's angle is the same for both the tree and the person. Because the triangles formed by each shadow, each object, and the sun's angle are proportional, the height of the tree can be calculated.

1. Write a proportion comparing the heights of objects to lengths of shadows (all measurements are in meters):

$$\frac{\text{height of person}}{\text{height of tree}} = \frac{\text{length of person's shadow}}{\text{length of tree's shadow}}$$

$$\frac{1.5}{h} = \frac{3}{187.8}$$

2. Find the cross products of the proportion:
$$1.5 \times 187.8 = 3 \times h$$
$$281.7 = 3 \times h$$

3. To find the value of h, divide both sides of the equation by 3:

$$\frac{281.7}{3} = \frac{3h}{3} \qquad 93.9 = h$$

The height of the tree is about 93.9 m.

Practice
PROBLEMS

1. The largest American elm tree grows in Louisville, Kansas. When the elm casts a shadow of 17.4 m, a nearby, 0.9 m fence post has a 0.6 m shadow. Find the height of the American elm.

2. Cuba, New Mexico, is home to the largest piñon pine. When it casts a shadow of 27.6 m, a nearby, 0.45 m shrub casts a shadow of 0.6 m. Find the height of the piñon pine.

3. Try this method on a tall object in your neighborhood at two different times on the same day. Did the time of day affect your calculations?

Seed Plant Reproduction

Gymnosperm Reproduction

Have you ever collected pine cones or used them in a craft project? If you have, you probably noticed that there are many shapes and sizes of pine cones. Cones are the reproductive structures on plants called gymnosperms (JIHM nuh spurmz). Each gymnosperm species has a different cone.

Pines are typical gymnosperms. Each pine produces male cones and female cones on the sporophyte plant. A mature female cone consists of a spiral of woody scales on a short stem. At the base of each scale are two ovules. Each **ovule** contains an egg cell, food-storage tissue, and a sticky fluid. **Pollen grains** develop on the smaller male cone. Two sperm eventually form in each pollen grain. As seen in **Figure 16-8,** a cloud of pollen grains is released from each male cone.

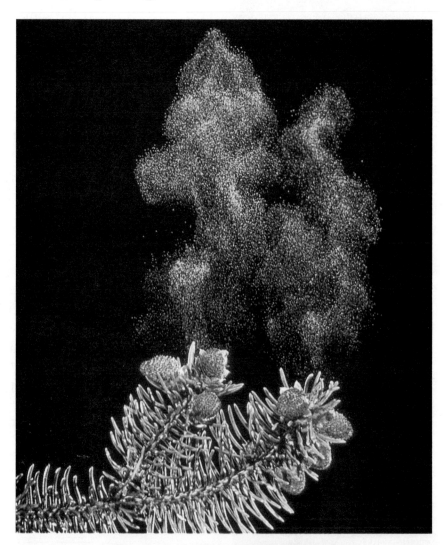

Figure 16-8 Male cones of a Norway spruce release clouds of tiny pollen grains.

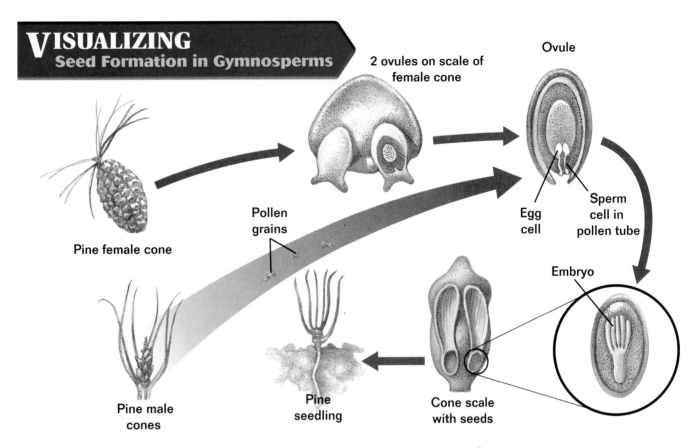

2 ovules on scale of female cone

Ovule

Pine female cone

Pollen grains

Egg cell

Sperm cell in pollen tube

Embryo

Pine male cones

Pine seedling

Cone scale with seeds

Wind carries the pollen to female cones. However, most of the pollen falls on other plants, the ground, and bodies of water. If a pollen grain is blown between the scales of a female cone, it may be trapped in the sticky fluid secreted by the ovule. When the pollen grain and female cone are the same species, a pollen tube grows from the pollen grain toward the ovule. Fertilization may happen as much as 15 months later. The two sperm move down the pollen tube. One fertilizes the egg cell, and the other breaks down. As a result, a zygote forms that develops into an embryo. **Figure 16-9** illustrates this process.

Female cones of pines mature, open, and release their seeds, usually during the fall or winter months. It may take a long time for seeds to be released from a pine cone. From the moment a pollen grain falls on the female cone until the time the seeds are released may take two or three years. Released seeds are carried away, eaten, or buried by animals. Under favorable conditions, the buried seeds will grow into new pines.

Figure 16-9 It may take two or three years for the seed of a female cone to form. **Where would you find the seed?**

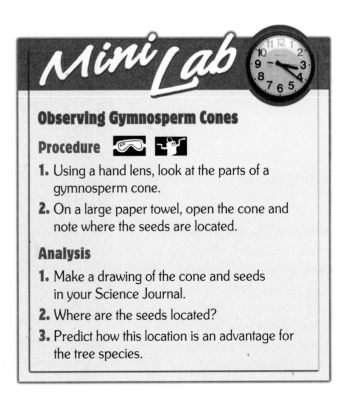

Mini Lab

Observing Gymnosperm Cones

Procedure

1. Using a hand lens, look at the parts of a gymnosperm cone.
2. On a large paper towel, open the cone and note where the seeds are located.

Analysis

1. Make a drawing of the cone and seeds in your Science Journal.
2. Where are the seeds located?
3. Predict how this location is an advantage for the tree species.

Angiosperm Reproduction

Angiosperms all produce flowers. Flowers are important because they contain the reproductive organs. When you think of a flower, you probably imagine something with a pleasant aroma and colorful petals. Although many such flowers do exist, some flowers are drab and have no aroma. Have you ever looked at the flowers of wheat, rice, or grass? Why do you think there is such variety among flowers?

The Flower

A flower's appearance may tell you something about the life of the plant it is part of. Large flowers with bright-colored petals often attract insects and other animals. These animals may eat the flower, its nectar, or pollen. As they move about the flower, the animals may get pollen on their wings, legs, or other body parts. As a result, these animals may spread the flower's pollen to other plants that they visit. Other flowers depend on wind, rain, or gravity to spread their pollen. Their petals may be small or absent. Flowers that open only at night, as seen in **Figure 16-10,** often have strong scents to attract animals.

Figure 16-10 Some flowers bloom only at night. They are usually light colored or white, and they produce large amounts of scent molecules, nectar, and pollen. **Aside from bats, what other animals might pollinate night-blooming plants?**

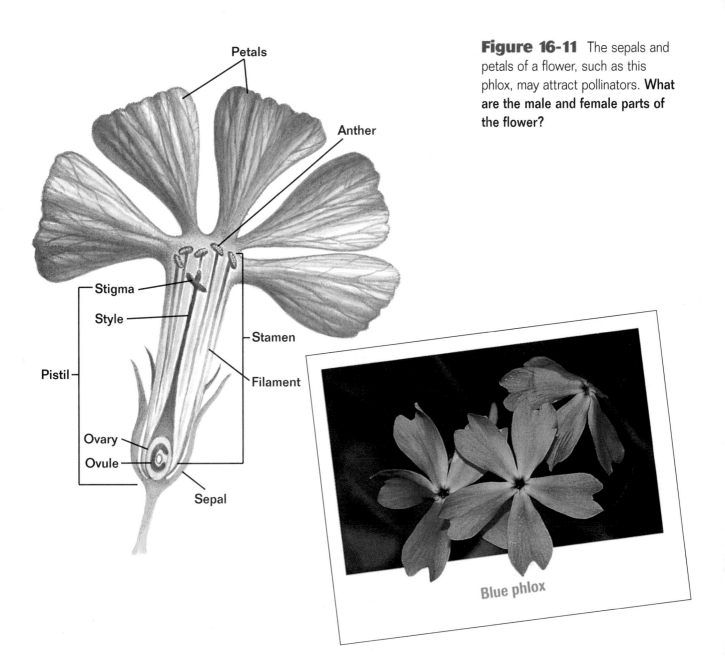

Petals

Anther

Stigma

Style

Stamen

Pistil

Filament

Ovary

Ovule

Sepal

Figure 16-11 The sepals and petals of a flower, such as this phlox, may attract pollinators. **What are the male and female parts of the flower?**

Blue phlox

Generally, the colored parts of a flower are the petals. Outside the petals are usually leaflike parts called sepals. Sepals are easy to see when a flower is still a bud. Sepals form the outside of the bud and cover the petals. In some flowers, the sepals are as colorful as the petals.

Inside the flower are the reproductive organs of the plant. The **stamen** is the male reproductive organ. A stamen consists of a filament and an anther. Pollen grains form inside the anther. The sperm develop in each pollen grain.

The **pistil** is the female reproductive organ. A pistil consists of a sticky stigma where the pollen grains land, a long stalklike style, and an ovary. The **ovary** is the swollen base of the pistil where ovules are formed. Eggs are produced inside the ovule as it develops. You can see the parts of a typical flower in **Figure 16-11.** ☑

Reading Check ☑

Where do pollen grains land in flowers?

VISUALIZING Pollination and Fertilization

Figure 16-12 The pollination process involves the transfer of pollen grains from the stamen to the stigma.

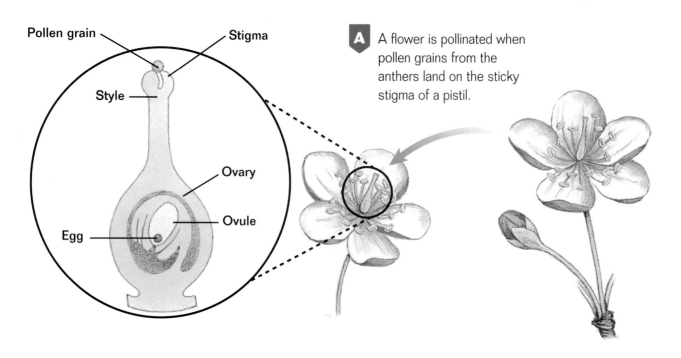

A A flower is pollinated when pollen grains from the anthers land on the sticky stigma of a pistil.

Pollen grain
Stigma
Style
Ovary
Ovule
Egg

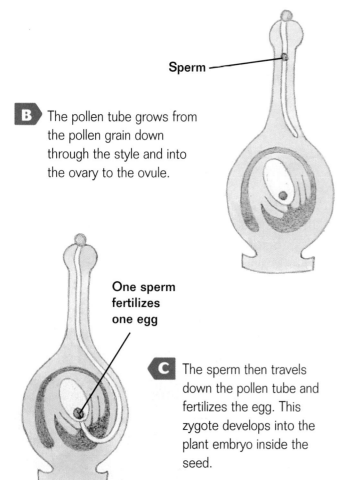

Sperm

B The pollen tube grows from the pollen grain down through the style and into the ovary to the ovule.

One sperm fertilizes one egg

C The sperm then travels down the pollen tube and fertilizes the egg. This zygote develops into the plant embryo inside the seed.

Development of a Seed

How does a seed develop? **Figure 16-12** illustrates this process. Pollen grains reach the stigma in a variety of ways. Pollen is carried by wind, rain, or animals such as insects, birds, and mammals. A flower is pollinated when pollen grains land on the sticky stigma. The transfer of pollen grains from the stamen to the stigma is the process of **pollination.** A pollen tube grows from the pollen grain down through the style. It enters the ovary and reaches an ovule. The sperm then travels down the pollen tube and fertilizes the egg. A zygote forms and grows into the plant embryo, which is inside the seed.

A seed is a mature ovule. It is surrounded by a protective seed coat. Inside the seed is the embryo. An embryo consists of an immature plant and stored food. The immature plant has structures that will eventually produce the plant's stem, leaves, and roots. In some plants, like beans and peanuts, the food is stored in structures called cotyledons. Other seeds like corn and wheat have food stored in a tissue called endosperm. This food provides the energy used by the seed as it sprouts. It also supplies energy for the immature plant's growth. You can see examples of these two seed types in **Figure 16-13.**

*inter***NET**
CONNECTION

What is a seed bank? Visit the Glencoe Science Web Site at **www.glencoe.com/ sec/science** for more information about seed banks.

Figure 16-13 Seeds of land plants are capable of surviving unfavorable environmental conditions.

1. **Immature plant**
2. **Cotyledon(s)**
3. **Seed coat**
4. **Endosperm**

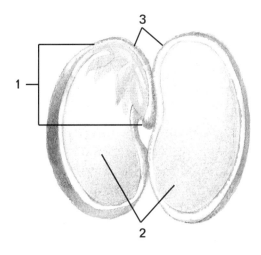

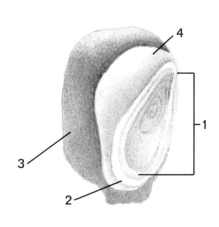

Problem Solving

Using Numbers to Test Seeds

While purchasing seeds to plant in his vegetable garden, Ling noticed that each seed packet had useful information on it. On each packet, he found a seed count, planting instructions, and germination rate for the seeds inside. The packet he chose stated that it contained about 200 carrot seeds. The planting instructions were to plant seeds about 5 cm apart and 6 mm deep. It also claimed that 95 percent of the seeds would germinate. Ling decided that he would test the seed company's claims.

Think Critically: What should Ling do to determine whether the claims are true? How could Ling use the weight of the seeds to determine the number of seeds in the packet?

Seed Dispersal

Most seeds grow only when placed on or in the ground. But, how do seeds naturally get from a plant to the ground? For many seeds, gravity is the answer.

Have you ever noticed how some plants just seem to appear in lawns, gardens, or the cracks of sidewalks? How did they get there? They probably grew from a seed, but where did the seed come from? In nature, seeds may travel great distances from the plants they grew on. Wind, water, and animals spread seeds. Some plants even have ways of ejecting their seeds. **Figure 16-14** shows ways that seeds are dispersed.

Wind dispersal happens usually because a seed has a structure attached to it that allows it to move with air currents. Dandelion, milkweed, and maple seeds are dispersed by the wind. Sometimes, seeds are so small that they become airborne when released by the plant.

Animals, including humans, disperse many seeds. Some seeds are eaten with fruits and dispersed as animals move from place to place. Often, for a seed to germinate, it must pass through an animal's digestive system. Hitchhiking on fur, feathers, and clothing is another way that animals disperse seeds. The fruit or seed may have a hooklike structure(s) or be coated with a sticky substance that allows it to stick to a passing animal. Humans often carry seeds without knowing it. Seeds wedge in the bottoms of shoes, drop into pockets or pant cuffs, and travel in our belongings.

Figure 16-14 Seeds can be dispersed by various methods.

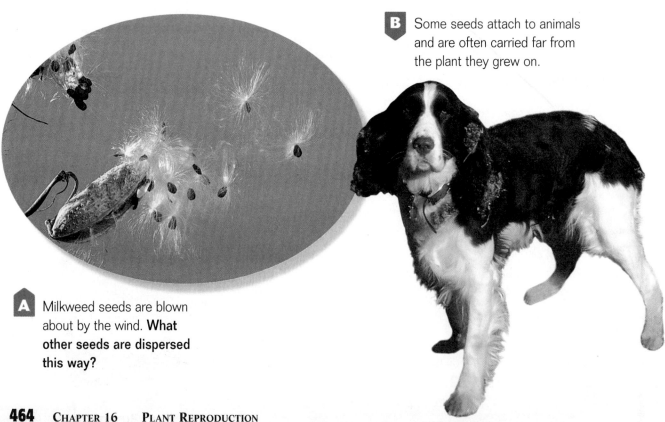

B Some seeds attach to animals and are often carried far from the plant they grew on.

A Milkweed seeds are blown about by the wind. **What other seeds are dispersed this way?**

Water also disperses seeds. Raindrops may knock seeds out of a dry fruit. Some fruits and seeds contain trapped air, which allows them to float on water. They also may have waxy coatings that delay water absorption. Floating seeds may travel great distances. The coconut palm's seed shown in **Figure 16-14C** has been dispersed hundreds of kilometers on ocean currents.

Have you ever touched the seedpod of an impatiens flower and watched as it exploded? The tiny seeds are ejected and spread some distance from the plant. This is another way that some plants disperse seeds.

Germination

Some seeds sprout or germinate in just a few days and other seeds take weeks or months to grow. Seeds will not sprout until environmental conditions are right. Some seeds can stay in a resting stage for hundreds of years. In 1982, seeds of the East Indian lotus sprouted after 466 years!

Mini Lab

Identifying How Seeds Disperse

Procedure

1. Make a list of ten different seeds, including those pictured in **Figure 16-14**.
2. Research each of the ten seeds to determine how they are dispersed.

Analysis

1. How are the seeds of each plant on your list dispersed—by wind, water, insects, birds, or mammals?
2. Identify features that tell you how each kind of seed is dispersed.

D The plant may disperse seeds by ejecting them.

C This coconut seed floats in the surf.

Figure 16-15 Germination is different in dicots and monocots.

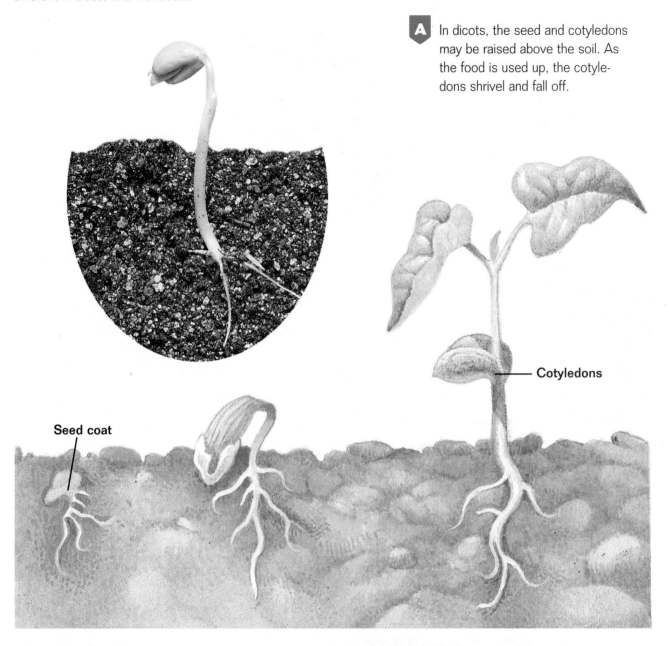

A In dicots, the seed and cotyledons may be raised above the soil. As the food is used up, the cotyledons shrivel and fall off.

Cotyledons

Seed coat

Germination, as shown in **Figure 16-15,** is a series of events that results in the growth of a plant from a seed. Temperature, the presence or absence of light, availability of water, and amount of oxygen present may affect germination. If the right combination of factors occurs, the seed will germinate. Germination begins when seed tissues absorb water. This causes the seed to swell. Then, a series of chemical reactions happens that releases energy from the stored food in the cotyledons or endosperm. Eventually, a root grows from the seed, followed by a stem and leaves. Once the plant is out of the soil, photosynthesis begins. Photosynthesis provides food and energy for the plant.

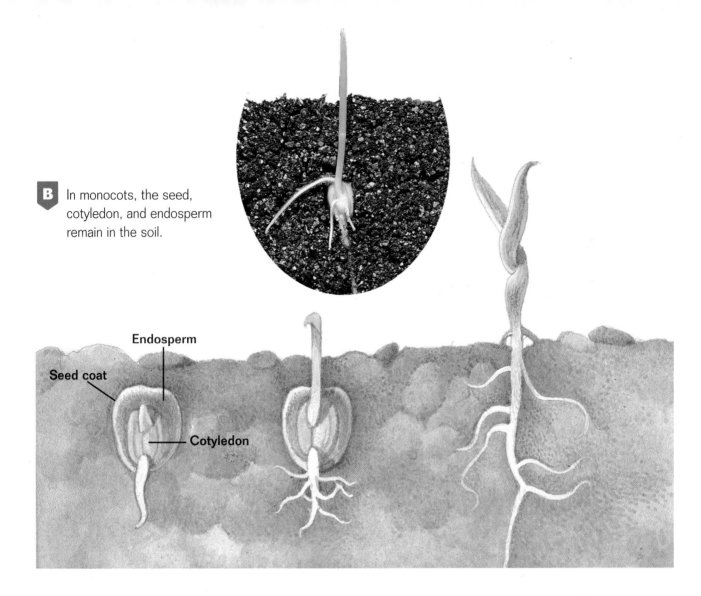

B In monocots, the seed, cotyledon, and endosperm remain in the soil.

Endosperm

Seed coat

Cotyledon

Section Assessment

1. **Compare** life cycles of angiosperms and gymnosperms.
2. Diagram a flower and label its parts.
3. List three methods of seed dispersal in plants.
4. **Think Critically:** Some conifers have female cones on the top half of the tree and male cones on the bottom half. Why do you think this arrangement of cones is important?
5.  **Skill Builder**
   Forming a Hypothesis A corn plant produces thousands of pollen grains on top of the plant in flowers that have no odor or color. The pistils grow from the cob lower down on the plant. Hypothesize how a corn plant is probably pollinated. If you need help, refer to Forming a Hypothesis in the **Skill Handbook** on page 722.

Science Journal Observe live specimens of several different types of flowers. In your Science Journal, describe their structures. Include numbers of petals, sepals, stamens, and pistil.

Germination Rate of Seeds

Possible Materials

- Seeds
- Water
- Salt
- Potting soil
- Plant trays or plastic cups
  * *seedling warming cables*
- Thermometer
- Graduated cylinder
- Beakers
  * *Alternate Materials*

Many environmental factors affect the germination rate of seeds. Among these are soil temperature, air temperature, moisture content of soil, and salt content of soil. What happens to the germination rate when one of these variables is changed? Can you determine a way to predict the best conditions for seed germination?

Recognize the Problem

How does an environmental factor affect seed germination?

Form a Hypothesis

Based on your knowledge of seed germination, state a hypothesis about how environmental factors affect germination rates.

Goals

- **Design an experiment** to test the effect of an environmental factor on seed germination rate.
- **Compare** germination rates under different conditions.

Safety Precautions

Some kinds of seeds are poisonous. Do not place any seeds in your mouth. Be careful when using any electrical equipment to avoid shock hazards.

Test Your Hypothesis

Plan

1. As a group, agree upon and **write** out your hypothesis statement.

2. As a group, list the steps that you need to take to test your hypothesis. Be specific, and **describe** exactly what you will do at each step. List your materials.

3. **Identify** any constants, variables, and controls of the experiment.

4. What measurements will you take? What data will you collect?

Do

1. Make sure your teacher approves your plan before you proceed.

2. Carry out the experiment as planned.

3. While the experiment is going on, **record** any observations

How often will you collect data? If you need a data table, **design** one in your Science Journal so that it is ready to use as your group collects data. Will the data be summarized in a graph?

5. **Read** over your entire experiment to make sure that all steps are in logical order. How many tests will you run?

that you make and complete the data table in your Science Journal.

Analyze Your Data

1. **Compare** your results with those of other groups.

2. Did changing the variable affect germination rates? Explain.

3. **Graph** your results using a bar graph, placing germination rate on the *y*-axis and the environmental variables on the *x*-axis.

Draw Conclusions

1. **Interpret** your graph to estimate the conditions that give the best germination rate.

2. What things affect the germination rate?

to Cones

FIELD *ACTIVITY*

FIELD *ACTIVITY*

Find three different cones in your neighborhood, a park, around your school or as part of a craft item. Using this guide, identify the genus of each cone. In your Science Journal, make a sketch of each cone and write a description of the plant it came from.

When we hear the word *cone*, we may think of a holder for our favorite ice cream. Or, we may think of the orange cones that we see on highways and in public places to direct traffic. But, there's another type of cone in our environment that plays an important role for some plants. They are the reproductive organs of a large plant group called the *conifers*, or cone bearers. The seeds of pines, firs, spruces, and redwoods are formed on cones.

Types of Cones

All conifers have two types of cones, male and female. The male cones produce pollen grains. They are short lived, breaking apart shortly after they release pollen. Depending on the species of conifer, the familiar female cones may stay on plants for nearly one year, two years, or three years. Female cones may be woody or berrylike. Woody cones consist of scales growing from a central stalk. Berrylike cones are round and may be either hard or soft. Each genus of conifers has a different female cone. They are so different from one another that you can use them to identify a conifer's genus.

Cone Characteristics

- **cylindrical**—shaped like a cylinder; nearly uniform in size from the base to the tip of the cone

- **ovoid**—shaped like a cylinder but smaller at the ends than in the middle

- **globose**—rounded like a globe

- **conic**—shaped like a cone; decreasing in diameter from the base to the tip of the cone

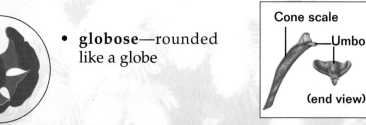

Cone scale

Umbo

(end view)

- **umbo**—a raised, triangular area at the tip of a cone scale; size and thickness of area varies

Cone Identification

This field guide contains some of the conifers. **Remember** that plant features may differ in appearance because of environmental conditions.

Juniper—*Juniperus*

- Hard, berrylike structures that stay on the tree or shrub for two to three years
- About 1.3 cm in diameter
- May be bluish, pale green, reddish, or brown and covered with a whitish, waxy coating called a bloom

Douglas Fir—*Psuedotsuga*

- Three-pointed, papery structure extends from below each cone scale
- Ovoid, on short stalks
- 5 cm to 10 cm in length

Spruce—*Picea*

- Cylindrical and brown, 6 cm to 15 cm in length
- Hang from branches on the upper third of the tree
- Thin cone scales, tips are usually pointed; brittle when mature
- Stay on the plant for two years

Redwood—*Sequoia*

- Ovoid, reddish brown, hang from the tips of neddled twigs
- Small in comparison to the size of the tree, only 1.2 cm to 3 cm
- Cone scales flattened on the end
- Mature in one year

Hemlock—*Tsuga*

- Small, ovoid to cylindrical, 2 cm to 7 cm long, hang from twigs
- Cone scales are few and have rounded tips
- Mature in one year but usually stay on tree for more than one year

Pine—*Pinus*

- Each thick, woody scale tipped with an umbo; the umbo may have a small spine or prickle
- Most cylindrical or conic and grow on a small stalk
- Varies in length from about 4 cm (scrub pine) to 45 cm (sugar pine)
- Remain on tree or shrub two to three years

Arborvitae—*Thuja*

- Egg-shaped cones, 1.2 cm to 1.5 cm long
- Paired cone scales, usually six to twelve, straplike and end in a sharp point
- Remain attached to shrub after opening and releasing seeds

Cypress—*Cupressus*

- Globose, usually 2 cm to 2.5 cm in diameter, only six to eight scales
- Cone scales have raised point in the center
- Mature in about 18 months and stay closed and attached to the tree

False Cypress—*Chamaecyparis*

- Small globose, only 0.5 cm to 4 cm in diameter with four to ten cone scales
- Open at maturity (unlike cones of *Cupressus* trees)

Swamp or Bald Cypress—*Taxodium*

- Globose, about 2.5 cm across
- Tips of cone scales are four sided, forming irregular pattern on the surface of cone
- Ripen in one year
- Trees in this genus recognizable by "knees" that form around the base of the tree trunk.

Fir—*Abies*

- Grow upright on branch
- Seldom used for identification because scales drop off at maturity leaving only the bare, central stalk
- 5 cm to 20 cm in length

Cedar—*Cedrus*

- Barrel-shaped cones with flattened tips grow upright on branches
- 5 cm to 10 cm in length and nearly half as wide
- Scales drop off at maturity (like firs) after two years
- Not produced until trees are 40 to 50 years old

Chapter 16 Reviewing Main Ideas

For a **preview** of this chapter, study this Reviewing Main Ideas before you read the chapter. After you have studied this chapter, you can use the Reviewing Main Ideas to **review** the chapter.

GLENCOE TECHNOLOGY

The Glencoe MindJogger, Audiocassettes, and CD-ROM provide additional opportunities for review.

Section

16-1 INTRODUCTION TO PLANT REPRODUCTION

Plants reproduce sexually and asexually. Sexual reproduction involves the formation of sex cells and fertilization. Asexual reproduction does not involve sex cells and produces organisms genetically identical to the parent organism. Plant life cycles include a gametophyte and a sporophyte stage. The gametophyte stage begins with meiosis. The sporophyte stage begins when the egg is fertilized by a sperm. In some plant life cycles, these stages are separate and not dependent on each other. In other plant life cycles, they are part of the same organism. For liverworts and mosses, the **gametophyte stage** is the familiar plant form. The **sporophyte stage** produces spores. In ferns, the sporophyte stage, not the gametophyte stage, is the familiar plant form. Ferns, like mosses and liverworts, produce spores.

What does alternation of generations mean?

Reading Check ✔

Find five science words in this chapter that begin with the letter *a*. Identify the words in which *a* is the prefix that means "without."

Section
16-2 SEED PLANT REPRODUCTION

Seed plants include gymnosperms and angiosperms. The male reproductive organs produce **pollen grains** that eventually contain sperm. Eggs are produced in the **ovules** of the female reproductive organs. The reproductive organs of gymnosperms are called cones. Wind usually moves pollen from the male cone to the female cone for fertilization. The reproductive organs of angiosperms are in a flower. The male reproductive organ is the **stamen,** and the female reproductive organ is the **pistil.** Gravity, wind, rain, and animals may pollinate a flower. Seeds of gymnosperms and angiosperms are dispersed in many ways. *How are the reproductive organs of gymnosperms and angiosperms alike?*

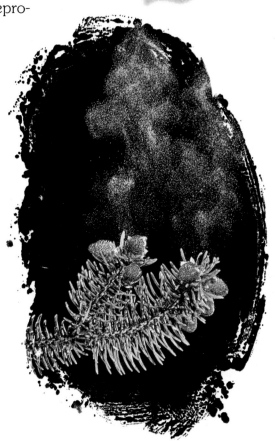

Career CONNECTION

Flora Ninomiya, Horticulturist

As a horticulturist, Flora Ninomiya is interested in the science of cultivating plants. She is responsible for 600 000 rose plants that occupy about 92 000 m² of greenhouse space. In addition to experimenting with new rose varieties, Flora schedules plant production, checks plants for diseases and insects, and oversees plant watering and fertilization. She uses the latest technologies, including computer-automated greenhouses and hydroponics.

Chapter 16 Assessment

Using Vocabulary

a. alternation of
   generations
b. frond
c. gametophyte
   stage
d. ovary
e. ovule
f. pistil
g. pollen grain
h. pollination
i. prothallus
j. rhizome
k. sori
l. sporophyte stage
m. stamen

Complete the following sentences with the best choices from the Vocabulary list.

1. A(n) _____ has an ovary and a(n) _____ has an anther.
2. In seed plants, the _____ contains the egg and the _____ contains the sperm.
3. Haploid cells make up the _____ _____ and diploid cells make up the _____ _____.
4. Moss capsules and moss plants are examples of _____ ___ _____.
5. Two parts of a sporophyte fern are _____ and _____.

Checking Concepts

Choose the word or phrase that best answers the question.

6. How are colorful flowers usually pollinated?
   A) insects   C) clothing
   B) wind   D) gravity
7. What is part of all plant life cycles?
   A) seeds   C) flowers
   B) fruits   D) alternation of
                      generations
8. What part of the flower receives the pollen grain?
   A) sepal   C) stamen
   B) ovary   D) stigma

9. What do ferns form when they reproduce sexually?
   A) spores   C) seeds
   B) vascular tissue   D) flowers
10. What contains food for the embryo?
    A) endosperm   C) stigma
    B) pollen grain D) root
11. What disperses most dandelion seeds?
    A) rain   C) wind
    B) animals   D) insects
12. What is the series of events that results in an organism from a seed?
    A) pollination C) germination
    B) alternation of   D) asexual
       generations   reproduction
13. What is another name for seed leaves?
    A) root hairs   C) stigmas
    B) cotyledons   D) stomata
14. Ovules and pollen grains are involved in what process?
    A) germination C) seed dispersal
    B) asexual   D) sexual
       reproduction   reproduction
15. Which of the following terms describes the cells in the gametophyte stage?
    A) haploid   C) diploid
    B) prokaryotic D) missing a nucleus

Thinking Critically

16. Explain why male cones produce so many pollen grains.
17. Describe a flower that is pollinated by a hummingbird.
18. Discuss the importance of water in the reproduction of bryophytes and ferns.
19. In mosses, why is the sporophyte stage dependent on the gametophyte stage?
20. What features of flowers ensure pollination?

Developing Skills

If you need help, refer to the **Skill Handbook**.

21. **Concept Mapping:** Complete this concept map of a moss life cycle.

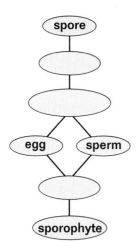

22. **Comparing and Contrasting:** Describe the differences and similarities between the fern sporophyte and gametophyte stages.

23. **Observing and Inferring:** Observe pictures of flowers or actual flowers and infer how each is pollinated. Explain your suggestion.

24. **Sequencing:** Number the following events in the correct order. *Pollen is trapped on the stigma; pollen tube reaches the ovule; fertilization; pollen released from the anther; pollen tube forms through the style; a seed forms.*

25. **Making and Using Graphs:** Make a bar graph for the following data table about onion seeds. Put the temperature on the horizontal axis and days on the vertical axis.

Onion Seed Data

Temperature (°C)	10	15	20	25	30	35
Days to germinate	13	7	5	4	4	13

THE PRINCETON REVIEW

Test-Taking Tip

Use as Much Time as You Can You will not get extra points for finishing early. Work slowly and carefully on any test and make sure you don't make careless errors because you are hurrying to finish.

Test Practice

Use these questions to test your Science Proficiency.

1. What does the gametophyte stage of a moss or fern life cycle produce?
   A) sex cells
   C) spores
   B) seeds
   D) fruits

2. What is the usual pollinator for gymnosperms?
   A) wind
   C) rain
   B) insects
   D) gravity

3. If a flower has a pistil but no stamen, what type of flower is it?
   A) pollinator
   C) infertile
   B) male
   D) female

4. You see a dandelion growing near a rose. Which of the following **BEST** explains how the dandelion came to be there?
   A) It grew from an underground dandelion.
   B) The seed was carried there by the wind and grew.
   C) The plant was put there by an animal.
   D) Dandelions often grow from the roots of roses.

6

Ecology

What's Happening Here?

A small plane flies over one of the soda lakes of eastern Africa (left). Dotted with islands of foam, where liquid and gas bubble through its salt crust, Tanzania's Lake Natron appears to be a wasteland. Yet, notice the color. Pink algae bloom everywhere. After a rain, fresh water collects on the salt flats, and there the algae survive. The algae feed the flamingos (below) that flock to the lake by the millions to breed, and the birds' droppings feed the algae. The algae also give the birds' feathers their pink hue. Moreover, the harsh salt crust keeps many predators from crossing the treacherous flats—thereby providing a safe place for the flamingos to nest. Thus, living and non-living parts of the environment—the algae and the salt crust—work together to support life. In this unit, you will learn that complex webs connect living things and are key to supporting life, even in hostile environments.

interNET CONNECTION

Explore the Glencoe Science Web Site at **www.glencoe.com/sec/ science** to find out more about topics found in this unit.

CHAPTER

17 Life and the Environment

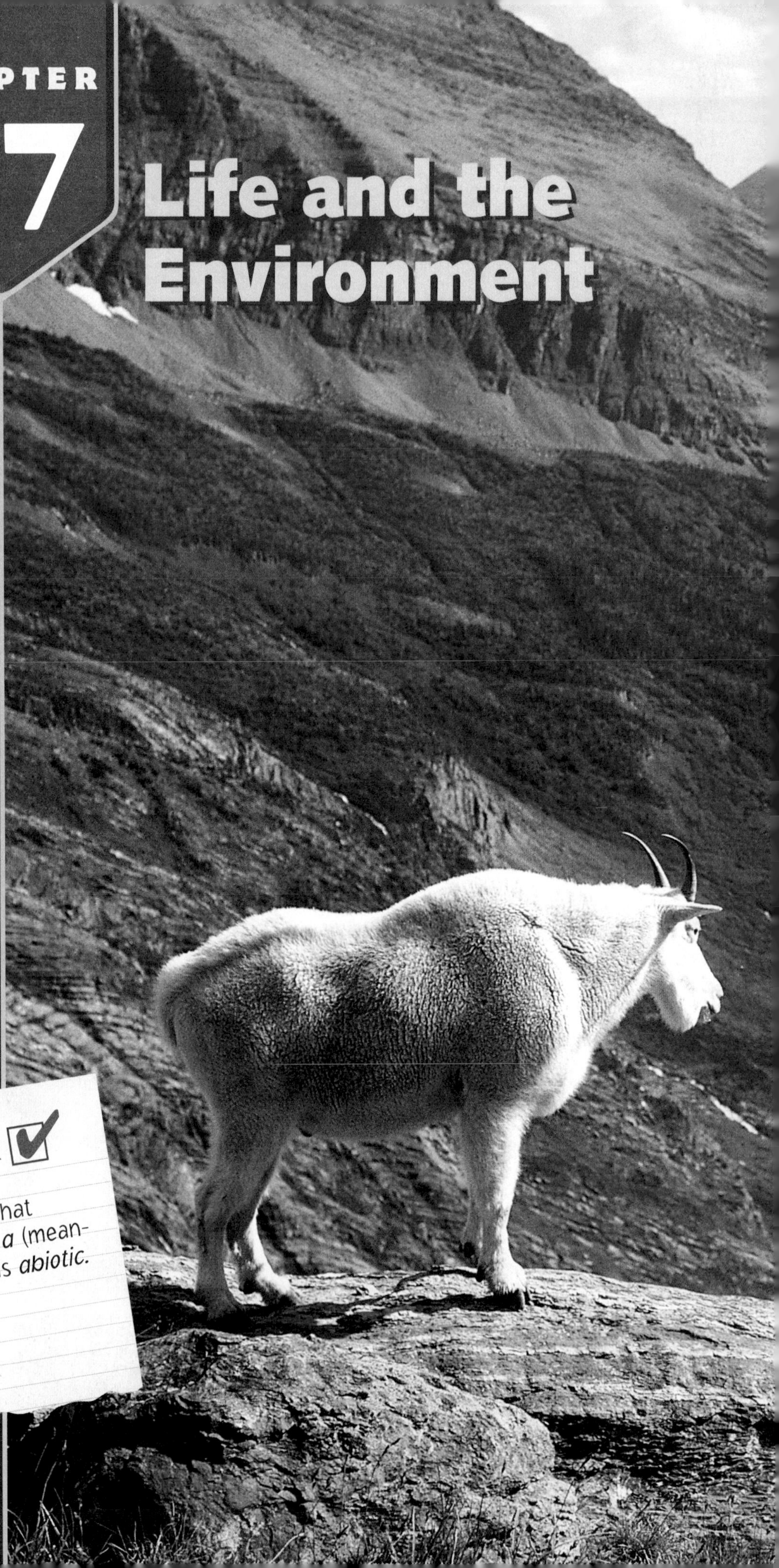

Chapter Preview

Skills Preview

Skill Builders
- Classify

Activities
- Graph

MiniLabs
- Infer

Reading Check ✓

Define several terms that begin with the prefix *a* (meaning "without"), such as *abiotic*.

Explore Activity

Mountain goats rely on winter winds to uncover food plants buried beneath the snow. Surefooted and strong, they scale high cliffs to get their next meal. A mountain goat's range consists of high terrain where few other animals dare to tread. This reduces competition from different organisms for food. How does the number of related organisms in an area affect each individual? You share your science classroom with other students. How much space is available to each student?

Measure Space

1. Use a meterstick to measure the length and width of the classroom.

2. Multiply the length times the width to find the area of the room in square meters.

3. Count the number of individuals in your class. Divide the number of square meters in the classroom by the number of individuals.

Science **Journal**

In your Science Journal, record how much space each person has. Determine the amount of space each person would have if the number of individuals in your class doubled. Predict how having that amount of space would affect you and your classmates.

17•1 The Living and Nonliving Environment

What You'll Learn

- How to identify biotic and abiotic factors in an ecosystem
- The characteristics of populations
- The levels of biological organization

Vocabulary
biosphere
ecology
abiotic factor
biotic factor
population
community
ecosystem

Why It's Important

- Abiotic and biotic factors work together to form your ecosystem.

The Biosphere

Think of all the organisms on Earth. Millions of species exist. Where do all these organisms live? Living things can be found 11 000 m below the surface of the ocean and on tops of mountains 9000 m high. The part of Earth that supports organisms is known as the **biosphere** (BI uh sfihr). The biosphere seems huge, but it is actually only a small portion of Earth. The biosphere includes the topmost portion of Earth's crust, all the waters that cover Earth's surface, and the surrounding atmosphere. Overall though, the thickness could be compared to the thickness of the skin of an apple.

Within the biosphere, many different environments can be found. For example, red-tailed hawks are found in environments where tall trees live near open grassland. The hawks nest high in the trees and soar over the land in search of rodents and rabbits to eat. In environments with plenty of moisture, such as the banks of streams, willow trees provide food and shelter for birds, mammals, and insects. All organisms interact

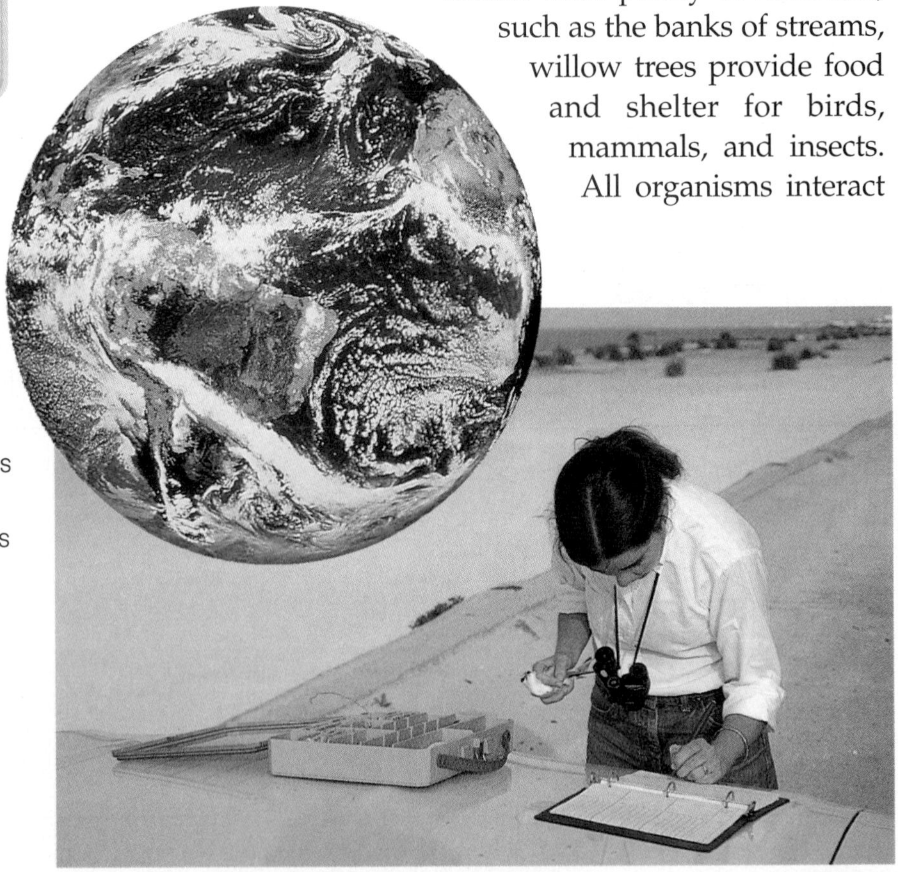

Figure 17-1 The biosphere is the region of Earth that contains all living organisms. An ecologist is a scientist who studies relationships among organisms and between organisms and the physical features of the biosphere.

with the environment. The science of **ecology** is the study of the interactions that take place among organisms and between organisms and the physical features of the environment. Ecologists, such as the one in **Figure 17-1,** are the scientists who study interactions between organisms and the environment.

Abiotic Factors

A forest environment is made up of trees, birds, insects, and other living things that depend on one another for food and shelter. But, these organisms also depend on factors that surround them such as soil, sunlight, water, temperature, and air. These factors—the nonliving, physical features of the environment—are called **abiotic factors.** Abiotic—*a* meaning "not" and *biotic* meaning "living"—factors have effects on living things and often determine the organisms that are able to live in a certain environment. Some abiotic factors are shown in **Figure 17-2.**

Figure 17-2 Abiotic factors help determine which species can survive in an area.

 A **Soil**
Soil consists of minerals mixed with decaying, dead organisms. It contains both living and nonliving components.

B **Light**
Seasonal events, such as flowering in plants or migration of birds, are often triggered by a change in the number of hours of daylight.

C **Water**
Many organisms live in water, such as this lake in Pennsylvania, rather than air.

D **Temperature**
Temperatures change with daily and seasonal cycles. Desert-dwelling rattlesnakes, like this sidewinder in the Colorado desert, are active only in the cool, early morning hours. During the hottest part of the day, they rest in the shade.

17-1   THE LIVING AND NONLIVING ENVIRONMENT   **483**

Water

Water is an important abiotic factor. The bodies of most organisms are 50 to 95 percent water. Water is an important part of cytoplasm and the fluid that surrounds cells. Respiration, photosynthesis, digestion, and other important life processes can take place only in the presence of water.

Soil

The type of soil in a particular location helps determine which plants and other organisms live in that location. Most soil is a combination of sand, clay, and humus. Soil type is determined by the relative amounts of sand, clay, and humus in the soil. Humus is the decayed remains of dead organisms. The greater the humus content, the more fertile the soil.

Light and Temperature

The abiotic factors of light and temperature also impact the environment. Through the process of photosynthesis, the radiant energy of sunlight is transformed into chemical energy that drives virtually all of life's processes. The availability of sunlight is a major factor in determining where green plants and other photosynthetic organisms live, as shown in **Figure 17-3.** Sunlight does not penetrate far into deep water. Most green algae benefit from living near the surface. In a similar situation, because little sunlight reaches the shady darkness of the forest floor, plant growth there is limited.

Figure 17-3 Many wildflowers that live on the forest floor, such as these padres shooting stars and Johnny jump-ups, produce seeds early in the spring. At this time, they receive the maximum amount of sunlight. When the leaves are fully out on the trees, they receive little direct sun.

Biotic Factors

Abiotic factors do not provide everything an organism needs for survival. Mushrooms would not be able to grow without the decaying bodies of other organisms to feed on. Honeybees could not survive without pollen from flowers. Some species of owls and woodpeckers prefer to nest in the hollow trunks of dead trees. Organisms depend on other organisms for food, shelter, protection, or reproduction. Living or once-living organisms in the environment are called **biotic factors.**

Reading Check ✔

What are the living organisms in the environment called?

Levels of Biological Organization

The living world is highly organized. Atoms are arranged into molecules, which are in turn organized into cells. Cells form tissues, tissues form organs, and organs form systems. Similarly, the biotic and abiotic factors studied by ecologists can be arranged into layers of organization, as shown in **Figure 17-4.**

Figure 17-4 The living world is organized into several levels.

Organism
An organism is a single individual from a population.

Population
A population is all of the individuals of one species that live and reproduce in the same area at the same time.

Community
A community is made up of populations of different species that interact in some way.

Ecosystem
An ecosystem consists of communities and the abiotic factors that affect them.

Biosphere
The biosphere is the highest level of biological organization. It is made up of all the ecosystems on Earth.

Figure 17-5 This coral reef is an example of an ecosystem. It is made up of hundreds of populations of organisms, as well as ocean water, sunlight, and other abiotic factors.

Populations

Individual organisms of the same species that live in the same place and can produce young form a **population.** Members of several populations on a coral reef are seen in **Figure 17-5.** Members of populations of organisms compete with each other for food, water, mates, and space. The resources of the environment and how the organisms use these resources determine how large a population can be.

Communities

Most populations of organisms do not live alone. They live and interact with populations of other organisms. Groups of populations that interact with each other in a given area form a **community.** Populations of organisms in a community depend on each other for food and shelter and for other needs.

Ecosystem

An **ecosystem** is made up of a biotic community and the abiotic factors that affect it. The rest of this chapter will discuss in more detail the kinds of interactions that take place between abiotic and biotic factors in an ecosystem.

Section Assessment

1. What is the difference between an abiotic factor and a biotic factor? Give at least five examples of each.

2. What is the difference between a population and a community? A community and an ecosystem?

3. **Think Critically:** Could oxygen in the atmosphere be considered an abiotic factor? Why or why not? What about carbon dioxide?

4. **Skill Builder**
   Observing and Inferring Each person lives in a population as part of a community. Describe your population and community. If you need help, refer to Observing and Inferring in the **Skill Handbook** on page 720.

Using Computers

Spreadsheet Obtain two months of temperature and rainfall data from your local newspaper or the Internet. Enter the data in a spreadsheet and then average the totals for temperature and the totals for rainfall. What kind of climate do you think you have based on your calculations? If you need help, refer to page 738.

Soil Composition

Soil is more than minerals mixed with the decaying bodies of dead organisms. It contains other biotic and abiotic factors.

What You'll Investigate

What are the components of soil?

Goals

* **Determine** what factors are present in soil.

Materials

* Small paper cups containing freshly dug soil (3)
* Newspaper
* Beaker of water
* Hand lens
* Jar with lid
* Scale

Procedure

1. **Obtain** 3 cups of soil from your teacher. **Record** the source of your sample in your Science Journal.

2. **Pour** one of your samples onto the newspaper. **Sort** through the objects in the soil. Try to separate abiotic and biotic items. Use a hand lens to help identify the items. **Describe** your observations in your Science Journal.

3. Carefully place the second sample in the jar, disturbing it as little as possible. Quickly fill the jar with water and screw the lid on tightly. Without moving the jar, **observe** its contents for several minutes. **Record** your observations in your Science Journal.

4. **Weigh** the third sample. **Record** the weight in your Science Journal. Leave the sample undisturbed for several days, then weigh it again. **Record** the second weight in your Science Journal.

Conclude and Apply

1. Can you **infer** the presence of any organisms? Explain.

2. **Describe** the abiotic factors in your sample. What biotic factors did you **observe?**

3. Did you **record** any change in the soil weight over time? If so, why?

Interactions Among Living Organisms

What You'll Learn

▶ The characteristics of populations
▶ The types of relationships that occur among populations in a community
▶ The habitat and niche of a species in a community

Vocabulary
population density
limiting factor
carrying capacity
symbiosis
habitat
niche

Why It's Important

▶ You must directly or indirectly interact with other organisms to survive.

Characteristics of Populations

As shown in **Figure 17-6,** populations can be described by their characteristics. These include the size of the population, spacing (how the organisms are arranged in a given area), and density (how many individuals there are in a specific area). Suppose you spent several months observing a population of field mice living in a pasture. You would probably observe changes in the size of the population. Older mice die, baby mice are born, some are eaten by predators, and some mice wander away to new homes. The size of a population—the number of individual organisms it contains—is always changing, although some populations change more rapidly than others. In contrast to a mouse population, the number of pine trees in a forest changes fairly slowly, but a forest fire could quickly reduce the population of pine trees in the forest.

Figure 17-6 Populations have several characteristics that define them.

Each dot represents 1000 people

A Spacing
A characteristic of populations is spacing. In some populations, such as the oak trees of an oak-hickory forest, individuals are spaced fairly evenly throughout the area.

B Density
Human population density is higher in and around cities than in rural areas. **Which part of the United States has the highest population density?**

Population Density

At the beginning of this chapter, when you figured out how much space is available to each student in your classroom, you were measuring another population characteristic. The size of a population that occupies an area of limited size is called **population density.** The more individuals there are in a given amount of space, as seen in **Figure 17-7,** the more dense the population. For example, if 100 mice live in an area of a square kilometer, the population density is 100 mice per km².

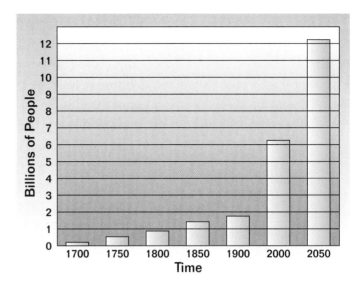

Figure 17-7 The size of the human population is increasing at a rate of about 1.6 percent per year. At the present time, it is about 6 billion. In 2050, the population will be about 12 billion.

Limiting Factors

Populations cannot continue to grow larger and larger forever. In any ecosystem, there are limits to the amount of food, water, living space, mates, nesting sites, and other resources available. A **limiting factor** is any biotic or abiotic factor that restricts the number of individuals in a population. A limiting factor can also indirectly affect other populations in the community. For example, a drought might restrict the growth of seed-producing plants in a forest clearing. Fewer plants means that food may become a limiting factor for a mouse population that feeds on the seeds. Food also may become a limiting factor for hawks and owls that feed on the mice, as well as for the deer in **Figure 17-8.**

Competition is the struggle among organisms to obtain the resources they need to survive and reproduce. As population density increases, so does competition among individuals.

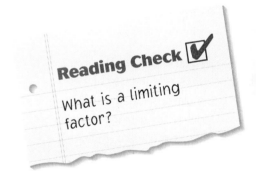

Reading Check
What is a limiting factor?

Figure 17-8 In many parts of the United States, deer populations, such as this one in northern Wisconsin, have become large enough to exceed the environment's ability to produce adequate food. Individuals starve or, weakened from lack of food, fall victim to disease.

Carrying Capacity

Suppose a population of robins continues to increase in size, year after year. At some point, food, nesting space, or other resources become so scarce that some individuals may not be able to survive or reproduce. When this happens, the environment has reached its carrying capacity, as seen in **Figure 17-9. Carrying capacity** is the largest number of individuals an environment can support and maintain for a long period of time. If a population begins to exceed the environment's carrying capacity, some individuals will be left without adequate resources. They may die or be forced to move elsewhere.

Biotic Potential

What would happen if there were no limiting factors? A population living in an environment that supplies more than enough resources for survival will continue to grow. The maximum rate at which a population increases when there is plenty of food, water, ideal weather, and no disease or enemies is its biotic potential. However, most populations never reach their biotic potential, or do so for only a short period of time. Eventually, the carrying capacity of the environment is reached and the population stops increasing.

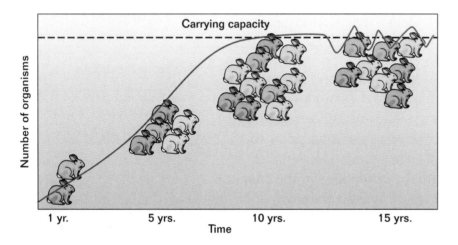

Figure 17-9 This graph shows how the size of a population increases until it reaches the carrying capacity of its environment. At first, growth is fairly slow. It speeds up as the number of adults capable of reproduction increases. Once the population reaches carrying capacity, its size remains fairly stable. **Why don't most populations achieve their biotic potential?**

Interactions in Communities

Populations are regulated not only by the supply of food, water, and sunlight, but also by the actions of other populations. The most obvious way one population can limit another is by predation (prih DAY shun). One organism feeds on another. Owls and hawks are predators that feed on mice. Mice are their prey. Predators are biotic factors that limit the size of prey populations. Because predators are more likely to capture old, ill, or young prey, predation also helps maintain the health of a prey population. Predators leave the strongest individuals to reproduce. **Figure 17-10** shows how some predators work together to hunt their food.

Symbiosis

Many types of relationships exist between organisms in ecosystems. Many species of organisms in nature have close, complex relationships in order to survive. When two or more species live close together, their relationship is called a symbiotic relationship. **Symbiosis** (sihm bee OH sus) is any close relationship between two or more different species.

Using Math

Calculating Population Growth

Example Problem: Estimates show the total human population will be about 6 billion in the year 2000. This number is thought to increase by 1.6 percent each year. What will the population be in the year 2005?

Problem-Solving Steps

1. What is known? Current population is 6 000 000 000. Yearly increase is 1.6%.
2. What is unknown? The population in 2001, 2002, 2003, 2004, and 2005.
3. **Solution:** Calculate the population increase for one year. Then, repeat the process four more times using the answer you came up with as a starting point.

$$
\begin{array}{r}
6\ 000\ 000\ 000 \\
\times\ 0.016 \\
\hline
36\ 000\ 000\ 000 \\
60\ 000\ 000\ 000 \\
\hline
96\ 000\ 000\ \text{more people}
\end{array}
\qquad
\begin{array}{r}
6\ 000\ 000\ 000 \\
+\ 96\ 000\ 000 \\
\hline
6\ 096\ 000\ 000\ \text{people in 2001}
\end{array}
$$

The estimated population in the year 2005 is 6 495 607 732 people.

Practice Problem

An endangered species of fish currently has a population of 136 individuals. If the population increases by two percent every year, how many individuals will there be in three years?
Strategy Hint: When calculating percentages, remember to move your decimal two spaces to the left (0.02).

MiniLab

Observing Symbiosis

Procedure

1. Carefully wash then examine the roots of a legume plant and a nonlegume plant.
2. Examine a prepared microscope slide of the bacteria that live in the roots of legumes.

Analysis

1. What differences do you observe in the roots of the two plants?
2. The bacteria help legumes thrive in poor soil. What type of symbiotic relationship is this? Explain.

Not all relationships benefit one organism at the expense of another as in predation. Symbiotic relationships can be identified by the type of interaction between organisms, as shown in **Figure 17-11.** Many types of symbiotic relationships occur between organisms. These are usually described by how each organism in the relationship is affected by the relationship.

A symbiotic relationship that benefits both species is called mutualism. An example of mutualism is the lichen. Each lichen species is made up of a fungus and an alga or cyanobacterium. The fungus provides a protected living space, and the alga or bacterium provides the fungus with food.

Figure 17-11 Many examples of symbiotic relationships occur in nature.

B Tropical orchids grow on the trunks of trees. The tree provides the orchid with a sunlit living space high in the forest canopy. This relationship is an example of commensalism because the orchid benefits from the relationship without harming or helping the tree.

A The partnership between the desert yucca plant and the yucca moth is an example of mutualism. Both species benefit from the relationship. The yucca depends on the moth to pollinate its flowers. The moth depends on the yucca for a protected place to lay its eggs and a source of food for its larvae.

C Tapeworms are parasites that feed inside the intestines of some mammals. This one was found inside a cat.

In shallow tropical seas, brightly colored anemone fish find protection from predators by swimming among the stinging tentacles of sea anemones. The presence of the fish does not affect the anemone in a harmful or beneficial way. Commensalism is a symbiotic relationship that benefits one partner but does not harm or help the other.

Parasitism is a symbiotic relationship that benefits the parasite and does definite harm to the parasite's host. Many parasites live on or in the body of the host, absorbing nutrients from the host's body fluids. Tapeworms live as parasites in the intestines of mammals. Mistletoe is a parasitic plant that penetrates tree branches with its roots.

Habitats and Niches

In a community, every species plays a particular role. Each also has a particular place to live. The physical location where an organism lives is called its **habitat.** The habitat of an earthworm is soil. The role of an organism in the ecosystem is called its **niche.** The niche of an earthworm is shown in **Figure 17-12.** What a species eats, how it gets its food, and how it interacts with other organisms are all parts of its niche. An earthworm takes soil into its body to obtain nutrients. The soil that leaves the worm enriches the soil. The movement of the worm through soil also loosens it and aerates it, creating a better environment for plant growth.

Figure 17-12 Each organism in an ecosystem uses and affects its environment in particular ways. **What role does the earthworm play in the environment?**

EARTH SCIENCE
◄INTEGRATION

Section Assessment

1. Describe how limiting factors can affect the organisms in a population.

2. Describe the difference between a habitat and a niche.

3. **Think Critically:** A parasite can obtain food only from its host. Most parasites weaken but do not kill their hosts. Why?

4. **Skill Builder**
   Observing and Inferring There are methods used to determine the size of a population without counting each organism. Do the **Chapter 17 Skill Activity** on page 758 to learn how to infer population size.

Using Math

In a 12 m² area of weeds, 46 dandelion plants, 212 grass plants, and 14 bindweed plants are growing. What is the population density per square meter of each species?

Activity 17·2

Identifying a Limiting Factor

Possible Materials

- Bean seeds
- Small planting containers
- Soil
- Water
- Labels
- Trowel or spoon
- Aluminum foil
- Sunny window or other light source
- Refrigerator or oven

Organisms depend on many biotic and abiotic factors in their environment to survive. When these factors are limited or are not available, it can affect an organism's survival. By experimenting with some of these limiting factors, you will see how organisms depend on all parts of their environment.

Recognize the Problem

How do abiotic factors such as light, water, and temperature affect the germination of seeds?

Form a Hypothesis

Based on what you have learned about limiting factors, make a hypothesis about how one specific abiotic factor may affect the germination of a bean seed. Be sure to consider factors that you can change easily.

Goals

- **Observe** the effects of an abiotic factor on the germination and growth of bean seedlings.

- **Design** an experiment that demonstrates whether or not a specific abiotic factor limits the germination of bean seeds.

Safety Precautions

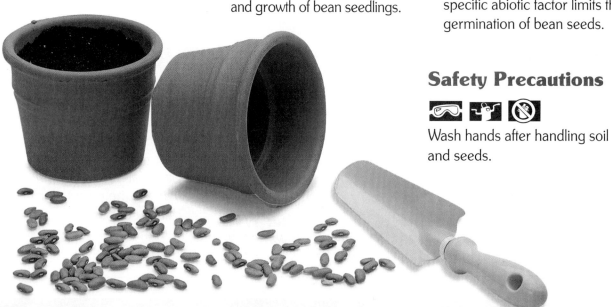

Wash hands after handling soil and seeds.

Test Your Hypothesis

Plan

1. As a group, agree upon and write out a hypothesis statement.

2. Decide on a way to test your group's hypothesis. Keep available materials in mind as you plan your procedure. **List** your materials.

3. **Prepare** a data table in your Science Journal.

4. Remember to **test** only one variable at a time and use suitable controls.

5. **Read** over your entire experiment to make sure that all steps are in logical order.

6. **Identify** any constants, variables, and controls in your experiment.

7. Be sure the factor you test is measurable.

Do

1. Make sure your teacher has approved your plan before you proceed.

2. Carry out the experiment as planned.

3. While the experiment is going on, write down any observations that you make and complete the data table in your Science Journal.

Analyze Your Data

1. **Compare** your results with those of other groups.

2. **Infer** how the abiotic factor you tested affected the germination of bean seeds.

3. **Graph** your results in a bar graph that compares the number of bean seeds that germinated in the experimental container with the number of seeds that germinated in the control container.

Draw Conclusions

1. **Identify** which factor had the greatest effect on the seeds.

2. **Determine** whether you could substitute one factor for another and still grow the seeds.

Matter and Energy

Energy Flow Through Ecosystems

What You'll Learn

► How energy flows through ecosystems
► The cycling of matter in the biosphere

Vocabulary
food chain
food web
ecological pyramid
water cycle
nitrogen cycle

Why It's Important

► You depend on the recycling of matter and energy to survive.

As you can see, life on Earth is not simply a collection of living organisms. Even organisms that seem to spend most of their time alone interact with other members of their species. They also interact with other organisms. Most of the interactions between members of different species are feeding relationships. They involve the transfer of energy from one organism to another. Energy moves through an ecosystem in the form of food. Producers are organisms that capture energy from the sun. They use the sun's energy for photosynthesis to produce chemical bonds in carbohydrates. Consumers are organisms that

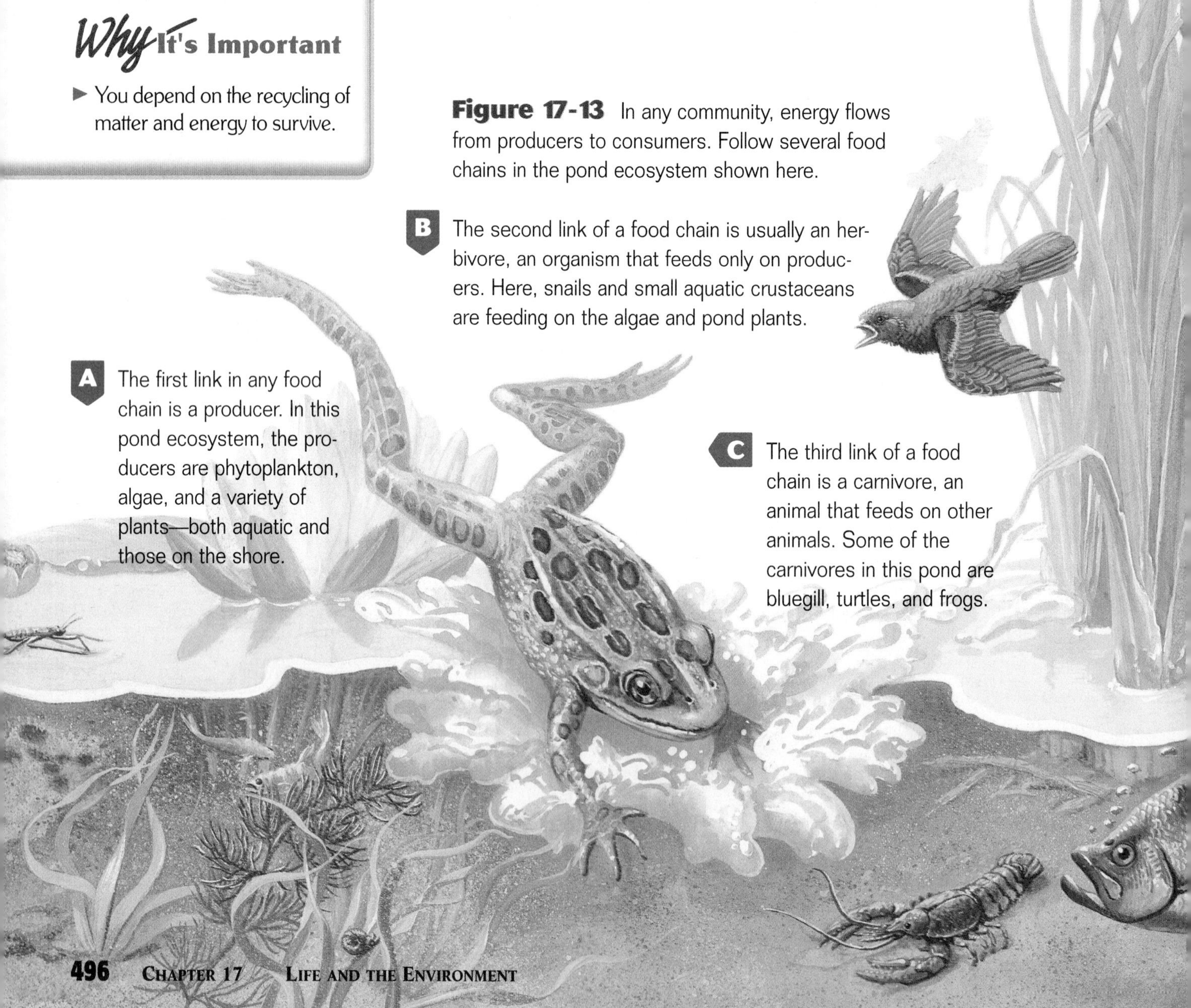

Figure 17-13 In any community, energy flows from producers to consumers. Follow several food chains in the pond ecosystem shown here.

B The second link of a food chain is usually an herbivore, an organism that feeds only on producers. Here, snails and small aquatic crustaceans are feeding on the algae and pond plants.

A The first link in any food chain is a producer. In this pond ecosystem, the producers are phytoplankton, algae, and a variety of plants—both aquatic and those on the shore.

C The third link of a food chain is a carnivore, an animal that feeds on other animals. Some of the carnivores in this pond are bluegill, turtles, and frogs.

obtain energy when they feed on producers or other consumers. The transfer of energy does not end there. When organisms die, other organisms called decomposers obtain energy when they break down the bodies of the dead organisms. This movement of energy through a community can be drawn as food chains, and food webs.

Food Chains and Food Webs

A **food chain** is a simple way of showing how energy in the form of food passes from one organism to another. The pond community pictured in **Figure 17-13** shows examples of several aquatic food chains. When drawing a food chain, arrows between organisms indicate the direction of energy transfer. An example of a pond food chain would be as follows.

phytoplankton → insects → bluegill → bass

Food chains usually have three or four links. Most have no more than five links. This is due to the decrease in energy available at each link. The amount of energy left by the fifth link is only a small portion of the total amount of energy available at the first link. This is because at each transfer of energy, a portion of the energy is lost as heat due to the activities of the organisms as they search for food and mates.

CHEMISTRY
INTEGRATION

Making Food
Certain bacteria obtain their energy through a process called chemosynthesis. In chemosynthesis, the bacteria produce food and oxygen using chemical compounds. Where do you think these bacteria are found?

D The fourth link of a food chain is a top carnivore, which feeds on other carnivores. Examples of these consumers in this pond are large fish such as crappies and bass.

E When an organism dies in any ecosystem, bacteria and fungi, which are decomposers, feed on the dead organism, breaking down the remains of the organism.

Figure 17-14 A food web includes many food chains. It provides a more accurate model of the complex feeding relationships in a community than a single food chain does.

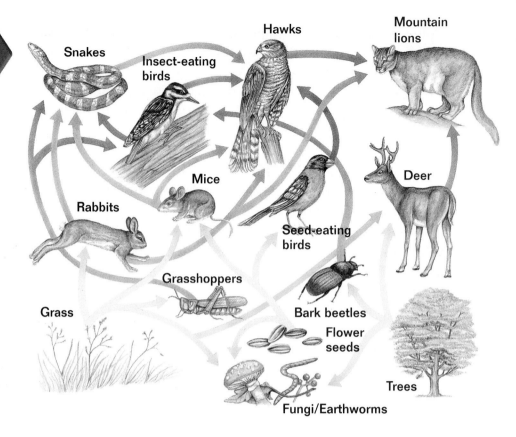

Snakes
Hawks
Mountain lions
Insect-eating birds
Mice
Deer
Rabbits
Seed-eating birds
Grasshoppers
Grass
Bark beetles
Flower seeds
Trees
Fungi/Earthworms

Single food chains are too simple to describe the many interactions among organisms in an ecosystem. Many food chains exist in any ecosystem. A **food web** is a series of overlapping food chains, as seen in **Figure 17-14.** This concept provides a more complete model of the way energy moves through a community. Food webs are also more accurate models because they show the many organisms that feed on more than one level in an ecosystem.

Ecological Pyramids

Almost all the energy used in the biosphere comes from the sun. Producers capture and transform only a small part of the energy that reaches Earth's surface. When an herbivore eats a plant, some of the energy in the plant is passed on to the herbivore. However, most of it is given off into the atmosphere as heat. The same thing happens when a carnivore eats an herbivore. This transfer of energy can be modeled by an **ecological pyramid.** The bottom of an ecological pyramid represents the producers of an ecosystem. The rest of the levels represent successive organisms in the food chain. ☑

Energy Pyramid

The flow of energy from grass to the hawk in **Figure 17-15** can be illustrated by an energy pyramid. An energy pyramid compares the energy available at each level of the food chain in an ecosystem. Just as most food chains have three or four links,

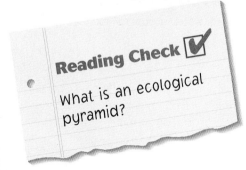

Reading Check ☑

What is an ecological pyramid?

a pyramid of energy usually has three or four levels. Only about ten percent of the energy available at each level of the pyramid is available to the next level. By the time the top level is reached, the amount of energy is greatly reduced.

The Cycles of Matter

The energy available at each link in the food chain is constantly renewed by sunlight. But, what about the physical matter that makes up the bodies of living organisms? The laws of conservation of mass and energy state that matter on Earth is never lost or gained. It is used over and over again. In other words, it is recycled. The carbon atoms present in your body right now have been on Earth since the planet formed billions of years ago.

Figure 17-15

An energy pyramid illustrates that energy decreases at each successive feeding step. **Why aren't there more levels in an energy pyramid?**

Problem Solving

Changes in Antarctic Food Webs

The food chain in the ice-cold Antarctic Ocean is based on phytoplankton—microscopic algae that float near the water's surface. The algae are eaten by tiny shrimp-like krill, which are consumed by baleen whales, squid, and fish. The fish and squid are eaten by toothed

whales, seals, and penguins. In the past, humans have hunted baleen whales. Now with laws against it, there is hope that the population of baleen whales will increase. How will an increase in the whale population affect this food web? Which organisms compete for the same source of food?

Think Critically

1. Populations of seals, penguins, and krill-eating fish increased in size as populations of baleen whales declined. Why?

2. What might happen if the number of baleen whales increases, but the amount of krill does not?

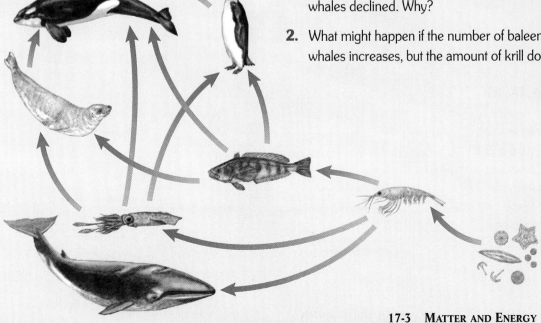

Modeling the Water Cycle

Procedure 🥽

1. With a marker, make a line halfway up on a plastic cup. Fill the cup to the mark with water.
2. Cover the top with plastic wrap and secure it with a rubber band or tape.
3. Put the cup in direct sunlight. Observe the cup for three days. Record your observations.
4. Remove the plastic wrap and observe it for a week.

Analysis

1. What parts of the water cycle did you observe in this activity?
2. What happened to the water level in the cup when the plastic wrap was removed?

They have been recycled untold billions of times. Many important materials that make up your body cycle through ecosystems. Some of these materials are water, carbon, and nitrogen.

The Water Cycle

Water molecules on Earth are on a constant journey, rising into the atmosphere, falling to land or the ocean as rain or snow, and flowing into rivers and oceans. The **water cycle** involves the processes of evaporation, condensation, and precipitation.

When energy, such as heat, is added to a liquid, its molecules begin to move faster. The more energy the molecules absorb, the faster they move, until they are moving so fast they break free and rise into the atmosphere. The liquid evaporates, or changes from a liquid to a gas. The heat of the sun causes water on the surface of Earth to evaporate and rise into the atmosphere as water vapor.

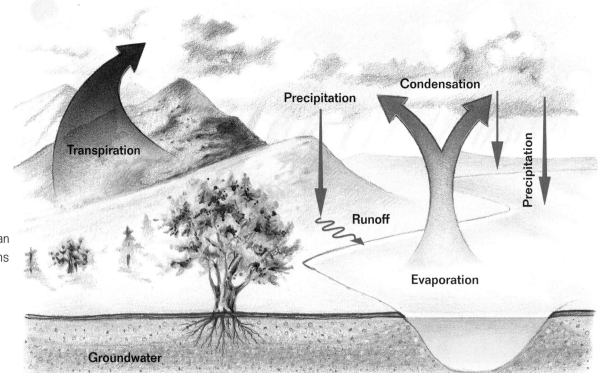

Figure 17-16
A water molecule that falls as rain can follow several paths through the water cycle. **Identify as many of these paths as you can in this diagram.**

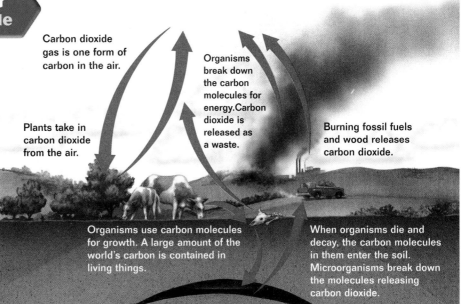

VISUALIZING
The Carbon Cycle

Figure 17-17 Carbon is cycled between the atmosphere and living organisms. **Why is the carbon cycle important?**

Carbon dioxide gas is one form of carbon in the air.

Plants take in carbon dioxide from the air.

Organisms break down the carbon molecules for energy. Carbon dioxide is released as a waste.

Burning fossil fuels and wood releases carbon dioxide.

Organisms use carbon molecules for growth. A large amount of the world's carbon is contained in living things.

When organisms die and decay, the carbon molecules in them enter the soil. Microorganisms break down the molecules releasing carbon dioxide.

As the water vapor rises, it encounters colder and colder air temperatures. As the molecules of water vapor become colder, they slow down. Eventually, the water vapor changes back into tiny droplets of water. It condenses, or changes from a gas to a liquid. These water droplets clump together to form clouds. When the droplets become large and heavy enough, they fall back to Earth as rain, or precipitation. This process is illustrated in **Figure 17-16.**

The Carbon Cycle

What do you have in common with all organisms? You all contain carbon. Earth's atmosphere contains about 0.03 percent carbon in the form of a gas called carbon dioxide. The movement of the element carbon through Earth's ecosystem is called the carbon cycle.

The carbon cycle begins with plants. During photosynthesis, plants remove carbon from the air and use it along with sunlight and water to make carbohydrates. These carbohydrates are used by other organisms and then returned to the atmosphere through cellular respiration, combustion, and erosion. See **Figure 17-17.** Once the carbon is returned to the atmosphere, the cycle begins again.

The Nitrogen Cycle

Nitrogen is an important element that is used by organisms to make proteins. Even though nitrogen gas makes up 78 percent of the atmosphere, most living organisms cannot use nitrogen in this form. It has to be combined with other elements through a process that is called nitrogen fixation.

*inter*NET
CONNECTION

Visit the Glencoe Science Web Site at **www.glencoe.com/ sec/science** for more information about food chains and food webs.

You can see in **Figure 17-18** how nitrogen is changed into usable compounds by bacteria associated with certain plants. A small amount is changed into nitrogen compounds by lightning. The transfer of nitrogen from the atmosphere to plants and back to the atmosphere or directly into plants again is the **nitrogen cycle.**

Phosphorus, sulfur, and other elements needed by living organisms also are used and returned to the environment. Just as we recycle aluminum, glass, and paper products, the materials that organisms need to live are recycled continuously in the biosphere.

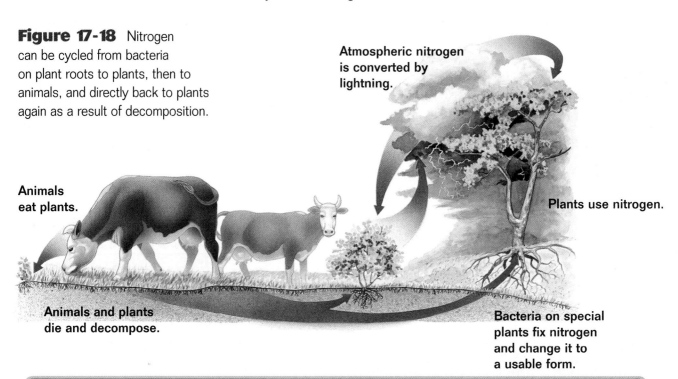

Figure 17-18 Nitrogen can be cycled from bacteria on plant roots to plants, then to animals, and directly back to plants again as a result of decomposition.

Atmospheric nitrogen is converted by lightning.

Plants use nitrogen.

Animals eat plants.

Animals and plants die and decompose.

Bacteria on special plants fix nitrogen and change it to a usable form.

Section Assessment

1. What is the difference between a food chain and a food web?
2. How does the cycling of matter affect a food chain?
3. **Think Critically:** Use your knowledge of food chains and the energy pyramid to explain why fewer lions than gazelles live on the African plains.
4.  **Skill Builder**
   Classifying Look at the food web pictured in **Figure 17-14.** Classify each organism pictured as a producer, an herbivore, a carnivore, or a decomposer. If you need help, refer to Classifying in the **Skill Handbook** on page 713.

Science **Journal**
In your Science Journal, compare the water cycle, carbon cycle, and nitrogen cycle. Use this information to discuss the processes that are involved in each cycle and how each cycle is important to living organisms.

Never Cry Wolf
by Farley Mowat

In the book *Never Cry Wolf*, Canadian biologist Farley Mowat details his yearlong expedition learning about wolves and surviving on the frozen tundra of northern Canada. When Mowat set up camp in a remote wilderness area, he didn't know he would end up eating mice to prove a point. Mowat was hired by the Canadian Wildlife Service to investigate and live among the wolves to help solve the country's growing "*Canis lupus* problem." Hunters were reporting that packs of bloodthirsty wolves were slaughtering caribou by the thousands and contributing to their extinction.

Mowat's Discovery

This action-packed book is more than just an adventure story. It's also the report of a stunning scientific discovery. Instead of fierce killers, Mowat found wolves to be gentle, skillful providers and devoted protectors of their young. Mowat challenged the idea that wolves were causing the decline in the caribou population. He showed that his wolf population fed almost exclusively on mice during the warmer summer months when the mouse population skyrocketed. To prove that a large mammal could survive on mice, he ate them himself. Following the publication of *Never Cry Wolf,* Mowat's conclusions about the habits and behaviors of wolves were criticized by people clinging to the old image of wolves as vicious killers.

Filled with beautiful images of animals in their natural setting, *Never Cry Wolf* describes one person's struggle to preserve a vanishing species. Mowat's heroic efforts to document never-before-seen behaviors in wild wolves focused international attention on wolves, which are threatened with extinction in North America and elsewhere. In 1983, Mowat's groundbreaking book was made into an entertaining movie.

Science JOURNAL

Never Cry Wolf was made into a movie based on the book. In your Science Journal, explain how books and movies like *Never Cry Wolf* can be used to persuade or to change a person's attitude toward a subject.

For a **preview** of this chapter, study this Reviewing Main Ideas before you read the chapter. After you have studied this chapter, you can use the Reviewing Main Ideas to **review** the chapter.

The Glencoe MindJogger, Audiocassettes, and CD-ROM provide additional opportunities for review.

17-1 THE LIVING AND NONLIVING ENVIRONMENT

The region of Earth in which all organisms live is the **biosphere.** The nonliving features of the environment are **abiotic factors,** and the organisms in the environment are **biotic factors. Populations** and **communities** make up an **ecosystem. Ecology** is the study of interactions among organisms and their environment. *How does the relationship between an organism, a population, and a community affect an ecosystem?*

17-2 INTERACTIONS AMONG LIVING ORGANISMS

A **population** can be described by characteristics that include size, spacing, and density. Any biotic or abiotic factor that limits the number of individuals in a population is a **limiting factor.** A close relationship between two or more species is a symbiotic relationship. The place where an organism lives is its **habitat,** and its role in the environment is its **niche.** *How could two similar species of birds live in the same area and nest in the same tree without occupying the same niche?*

Section
17-3 MATTER AND ENERGY

Food chains and **food webs** are models that describe the feeding relationships in a community. An **energy pyramid** describes the flow of energy through a community. Energy is distributed at each level of the food chain but is replenished by the sun. Matter is never lost or gained but is recycled. *If the rabbits, birds, mice, beetles, and deer were removed from the food web shown in this figure, which organisms would be affected and how?*

Career CONNECTION   **Isidro Bosh, Aquatic Biologist**

As an aquatic biologist, Isidro Bosh studies ocean invertebrates such as sea urchins, sea slugs, and sponges. He is interested in how these animals live in tough environmental conditions, such as cold polar oceans and the dark deep sea with its high pressure. He has explored the oceans in everything from huge research vessels to small, inflatable rafts. He also has explored tropical coral reefs and giant kelp forests. *Why is it important to study how animals adapt to tough environments?*

Chapter 17 Assessment

Using Vocabulary

a. abiotic factor
b. biosphere
c. biotic factor
d. carrying capacity
e. community
f. ecological pyramid
g. ecology
h. ecosystem
i. food chain
j. food web
k. habitat
l. limiting factor
m. niche
n. nitrogen cycle
o. population
p. population density
q. symbiosis
r. water cycle

Match each phrase with the correct term from the list of Vocabulary words.

1. any living thing in the environment
2. number of individuals of a species living in the same place at the same time
3. all the populations in an ecosystem
4. series of overlapping food chains
5. where an organism lives in an ecosystem

Checking Concepts

Choose the word or phrase that best answers the question.

6. Which of the following is a biotic factor?
   A) animals   C) sunlight
   B) air   D) soil

7. What are coral reefs and oak-hickory forests examples of?
   A) niches   C) populations
   B) habitats   D) ecosystems

8. What is made up of all populations in an area?
   A) niche   C) community
   B) habitat   D) ecosystem

9. What does the number of individuals in a population occupying an area of a specific size describe?
   A) clumping   C) spacing
   B) size   D) density

10. Which of the following is an example of an herbivore?
    A) wolf   C) tree
    B) moss   D) rabbit

11. Which level of the food chain has the most energy?
    A) omnivores   C) decomposers
    B) herbivores   D) producers

12. What is a relationship in which one organism is helped and the other is harmed?
    A) mutualism   C) commensalism
    B) parasitism   D) symbiosis

13. Which of the following is **NOT** cycled in the biosphere?
    A) nitrogen   C) water
    B) soil   D) carbon

14. Which of the following is a model that shows how energy is lost as it flows through an ecosystem?
    A) pyramid of biomass
    B) pyramid of numbers
    C) pyramid of energy
    D) niche

15. What does returning wolves to Yellowstone National Park add to the food web?
    A) producer   C) top carnivore
    B) herbivore   D) decomposer

Thinking Critically

16. What would be the advantage to a human or other omnivore of eating a diet of organisms that are lower rather than higher on the food chain?

17. Why are viruses considered parasites?

18. What does carrying capacity have to do with whether or not a population reaches its biotic potential?

19. Why are decomposers vital to the cycling of matter in an ecosystem?

20. Describe your own habitat and niche.

Developing Skills

If you need help, refer to the **Skill Handbook.**

21. **Classifying:** Classify each event in the water cycle as the result of either evaporation or condensation.

    A) A puddle disappears after a rainstorm.

    B) Rain falls.

    C) A lake becomes shallower.

    D) Clouds form.

22. **Making and Using Graphs:** Use the following data to graph the population density of a deer population over the years. Plot the number of deer on the *y*-axis and years on the *x*-axis. Propose a hypothesis to explain what might have happened to cause the changes in the size of the population.

Arizona Deer Population	
Year	**Deer per 400 hectares**
1905	5.7
1915	35.7
1920	142.9
1925	85.7
1935	25.7

23. **Observing and Inferring:** A home aquarium contains water, an air pump, a light, algae, a goldfish, and algae-eating snails. What are the abiotic factors in this environment? Which of these items would be considered a population? A community?

24. **Concept Mapping:** Use the following information to draw a food web of organisms living in a goldenrod field. *Goldenrod sap is eaten by aphids, goldenrod nectar is eaten by bees, goldenrod pollen is eaten by beetles, goldenrod leaves are eaten by beetles, stinkbugs eat beetles, spiders eat aphids, assassin bugs eat bees.*

THE PRINCETON REVIEW

Test-Taking Tip

Skip Around, If You Can Just because the questions are in order doesn't mean you have to answer them that way. You may want to skip over hard questions and come back to them later. Answer all the easier questions first to guarantee you more points toward your score.

Test Practice

Use these questions to test your Science Proficiency.

1. According to the table, at which point are there more deer than available food?
   A) 1
   B) 2
   C) 3
   D) 4

2. In the water cycle, how is water returned to the atmosphere?
   A) evaporation
   B) condensation
   C) precipitation
   D) fixation

3. What are the food relationships among all organisms in the same environment called?
   A) food chain
   B) ecological pyramid
   C) food web
   D) energy pyramid

4. In an energy pyramid, which level has the most available energy?
   A) first
   B) second
   C) third
   D) fourth

CHAPTER

18 Ecosystems

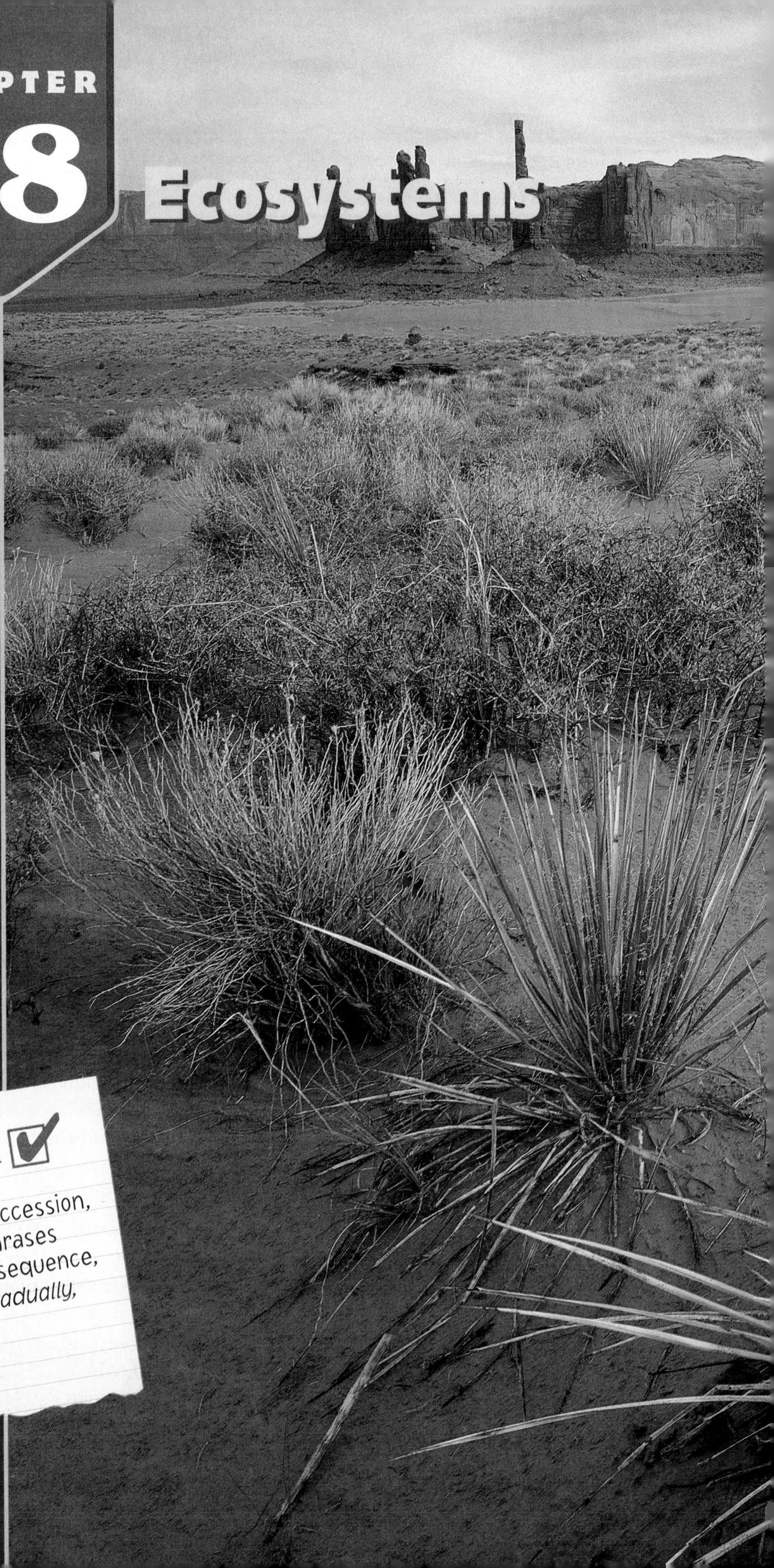

Chapter Preview

Skills Preview

Skill Builders
- Map Concepts
- Compare and Contrast

Activities
- Observe

MiniLabs
- Observe
- Infer

Reading Check

As you read about succession, record words and phrases that indicate a time sequence, such as *long ago, gradually,* and *as time passed.*

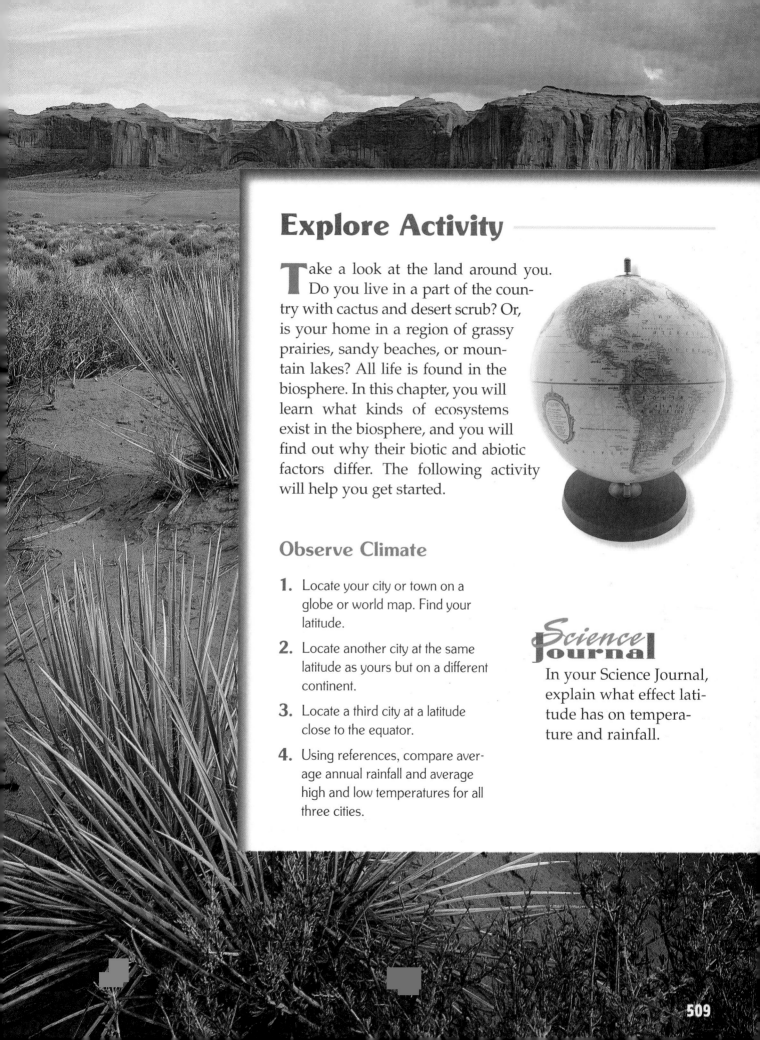

Explore Activity

Take a look at the land around you. Do you live in a part of the country with cactus and desert scrub? Or, is your home in a region of grassy prairies, sandy beaches, or mountain lakes? All life is found in the biosphere. In this chapter, you will learn what kinds of ecosystems exist in the biosphere, and you will find out why their biotic and abiotic factors differ. The following activity will help you get started.

Observe Climate

1. Locate your city or town on a globe or world map. Find your latitude.

2. Locate another city at the same latitude as yours but on a different continent.

3. Locate a third city at a latitude close to the equator.

4. Using references, compare average annual rainfall and average high and low temperatures for all three cities.

Science Journal

In your Science Journal, explain what effect latitude has on temperature and rainfall.

18·1 How Ecosystems Change

What You'll Learn

▶ How ecosystems change over time

▶ How new communities arise in areas that were bare of life

▶ How to compare and contrast pioneer communities and climax communities

Vocabulary

ecological succession
primary succession
pioneer community
secondary succession
climax community

Why It's Important

▶ Your ecosystem is changing right now.

Ecological Succession

Imagine hiking through a forest. Huge trees tower over the trail. You know it can take many years for trees to grow this large, so it's easy to think of the forest as something that has always been here. But, this area has not always been covered with trees. Long ago, it may have been a pond full of fish and frogs surrounded by water-loving plants. As time passed, the decomposed bodies of plants and animals slowly filled in the pond until it eventually became a lush, green meadow full of grass and wildflowers. Gradually, over many more years, seeds blew in, trees began to grow, and a forest developed. The process of gradual change from one community of organisms to another is called **ecological succession.** The changes associated with succession usually take place in a fairly predictable order and involve animals, plants, and other organisms.

VISUALIZING Succession

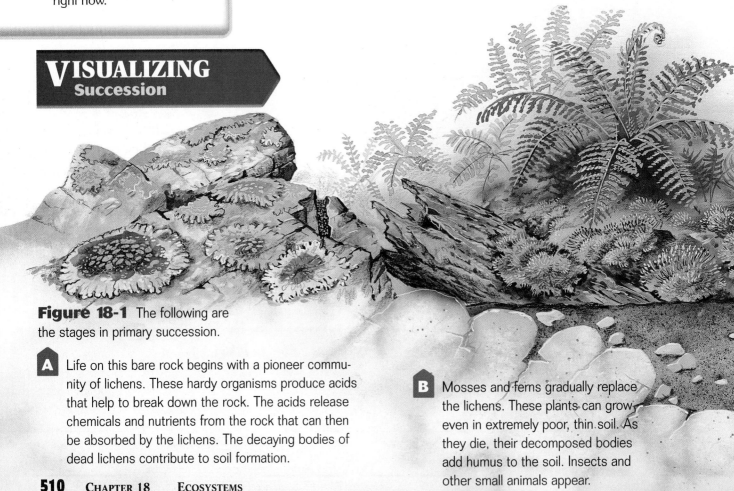

Figure 18-1 The following are the stages in primary succession.

A Life on this bare rock begins with a pioneer community of lichens. These hardy organisms produce acids that help to break down the rock. The acids release chemicals and nutrients from the rock that can then be absorbed by the lichens. The decaying bodies of dead lichens contribute to soil formation.

B Mosses and ferns gradually replace the lichens. These plants can grow even in extremely poor, thin soil. As they die, their decomposed bodies add humus to the soil. Insects and other small animals appear.

Primary Succession

Think about conditions around an erupting volcano. Incredibly hot, molten lava flows along the ground, destroying everything in its path. As the lava cools, it forms new land. Soil is formed from bare rock. Similar events happen to this newly formed land. Particles of dust and ash fall to the ground. The forces of weather and erosion break up the lava rock. A thin layer of soil begins to form. Birds, wind, and rain deposit more dust, along with bacteria, seeds, and fungal spores. Plants start to grow and decay. A living community has begun to develop.

Ecological succession that begins in a place that does not have soil is called **primary succession.** The first community of organisms to move into a new environment is called the **pioneer community,** as shown in **Figure 18-1.** Members of pioneer communities are usually hardy organisms that can survive drought, extreme heat and cold, and other harsh conditions. Pioneer communities change the conditions in their environments. These new conditions support the growth of other types of organisms that gradually take over.

CHEMISTRY INTEGRATION

Freezing Water

Freezing temperatures are harmful to living organisms because water is the main component of cells. As water freezes, it expands. Infer what happens to cells if ice crystals form inside them.

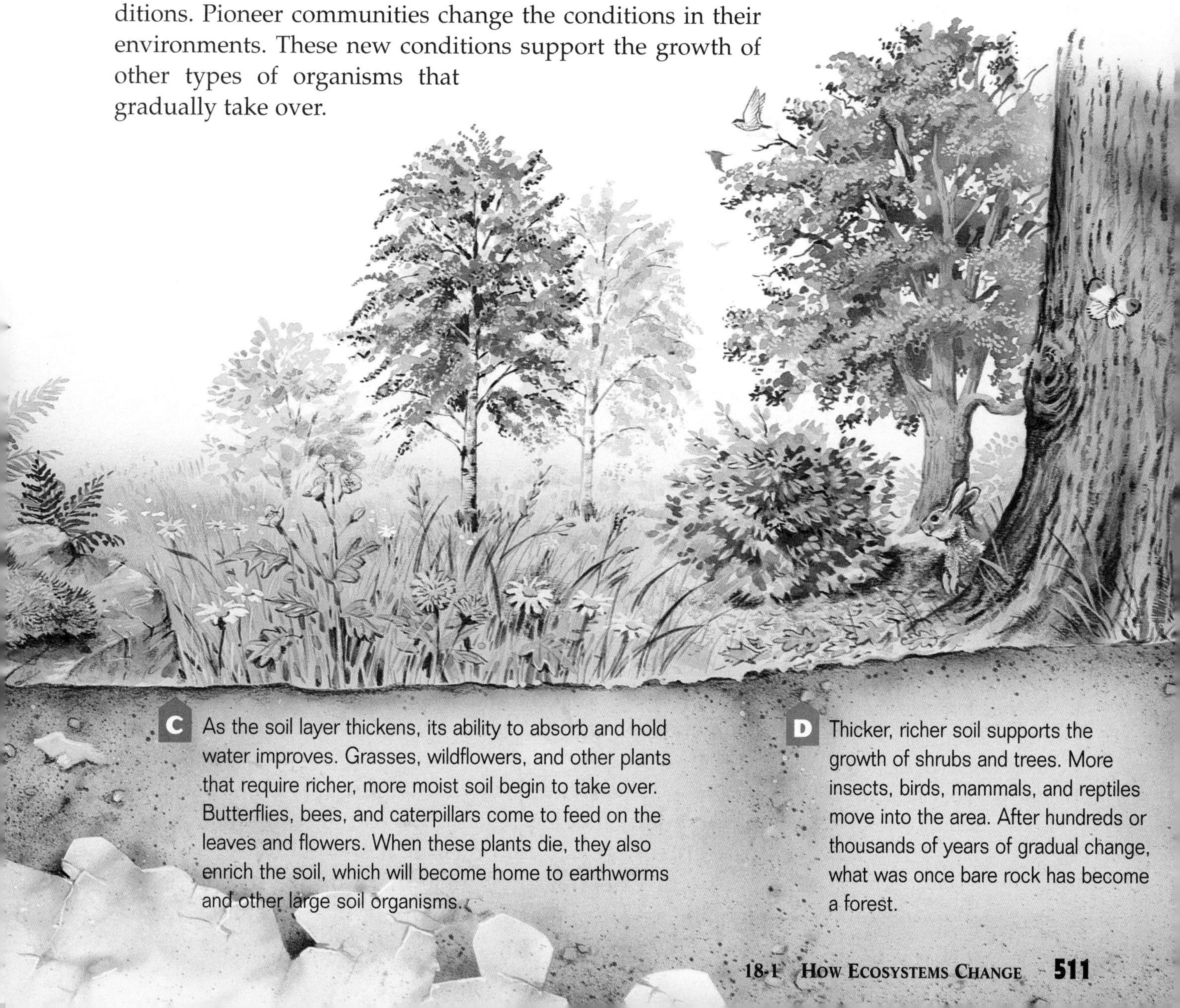

C As the soil layer thickens, its ability to absorb and hold water improves. Grasses, wildflowers, and other plants that require richer, more moist soil begin to take over. Butterflies, bees, and caterpillars come to feed on the leaves and flowers. When these plants die, they also enrich the soil, which will become home to earthworms and other large soil organisms.

D Thicker, richer soil supports the growth of shrubs and trees. More insects, birds, mammals, and reptiles move into the area. After hundreds or thousands of years of gradual change, what was once bare rock has become a forest.

Figure 18-2 The tangled growth of weeds and grasses in untended yards and vacant lots, on abandoned farms, and along country roadsides is the beginning stage of secondary succession.

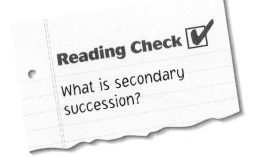

Reading Check

What is secondary succession?

interNET
CONNECTION

Visit the Glencoe Science Web Site at **www. glencoe.com/sec/ science** for more information about the Yellowstone fires and how they contributed to succession.

Secondary Succession

What happens when a forest is destroyed by a fire or a city building is torn down? After a forest fire, nothing is left except dead trees and ash-covered soil. Once the rubble of a demolished building has been taken away, all that remains is bare soil. But, these places do not remain lifeless for long. The soil may already contain the seeds of weeds, grasses, and trees. More seeds are carried to the area by wind and birds. As the seeds germinate and plants begin to grow, insects, birds, and other wildlife move in. Ecological succession has begun again. Succession that begins in a place that already has soil and was once the home of living organisms is called **secondary succession,** shown in **Figure 18-2.**

Climax Communities

Succession involves changes in abiotic factors as well as biotic factors. You have already seen how lichens, mosses, and ferns change the environment by helping to form the rich, thick soil needed for the growth of shrubs and trees. Shrubs and trees also cause changes in abiotic factors. Their branches shade the ground beneath them, reducing the temperature. Shade also reduces the rate of evaporation, increasing the moisture content of the soil. Amount of sunlight, temperature, and moisture level determine which species will grow in soil.

The redwood forest shown in **Figure 18-3** is an example of a community that has reached the end of succession. As long as the trees are not cut down or destroyed by fire or widespread disease, the species that make up the redwood community tend to remain the same. When a community has reached the final stage of ecological succession, it is called a **climax community.** Because primary succession begins in areas with no life at all, it can take hundreds or even thousands of years for a pioneer community to develop into a climax community. Secondary succession is a shorter process, but it still may take a century or more.

Comparing Communities

As you have seen, pioneer communities are simple. They contain only a few species, and feeding relationships usually can be described with simple food chains. Climax communities are much more complex. They may contain hundreds of thousands of species, and feeding relationships usually involve complex food webs. Interactions among the many biotic and abiotic factors in a climax community create a more stable environment that does not change much over time. Climax communities are the end product of ecological succession. A climax community that has been disturbed in some way will eventually return to the same type of community, as long as all other factors remain the same. However, it may take a century or more for the community to return to its former state.

Figure 18-3 This forest of redwood trees in California is an example of a climax community. Redwoods live for hundreds of years. They create shade on the ground beneath them. Needles constantly fall from their branches. Eventually, they form an acidic soil that allows the growth of young redwoods but prevents the growth of many other types of plants.

Section Assessment

1. What is ecological succession?
2. What is the difference between primary and secondary succession?
3. What is the difference between pioneer and climax communities?
4. **Think Critically:** What kind of succession will take place on an abandoned, unpaved country road? Why?
5. **Skill Builder**
   Sequencing Describe the sequence of events in primary succession. Include the term *climax community.* If you need help, refer to Sequencing on page 714.

In your Science Journal, draw a food chain for a pioneer community of lichens and a food web for the climax community of an oak-maple forest. Write a short paragraph comparing the two communities.

Activity 18•1

Endangered and Threatened Species

A species becomes endangered when its numbers are so low that it is in danger of extinction in the near future. The list of threatened and endangered species in the United States and around the world is constantly growing due to a variety of reasons. In 1998, about 965 species in the United States were listed as endangered or threatened.

Recognize the Problem

What endangered or threatened species have been identified for your region of the country?

Form a Hypothesis

Form a hypothesis to explain some of the reasons why the organisms identified as threatened or endangered in your region are on the list.

Goals

- **Obtain** and **organize** data.
- **Infer** relationships between the plant or animal and its environment.
- **Use the Internet** to collect and compare data from other students.

Data Sources

Go to the Glencoe Science Web Site at **www.glencoe. com/sec/science** to find links to information about endangered plants and animals around the country. You also will find information posted by other students from around the country.

Species Data				
Organism Genus species	Threatened or Endangered	Length of Time on List	Recovery Plan	General Information

Test Your Hypothesis

Plan

1. Find links to information on the Glencoe Science Web Site. You can also find information on endangered species at the local library or a local zoo.

2. Prepare a data table similar to the one below to record your findings.

3. If possible, observe one of the endangered or threatened species you've identified either in a zoo or in the wild.

Do

1. **Describe** the habitat and range of the organism you chose to study.

2. **Identify** any steps being taken to protect the organism. Outline the recovery plan written for one of the organisms in your region.

3. **Post** the information you collected in the table provided for this activity on the Glencoe Science Web Site.

4. **Check** the postings by other students for more information on your organism and on other organisms.

Analyze Your Data

1. Brainstorm possible reasons why your organism is threatened or endangered.

2. What factors were you able to identify as reasons for the organism becoming endangered?

3. Was your hypothesis supported by the information you collected? **Explain** your answer.

Draw Conclusions

1. What might help the organism you are studying survive the changes in conditions or other changes that have occurred in its range that caused its numbers to decrease.

2. How successful have any techniques established to protect the organism been?

3. Did you find more threatened or endangered species of plants or animals in your region? What explanation might there be for your findings?

4. What steps do you think should be taken, if any, to protect endangered or threatened species in your region? What objections might be raised for the steps taken to protect a species?

Land Environments

Factors That Determine Climate

What does a desert in Arizona have in common with a desert in Africa? They both have water-conserving plants with thorns, lizards, heat, little rain, and poor soil. How are the plains of the American West like the veldt of central Africa? Both regions have dry summers, wet winters, and huge expanses of grassland that support grazing animals such as elk and antelope. Many widely separated regions of the world have similar ecosystems. Why? Because they have similar climates. Climate is the general weather pattern in an area. The factors that determine a region's climate include temperature and precipitation.

Temperature

The sun supplies life on Earth not only with light energy for photosynthesis, but also with heat energy for warmth. The temperature of a region is regulated primarily by the amount of sunlight that reaches it. In turn, the amount of sunlight is determined by an area's latitude and elevation.

Latitude

As **Figure 18-4** shows, not all parts of Earth receive the same amount of energy from the sun. When you conducted the Explore Activity at the beginning of this chapter, you probably concluded that temperature is affected by latitude.

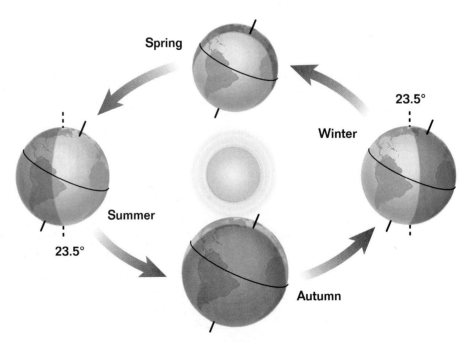

Figure 18-4 Because Earth is tilted on its axis, the angle of the sun's rays changes during the year. These changes create the seasons. The tilt of Earth's axis does not have as much of an effect on regions near the equator.

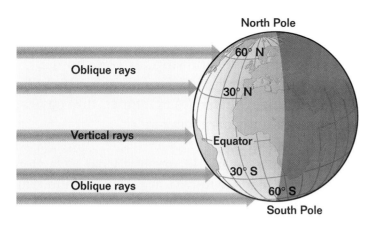

North Pole

Oblique rays

60° N

30° N

Vertical rays

Equator

30° S

Oblique rays

60° S

South Pole

Figure 18-5 Because Earth is curved, oblique rays of sunlight reaching higher latitudes near the poles are more spread out. These rays are therefore weaker than the sunlight reaching lower latitudes near the equator. Climates near the equator are warmer, and those near the poles are colder.

The nearer a region is to the north or south pole, the higher its latitude, the smaller the amount of energy it receives from the sun, as seen in **Figure 18-5,** and the colder its climate.

Seasonal changes in sunlight also have an effect on the temperature of a climate. Because Earth is tilted on its axis, the angle of the sun's rays changes as Earth moves through its yearly orbit. During winter in the northern hemisphere, regions north of the equator are tilted away from the sun. Rays of sunlight are spread over a larger area, reducing their warming effect. As a result, winter temperatures are colder than summer temperatures.

Elevation

A region's elevation, or distance above sea level, also has an influence on temperature. Earth's atmosphere acts as insulation that traps some of the heat that reaches Earth's surface. At higher elevations, the atmosphere is thinner, so more heat escapes back into space. As a result, the higher the elevation, the colder the climate. The climate on a mountain will be cooler than the climate at sea level at the same latitude. Higher elevations affect plant growth, as seen in **Figure 18-6.**

EARTH SCIENCE
◄ **INTEGRATION**

Using Math

Earth is tilted at an angle of 23.5°. Without using a protractor, sketch an angle that measures about 23.5°. Then, check your angle by measuring it with a protractor.

Figure 18-6 These Rocky Mountain bristlecone pines show the effects of higher elevations on plants. These trees are shaped by the wind and stunted by the cold, harsh conditions.

Precipitation

Water is one of the most important factors affecting the climate of an area. Precipitation (prih sihp uh TAY shun) is the amount of water that condenses and falls in the form of rain, snow, sleet, hail, and fog. Differences in temperature have an important effect on patterns of precipitation.

Have you heard the expression "Hot air rises"? Actually, hot air is pushed upward whenever cold air sinks. Cold air is more dense than hot air, so it tends to move toward the ground. This pushes warm air near Earth's surface upward. In warm tropical regions near the equator, the air, land, and oceans are constantly being heated by the direct rays of the sun. As the cooler air sinks, the warm air is pushed upward into the atmosphere. This warm air carries large amounts of water vapor from the oceans. When the air reaches a high enough altitude in the atmosphere, the water vapor it contains cools and condenses as rain. While the air rises, it also moves slowly toward either the north or south pole. The air loses virtually all of its moisture by the time it reaches a latitude of about 30°. Because of this pattern, deserts are common at latitudes near 30° in both the northern and southern hemispheres. Latitudes between 0° and 22° receive much larger amounts of rain.

The Rain Shadow Effect

The presence of mountain ranges also has an effect on rainfall patterns. As **Figure 18-7** shows, air that is moving toward a mountain range is forced upward by the shape of the land. As warm air is forced upward, it cools, condensing the water vapor it contains and creating rain or snow. By the time the air has passed over the mountains, it has lost its moisture. The region on the opposite side of the mountain range receives very little rain because it is in a "rain shadow" created by the mountains.

interNET CONNECTION

Little precipitation falls in the desert. Visit the Glencoe Science Web Site at **www.glencoe.com/sec/science** for more information about how cacti thrive.

Figure 18-7 Moist air moving into California from the Pacific Ocean is forced upward when it reaches the Sierra Nevada Mountains. As air rises, it cools and loses its moisture in the form of rain or snow. By the time the air reaches Nevada and Utah, on the other side of the mountains, it is dry. This area is in the mountains' "rain shadow." It receives so little rain that it has become a desert.

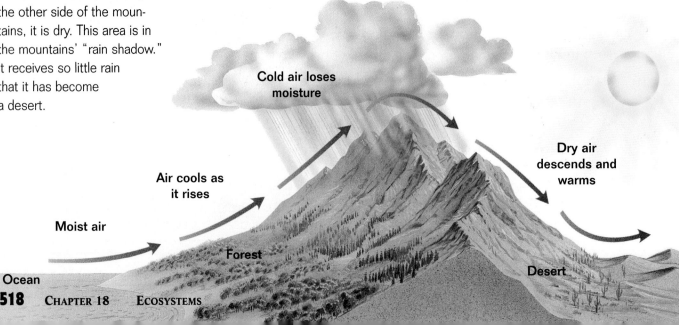

Cold air loses moisture

Dry air descends and warms

Air cools as it rises

Moist air

Forest

Ocean

Desert

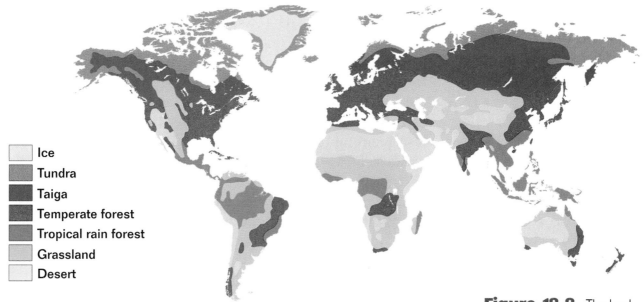

- Ice
- Tundra
- Taiga
- Temperate forest
- Tropical rain forest
- Grassland
- Desert

Figure 18-8 The land portion of the biosphere can be divided into several biomes. Tundra, taiga, temperate forest, tropical rain forest, grassland, and desert are the most commonly known. **Which biome is most common in the United States?**

Land Biomes

As you will see in the **Field Guide to Biomes** at the end of this chapter, regions with similar climates tend to have ecosystems with climax communities of similar structure. Tropical rain forests are climax communities found near the equator, where temperatures are warm and rainfall is plentiful. Coniferous forests grow where winter temperatures are cold and rainfall is moderate. Large geographic areas that have similar climates and ecosystems are called **biomes** (BI ohmz). The six most common biomes are mapped in **Figure 18-8.**

Tundra

At latitudes surrounding the north pole lies a biome that receives little precipitation but is covered with ice most of the year. The **tundra** (TUN dra) is a cold, dry, treeless region, sometimes called a cold desert, where winters are six to nine months long. For some of those months, the land remains dark because the sun never rises above the horizon. For a few days during the short, cold summer, the sun never sets. Precipitation averages less than 25 cm per year, and winter temperatures drop to −40°C, so water in the tundra soil remains frozen solid during the winter. During the summer, only the top few inches thaw.

Try at Home

Mini Lab

Comparing Tundra and Taiga

Procedure

1. Compare the latitudes where tundra is found in the northern hemisphere with the same latitudes in South America.
2. Compare the latitudes where taiga is found in the northern hemisphere with the same latitudes in South America.

Analysis

Are either of these biomes found in South America? Explain why or why not.

Below the thawed surface is a layer of permanently frozen soil called permafrost. The cold temperatures slow down the process of decomposition, so the soil is also poor in nutrients.

Tundra plants are resistant to drought and cold. They include species of lichens known as reindeer moss, true mosses, grasses, and small shrubs, as seen in **Figure 18-9.** During the summer, mosquitoes, blackflies, and other biting insects are abundant. Many birds, including ducks, geese, various shorebirds, and songbirds, migrate to the tundra to nest during the summer. Hawks, snowy owls, mice, voles, lemmings, arctic hares, caribou, and musk oxen are also found there.

Taiga

Just below the tundra, at latitudes between about 50°N and 60°N, and stretching across Canada, northern Europe, and Asia, lies the world's largest biome. The **taiga** (TI guh), as shown in **Figure 18-10,** is a cold region of cone-bearing evergreen trees. This biome is also called the northern coniferous forest. Although the winter is long and cold, the taiga is warmer and wetter than the tundra. Precipitation is mostly snow and averages 35 cm to 100 cm each year.

Figure 18-9 Land is so flat in the tundra that water does not drain away. Because the frozen soil also prevents water from soaking into the soil, part of the tundra becomes wet and marshy during the summer. Frozen soil also prevents trees and other deep-rooted plants from growing in the tundra biome.

Figure 18-10 The climax community of the taiga is dominated by fir and spruce trees. Mammal populations include moose, black bears, lynx, and wolves.

No permafrost is found in a taiga. The ground thaws completely during the summer, making it possible for trees to grow. There are few shrubs and grasses, primarily because the forests of the taiga are so dense that little sunlight penetrates through the trees. Lichens and mosses grow on the forest floor.

Temperate Deciduous Forest

Temperate forests are found in both the northern and southern hemispheres, at latitudes below about 50°. Temperate regions usually have four distinct seasons each year. Precipitation ranges from about 75 cm to 150 cm and is distributed evenly throughout the year. Temperatures range from below freezing during the winter to 30°C or more during the warmest days of summer.

Many coniferous forests exist in the temperate regions of the world, particularly in mountainous areas. However, most of the temperate forests in Europe and North America are dominated by climax communities of deciduous trees, which lose their leaves every autumn. These forests, like the one in **Figure 18-11,** are called **temperate deciduous forests.** In the United States, they are found primarily east of the Mississippi River. ☑

The loss of leaves in the fall signals a dramatic change in the life of the deciduous forest. Food becomes less abundant, and the leafless trees no longer provide adequate shelter for many organisms. Some animals, particularly birds, migrate to warmer regions during the winter. Other organisms reduce their activities and their need for food by going into hibernation until spring.

Reading Check ☑

Where are temperate deciduous forests found?

Figure 18-11 The mild climate and rich soil of the temperate deciduous forest support a wide variety of organisms. Animal life includes deer, foxes, squirrels, mice, snakes, and a huge number of bird and insect species. **Why do you think the temperate forests support a wide variety of organisms?**

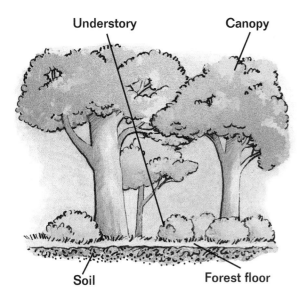

Understory   Canopy

Soil   Forest floor

Figure 18-12 All forests are made up of layers with distinctly different biotic and abiotic factors.

Layers of Vegetation

Forests form layers of vegetation, as illustrated in **Figure 18-12.** At the top of the forest is the canopy, which consists of the leafy branches of trees. The *canopy* shades the ground below and provides homes for birds, insects, mammals, and many other organisms.

Beneath the canopy and above the forest floor is the shrub layer, or *understory*. The understory is made up of shorter plants that tolerate shade, along with organisms that depend on these plants for food and shelter.

The forest floor is dark and moist. It is home to many insects, worms, and fungi, as well as plants that can survive in dim light. Leaves, twigs, seeds, and the bodies of dead animals that fall to the forest floor either decompose or are eaten.

Problem Solving

Saving the Rain Forests

Many of the world's rain forests are being destroyed for economic reasons. Logging and farming provide income for people living in these areas. When a section of rain forest is cleared, trees that can be used as lumber are removed and sold. The remaining plants are cut down and burned, the ash is used to fertilize the soil, and food crops are planted. After a couple of years, the soil becomes too poor to produce a harvest, so the land is abandoned and another patch of forest is cleared.

People can make a living from the rain forest in other ways. Latex, a material used in surgical gloves, rubber bands, tires, and shoes, is the sap of rubber trees. Carefully tapping the trees provides a continual harvest without harming the forest. Many rain forest plants produce edible fruits, nuts, and oils that can be harvested year after year, without the need for clearing land. Harvesting these plants, rather than clearing land on which other crops can be grown for only a short time, could provide people with a sustainable income.

Think Critically: Suppose a family could earn the same amount of money in two different ways. One is to clear several hectares of rain forest, sell the timber, and grow food crops for two years. The other is to harvest latex and edible fruits and nuts from a larger area of rain forest for four years. Which course of action would you recommend? Why? Give reasons why the family might choose the other method.

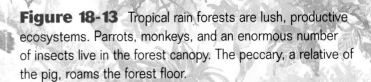

Figure 18-13 Tropical rain forests are lush, productive ecosystems. Parrots, monkeys, and an enormous number of insects live in the forest canopy. The peccary, a relative of the pig, roams the forest floor.

Tropical Rain Forest

The most important climax community in the equatorial regions of the world is the lush, green plant growth of the **tropical rain forest.** Rainfall averages 200 cm to 225 cm each year, and some areas receive as much as 400 cm of rain annually. Temperatures are warm and stable, never varying much above or below about 25°C. The abundant rainfall and high temperatures combine to create a hot, humid environment that can be compared to the atmosphere inside a greenhouse.

Plants

The highest part of the rain forest canopy is formed by the leaves and branches of trees that may reach 30 m to 40 m in height. A rain forest may contain more than 700 species of trees and more than 1000 species of flowering plants. The canopy is so dense that it prevents much sunlight from filtering through to the regions below. Vines that are rooted in the soil grow up along tree trunks to reach the sun. Some types of plants such as orchids reach the light by anchoring themselves on tree trunks instead of in the soil. The understory is only dimly lit. Many of the plants growing here have huge leaves that catch what little sunlight is available. The forest floor is almost completely dark, with few plants other than ferns and mosses. Many of the tallest trees have support roots that rise above the ground. Most plants have shallow roots that form a tangled mat at the soil surface.

Animals

The rain forest is home to a huge number of animals. It is estimated that 1000 hectares (about 2500 acres) of rain forest in South America contain thousands of insect species, including 150 different

Using Math

Make a bar graph that shows the average yearly precipitation in each of the land biomes.

kinds of butterflies. The same patch of forest also contains dozens of species of snakes, lizards, frogs, and salamanders, and hundreds of varieties of brightly colored birds, including parrots, toucans, cockatoos, and hummingbirds. Tree-dwelling mammals include monkeys, sloths, and bats. Ocelots and jaguars are tropical cats that prowl the forest floor in search of small mammals such as pacas and agoutis, or piglike peccaries, shown in **Figure 18-13.**

Grassland

Temperate and tropical regions that receive between 25 cm and 75 cm of precipitation each year and are dominated by climax communities of grasses are known as **grasslands.** Most grasslands have a dry season, when little or no rain falls, which prevents the development of forests. Virtually every continent has grasslands, like the one in **Figure 18-14,** and they are known by a variety of names. The prairie and plains of North America, the steppes of Asia, the veldts of Africa, and the pampas of South America are all grasslands.

Grass plants have extensive root systems, called sod, that absorb water when it rains and can withstand drought during long dry spells. The roots remain dormant during winter and sprout new stems and leaves when the weather warms in the spring. The soil is rich and fertile, and many grassland regions of the world are now important farming areas. Cereal grains such as wheat, rye, oats, barley, and corn, which serve as staple foods for humans, are types of grasses.

The most noticeable animals in grassland ecosystems are usually mammals that graze on the stems, leaves, and seeds of grass plants. Kangaroos graze in the grasslands of Australia. In Africa, common grassland inhabitants include wildebeests and zebras.

Figure 18-14 Grasslands, like this one in South Dakota, are hot and dry during the summer and cold and wet during the winter. They once supported huge herds of bison. Today, they are inhabited by pronghorn, gophers, ground squirrels, prairie chickens, and meadowlarks.

Desert

The **desert,** the driest biome on Earth, receives less than 25 cm of rain each year and supports little plant life. Some desert areas may receive no rain for years. When rain does come, it quickly drains away due to the sandy soil. Any water that remains on the ground evaporates rapidly, so the soil retains almost no moisture.

Because of the lack of water, desert plants are spaced widely apart, and much of the ground is bare. Some areas receive enough rainfall to support the growth of a few shrubs and small trees. Barren, windblown sand dunes are characteristic of the driest deserts, where rain rarely falls. Most deserts are covered with a thin, sandy or gravelly soil that contains little humus.

Adaptations of Desert Plants and Animals

Desert plants have developed a variety of adaptations for survival in the extreme dryness and hot and cold temperatures of this biome. Cactus plants, like the one in **Figure 18-15A,** with their reduced, spiny leaves, are probably the most familiar desert plants. Cacti have large, shallow roots that quickly absorb any water that becomes available.

Water conservation is important to all desert animals. Some, like the kangaroo rat, never need to drink water. They get all the moisture they need from the breakdown of food during digestion. Other adaptations involve behavior. Most animals are active only during the early morning or late afternoon, when temperatures are less extreme. Few large animals are found in the desert because there is not enough water or food to support them.

Figure 18-15 Desert organisms are adapted to hot, dry conditions.

A Giant saguaro cacti expand to store water after it rains.

B Desert iguanas, common in deserts of the southwestern United States and Mexico, prefer temperatures above 100°F.

Section Assessment

1. Name two biomes that receive less than 25 cm of rain each year.

2. Compare the adaptations of tundra organisms to their environment with those of a desert organism to its environment.

3. **Think Critically:** Compare and contrast the canopies of temperate deciduous forests and tropical rain forests.

4. **Skill Builder**
   Observing and Inferring Animals adapt to their environments in order to survive. Do the **Chapter 18 Skill Activity** on page 759 to infer how some organisms adapt.

Using Computers

Database Create a database of information on Earth's land biomes. Include data on temperature range, precipitation, limiting factors, and descriptions of climax communities. If you need help, refer to page 733.

Materials

- Graph paper
- Thermometer
- Tape measure
- Hand lens
- Notebook
- Binoculars
- Pencil
- Field guides

Studying a Land Environment

An ecological study includes observation and analysis of living organisms and the physical features of the environment.

What You'll Investigate

How do you study an ecosystem?

Goals

- **Observe** biotic and abiotic factors of an ecosystem.
- **Analyze** the relationships among organisms and their environment.

Procedure

1. **Choose** a portion of an ecosystem near your school or home as your area of study. You might choose to study a pond, a forest area in a park, a garden, or another area.

2. **Decide** the boundaries of your study area.

3. Using a tape measure and graph paper, **make a map** of your study area.

4. Using a thermometer, **measure and record** the air temperature in your study area.

5. **Observe** the organisms in your study area. Use field guides to identify them. Use a hand lens to study small organisms. Use binoculars to study animals you cannot get near. Also, look for evidence (such as tracks or feathers) of organisms you do not see.

6. Record your observations in a table like the one shown. Make drawings to help you remember what you see.

7. Visit your study area as many times as you can and at different times of the day for four weeks. At each visit, be sure to make the same measurements and record all observations. Note how biotic and abiotic factors interact.

Conclude and Apply

1. **Identify** relationships among the organisms in your study area, such as predator-prey or symbiosis.

2. **Diagram** a food chain or food web for your ecosystem.

3. **Predict** what might happen if one or more abiotic factors were changed suddenly.

4. **Predict** what might happen if one or more populations were removed from the area.

Environmental Data				
Date	Time of Day	Temperature	Organisms Observed	Observations and Comments

Protecting Antarctica

The Coldest Place on Earth

Antarctica is a vast continent of rock covered with ice and surrounded by ocean. It is the least changed landmass in the world, in part because it is an environment hostile to humans. Winters are dark and long, with temperatures dipping to –90°C. During winter, shelves of ice extend from the land out over the ocean, essentially doubling the size of the continent. The yearly freezing and thawing of this ice has important effects on worldwide weather patterns and is a force that drives ocean currents.

Antarctica's Resources

Although the land is barren, seals and penguins, like the ones at left, use the shores as breeding grounds, and the waters of the Antarctic Ocean teem with life. Under the surface of Antarctica lie untouched mineral resources. Coal and oil probably exist in enormous quantities, as do other minerals that have already been discovered.

Antarctica and its remarkable natural resources are fully protected by a treaty that was drawn up in 1959 and signed by 12 nations—the United States, Great Britain, Argentina, Chile, France, Belgium, Norway, Australia, New Zealand, Japan, South Africa, and what was then the USSR. The Antarctic Treaty made the entire continent "a natural reserve, devoted to peace and science." Military activities, hunting, mining, and other actions that might harm the environment and its wild inhabitants are banned.

Since 1959, the Antarctic Treaty has been expanded to promote even greater environmental protection, international cooperation, and freedom for scientific research. Thanks to this agreement, Antarctica will remain an essentially undisturbed wilderness far into the future.

interNET CONNECTION

Visit the Glencoe Science Web Site at **www.glencoe.com/sec/ science** to find out more about research in Antarctica.

18•3 Water Environments

What You'll Learn

▶ The difference between flowing freshwater and standing freshwater ecosystems

▶ Important seashore and deep-ocean ecosystems

Vocabulary
plankton
estuary
intertidal zone

Why It's Important

▶ You depend on water for your life processes.

Figure 18-16

 Freshwater streams are important in the ecosystem.

Freshwater Biomes

You've learned that temperature and precipitation are the most important factors determining which species can survive in a land environment. The limiting factors in water environments are the amount of salt in the water, dissolved oxygen, water temperature, and sunlight. The amount of salts dissolved in the water is called salinity. Freshwater contains little or no dissolved salts, and so has a low salinity. Earth's freshwater biomes include flowing water like these rivers and streams, as well as still or standing water, such as lakes and ponds.

Rivers and Streams

Flowing freshwater environments range from small, swiftly flowing streams, like the one in **Figure 18-16A,** to large, slow rivers. The faster a stream flows, the clearer its water tends to be and the higher its oxygen content. Swift currents quickly wash loose particles downstream, leaving a rocky or gravelly bottom. The tumbling and splashing of swiftly flowing water mixes in air from the atmosphere, increasing the oxygen content of the water.

Most of the nutrients that support life in flowing-water ecosystems are washed into the water from land. In areas where the water movement slows down, such as wide pools in streams or large rivers, debris settles to the bot-

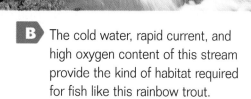

B The cold water, rapid current, and high oxygen content of this stream provide the kind of habitat required for fish like this rainbow trout.

Figure 18-17 Ponds and lakes differ in the types of communities inhabiting them. **What are some other differences between ponds and lakes?**

A The warm, sunlit waters of this pond are home to a large variety of organisms. Plants and algae form the basis of a food web that includes snails, insects, frogs, snakes, turtles, and fish.

tom. These environments tend to have higher nutrient levels and lower dissolved oxygen levels. They contain organisms such as freshwater mussels, minnows, and leeches that are not so well adapted for swiftly flowing water. They also tend to have more plant growth.

Lakes and Ponds

A lake or pond forms when a low place in the land fills with rainwater, snowmelt, or water from a stream. The waters of lakes and ponds hardly move at all. They contain more plant growth than flowing-water environments contain.

Ponds, like the one in **Figure 18-17A,** are smaller, shallow bodies of water. Because they are shallow, sunlight can usually penetrate all the way to the bottom, making the water warmer and promoting the growth of plants and algae. In fact, many ponds are almost completely filled with plant material, so the only clear, open water is at the center. Because of the lush growth in pond environments, they tend to be high in nutrients.

Lakes are larger and deeper than ponds. They tend to have more open water because most plant growth is limited to shallow areas along the shoreline. In fact, organisms found in the warm, sunlit waters of the lakeshore are often similar to those found in ponds.

Floating in the warm, sunlit waters near the surface of freshwater lakes and ponds are microscopic organisms known as plankton. **Plankton** includes algae, plants, and other organisms. If you were to dive all the way to the bottom, you would discover few, if any, plants or algae growing. Colder temperatures and lower light levels limit the types of organisms that can live in deep lake waters. Most lake organisms are found along the shoreline and in the warm water near the surface. ☑

B The population density of the warm, shallow water of the lakeshore is high. Fewer types of organisms live in the deeper water.

Reading Check ☑

What is plankton?

Saltwater Biomes

Figure 18-18 These Canada geese are swimming in an estuary of the Chesapeake Bay.

About 95 percent of the water on the surface on Earth contains high concentrations of salts. The saltwater biomes include the oceans, seas, and a few inland lakes, such as the Great Salt Lake in Utah.

Estuaries

Virtually every river on Earth eventually flows into the ocean. The area where a river meets the ocean and contains a mixture of freshwater and salt water is called an **estuary.** Estuaries are located near coastlines and border the land. Salinity changes with the amount of freshwater brought in by rivers and streams, and with the amount of salt water pushed inland by the tides.

Estuaries like the one in **Figure 18-18** are extremely fertile, productive environments because freshwater streams bring in tons of nutrients from inland soils. Nutrient levels in estuaries are higher than those in freshwater or other saltwater ecosystems. Estuarine organisms include many species of algae, a few salt-tolerant grasses, shrimp, crabs, clams, oysters, snails, worms, and fish. Estuaries serve as important nursery grounds for many species of ocean fish.

Seashores

All of Earth's landmasses are bordered by ocean water. The fairly shallow waters along the world's coastlines contain a variety of saltwater ecosystems, all of which are influenced by the tides and by the action of waves. The gravitational pull of the sun and moon causes the tides to rise and fall twice each day in most parts of the world. The **intertidal zone** is the portion of the shoreline that is covered with water at high tide and exposed to the air during low tide. Organisms living in the intertidal zone must not only be adapted to dramatic changes in temperature, moisture, and salinity, but also be able to withstand the force of wave action. Two kinds of intertidal zones are shown in **Figure 18-19.**

Mini Lab

Modeling Freshwater Environments

Procedure

1. Cover the bottom of a 2-L bottle with about 2 cm of gravel, muck, and other debris from the bottom of a pond. If plants are present, add one or two to the bottle. Use a dip net to capture small fish, insects, or tadpoles.
2. Carefully pour pond water into the bottle until it is about two-thirds full. Seal the bottle.
3. Keep the bottle indoors at room temperature and out of direct sunlight.

Analysis

1. Using a hand lens, observe as many organisms as possible. Record your observations. After two or three days, return your sample to the original habitat.
2. Write a short paper describing the organisms in your sample ecosystem and explaining their interactions.

Figure 18-19 Organisms living in intertidal zones have adaptations to survive in these changing environments.

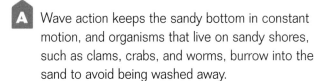

A Wave action keeps the sandy bottom in constant motion, and organisms that live on sandy shores, such as clams, crabs, and worms, burrow into the sand to avoid being washed away.

Open Ocean

Life abounds in the open ocean, where there is no land. The ocean can be divided into life zones based on the depth to which sunlight can penetrate the water. The lighted zone of the ocean is the upper 200 m or so. It is the home of the plankton that make up the foundation of the food chain in the open ocean. Below about 200 m, where sunlight cannot reach, is the dark zone of the ocean. Animals living in this region feed on material that floats down from the lighted zone, or they feed on each other.

B Algae, mussels, barnacles, snails, and other organisms adapted for clinging to the rocks are typically found on rocky shores. These organisms must be able to tolerate the heavy force of breaking waves.

Section Assessment

1. What are the similarities and differences between a lake and a stream?

2. What biotic or abiotic factor limits life on the floor of a tropical rain forest and the bottom of the deep ocean? Why?

3. **Think Critically:** Why do few plants grow in the waters of a swift-flowing mountain stream?

4. 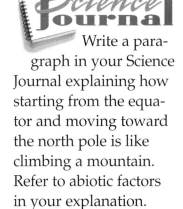 **Skill Builder**

   Comparing and Contrasting Compare and contrast the effects of (1) temperature in the tundra and desert and (2) sunlight in deep-lake and deep-ocean waters. If you need help, refer to Comparing and Contrasting in the **Skill Handbook** on page 720.

Science Journal
Write a paragraph in your Science Journal explaining how starting from the equator and moving toward the north pole is like climbing a mountain. Refer to abiotic factors in your explanation.

FIELD GUIDE to BIOMES

FIELD ACTIVITY

Research the average monthly rainfall, high temperature, and low temperature for each month of the past year for the area where you live. Prepare a graph of data using the example below. Based on your findings, which biome graph most closely matches your data? What biome do you live in? What type of plant and animal life do you expect to find in your biome?

Have you ever wondered why you do not find polar bears in Florida or palm trees in Alaska? Organisms are limited to where they can live and survive due to temperature, amount of rainfall, and type of soil found in a region. A biome's boundaries are determined by climate more than anything else. Climate is a way of categorizing temperature extremes and yearly precipitation patterns. Use this field guide to identify some of the world's biomes and to determine which biome you live in.

Interpreting Land Biome Climates

The following graphs represent the climates of six different biomes. To read each biome graph, use the following information. Axis A shows the months of the year. Axis B shows the average amount of precipitation for each month. Axis C shows the average high and low temperature for each month.

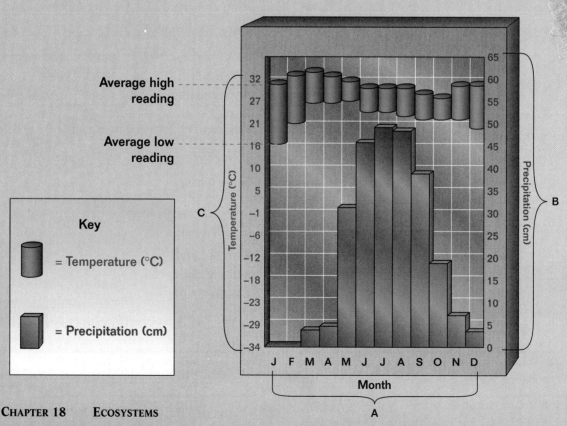

Key

▮ = Temperature (°C)

▮ = Precipitation (cm)

Average high reading

Average low reading

Biome: Tundra

- Seasons: long, harsh winters; short summers; very little precipitation
- Plants: mosses, lichens, grasses, and sedges
- Animals: weasels, arctic foxes, snowshoe hares, snowy owls, and hawks

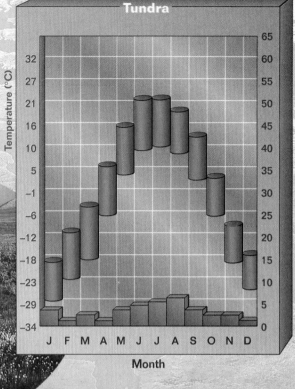

Tundra

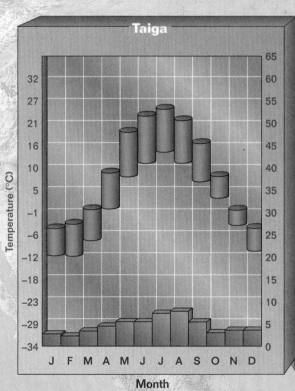

Biome: Taiga

Taiga

- Seasons: cold, severe winters with much snow; short growing seasons
- Plants: conifers such as spruces, firs, and larches
- Animals: caribou, wolves, moose, bear, and summer birds

Temperate Deciduous Forest

Biome: Temperate Deciduous Forest

- Seasons: cold winters, hot summers, and moderate precipitation
- Plants: deciduous trees such as oak, hickory, and beech, which lose their leaves every autumn
- Animals: wolves, deer, bears, small mammals, and birds

Biome: Grassland

- Seasons: cold winters, hot summers with little precipitation
- Plants: grasses and a few trees
- Animals: grazing animals, wolves, prairie dogs, foxes, ferrets, snakes, lizards, and insects

Grassland

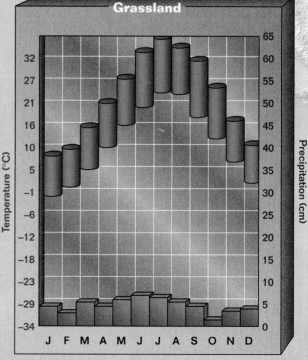

Biome: Desert

- Seasons: warm to hot in daytime, cool in the evening, little precipitation
- Plants: cacti, yuccas, Joshua trees, and bunchgrasses
- Animals: small rodents, jackrabbits, birds of prey, and snakes

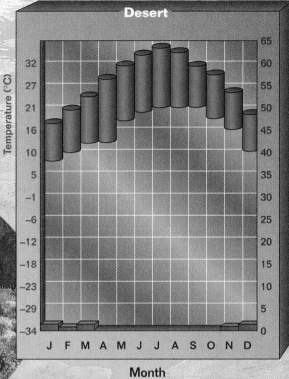

Desert

Biome: Tropical Rain Forest

- Seasons: hot all year with precipitation almost every day
- Plants: trees and orchids
- Animals: birds, reptiles, insects, monkeys, and sloths

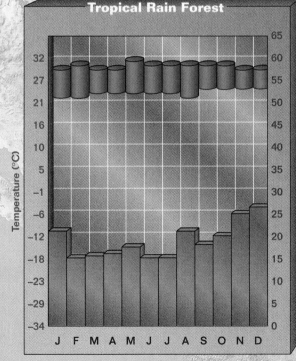

Tropical Rain Forest

For a **preview** of this chapter, study this Reviewing Main Ideas before you read the chapter. After you have studied this chapter, you can use the Reviewing Main Ideas to **review** the chapter.

The Glencoe MindJogger, Audiocassettes, and CD-ROM provide additional opportunities for review.

Section
18-1 HOW ECOSYSTEMS CHANGE

The process of gradual change from one community of organisms to another is **ecological succession.** It involves changes in both abiotic and biotic factors. Succession can be divided into **primary** and **secondary succession. Pioneer communities** are the first to move into an environment, and **climax communities** are the final organisms to move in. *How can you explain that lawns usually do not go through succession?*

Section
18-2 LAND ENVIRONMENTS

Climate is the general weather pattern in an area. The factors that determine a region's climate are temperature and precipitation. Large geographic areas with similar climates and climax communities are biomes. The six major biomes are the **tundra, taiga, temperate deciduous forests, tropical rain forests, grasslands,** and **deserts.** *How does climate influence the type of biomes?*

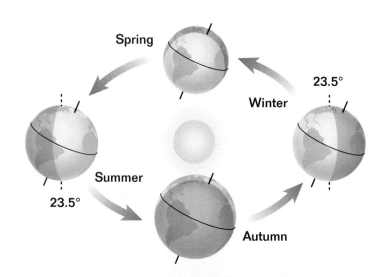

Spring

Winter

23.5°

Summer

23.5°

Autumn

Reading Check ✓

Diagram changes in an ecosystem as a series of causes and effects. You might start with this cause: an ecosystem's soil is thin and poor. What is a possible effect?

Section
18-3 WATER ENVIRONMENTS

The limiting factors in water environments include the amount of salt in the water, dissolved oxygen, water temperature, and sunlight. Freshwater ecosystems include rivers, streams, lakes, and ponds. Saltwater ecosystems include the oceans, seas, and a few inland lakes. An area where a river meets the ocean is called an **estuary.** All land on Earth is surrounded by ocean water. The **intertidal zone** is the portion of the shoreline that is covered with water at high tide and exposed to the air during low tide. The open ocean is divided into life zones based on the depth to which sunlight can penetrate the water. *Describe where estuaries form. How are they important?*

Chapter 18 Assessment

Using Vocabulary

a. biome
b. climax community
c. desert
d. ecological succession
e. estuary
f. grassland
g. intertidal zone
h. pioneer community
i. plankton
j. primary succession
k. secondary succession
l. taiga
m. temperate deciduous forest
n. tropical rain forest
o. tundra

Each of the following sentences is false. Make the sentence true by replacing the italicized word with a word from the list above.

1. *Primary succession* has occurred when one community of organisms replaces another.
2. *Plankton* are the first organisms to inhabit an area.
3. An *estuary* is a region with similar climate and climax communities.
4. A *biome* is an equatorial region that receives large amounts of rainfall.
5. A *tropical rain forest* is where freshwater mixes with salt water.

Checking Concepts

Choose the word or phrase that best answers the question.

6. What determines the climate of an area?
   A) plankton
   B) succession
   C) limiting factors
   D) abiotic factors

7. What are tundra and desert examples of?
   A) ecosystems
   B) biomes
   C) habitats
   D) communities

8. What is a treeless, cold, and dry biome called?
   A) taiga
   B) tundra
   C) desert
   D) grassland

9. Which is **NOT** a grassland?
   A) pampas
   B) veldts
   C) steppes
   D) estuaries

10. Mussels and barnacles have adapted to the wave action of what?
    A) sandy beach
    B) rocky shore
    C) open ocean
    D) estuary

11. Which biome contains the largest number of species?
    A) taiga
    B) temperate deciduous forest
    C) tropical rain forest
    D) grassland

12. What is the end result of succession?
    A) pioneer community
    B) limiting factor
    C) climax community
    D) permafrost

13. Which biome does **NOT** have trees as a climax community?
    A) tundra
    B) taiga
    C) tropical rain forest
    D) grassland

14. Which does **NOT** contain freshwater?
    A) lakes
    B) ponds
    C) rivers
    D) oceans

15. Which does **NOT** have flowing water?
    A) ponds
    B) rivers
    C) seashores
    D) streams

Thinking Critically

16. Would a soil sample from a temperate deciduous forest contain more or less humus than soil from a tropical rain forest? Explain.

17. A grassy meadow borders an oak-maple forest. Is one of these ecosystems undergoing succession? Why?

18. Describe how ecological succession eventually results in the layers of vegetation found in forests.

19. Why do many tropical rain forest plants make good houseplants?

Developing Skills

If you need help, refer to the **Skill Handbook**.

20. **Concept Mapping:** Make a concept map for water environments. Include these terms: *saltwater ecosystems, freshwater ecosystems, intertidal zone, lighted zone, dark zone, lake, pond, river, stream, flowing water,* and *standing water.*

21. **Making and Using Graphs:** Make a bar graph of the amount of rainfall per year in each biome.

Rainfall Amounts

Biome	Rainfall/Year
Deciduous forests	100 cm
Tropical rain forests	225 cm
Grasslands	50 cm
Deserts	20 cm

22. **Hypothesizing:** Make a hypothesis as to what would happen to succession in a pond if the pond owner removed all the cattails and reeds from around the pond edges every summer.

23. **Comparing and Contrasting:** Compare and contrast the adaptations of organisms living in swiftly flowing streams and organisms living in the rocky intertidal zones.

24. **Recognizing Cause and Effect:** Devastating fires, like the one in Yellowstone National Park in 1988, cause many changes to the land. Determine the effect of a fire to an area that has reached its climax community.

THE PRINCETON REVIEW

Test-Taking Tip

Where's the fire? Slow down! Go back over reading passages and double check your math. Remember that doing most of the questions and getting them right is always better than doing all the questions and getting lots of them wrong.

Test Practice

Use these questions to test your Science Proficiency.

1. What determines whether a land supports a deciduous forest or a grassland?
   A) temperature
   B) latitude
   C) precipitation
   D) length of growing season

2. What causes the vertical distribution of plants in a deep lake?
   A) color of the water
   B) depth that light can penetrate
   C) kind of plants in the lake
   D) kind of animals in the lake

3. How are primary succession and secondary succession similar?
   A) both begin where no soil is present
   B) both end in climax communities
   C) both begin with a pioneer community
   D) both develop where lava has cooled

4. What is the layer of vegetation that shades the ground below and provides homes for birds, insects, and mammals called?
   A) soil
   B) understory
   C) canopy
   D) forest floor

CHAPTER

19 Resources and the Environment

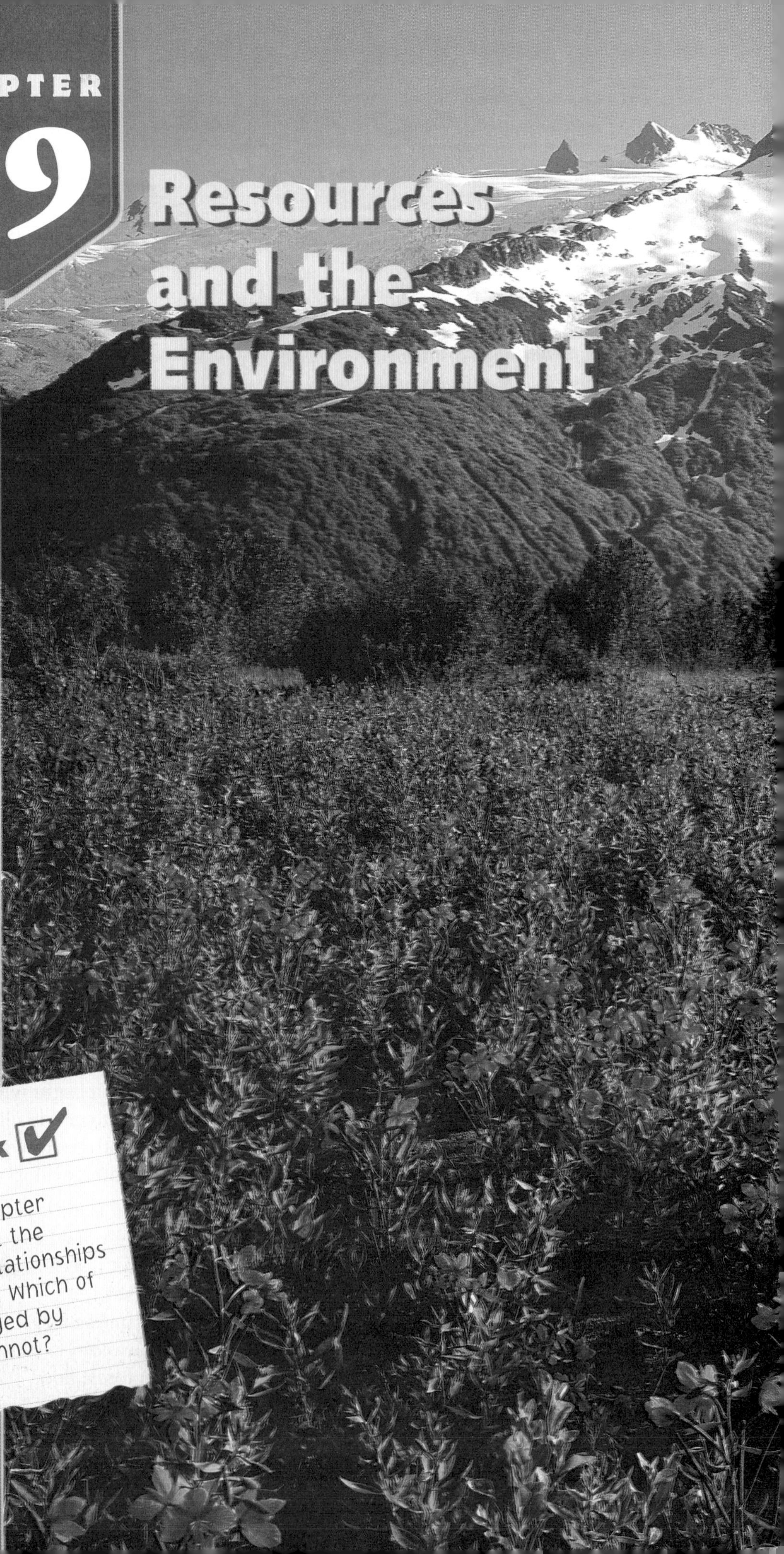

Chapter Preview

Skills Preview

Skill Builders

- Map Concepts

MiniLabs

- Observe
- Infer

Activities

- Measure and Graph

Reading Check ✓

As you read this chapter about resources, list the cause and effect relationships that are described. Which of them can be changed by humans? Which cannot?

Explore Activity

Nothing is so reliable as the ground beneath our feet. We walk on it, plant lawns and flowers in it, and pave it over to drive cars on it. But, topsoil is something we shouldn't take for granted. Topsoil is the loose, nutrient-rich, top layer of soil that is vital to the growth of everything. Layers of plants, like these wildflowers in Glacier Bay National Park in Alaska, help protect topsoil and keep it in place. What happens when topsoil is left unprotected? Do the activity below to find out.

Model Topsoil Loss

1. Use a mixture of moist sand and potting soil to create a miniature landscape in a plastic basin or aluminum-foil baking pan. Include hills and valleys in your landscape.

2. Cover portions of your landscape with clumps of moss as a plant cover. Leave some sloping portions of your landscape without plant cover.

3. Simulate a rainstorm by pouring water from a dropper or spraying water from a spray bottle over your landscape.

Science Journal

In your Science Journal, record what happens to the land that is not protected by plant cover.

19•1 Natural Resources

Earth's Resources

A robin eats an earthworm, then collects twigs for a nest. A fox burrows underground, preparing a den for pups that will soon be born. The leaves of a tree absorb carbon dioxide from the air. A sea otter stays afloat by wrapping itself in a strand of giant kelp, while it uses a stone to hammer open the shell of a sea urchin. A group of young humans climbs aboard a bus for the ride to school.

What do these organisms have in common? They rely on Earth's natural resources for their survival. **Natural resources** are materials found in nature that are useful or necessary for living things. The natural resources people use include food, air, water, and the materials and energy needed to make everything from clothes and buildings to automobiles, books, computers, gasoline, and electricity.

Renewable Resources

Water moves from the surface of Earth to the atmosphere and back again via the water cycle. Oxygen is produced by plants during photosynthesis. Oxygen and water are examples of renewable resources. A **renewable resource** is a natural resource that is recycled or replaced by ongoing natural processes. Cotton used to make a pair of blue jeans is renewable because a new crop of cotton plants can be grown every year. Plants such as those in **Figure 19-1,** animals, water, and air are all renewable resources.

Figure 19-1 Renewable natural resources include forests, wildlife, and food crops like this grove of orange trees in Phoenix, Arizona.

Figure 19-2 Nonrenewable resources include many metals and minerals, as well as fossil fuels such as coal and oil.

A Oil wells, like this one in the North Sea, provide oil that is used to heat homes and fuel cars.

B Lightbulbs contain a filament made of the metal tungsten, a nonrenewable substance.

Nonrenewable Resources

Although some resources will never run out, we do have to worry about running out of some natural resources. Whenever you take home a plastic grocery bag; drink from a plastic cup; paint a wall; or travel by car, bus, or airplane, you are using products made from a natural resource called petroleum. Petroleum, also known as crude oil, is a thick, greasy liquid formed from the bodies of organisms that died hundreds of millions of years ago. It is the raw material used to make fuel oil, gasoline, plastics, paints, chemicals, fertilizers, pesticides, and a huge number of other products that have become essential to modern life. Petroleum is an example of a nonrenewable resource. A **nonrenewable resource** is a natural resource that is available only in limited amounts and is not quickly replaced by natural processes. A lightbulb made from nonrenewable resources is shown in **Figure 19-2.**

Try at Home

Mini Lab

Observing Mineral Mining Effects

Procedure 🥽 👕 🧤 🚫

1. Place a chocolate-chip cookie or nut-filled brownie on a paper plate. Pretend the cookie is Earth's crust and the nuts or chips are mineral deposits. **CAUTION:** *Never eat food or put anything in your mouth from an experiment.*

2. Use a toothpick to locate and dig up mineral deposits. Try to disturb the "land" as little as possible.

3. When mining is completed, do your best to restore the land to its original condition.

Analysis

1. Were you able to restore the land to its original condition? Describe the kinds of changes in an ecosystem that might result from a mining operation.

2. How do mining deposits found close to the surface compare with mining deposits found deeper within Earth's crust?

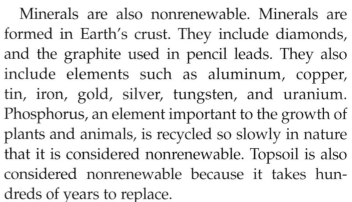

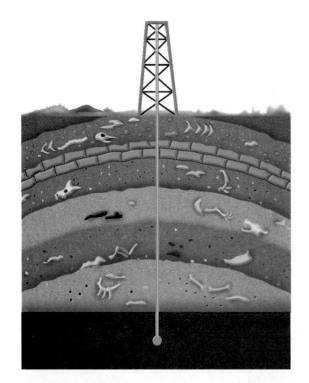

Figure 19-3 Fossil fuels—coal, oil, and natural gas—are formed when organisms die and are buried by layers of rock and sediment. **Why are fossil fuels considered non-renewable?**

Minerals are also nonrenewable. Minerals are formed in Earth's crust. They include diamonds, and the graphite used in pencil leads. They also include elements such as aluminum, copper, tin, iron, gold, silver, tungsten, and uranium. Phosphorus, an element important to the growth of plants and animals, is recycled so slowly in nature that it is considered nonrenewable. Topsoil is also considered nonrenewable because it takes hundreds of years to replace.

Meeting Energy Needs

Imagine what life was like before the invention of the electric lightbulb or the internal combustion engine. Candles were used for light at night, wood for cooking and heating, and horse-drawn wagons or walking for getting from one place to another. Today, we have electric lights, TV and radio, electric ranges, gas stoves, gasoline-powered vehicles, and jet-fueled airplanes. However, it takes energy to operate and manufacture all these modern conveniences. Where does all this energy come from?

Fossil Fuels

Right now, much of this energy comes from fossil fuels. **Fossil fuels** include coal; natural gas; and fuels made from oil including gasoline, diesel fuel, jet fuel, heating oil, and kerosene. **Figure 19-3** describes how fossil fuels form. Fossil fuels power everything from automobiles and lawn mowers to factories. They provide us with many of the conveniences we consider essential to modern life. However, burning fossil fuels contaminates air and water. Other forms of energy can provide some or all of the power we need without polluting the environment the way fossil fuels do. These alternatives include solar power and geothermal energy. Nuclear energy is another energy source, but it has its own pollution problems. ✔

Reading Check ✔

What are fossil fuels?

Solar Energy

You've probably heard many times that you should never leave a pet or a child in a parked car with the windows closed when it's hot. Sunlight entering through the windows heats the interior of the car. This heat cannot escape through the closed windows, and the temperature inside can rise rapidly to dangerous levels. Ways in which solar energy can be trapped and used are seen in **Figure 19-4.**

Solar Cells

Do you know how a solar-powered calculator works or how the solar-powered satellites that orbit Earth generate their electricity? These devices use photovoltaic (foh toh vohl TAY ihk) solar cells to turn sunlight directly into electric current. **Photovoltaic (PV)** cells are wafers made of the element silicon that is covered with thin layers of metals. When the sun's light hits these layers, a stream of electrons, called electricity, is created. PV cells are small, and they are easy to use because they don't have any moving parts. However, at the present time, they are too expensive to use for generating large amounts of electricity. But, improvements in the materials used to make them could bring prices down in the future. In the meantime, PV cells are being used to power a variety of small items, including flashlights, radios, watches, and toys.

Figure 19-4 Solar energy can be captured in a number of ways and used instead of fossil fuels to heat homes and water, generate electricity, and even cook food.

A Solar-powered satellites use the continuous energy of the sun as they orbit Earth.

B This home has been designed to use solar heating. The floors and walls are made of heat-absorbing stone, tile, or brick. At night, the heat stored in the walls and floors keeps the building warm.

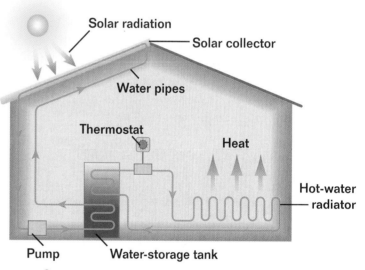

C Active solar designs use a combination of solar collectors, pumps, and fans to heat indoor air and to heat water for household use.

D In the Mojave Desert in southern California, an electric utility company constructed a huge array of mirrors to focus sunlight on a water-filled tower. The steam produced by this system was used to generate electricity.

Wind and Water Power

Wind can be used to generate electricity. In regions with frequent winds, electricity is produced on wind farms, on which large numbers of windmills are placed. A windmill like the one in **Figure 19-5A** is a turbine that is rotated by the wind instead of by steam or water. Wind power is a nonpolluting, renewable energy source. However, much open space is needed for a wind farm so use of this resource is limited.

Electricity also can be created by water. Water that is prevented from flowing downstream by a dam contains a tremendous amount of stored, or potential, energy. When the water flows through openings in the dam, that stored energy is released. Hydroelectric power plants, located inside dams, use the energy of flowing water to turn gigantic turbines that generate enormous amounts of electricity. **Hydroelectric power,** or hydropower, is electricity produced by the energy of flowing water. Hydroelectric power plants like the one in **Figure 19-5B** are a renewable energy resource because the water in the reservoir behind the dam is continually replaced by Earth's water cycle. They are also efficient and produce little pollution.

Geothermal Energy

When a volcano erupts, lava and hot gases pour out of the ground. When a geyser erupts, steam and hot water spew out of the ground. Where does the energy for these eruptions come from? It comes from hot, molten rock that lies deep underground. Volcanoes erupt when molten rock is forced to the surface. Geysers develop when underground water that has been trapped in hot rock is heated to the boiling point and forced up through cracks and openings in the ground. The thermal energy contained in Earth's crust is called **geothermal energy.** Geothermal power plants use the thermal energy that lies in Earth's crust to generate electricity.

Figure 19-5
Water power and wind power are actually indirect forms of solar power. **Describe why.**

A Wind turning the turbine blades of this windmill produces electricity.

B When the water in this reservoir flows through narrow channels inside the dam, it turns the blades of turbines to generate electricity.

Nuclear Energy

Another form of energy that does not require burning fossil fuels takes advantage of the huge amounts of energy bound up in the nuclei of atoms. **Nuclear energy** is produced when billions of nuclei from uranium, a radioactive element, split apart in a nuclear fission reaction. This energy can be used to heat water to produce steam, which turns turbines that produce electricity. A primary advantage of nuclear power is that it does not contribute to air pollution. However, mining uranium does disrupt land ecosystems, and nuclear power plants, such as the one shown in **Figure 19-6,** produce radioactive waste materials. These materials remain radioactive for thousands of years. Safe disposal of nuclear wastes is a problem that has not yet been solved. Therefore, nuclear energy is not widely used.

PHYSICS
INTEGRATION

Nuclear Power
Use references to determine the advantages and disadvantages of nuclear power.

Figure 19-6 Nuclear energy is an alternative energy source that can be produced cleanly and cheaply. **Why isn't nuclear energy more widely used?**

Section Assessment

1. What are natural resources?
2. Compare and contrast renewable and nonrenewable resources, and give five examples of each.
3. Name five alternative energy sources.
4. **Think Critically:** Explain how fossil fuels could be considered a form of solar energy.
5. **Skill Builder**
   Comparing and Contrasting Deciding which energy source to use is easier when you compare and contrast all the alternative sources. Do the **Chapter 19 Skill Activity** on page 760 to learn how to decide which energy source is best for you.

Science Journal
In your Science Journal, invent a new alternative energy source. The source should be available in your community.

Conservation and Wildlife Protection

What We Can Do

Many Native American traditions teach people to think about their actions and how they will affect the next seven generations of their descendants. That means thinking of your children, grandchildren, and great-grandchildren. It means thinking about what Earth will be like 200 years from now. We can take actions to make sure we leave Earth's land, soil, minerals, wildlife, and other resources in good condition for the generations who will live on this planet after us.

Energy Conservation

Nonrenewable resources can be conserved by using less, using a renewable resource, or recycling. You already know about some of the alternatives to nonrenewable fossil fuels. More and more home builders are designing houses that take advantage of sunlight, not only for warmth but also for lighting. Well-placed windows and skylights can reduce the need for electric lights during the day. The amount of electricity produced by solar, wind, and geothermal power plants also will increase. But, the fact remains that most of the energy we

VISUALIZING
Energy Conservation

Figure 19-7
Individuals can take many actions to save energy.
What are some ways you can conserve energy?

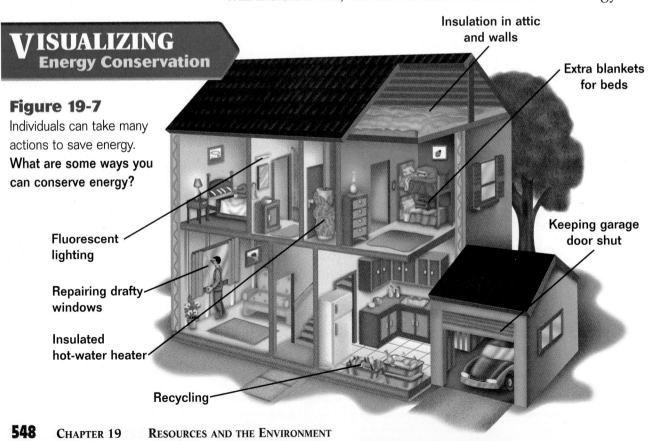

Insulation in attic and walls

Extra blankets for beds

Fluorescent lighting

Repairing drafty windows

Insulated hot-water heater

Keeping garage door shut

Recycling

use today still is produced by fossil fuels. In order to conserve those resources, we need to reduce our energy use. Recycling is one way to do that, as well as reducing energy use as shown in **Figure 19-7.** Using recycled aluminum cans to make new cans uses only about ten percent of the energy required to make new cans from aluminum ore. Recycling glass also saves energy.

Soil Conservation

When soil is used for agriculture, native plants are replaced with crops. The crops use the nutrients in the soil to grow. When the crops are harvested, little material is left to decay and replenish the nutrients in the soil. This removal of soil nutrients is called **soil depletion.** Over a period of time, if the nutrients are not replaced, the soil may become too poor to grow crops.

Farmers replenish the soil in several ways, including crop rotation and the addition of fertilizers. Crop rotation is the process of changing the crops that are grown in a field from one season to the next. Every few seasons, a nonfood crop is grown and tilled back into the soil to help replenish nutrients. Fertilizers include materials such as compost and chemicals made from petroleum. Other methods of soil conservation are shown in **Figure 19-8.**

Figure 19-8 Soil management helps reduce the erosion of farmland. **Why is erosion a concern for farmers?**

A By plowing at right angles to the slope of the land, contour farming reduces erosion from the downhill flow of water.

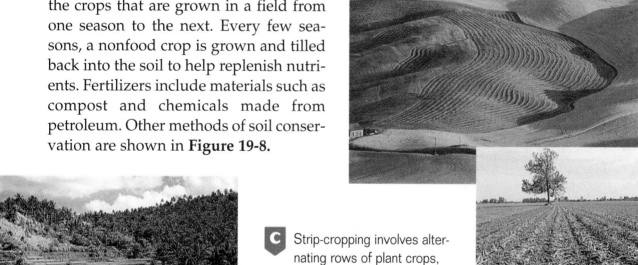

C Strip-cropping involves alternating rows of plant crops, such as corn, with a cover crop such as wheat or hay.

B In areas with steep hillsides, the downhill flow of water is reduced by creating flat areas, called terraces.

D No-till farming is a soil-management method that involves planting crops in untilled, undisturbed soil.

Figure 19-9 Species can become endangered because of pollution, habitat destruction, illegal hunting, or competition with introduced species.

Erosion

Another process that destroys soil fertility is erosion. **Erosion** is the wearing away of soil by wind and water. If you conducted the Explore Activity at the beginning of the chapter, you noticed that flowing water can pick up loose topsoil and wash it away. An important part of farming is soil management. As shown in **Figure 19-8** on the previous page, **soil management** is the use of plowing methods that reduce soil erosion. These methods include contour plowing, strip-cropping, terracing, and no-till farming. Plowing loosens the soil, making it easier for seedlings to take root, but also making it easier for water and wind to carry away the soil.

Wildlife Conservation

A hundred years ago, up to a million passenger pigeons would darken the skies above North America. Today, there are none. The last member of the species died in a New York zoo in 1914. Human hunters killed them by the thousands until the species became extinct. **Extinction** is the dying out of an entire species. Extinction does occur naturally. Over time, many species that once lived on Earth have become extinct. But, changes in the environment due to competition among organisms have increased the rate of extinction.

A The destruction of habitat and breeding ground is the reason many species have become endangered, including the sea turtle in the United States.

B Close to 200 plants that grow only in the Hawaiian Islands, including this silver sword plant, are endangered. **What could cause plants like this one to become endangered?**

Figure 19-10 When the pesticide DDT was sprayed on farmland, runoff from rainwater carried it into nearby streams, where it entered the food chain. DDT built up in the tissues of fish, which were eaten by ospreys. DDT buildup in the bodies of the ospreys caused them to produce eggs with shells so thin that the eggs broke open before the young could develop. This resulted in a decline of the osprey population.

An **endangered species** is a species that is in danger of becoming extinct unless action is taken to protect it. The bald eagle, the national bird of the United States, is an example of a species that was endangered for a time. In the early 1960s, only about 400 bald eagles were left in the 48 lower states. By 1999, because of preservation efforts, the population had increased to approximately 5000 and is still rising.

Most species become endangered because of damage to their habitat such as that caused by building roads, clearing forest, or draining marshes to provide dry land for buildings. In other cases, pollution is to blame. The pesticide DDT was used in the United States from the 1940s to the 1970s. This chemical provided farmers with relief from large populations of insect pests that were damaging crops. But, as **Figure 19-10** describes, DDT remains in the environment for many years after it is used and is passed along the food chain from one organism to another. When it entered the bodies of large predatory birds, such as eagles, ospreys, falcons, and pelicans, the birds began to have difficulty reproducing. After DDT use was stopped, the bird populations began to recover. Bald eagles had recovered enough by 1995 to be removed from the list of endangered species. As **Figure 19-9** shows, a species also may become endangered because it is overhunted by predators or it is crowded out by a species that has been introduced to the area from another part of the world.

Wildlife conservation involves determining what species are endangered and why, and devises methods to help the species recover. Recovery may involve ridding the environment of a harmful pollutant, as was the case with DDT, preserving the habitat of a species, or even breeding a disappearing species in captivity and then restoring it to the wild as with the California condor. ✓

Reading Check ✓

What does wildlife conservation involve?

Figure 19-11 From the human perspective, wetlands may look like nothing more than a swamp. In the past, wetlands have been destroyed by filling them in with soil and using the land for roads and buildings. Today, many remaining wetlands have been set aside as protected areas.

Land Conservation

When European settlers first came to North America, much of the continent was covered with forests. Settlers cut down many of these forests to farm and to obtain fuel and lumber for building. About 100 years ago, people began to realize that if this kept up, we eventually would lose all of our forests. The U.S. government began a conservation program that involved setting aside wilderness areas, including forests, to protect them from development.

Many other countries also have made efforts to protect forests and wildlife habitat. **Figure 19-12** shows a map of U.S. national parks. Worldwide, more than 4000 national parks

Figure 19-12 The United States has set aside land as national parks. **Which state has the most land set aside as national parks?**

A Plastic can be recycled into items like this picnic table.

B This jacket is actually made from soda-pop bottles.

C This mountain lion sculpture is made from discarded bumpers. This is an example of reuse.

Figure 19-13 Many products can be made from recycled or reused materials. **What are some other products you can think of that are made from recycled materials?**

and other protected areas, covering about 8.5 million km² (an area slightly larger than the country of Brazil), have now been set aside. In many areas, including the United States, land that was once forested is being replanted. The replanting of a forest is called reforestation. Reforestation not only restores forest ecosystems, it also helps preserve topsoil because the roots of young trees help hold the soil in place.

Recycling

How many garbage bins do you set beside the curb for pickup every week? As the world population grows, more and more garbage is produced. As a result, landfills are slowly taking up valuable land space. They often disrupt the local ecosystem, smell bad, and contain toxic materials that can pollute air and water.

One way to prevent this waste is to reuse items or purchase items that have little packaging. For example, you can reuse old clothes by giving them to someone else or cutting them up into rags. **Recycling** is a process that changes or reprocesses an item or resource. Not only does it conserve the resource being recycled, it conserves land space that would normally become the next landfill. **Figure 19-13** shows some products made from recycled and reused materials.

*inter*NET
CONNECTION

Paper accounts for more than 30 percent of discarded waste. Visit the Glencoe Science Web Site at **www.glencoe. com/sec/science** for more information about how to recycle your own paper by making hand-made paper from scraps.

Mineral Conservation

Minerals are nonrenewable resources. Because we can't replace them, the way to conserve them is to use less and to recycle whenever we can. Not only does this save them for future generations, but it also helps avoid the need for mining. Most minerals—and fossil fuels—are obtained by digging mines into the earth. Mining disrupts ecosystems, destroys topsoil, and sometimes releases toxic substances into air and water, as you can see in **Figure 19-14.** Recycling aluminum, steel, silver, and other minerals reduces the need for mining operations.

Figure 19-14 This open-pit copper mine cuts into the Arizona landscape.

Section Assessment

1. Compare and contrast soil depletion and erosion.

2. Describe four ways in which a species can become endangered.

3. Name three ways to conserve nonrenewable resources.

4. **Think Critically:** What might happen to top-soil during the first rain after a forest fire? Why?

5. **Skill Builder**
   Comparing and Contrasting
   Compare and contrast biodegradable and non-biodegradable materials and give five examples of each. If you need help, refer to Comparing and Contrasting in the **Skill Handbook** on page 720.

Using Computers

Database Use references to create an endangered species database. Include each organism's common and scientific names, biome in which it's found, habitat description, and reasons why it is threatened. Sort the database by biome to obtain a list of endangered species from each of the world's biomes. If you need help, refer to page 733.

What did Chief Seattle really say?

Before tape recorders and video cameras, the record of what someone said depended on a quick pencil or the good memory of a listener. In 1854, Chief Seattle (left), a leader of the Suquamish, an indigenous people of Puget Sound, gave a speech in response to an offer to move his people to a reservation.

Dr. Henry Smith witnessed Chief Seattle's original speech and took notes. More than 30 years later, he published a translation of the speech in the newspaper *Seattle Sunday Star*. In Smith's version of the speech, Chief Seattle was concerned with his people being able to visit their ancient burial grounds.

Every part of this country is sacred to my people. Every hillside, every valley, every plain and grove has been hallowed by some fond memory or some sad experience of my tribe. Even the rocks that seem to lie dumb as they swelter in the sun ... thrill with memories of past events connected with the fate of my people, and the very dust under your feet responds more lovingly to our footsteps than to yours, because it is the ashes of our ancestors, and our bare feet are conscious of the sympathetic touch, for the soil is rich with the life of our kindred.

In 1972, another version of the speech was written by Ted Perry for a film about ecology. This version has been widely quoted in newspapers, books, and speeches by environmentalists, politicians, and religious leaders. The following is a quote from Perry's version:

How can you buy or sell the sky, the warmth of the land? The idea is strange to us. If we do not own the freshness of the air and the sparkle of the water, how can you buy them? Every part of the Earth is sacred to my people.

Science JOURNAL

Write an essay that compares and contrasts Dr. Smith's version with that of Ted Perry's. Use the library to locate both versions of the speech and read about the controversy surrounding them.

Materials

- Soft-drink bottles (2 L) (2)
- Plastic wrap
- Potting soil
- Gravel or sand
- Labels
- Biodegradable and nonbiodegradable waste materials
- Hand lens
- Plastic teaspoon
- Transparent tape
- Scissors

Is it biodegradable?

As you probably know, all trash is not the same. One important way in which one waste material may differ from another is whether or not the material is biodegradable. A biodegradable substance is anything that can be broken down by organisms in the environment. After it is broken down, the substance can become part of the environment. Whether a material is biodegradable or not can make a big difference in how it affects the environment.

What You'll Investigate

What kinds of materials are biodegradable?

Goals

- **Distinguish** between biodegradable and non-biodegradable substances.
- **Observe** the decomposition of biodegradable materials.

Safety Precautions

Wash hands after handling soil or waste materials.

Procedure

1. **Cut** a square in the side of the soft-drink bottles as shown.

2. **Label** the bottles 1 and 2.

3. **Add** 1 cm of sand or gravel to each bottle and then fill with 4 cm of potting soil.

4. Your teacher will give you ten substances. **Hypothesize** which substances are biodegradable and which ones are not. **Record** your hypotheses in your Science Journal. **Make a table** in your Science Journal to record your observations.

5. **Place** the substances you think are biodegradable in bottle 1 and the others in bottle 2.

6. **Cover** the substances with 1 cm to 2 cm of potting soil.

7. **Sprinkle water** on the top of the soil. Cover the hole in the bottle with plastic wrap and secure it with transparent tape.

8. **Observe** each bottle at the end of five days. Note any change in the level of the layers. Use the teaspoon to carefully remove the soil from each substance. Use your hand lens to observe the substance and record your observations. Carefully replace each substance and cover with soil.

9. **Observe** the contents of the bottles after five more days and record your results.

Conclude and Apply

1. Which substances decomposed?

2. Which substances decomposed partially?

3. Was your hypothesis supported? Why or why not?

4. Describe any organisms you observed.

5. Explain how substances that are biodegradable affect the environment.

6. Explain how substances that are not biodegradable affect the environment.

Maintaining a Healthy Environment

What You'll Learn

▶ The origins and effects of pollutants that contaminate air, land, and water
▶ The causes of acid rain, ozone depletion, and the greenhouse effect

Vocabulary
pollutant
smog
acid rain
ozone depletion
greenhouse effect
global warming
hazardous waste
groundwater

Why It's Important

▶ Clean air and water promote good health.

CHEMISTRY
INTEGRATION ▶

How We Affect the Environment

Safeguarding our air, land, and water requires more than conserving resources. It also means paying attention to how our use of those resources affects the health of the environment. Every action we take—from starting the car or revving up the lawn mower to painting a building, using bug spray, cutting down a tree, turning on a light, and even recycling—has an effect on the environment.

Air Pollution

On almost any warm, sunny, windless day in any populated area in the world, you can see a distinct layer of brown haze hanging in the air. The brown color comes from smoke, dust, and exhaust fumes that pollute the air. Wherever there are cars, trucks, airplanes, factories, furnaces, fireplaces, cookstoves, or power plants, there is air pollution. Although it also is caused by volcanic eruptions, forest fires, and the evaporation of chemicals such as paints and dry-cleaning fluid, most air pollution results from the burning of fossil fuels.

Figure 19-15 Some components of smog are nitrogen oxide, nitrogen dioxide, ozone, and soot particles. Tiny particles of soot suspended in the air make visibility difficult in Los Angeles. These particles irritate the eyes and respiratory system.

Smog

Burning wood or coal in a fireplace produces smoke and ash as well as heat. Burning gasoline not only provides the energy to run a car engine, but also creates a number of unwanted chemicals, including tiny particles of soot and a number of gases, such as carbon monoxide, carbon dioxide, and oxides of nitrogen and sulfur. The unwanted by-products created when wood and fossil fuels are burned are examples of pollutants. Any substance that contaminates the environment and causes pollution is a **pollutant.** The brown haze as shown in **Figure 19-15** that hangs over cities and other heavily populated areas is **smog,** a form of air pollution that is created when sunlight reacts with pollutant chemicals produced by burning fuels.

Acid Rain

When you studied the water cycle, you learned that water evaporates from Earth's surface and rises into the air as water vapor. While in the atmosphere, it comes into contact with air pollutants. When it condenses and falls to the ground, it may bring pollutants with it.

Figure 19-16 Acid rain is formed when pollutants mix with water vapor to create acidic solutions. **What activities in this picture could cause acid rain?**

Problem Solving

Why should you repair a leaky faucet?

Have you ever heard a faucet dripping in your home? Perhaps you tried to turn it off but it still leaked. Not only can a leaky faucet be annoying, but it can also be expensive if it is not repaired.

There are 20 drops of water in 1 cm^3 of water. If a faucet drips 20 times per minute, how much water would be lost in one hour? How much water would be lost in one day?

Think Critically

1. Name three reasons why it is important to fix leaky faucets.

2. Why is cost an important factor in water usage?

3. What are some other things you can do to conserve water in your home?

Figure 19-17 The pH scale shows whether a solution is acidic or basic. Acid rain can have damaging effects.

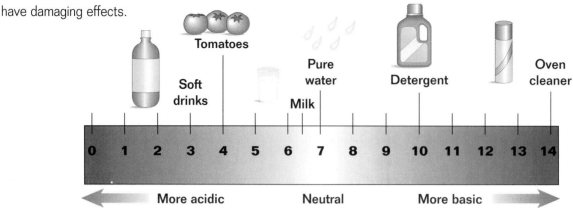

More acidic   Neutral   More basic

Acidic solutions have a pH below 7.0. Basic solutions have a pH greater than 7.0. Neutral solutions have a pH of 7.0.

Mini Lab

Measuring Acid Rain

Use a container to collect samples of rain.

Procedure

1. Dip a piece of pH indicator paper into the sample.
2. Compare the color of the paper with the pH chart provided. Record the pH of the rainwater.
3. Use separate pieces of pH paper to test the pH of tap water and distilled water. Record these values.

Analysis

1. Is the rainwater acidic, basic, or neutral?
2. How does the pH of the rainwater compare with the pH of tap water? Distilled water?

Air pollutants can increase the acidity of rain. As shown in **Figure 19-16,** the pollutants released by the burning of fossil fuels can react with water vapor in the atmosphere to form strong acids, including sulfuric acid and nitric acid. Acids are measured by a value called pH. **Acid rain** is rain or snow with a pH below 5.6. It washes valuable nutrients from the soil, which can lead to the death of trees and other plants. When the runoff from acid rain flows into a lake or pond, it changes the pH of the water. Algae and microscopic plankton cannot survive, so fish and other organisms that depend on them for food also die. A lake damaged by acid rain may look clear. But, the water is clear because few organisms can survive in it.

Ozone Depletion

When ozone forms in the lower atmosphere, it is considered an air pollutant. But, ozone also forms in the upper atmosphere. This upper ozone layer acts as a sunscreen that helps protect living organisms from exposure to harmful ultraviolet (UV) radiation that comes from the sun. When ultraviolet rays from the sun strike molecules of oxygen in the upper atmosphere, ozone is formed. Ozone absorbs UV rays, preventing some of the rays from reaching Earth's surface.

Scientists have discovered that Earth's protective ozone layer is becoming thinner. The thinning of the ozone layer is called **ozone depletion.** It is being caused by air pollutants, but not pollutants that are created by the burning of fossil fuels. Chemicals known as chlorofluorocarbons (CFCs), used in the cooling systems of refrigerators, freezers, and air conditioners, are the primary cause of ozone depletion. These chemicals contain chlorine and fluorine molecules. When these molecules escape into the air, they rise in the atmosphere until they reach the level of the protective ozone layer. Once there, they react with and destroy ozone molecules. The ozone layer is so important to the survival of life on Earth that world governments have agreed to stop producing CFCs by the year 2000. ☑

Greenhouse Effect

Earth's atmosphere allows sunlight to penetrate the surface but prevents much of the resulting heat from radiating back into space. This heat-trapping feature of the atmosphere shown in **Figure 19-18** is known as the **greenhouse effect.** Without it, temperatures would be too cold to support life as we know it.

The heat-reflecting atmospheric gases responsible for the greenhouse effect are called greenhouse gases. The most important is carbon dioxide. Although carbon dioxide is a normal part of the atmosphere, it is also a by-product when fossil fuels are burned. Over the past hundred years or so, larger and larger quantities of fossil fuels have been burned and more and more carbon dioxide and other greenhouse gases have been released into the atmosphere. These extra greenhouse gases could cause Earth to get warmer. **Global warming** is an increase in the average yearly temperature.

CHEMISTRY
INTEGRATION

CFCs
Chlorofluorocarbon, or CFC, molecules found in certain cooling systems contain atoms of chlorine, fluorine, and carbon. When they reach the ozone layer in the upper atmosphere, they are broken apart. The breakdown of CFCs releases chlorine atoms that destroy ozone. Explain how this information persuaded world leaders to agree that CFC use should be stopped.

Reading Check ☑
How do CFCs affect the environment?

Solar radiation

Carbon dioxide in atmosphere

Heat trapped near Earth's surface

Figure 19-18 The moment you step inside a greenhouse, you feel the greenhouse effect. Heat trapped by the glass walls warms the air inside. Similarly, atmospheric greenhouse gases, particularly carbon dioxide, trap heat close to Earth's surface.

Effects of Global Warming

Scientists disagree about whether or not the increase in atmospheric carbon dioxide and other greenhouse gases is actually warming up Earth. What might happen if the temperature of Earth did increase? Rainfall amounts could decrease, which could affect the production of food, as well as affect the health of wildlife. A rise in temperature of just 5°C would begin to melt the polar ice caps, which would raise sea levels and flood coastal communities. There also could be an increase in the number and severity of storms and hurricanes. Many people feel that the possibility of global warming is a good reason to slow our consumption of fossil fuels.

Land Pollution

As you learned earlier in this chapter, the human population is running out of land space for burying solid waste. For a long time, most people expected that biodegradable items in landfills would eventually decompose. But, it turns out that they decompose quite slowly. A newspaper thrown away in the 1950s was still readable when scientists dug it out of a landfill almost 40 years later. What about the nonbiodegradable substances we put in landfills? They won't break down at all. Any toxic materials that are disposed of in landfills can pollute the soil and surrounding waterways.

Waste materials that are harmful to human health or poisonous to living organisms in general are known as **hazardous wastes.** Pesticides, medical wastes that may contain disease organisms, nuclear waste, chemicals used in industry, and even items you might have around the house such as dead batteries, paints, and household cleaning products are all examples of hazardous waste. If hazardous wastes are not properly contained, as in **Figure 19-19,** they may leak out of the landfill and into the surrounding soil and waterways.

interNET
CONNECTION

Hazardous waste can be found in many homes. Visit the Glencoe Science Web Site at **www.glencoe.com/ sec/science** for more information about house-hold hazardous waste and what you can do to eliminate it.

Figure 19-19 Special steps must be taken to ensure that hazardous wastes are properly disposed of. They must also be clearly marked as a hazardous waste. **What steps have been taken in this photo?**

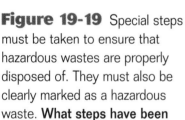

Water Pollution

Many pollutants released into the air may pollute water, as well. Acid rain starts as an air pollution problem but ends up affecting waterways because rain eventually flows into rivers and lakes. Water flowing over or through soil that contains hazardous wastes can pick up and carry some of those wastes along with it, as shown in **Figure 19-20.**

Water pollution can have more direct sources. Wastewater from factories and sewage-treatment plants is released into streams, rivers, or sometimes directly into the ocean. In the United States and many other countries, this wastewater is treated to remove some or all pollutants before it is released into the environment. But, in many parts of the world, wastewater treatment is not always possible.

Groundwater Pollution

Water pollution can also affect **groundwater.** Groundwater comes from rainfall and runoff that gets trapped in underground pockets. The water in these underground pools, or aquifers, comes from rainfall and runoff that soaks down through the soil. If the water contacts waste materials as it makes its way underground, the aquifer may become contaminated. Groundwater contamination has already become a problem for rural residents and communities that draw their water supply from wells that tap into underground aquifers, as shown in **Figure 19-21.** ☑

Figure 19-20 When rain falls on roads and parking lots, it can wash oil and grease into nearby waterways. When rain falls on agricultural land that has been sprayed with pesticides, chemical residues may be washed into neighboring streams.

Reading Check ☑

How can groundwater become polluted?

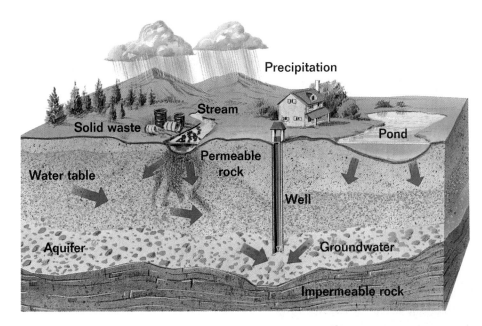

Figure 19-21 Pollutants leaking from storage containers can eventually reach and contaminate groundwater.

Figure 19-22 Oil spill cleanup, like this one in Wales, is a messy task. Oil-soaked sand has to be shoveled into bags by hand. If the water is contaminated, it must be skimmed from the surface. **What would happen if the beach wasn't cleaned up?**

Ocean Pollution

Rivers eventually flow into the ocean, bringing their pollutants along. The areas of the ocean most seriously affected by pollution are those near the coastlines, where freshwater enters the sea or where factories, sewage-treatment plants, and shipping activities are concentrated. As is the case with freshwater pollution, the discharge of raw sewage into coastal waters can encourage the overgrowth of algae and plankton. Wastes produced by many of these species are poisonous to fish and wildlife.

Another well-known ocean pollution problem involves oil spills. About 4 million metric tons of oil are released into ocean waters every year. Some of that total comes from freshwater runoff and some comes from ships, including oil tankers that use ocean water to wash out empty tanks before refilling them. Some also is spilled by accident. One of the worst oil spills ever seen occurred during the Persian Gulf War, when a huge amount of crude oil was released into the water on purpose. Tens of thousands of seabirds died, and salt marshes and other estuarine ecosystems were destroyed.

Section Assessment

1. List four ways in which air pollution affects the atmosphere.
2. Describe global warming.
3. How does acid rain affect the environment?
4. What causes ozone depletion?
5. **Think Critically:** How can hazardous chemicals deposited in landfills affect groundwater? Surface streams?
6. ### Skill Builder
   Comparing and Contrasting
   Compare and contrast the causes and effects of air and water pollution. If you need help, refer to Comparing and Contrasting in the **Skill Handbook** on page 720.

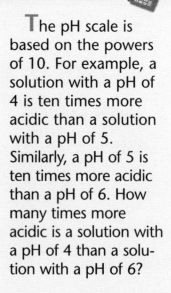

Using Math

The pH scale is based on the powers of 10. For example, a solution with a pH of 4 is ten times more acidic than a solution with a pH of 5. Similarly, a pH of 5 is ten times more acidic than a pH of 6. How many times more acidic is a solution with a pH of 4 than a solution with a pH of 6?

Modeling the Greenhouse Effect

You can create models of Earth with and without heat-reflecting greenhouse gases. Then, experiment with the models to observe the greenhouse effect.

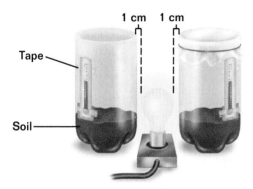

Tape

1 cm   1 cm

Soil

What You'll Investigate

How does the greenhouse effect influence temperatures on Earth?

Goals

- **Observe** the greenhouse effect.
- **Describe** the effect that a heat source has on an environment.

Procedure

1. Copy the data table and use it to record your temperature measurements.
2. Put an equal volume of potting soil in the bottom of each container.

Changes in Temperature		
Time	Open Container Temperature (°C)	Sealed Container Temperature (°C)
0 minutes		
2 minutes		
4 minutes		
6 minutes		

Materials

- Clear, plastic, 2-L soft-drink bottles with tops cut off and labels removed (2)
- Thermometers (2)
- Cups of potting soil (4)
- Masking tape
- Plastic wrap
- Rubber band
- Lamp with 100-watt lightbulb
- Watch or clock

3. Use masking tape to affix a thermometer to the inside of each container. Place the thermometers at the same height relative to the soil. Shield each thermometer bulb by putting a double layer of masking tape over it.

4. Seal the top of one container with plastic wrap held in place with the rubber band.

5. Place the lamp with the exposed 100-watt bulb between the two containers, exactly 1 cm from each, as shown in the diagram. Do not turn on the light.

6. Let the apparatus sit undisturbed for five minutes, then record the temperature in each container.

7. Turn on the light. Record the temperature in each container every two minutes for the next 15 to 20 minutes.

8. **Record** the results on a graph.

Conclude and Apply

1. How did the temperature of each container change during the experiment?

2. **Compare and contrast** the temperature of the two containers at the end of the experiment.

3. What does the lightbulb represent in this experimental model? What does the plastic wrap represent?

Chapter 19 Reviewing Main Ideas

For a **preview** of this chapter, study this Reviewing Main Ideas before you read the chapter. After you have studied this chapter, you can use the Reviewing Main Ideas to **review** the chapter.

The Glencoe MindJogger, Audiocassettes, and CD-ROM provide additional opportunities for review.

19-1 NATURAL RESOURCES

Natural resources are materials in the environment that are useful for living things. Some of these resources are **renewable** and replenished by the environment, but **nonrenewable resources** cannot be replaced or are only replaced slowly. **Fossil fuels,** solar energy, water and wind power, **geothermal energy,** and **nuclear energy** are energy sources used today. *How are renewable and nonrenewable resources different? Give examples of each.*

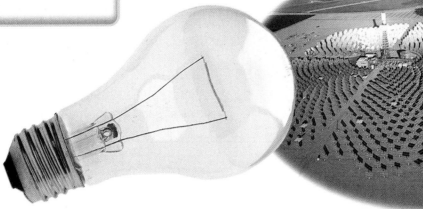

Section

19-2 CONSERVATION AND WILDLIFE PROTECTION

Conservation is the process of saving resources. A nonrenewable resource can be conserved by using less of that resource or using a renewable resource instead. **Recycling,** the process of changing a used item into a new item for a different use, is one method used to reduce energy use. Wildlife, land, and mineral conservation are methods used to preserve natural resources. *What methods are used to preserve our natural resources?*

Reading Check ✓

You can better understand new words if you analyze their parts. What do the parts of these words mean: *nonrenewable, photovoltaic, geothermal?*

Section

19-3 MAINTAINING A HEALTHY ENVIRONMENT

Any substance that contaminates the environment and causes pollution is a **pollutant.** There are three types of pollution: air pollution, water pollution, and land pollution. **Smog** is air pollution created when sunlight reacts with the by-products of fossil fuels. **Acid rain** results from the mixture of water vapor and air pollutants in the atmosphere.

THE GREENHOUSE EFFECT

The **greenhouse effect** is the warming of Earth due to a blanket of gases in the atmosphere. It is essential to life on Earth. Without it, temperatures would be too cold to support life as we know it. However, the burning of fossil fuels has added to the amount of greenhouse gases in the atmosphere. These gases are responsible for **global warming.** *What could happen if Earth temperatures rise by 5°C?*

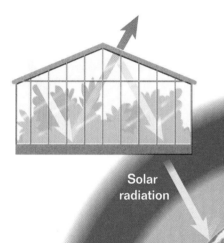

Solar radiation

Carbon dioxide in atmosphere

Heat trapped near Earth's surface

Career CONNECTION

Alice Derby Erickson, Pipestone Carver

Alice Derby Erickson works as a park ranger at the Pipestone National Monument in southwestern Minnesota. She is a full-blooded Dakota Sioux and a pipestone carver. Carrying on a longtime family tradition, Alice started carving pipestone at the age of ten. She starts with a piece of carefully quarried pipestone and shapes it using various files and sandpaper. Heating the stone and applying beeswax produces a rich, red color. *What are the physical properties that make a rock desirable for carving?*

Chapter 19 Assessment

Using Vocabulary

a. acid rain
b. endangered species
c. erosion
d. extinction
e. fossil fuel
f. geothermal energy
g. global warming
h. greenhouse effect
i. groundwater
j. hazardous waste
k. hydroelectric power

l. natural resource
m. nonrenewable resource
n. nuclear energy
o. ozone depletion
p. photovoltaic (PV) cell
q. pollutant
r. recycling
s. renewable resource
t. smog
u. soil depletion
v. soil management

The sentences below include terms that have been used incorrectly. Change the italicized terms so that the sentence reads correctly. Underline your change.

1. *Geothermal energy* is a natural resource that is not replaceable.
2. *Hydroelectric power* is heat energy from below the surface of Earth.
3. Reducing the use of natural resources by reusing an item after it has been reprocessed is called *soil depletion.*
4. *Erosion* is a combination of smoke, dust, and oxides of nitrogen and sulfur.
5. The *greenhouse effect* is an increase in the temperature of Earth due to an increase in the levels of certain gases in the atmosphere.

Checking Concepts

Choose the word or phrase that best answers the question.

6. What does smog **NOT** include?
   A) ozone
   B) nitrogen oxides
   C) soot
   D) acid rain

7. Which of the following is **NOT** a fossil fuel?
   A) wood
   B) oil
   C) natural gas
   D) coal

8. Which of the following is **NOT** a renewable resource?
   A) wood
   B) water
   C) sunlight
   D) aluminum

9. Which of the following is **NOT** either directly or indirectly caused by the sun?
   A) hydroelectric power
   B) nuclear energy
   C) photosynthesis
   D) wind power

10. What kind of renewable energy source is found deep in the crust of Earth?
    A) groundwater
    B) solid waste
    C) geothermal energy
    D) nuclear power

11. What are methods used to prevent or reduce soil depletion and erosion forms of?
    A) crop rotation
    B) soil management
    C) fertilizers
    D) terracing

12. Which of the following is **NOT** a description of carbon dioxide?
    A) component of acid rain
    B) greenhouse gas
    C) ozone-depleting gas
    D) waste product from the burning of fossil fuels

13. What is ozone depletion caused by?
    A) acid rain
    B) oxygen
    C) carbon dioxide
    D) chlorine molecules

14. Which of the following does **NOT** cause water pollution?
    A) air pollution
    C) solid-waste disposal
    B) ozone depletion
    D) runoff from rainfall

Thinking Critically

15. Why does the burning of wood produce similar pollutants to the burning of fossil fuels?

16. What would make a better location for a solar power plant—a polar region or a desert region? Why?

17. Why is it beneficial to grow another crop in soil after the major crop has been harvested?

Developing Skills

If you need help, refer to the **Skill Handbook**.

18. **Comparing and Contrasting:** Compare and contrast the reasons for using crop rotation, strip-cropping, contour plowing, terracing, and no-till farming.

19. **Making and Using a Concept Map:** Complete the concept map describing how air can be polluted. Use the following terms and events: *nitrogen oxides, sulfur dioxides, acid rain,* and *smog.*

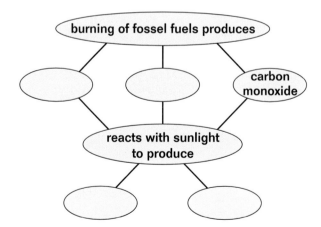

THE PRINCETON REVIEW

Test-Taking Tip

Stock Up on Supplies Be sure to supply yourself with the test-taking essentials: number two pencils, pens, erasers, a ruler, and a pencil sharpener. If the room doesn't have a pencil sharpener, a broken pencil can be a problem.

Test Practice

Use these questions to test your Science Proficiency.

1. What are renewable resources?
   A) minerals such as phosphorus
   B) fuel oil, gasoline, plastics, and paint
   C) oxygen, water, plants, and animals
   D) petroleum products

2. Where does most of the energy we use today come from?
   A) solar cells
   B) fossil fuels
   C) geothermal energy
   D) wind farms

3. Why must topsoil be conserved?
   A) It is fertile soil that has accumulated over thousands of years.
   B) Its underground reservoir is being used up at a fast rate.
   C) Terracing has caused the loss of several centimeters of topsoil each decade.
   D) No-till farming has caused topsoil to be used up.

4. What causes water pollution?
   A) solid-waste disposal
   B) runoff from rainfall
   C) air pollution
   D) all of the above

Astronomy

What's Happening Here?

Much of the light you see twinkling in the night sky bears witness to a distant past. How so? If you peered at one of those stars through a powerful telescope, you would discover not how the star appears today but how it appeared millions of years ago. Likewise, if people on a distant planet were to aim a telescope at you, they would see Earth as it existed in the age of the dinosaurs. Outer space is so vast that light traveling at 300 000 kilometers a second takes millions of years to span the distance from a distant star to Earth. To grasp the subject of astronomy, you must expand your notion of distance to the unfathomable. In this unit, you will learn how the lure of this vastness has triggered a new age of exploration. En route into deep space, the *Voyager* probes launched in 1977 photographed Jupiter's Great Red Spot (left), a massive storm in the planet's outer gases. In 1996, this astronaut (inset) tested a minirocket backpack by flying solo above the space shuttle *Discovery*.

CHAPTER

20 Exploring Space

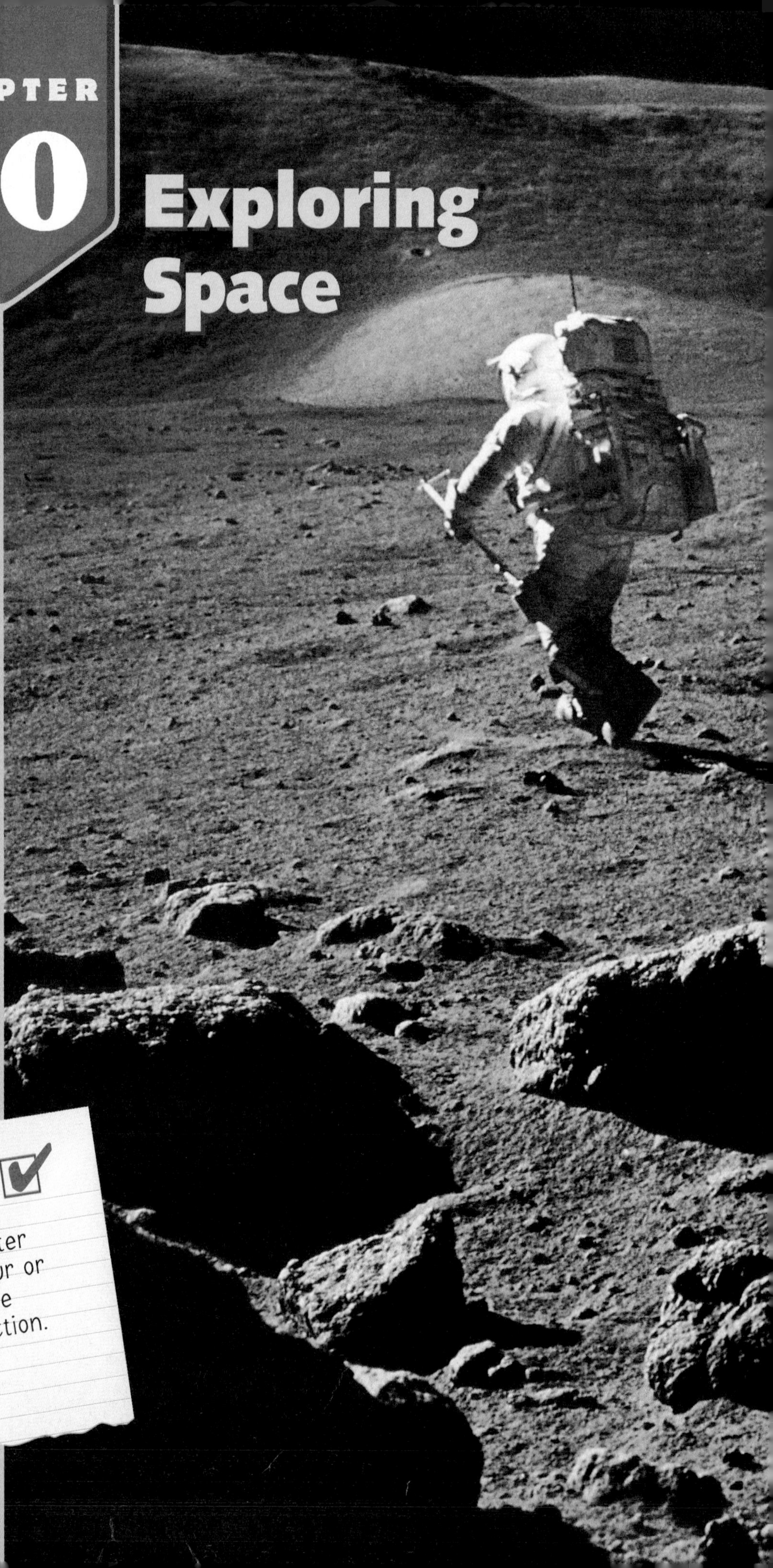

Chapter Preview

Skills Preview

Skill Builders
- Sequence
- Map Concepts

MiniLabs
- Analyze Data
- Infer

Activities
- Draw Conclusions

Reading Check

As you read this chapter about space, write four or five questions that are answered in each section.

Explore Activity

The first space exploration didn't occur in a spaceship or a satellite. Instead, it was done by a person simply looking upward, studying countless points of shimmering light. Over time, people devised more and more accurate ways to study the moon, the planets, and the stars. We can learn a lot about a star's temperature, size, and composition, for instance, by studying its light. In this activity, you'll observe some of the colors that make up visible light, which is one form of radiation emitted by stars.

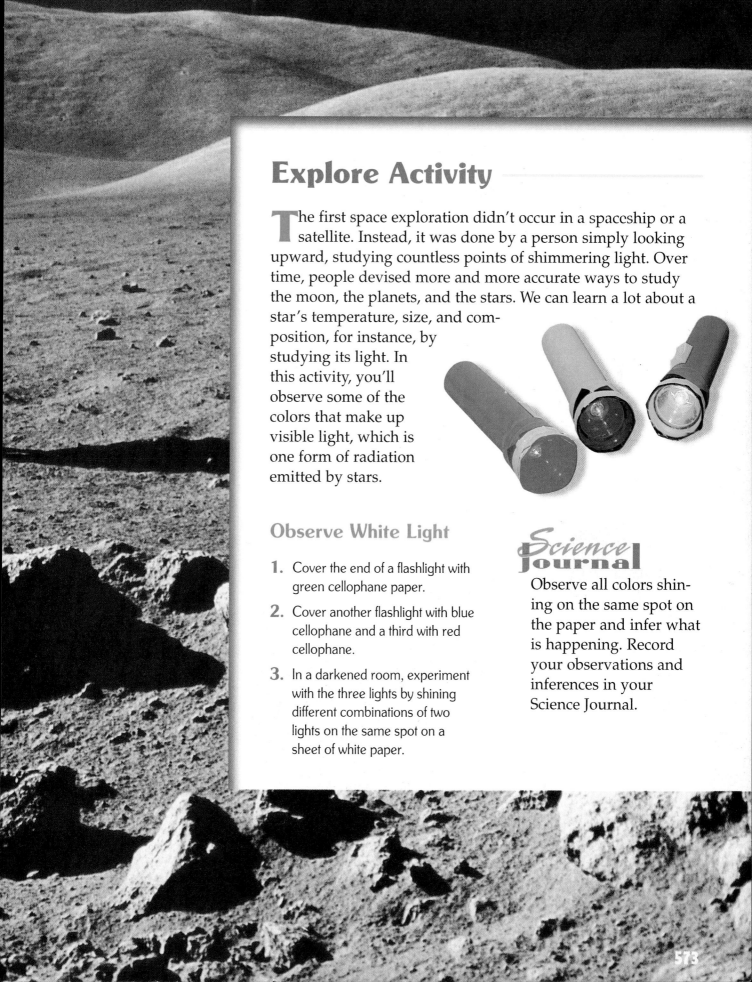

Observe White Light

1. Cover the end of a flashlight with green cellophane paper.

2. Cover another flashlight with blue cellophane and a third with red cellophane.

3. In a darkened room, experiment with the three lights by shining different combinations of two lights on the same spot on a sheet of white paper.

Science Journal

Observe all colors shining on the same spot on the paper and infer what is happening. Record your observations and inferences in your Science Journal.

Radiation from Space

What You'll Learn

▶ The electromagnetic spectrum
▶ The differences between refracting and reflecting telescopes
▶ The differences between optical and radio telescopes

Vocabulary

electromagnetic spectrum
refracting telescope
reflecting telescope
observatory
radio telescope

Why It's Important

▶ You'll learn about the tools and methods used to study space.

Figure 20-1 The electromagnetic spectrum ranges from gamma rays with wavelengths of less than 0.000 000 000 01 m to radio waves more than 100 000 m long. **What happens to frequency (the number of waves that pass a point per second) as wavelength shortens?**

Electromagnetic Waves

On a crisp, autumn evening, you take a break from your homework to gaze out the window at the many stars that fill the night sky. Looking up at the stars, it's easy to imagine future spaceships venturing through space and large space stations circling above Earth, where people work and live. But, when you look into the night sky, what you're really seeing is the distant past, not the future.

Light from the Past

When you look at a star, you see light that left the star many years ago. The light that you see travels fast. Still, the distances across space are so great that it takes years for the light to reach Earth—sometimes millions of years.

The light and other energy leaving a star are forms of radiation. Recall that radiation is energy that's transmitted from one place to another by electromagnetic waves. Because of the electric and magnetic properties of this radiation, it's called electromagnetic radiation. Electromagnetic waves carry energy through empty space as well as through matter.

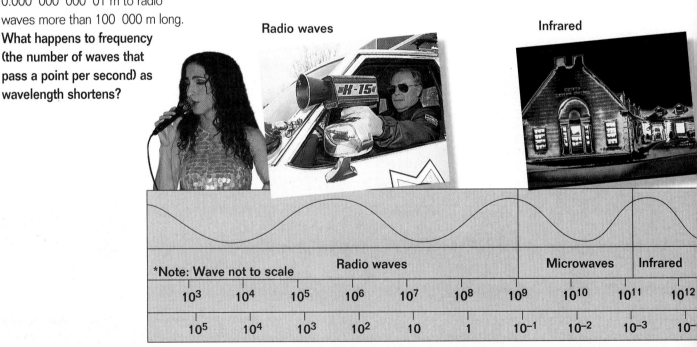

Radio waves

Infrared

*Note: Wave not to scale		Radio waves						Microwaves		Infrared
10^3	10^4	10^5	10^6	10^7	10^8	10^9	10^{10}	10^{11}	10^{12}
10^5	10^4	10^3	10^2	10	1	10^{-1}	10^{-2}	10^{-3}	10^-

Electromagnetic Radiation

Sound waves, a type of mechanical wave, can't travel through empty space. How do we hear the voices of the astronauts while they're in space? When they speak into a microphone, the sound is converted into electromagnetic waves called radio waves. The radio waves travel through space and through our atmosphere. They are then converted back into sound by electronic equipment and audio speakers.

Radio waves and visible light from the sun are just two types of electromagnetic radiation. The other types include gamma rays, X rays, ultraviolet waves, infrared waves, and microwaves. **Figure 20-1** shows these forms of electromagnetic radiation arranged according to their wavelengths. This arrangement of electromagnetic radiation is called the **electromagnetic spectrum.**

Although the various electromagnetic waves differ in their wavelengths, they all travel at the speed of 300 000 km/s in a vacuum. You're probably more familiar with this speed as the "speed of light." Visible light and other forms of electromagnetic radiation travel at this incredible speed, but the universe is so large that it takes millions of years for the light from some stars to reach Earth.

Once electromagnetic radiation from stars and other objects reaches Earth, we can use it to learn about the source of the electromagnetic radiation. What tools and methods do scientists use to discover what lies beyond our planet? One tool for observing electromagnetic radiation from distant sources is a telescope.

PHYSICS
INTEGRATION

Bending Light
Pass a beam of white light through a prism. Note that different colors of light are bent, forming a spectrum. Infer how the white light and prism form a spectrum with violet on one end and red on the other.

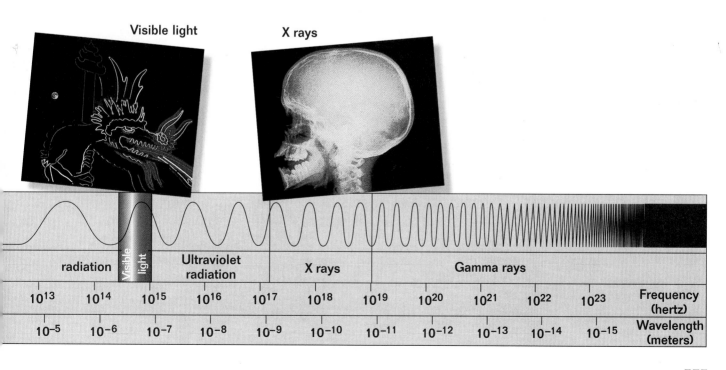

Visible light

X rays

radiation	Visible light	Ultraviolet radiation	X rays	Gamma rays	

10^{13}	10^{14}	10^{15}	10^{16}	10^{17}	10^{18}	10^{19}	10^{20}	10^{21}	10^{22}	10^{23}	Frequency (hertz)
10^{-5}	10^{-6}	10^{-7}	10^{-8}	10^{-9}	10^{-10}	10^{-11}	10^{-12}	10^{-13}	10^{-14}	10^{-15}	Wavelength (meters)

Optical Telescopes

Optical telescopes produce magnified images of objects. Light is collected by an objective lens or mirror, which then forms an image at the focal point of the telescope. The eyepiece lens then magnifies the image. The two types of optical telescopes are shown in **Figure 20-2.**

In a **refracting telescope,** the light from an object passes through a double convex objective lens and is bent to form an image on the focal point. The image is then magnified by the eyepiece.

A **reflecting telescope** uses a mirror as an objective to focus light from the object being viewed. Light passes through the open end of a reflecting telescope and strikes a concave mirror at its base. The light is then reflected to the focal point to form an image. A smaller mirror is often used to reflect the light into the eyepiece lens so the magnified image can be viewed.

Using Optical Telescopes

Most optical telescopes used by professional astronomers are housed in buildings called **observatories.** Observatories often have a dome-shaped roof that opens up to let in light. However, not all telescopes are in observatories.

Figure 20-2 These diagrams show how each type of optical telescope collects light and forms an image.

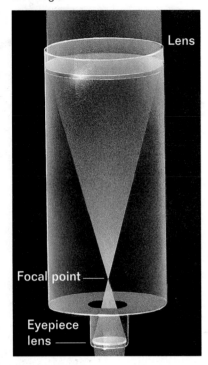

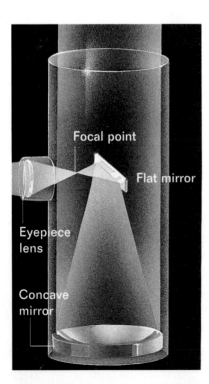

A In a refracting telescope, a double convex lens focuses light to form an image at the focal point.

B In a reflecting telescope, a concave mirror focuses light to form an image at the focal point.

C Which type of optical telescope is this student using?

The *Hubble Space Telescope,* shown in **Figure 20-3,** was launched in 1990 by the space shuttle *Discovery.* Earth's atmosphere absorbs and distorts some of the energy received from space. Because *Hubble* didn't have to view space through our atmosphere, it should have produced clear images. However, when the largest mirror of this reflecting telescope was shaped, there was a mistake. Images obtained by the telescope were not as clear as expected. In December 1993, a team of astronauts repaired *Hubble's* telescope mirror and other equipment. Now, the clear images obtained by *Hubble Space Telescope* are changing scientists' ideas about space.

Figure 20-3 The *Hubble Space Telescope* was released from the cargo bay of the space shuttle *Discovery* on April 25, 1990. It's now orbiting Earth, sending back images and data about distant space objects.

Problem Solving

Interpreting Telescope Data

The magnifying power *(Mp)* of a telescope is determined by the focal lengths of the telescope's objective lens and eyepiece. Once built, you cannot easily change the objective lens, but you can easily change the eyepiece. That's why telescopes are often sold with three or four eyepieces—each with a different focal length. The magnifying power of a telescope is equal to the focal length of its objective lens divided by the focal length of its eyepiece.

Telescopes also have light-gathering power (LGP). Generally, the larger the diameter (aperture) of a telescope's objective, the more light the telescope can gather. Therefore, a telescope with an objective aperture of 125 mm will gather more light than a telescope with an objective aperture of 75 mm.

The following table lists the characteristics of two telescopes. Study the data about each telescope and interpret which has the greater magnifying power and which has the greater light-gathering power.

Telescope Data			
Tele-scope	Aperture	Objective Focal Length	Eyepiece Focal Length
1	75 mm	1200 mm	9 mm, 12 mm
2	125 mm	900 mm	9 mm, 12 mm

Think Critically: Which telescope would you want to use to observe stars? Which telescope would you want to use to observe craters on the moon? Explain your selections.

Active Optics

Since the early 1600s, when the Italian scientist Galileo Galilei first turned a telescope toward the stars, people have been searching for better ways to study what lies beyond our atmosphere, such as the twin Keck telescopes shown in **Figure 20-4.** Today, the largest reflector has a segmented mirror 10 m wide. The most recent innovations in optical telescopes involve active and adaptive optics. With active optics, a computer is used to compensate for changes in temperature, mirror distortions, and bad viewing conditions. Even more ambitious is adaptive optics, which uses a laser to probe the atmosphere and relay information to a computer about air turbulence. The computer then adjusts the telescope's mirror thousands of times per second, thus reducing the effects of atmospheric turbulence. ✔

Reading Check ✔

How big is the mirror on the largest reflector?

Figure 20-4 The twin Keck telescopes on Mauna Kea in Hawaii can be used together, more than doubling the resolving power. Each individual telescope has an objective mirror 10 m in diameter. To cope with the difficulty of building such a large mirror, this telescope design used several smaller mirrors positioned to work as one. **Although the Keck telescopes are much larger than the** *Hubble Space Telescope*, **the** *Hubble* **is able to achieve better resolution. Why?**

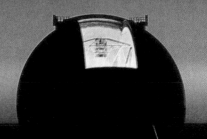

Radio Telescopes

As you know, stars and other objects radiate energy throughout the electromagnetic spectrum. A **radio telescope,** such as the one shown in **Figure 20-5,** is used to study radio waves traveling through space. Unlike visible light, radio waves pass freely through Earth's atmosphere. Because of this, radio telescopes are useful 24 hours a day under most weather conditions.

Radio waves reaching Earth's surface strike the large, curved dish of a radio telescope. This dish reflects the waves to a focal point where a receiver is located. The information allows scientists to detect objects in space, to map the universe, and to search for intelligent life on other planets.

In the remainder of this chapter, you'll learn about the instruments that travel into space and send back information that telescopes on Earth's surface cannot obtain.

Figure 20-5 This radio telescope is used to study radio waves traveling through space.

Section Assessment

1. What is the difference between radio telescopes and optical telescopes?

2. The frequency of electromagnetic radiation is the number of waves that pass a point in a specific amount of time. If red light has a longer wavelength than blue light, which would have a greater frequency?

3. **Think Critically:** It takes light from the closest star to Earth (other than the sun) about four years to reach us. If there were intelligent life on a planet circling that star, how long would it take for us to send them a radio transmission and for us to receive their reply?

4. **Skill Builder**
   Sequencing Sequence these electromagnetic waves from longest wavelength to shortest wavelength: *gamma rays, visible light, X rays, radio waves, infrared waves, ultraviolet waves,* and *microwaves.* If you need help, refer to Sequencing in the **Skill Handbook** on page 714.

Using Math

The magnifying power (Mp) of a telescope is determined by dividing the focal length of the objective lens (FL_{obj}) by the focal length of the eyepiece (FL_{eye}) using the following equation.

$$Mp = \frac{FL_{obj}}{FL_{eye}}$$

If $FL_{obj} = 1200$ mm and $FL_{eye} = 6$ mm, what is the telescope's magnifying power?

Telescopes

Materials

- Candle
- White cardboard (50 cm × 60 cm)
- Flashlight
- Hand lens
- Large glass of water
- Concave mirror
- Plane mirror
- Masking tape
- Convex mirror
- Empty paper-towel tube

You have learned that optical telescopes use lenses and mirrors as objectives to collect light from an object. They use eyepiece lenses to magnify images of that object. Try this activity to see how the paths of light differ in reflecting and refracting telescopes.

What You'll Investigate

In what way are paths of light affected by the lenses and mirrors in refracting and reflecting telescopes?

Goals

- **Observe** how different mirrors and lenses affect light and the appearance of objects.

Procedure

1. **Observe** your reflection in plane, convex, and concave mirrors.

2. Hold an object in front of each of the mirrors. **Compare** the size and position of the images.

3. **Darken** the room and hold the convex mirror in front of you at a 45° angle, slanting downward. Direct the flashlight toward the mirror. **Note** the size and position of the reflected light.

4. Repeat step 3 using a plane mirror. **Draw** a diagram to show what happens to the beam of light.

5. **Tape** the paper-towel tube to the flashlight so that the beam of light will pass through the tube. Direct the light into a glass of water, first directly from above, then from an angle 45° to the water's surface. **Observe** the direction of the light rays when viewed from the side of the glass.

6. **Light** a candle and set it some distance from the vertically held cardboard screen. **CAUTION:** *Keep hair and clothing away from the flame.* Using the hand lens as a convex lens, move it between the candle and the screen until you have the best possible image.

7. **Move** the lens closer to the candle. Note what happens to the size of the image. Move the cardboard until the image is in focus.

Conclude and Apply

1. How did you **determine** the position of the focal point of the hand lens in step 6? What does this tell you about the position of the light rays?

2. **Compare and contrast** the effect the three types of mirrors had on your reflection.

3. **Compare and contrast** the path of light in refracting and reflecting telescopes.

4. What is the purpose of the concave mirror in a reflecting telescope?

Seeing in 3-D

Why do humans have two eyes? One reason is that the second eye lets us see more of the world. It increases our field of view. Many animals have eyes set on opposite sides of their heads, so each eye sees a separate half of the world. But, human eyes are set closer together. They see almost the same scene but from a slightly different angle. Look at the student in front of you, first through only your right eye then only your left eye. You'll notice that each eye sees a slightly different view. But, your brain puts the two different views together, giving you the ability to figure out which object is closer to you and which is farther away. You see in three dimensions (3-D).

In the figure on the left, notice how the green block appears to the left of the yellow cylinder when seen by the left eye but to the right when seen by the right eye. Your brain interprets these two images, and you know that the yellow cylinder is in front of the green block.

Movies and Television

How can you have a 3-D experience at the movies or on a TV? A camera with two lenses a few inches apart records the images on film or videotape. But, one lens has a red filter in front of it and the other a blue, as shown in the figure on the right. So, the image recorded by one lens is in shades of red, while the one recorded by the other lens is in shades of blue. The viewer watches the film through 3-D glasses that have the same color filters. Because the red filter allows only red light through it, only the image meant for that eye passes through that filter. The filters send the images meant for the right eye only to the right eye and the images meant for the left only to the left. The brain does the rest of the work. It combines the two colors, giving different shades of gray and interprets the slightly different images so that you can tell which object is in front and which is behind.

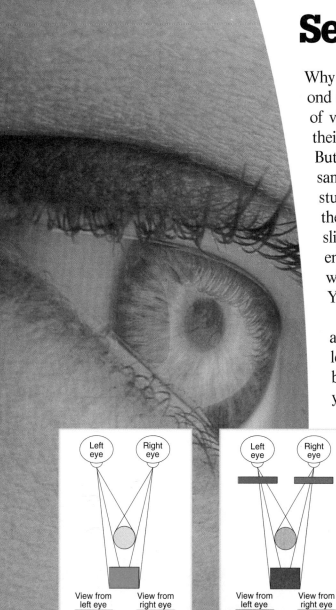

Left eye | Right eye
View from left eye | View from right eye

Left eye | Right eye
View from left eye | View from right eye

Career CONNECTION

Research how 3-D technology is being used in the latest computer animation software. Find out how the 3-D images used in computer animations are made.

Early Space Missions

What You'll Learn

► How to compare and contrast natural and artificial satellites

► The differences between artificial satellites and space probes

► The history of the race to the moon

Vocabulary

satellite
orbit
space probe
Project Mercury
Project Gemini
Project Apollo

Why It's Important

► Learning about space exploration will help you better understand the vastness of space.

The First Steps into Space

If you had your choice of watching your favorite sports team on television or from the stadium, which would you prefer? You would probably want to be as close as possible to the game so you wouldn't miss any of the action. Scientists feel the same way about space. Even though telescopes have taught them a great deal about the moon and planets, they want to learn more by actually going to those places or by sending spacecraft where they can't go.

Satellites

Space exploration began in 1957 when the former Soviet Union used a rocket to send *Sputnik I* into space. It was the first artificial satellite. A **satellite** is any object that revolves around another object. When an object enters space, it travels in a straight line unless a force such as gravity deflects it. When Earth's gravity pulls on a satellite, it falls toward Earth. The result of the satellite traveling forward while at the same time falling toward Earth is a curved path, called an **orbit,** around Earth. This is shown in **Figure 20-6.**

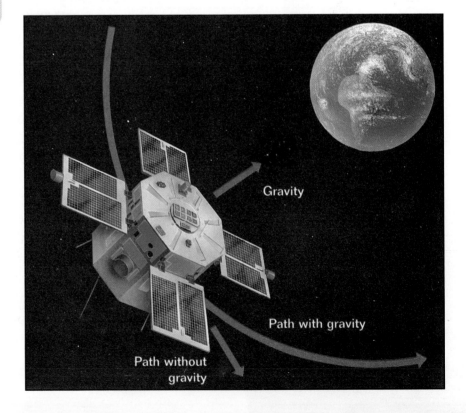

Figure 20-6 The combination of the satellite's forward movement and the gravitational attraction of Earth causes the satellite to travel in a curved path, called an orbit. **What would happen if the forward speed of the satellite decreased?**

Gravity

Path with gravity

Path without gravity

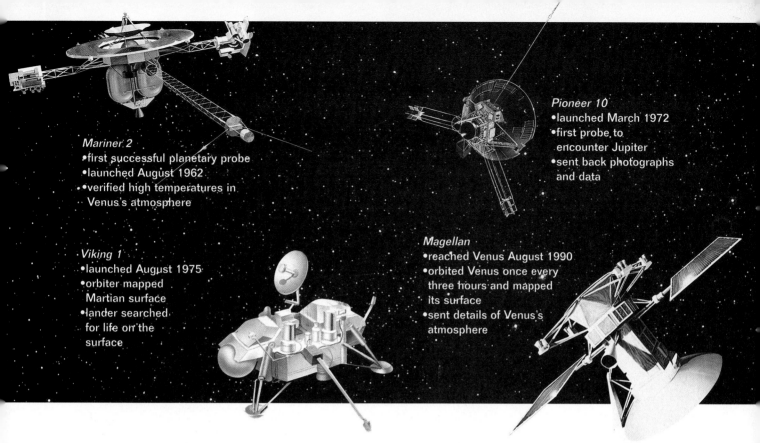

Mariner 2
•first successful planetary probe
•launched August 1962
•verified high temperatures in Venus's atmosphere

Pioneer 10
•launched March 1972
•first probe to encounter Jupiter
•sent back photographs and data

Viking 1
•launched August 1975
•orbiter mapped Martian surface
•lander searched for life on the surface

Magellan
•reached Venus August 1990
•orbited Venus once every three hours and mapped its surface
•sent details of Venus's atmosphere

Figure 20-7 Some early U.S. space probes and their missions provided much useful data.

Satellite Uses

The moon is a natural satellite of Earth. It completes one orbit every month. *Sputnik I* orbited Earth for 57 days before gravity pulled it back into the atmosphere, where it burned up. *Sputnik I* was an experiment to show that artificial satellites could be made. Today, thousands of artificial satellites orbit Earth.

Present-day communication satellites transmit radio and television programs to locations around the world. Other satellites gather scientific data that can't be obtained from Earth, and weather satellites constantly monitor Earth's global weather patterns.

Space Probes

Not all objects carried into space by rockets become satellites. Rockets also can be used to send instruments into space. A **space probe** is an instrument that gathers information and sends it back to Earth. Unlike satellites that orbit Earth, space probes travel far into the solar system. Some have even traveled out of the solar system. Space probes, like many satellites, carry cameras and other data-gathering equipment, as well as radio transmitters and receivers that allow them to communicate with scientists on Earth. **Figure 20-7** shows some of the early space probes launched by NASA (National Aeronautics and Space Administration).

Using Math

Suppose a spacecraft is launched at a speed of 40 200 km per hour. Express this speed in kilometers per second.

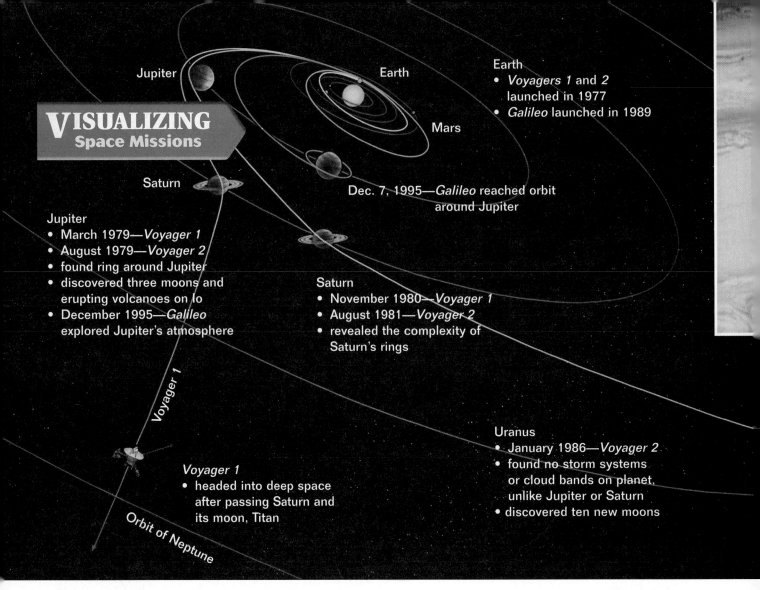

VISUALIZING
Space Missions

Jupiter

Earth

Earth
• *Voyagers 1* and *2* launched in 1977
• *Galileo* launched in 1989

Mars

Dec. 7, 1995—*Galileo* reached orbit around Jupiter

Saturn

Jupiter
• March 1979—*Voyager 1*
• August 1979—*Voyager 2*
• found ring around Jupiter
• discovered three moons and erupting volcanoes on Io
• December 1995—*Galileo* explored Jupiter's atmosphere

Saturn
• November 1980—*Voyager 1*
• August 1981—*Voyager 2*
• revealed the complexity of Saturn's rings

Voyager 1

Voyager 1
• headed into deep space after passing Saturn and its moon, Titan

Orbit of Neptune

Uranus
• January 1986—*Voyager 2*
• found no storm systems or cloud bands on planet, unlike Jupiter or Saturn
• discovered ten new moons

Figure 20-8 The *Voyager* and *Galileo* spacecraft helped make many major discoveries.

You've probably heard of the space probes *Voyager 1* and *Voyager 2*. These two probes were launched in 1977 and are now heading toward deep space. *Voyager 1* flew past Jupiter and Saturn. *Voyager 2* flew past Jupiter, Saturn, Uranus, and Neptune. **Figure 20-8** describes some of what we've learned from the *Voyager* probes. Now, these probes are exploring beyond our solar system as part of the Voyager Interstellar Mission. Scientists expect these probes to continue to transmit data to Earth for at least 20 more years.

The fate of a probe is never certain, and not all probes are successful. In 1993, *Mars Observer* was only days away from entering orbit around Mars when it was lost. The problem was most likely a critical failure in the propulsion system.

Galileo, launched in 1989, reached Jupiter in 1995. In July 1995, *Galileo* released a smaller probe that began a five-month approach to Jupiter. The small probe took a parachute ride through Jupiter's violent atmosphere in December 1995.

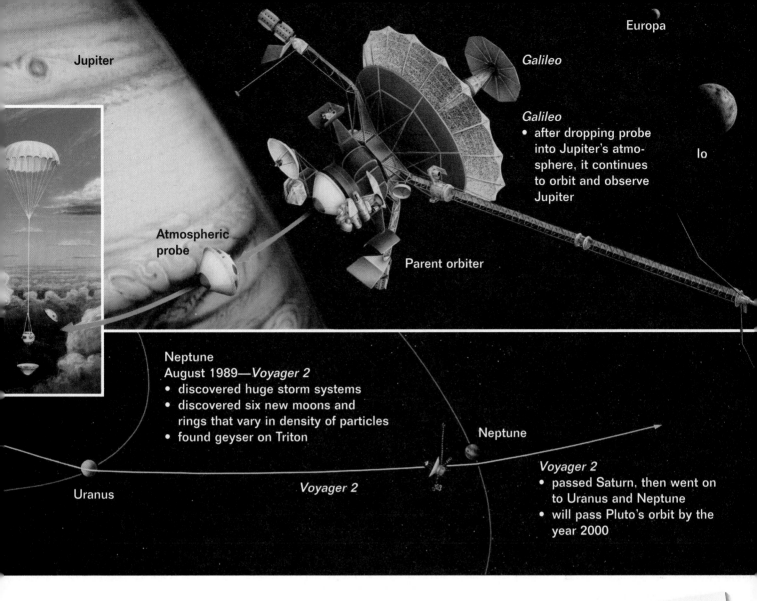

Jupiter

Europa

Galileo

Galileo
- after dropping probe into Jupiter's atmosphere, it continues to orbit and observe Jupiter

Io

Atmospheric probe

Parent orbiter

Neptune
August 1989—*Voyager 2*
- discovered huge storm systems
- discovered six new moons and rings that vary in density of particles
- found geyser on Triton

Neptune

Uranus

Voyager 2

Voyager 2
- passed Saturn, then went on to Uranus and Neptune
- will pass Pluto's orbit by the year 2000

Before being crushed by the atmospheric pressure, it transmitted information about Jupiter's composition, temperature, and pressure to the ship orbiting above. *Galileo* studied Jupiter's moons, rings, and magnetic fields and then relayed this information back to scientists who were eagerly waiting for it on Earth. ☑

Galileo

Recent studies of Jupiter's moon Europa by *Galileo* indicate that an ocean of water or ice may exist under the outer layer of ice that covers Europa's cracked surface. The cracks in the surface may be caused by geologic activity that heats the ocean underneath the surface. Sunlight penetrates these cracks, further heating the ocean and setting the stage for the possible existence of life on Europa. *Galileo* studied Europa through 1999. More advanced probes will be needed to determine whether molecular life actually does exist on this icy moon.

Reading Check ☑

What did the *Galileo* space probe study?

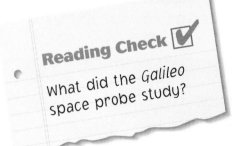

LIFE SCIENCE
◄ **INTEGRATION**

Mini Lab

Comparing the Effects of Light Pollution

Procedure

1. Obtain a cardboard tube from an empty roll of paper towels.
2. Select a night when clear skies are predicted. Go outside about two hours after sunset and look through the cardboard tube at a specific constellation decided upon ahead of time.
3. Count the number of stars you are able to see without moving the observing tube. Repeat this three times.
4. Determine the average number of observable stars at your location.

Analysis

1. Compare and contrast the number of stars visible from other students' homes.
2. Explain the cause and effect of differences in your observations.

The Race to the Moon

Throughout the world, people were shocked when they turned on their radios and television sets in 1957 and heard the radio transmissions from *Sputnik I* as it orbited over their heads. All that *Sputnik I* transmitted was a sort of beeping sound, but people quickly realized that putting a human into space wasn't far off.

In 1961, the Soviet cosmonaut Yuri A. Gagarin became the first human in space. He orbited Earth and then returned safely. Soon, President John F. Kennedy called for the United States to place people on the moon and return them to Earth by the end of that decade. The "race for space" had begun.

The U.S. program to reach the moon began with **Project Mercury.** The goals of Project Mercury were to orbit a piloted spacecraft around Earth and to bring it safely back. The program provided data and experience in the basics of space flight. On May 5, 1961, Alan B. Shepard became the first U.S. citizen in space. In 1962, *Mercury* astronaut John Glenn became the first U.S. citizen to orbit Earth. **Figure 20-9** shows Glenn preparing for liftoff. In 1998, Glenn returned to space aboard the space shuttle *Discovery.* You'll learn more about space shuttles in the next section.

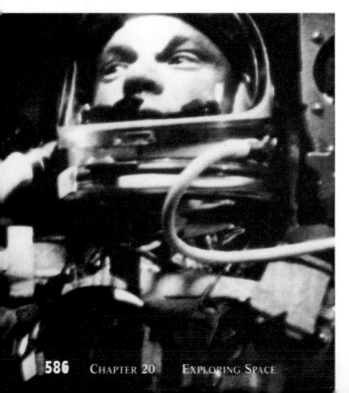

Figure 20-9 John Glenn was the first U.S. astronaut to orbit Earth.

Project Gemini

Project Gemini was the next step in reaching the moon. Teams of two astronauts in the same *Gemini* spacecraft orbited Earth. One *Gemini* team met and connected with another spacecraft in orbit—a skill that would be needed on a voyage to the moon.

Along with the *Mercury* and *Gemini* programs, a series of robotic probes was sent to the moon. *Ranger* proved we could get spacecraft to the moon. *Surveyor* landed gently on the moon's surface, indicating that the moon's surface could support spacecraft and humans. The mission of *Lunar Orbiter* was to take pictures of the moon's surface to help determine the best landing sites on the moon.

Project Apollo

The final stage of the U.S. program to reach the moon was **Project Apollo.** On July 20, 1969, *Apollo* 11 landed on the lunar surface. Neil Armstrong was the first human to set foot on the moon. His first words as he stepped onto its surface were, "That's one small step for man, one giant leap for mankind." Edwin Aldrin, the second of the three *Apollo* 11 astronauts, joined Armstrong on the moon, and they explored its surface for two hours. Michael Collins remained in the Command Module orbiting the moon, where Armstrong and Aldrin returned before beginning the journey home. A total of six lunar landings brought back more than 2000 samples of moon rock and soil for study before the program ended in 1972. **Figure 20-10** shows astronauts on the moon.

During the past three decades, most missions in space have been carried out by individual countries, often competing to be the first or the best. Today, there is much more cooperation among countries of the world to work together and share what each has learned. Projects are now being planned for cooperative missions to Mars and elsewhere. As you read the next section, you'll see how the U.S. program has progressed since the days of Project Apollo, and where it may be going in the future.

Figure 20-10 The Lunar Rover Vehicle was first used during the *Apollo 15* mission. Riding in the moon buggy, *Apollo 15, 16,* and *17* astronauts explored large areas of the lunar surface.

Section Assessment

1. Currently, no human-made objects are orbiting Neptune, yet Neptune has eight satellites. Explain.

2. *Galileo* was considered a space probe as it traveled to Jupiter. Once there, however, it became an artificial satellite. Explain.

3. **Think Critically:** Is Earth a satellite of any other body in space? Explain your answer.

4. **Skill Builder**
   Concept Mapping Make an events-chain concept map that lists the events in the U.S. space program to place people on the moon. If you need help, refer to Concept Mapping in the **Skill Handbook** on page 714.

Using Computers

Spreadsheet Use the spreadsheet feature on your computer to generate a table of recent successful satellites and space probes launched by the United States. Include a description of the craft, the date launched, and the mission. If you need help, refer to page 738.

Star Sightings

For thousands of years, humans have used the stars to learn about the planet we live on. From star sightings, you can map the change of seasons, navigate the oceans, and even determine the size of Earth.

Polaris, or the North Star, has occupied an important place in human history. The location of Polaris is not affected by Earth's rotation. At any given observation point, it always appears at the same angle above the horizon. At Earth's north pole, Polaris appears directly overhead. At the equator, it is just above the northern horizon. Polaris provides a standard from which other locations can be measured. Such star sightings can be made using the astrolabe, an instrument used to measure the height of a star above the horizon.

Recognize the Problem

How can you determine the size of Earth?

Form a Hypothesis

Think about what you have learned about sightings of Polaris. How does this tell you that Earth is round? Knowing that Earth is round, **form a hypothesis** about whether you can estimate the circumference of Earth based on star sightings.

Goals

- **Record** your sightings of Polaris.
- **Share** the data with other students to **calculate** the circumference of Earth.

Safety Precautions

Do not use the astrolabe during the daytime to observe the sun.

Data Sources

Go to the Glencoe Science Web Site at *www.glencoe.com/sec/science* to obtain instructions on how to make an astrolabe, for more information about the location of Polaris, and for data from other students.

Test Your Hypothesis

Plan

1. Obtain an astrolabe or **construct** one using the instructions posted on the Glencoe Science Web Site.
2. **Design** a data table in your Science Journal similar to the one below.

3. Decide as a group how you will make your observations. Does it take more than one person to make each observation? When will it be easiest to see Polaris?

Do

1. Make sure your teacher approves your plan before you proceed.
2. Carry out your observations.

3. **Record** your observations in your data table.
4. **Average** your readings and post them in the table provided on the Glencoe Science Web Site.

Analyze Your Data

1. **Research** the names of cities that are at approximately the same longitude as your hometown. **Gather** astrolabe readings at the Glencoe Science Web Site from students in one of those cities.
2. **Compare** your astrolabe readings. **Subtract** the smaller reading from the larger one.

3. Determine the distance between your star sighting location and the other city.
4. To calculate the circumference of Earth, use the following relationship.

$$\text{Circumference} = \frac{(360°)(\text{distance between locations})}{\text{difference between readings}}$$

Draw Conclusions

1. How does the circumference of Earth that you calculated compare with the accepted value of 40 079 km?
2. What are some possible sources of error in this method of determining the size of Earth? What improvements would you suggest?

Polaris Observations		
Your location:		
Date	Time	Astrolabe Reading
Average astrolabe reading:		

Recent and Future Space Missions

What You'll Learn

▶ The benefits of the space shuttle
▶ The usefulness of orbital space stations
▶ Future space missions

Vocabulary
space shuttle
space station

Why It's Important

▶ Many exciting things are planned for the future of space exploration.

The Space Shuttle

Imagine spending millions of dollars to build a machine, sending it off into space, and watching its 3000 metric tons of metal and other materials burn up after only a few minutes of work. That's exactly what NASA did for many years. The early rockets lifted a small capsule holding the astronauts into orbit. Sections of the rocket separated from the rest of the rocket body and burned as they reentered the atmosphere.

A Reusable Spacecraft

NASA administrators, like many others, realized that it would be less expensive and less wasteful to reuse resources. The reusable spacecraft that transports astronauts, satellites, and other materials to and from space is the **space shuttle.** The space shuttle is shown in **Figure 20-11.**

At launch, the space shuttle stands on end and is connected to an external liquid-fuel tank and two solid-fuel booster rockets. When the shuttle reaches an altitude of about 45 km, the emptied solid-fuel booster rockets drop off and parachute back to Earth. They are recovered and used again. The larger, external liquid-fuel tank eventually separates and falls back to Earth, but it isn't recovered.

Once the space shuttle reaches space, it begins to orbit Earth. There, astronauts perform many different tasks. The cargo bay can carry a self-contained laboratory, where astronauts conduct scientific experiments and determine the effects of space flight on the human body. On missions in which the cargo bay isn't used as a laboratory, the shuttle can launch, repair, and retrieve satellites.

To retrieve a satellite, a large mechanical arm in the cargo bay is extended. An astronaut inside the shuttle moves the arm by remote control. The arm grabs the satellite and pulls it back into the cargo bay. The doors are closed, and it is then returned to Earth.

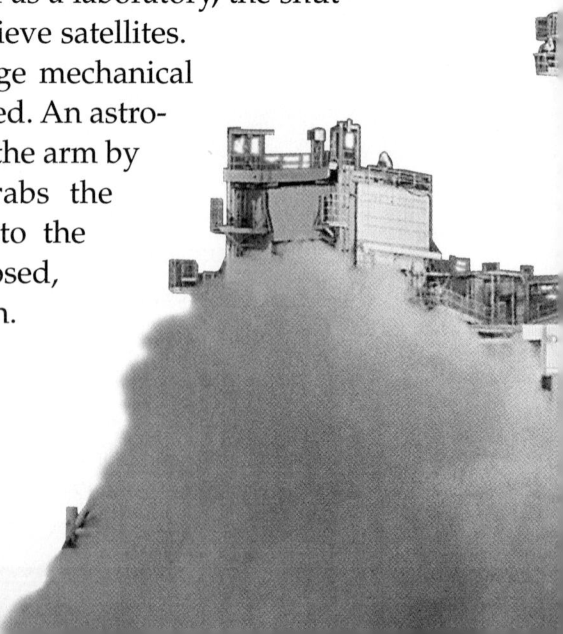

Figure 20-11 The space shuttle is designed to make many trips into space.

Similarly, the mechanical arm can be used to lift a satellite or probe out of the cargo bay and place it into space. In some cases, a defective satellite can be pulled in by the mechanical arm, repaired while in the cargo bay, and then placed into space once more.

After each mission is completed, the space shuttle glides back to Earth and lands like an airplane. A large landing field is needed because the gliding speed of the shuttle is 335 km/hr.

Space Stations

Astronauts can spend only a short time in space in the space shuttle. Its living area is small, and the crew needs more room to live, exercise, and work. A **space station** has living quarters, work and exercise areas, and all the equipment and support systems needed for humans to live and work in space.

The United States had such a station in the past. The space station *Skylab* was launched in 1973. Crews of astronauts spent up to 84 days in it performing experiments and collecting data on the effects that living in space had on humans. In 1979, the abandoned *Skylab* fell out of orbit and burned up as it entered Earth's atmosphere.

*inter*NET
CONNECTION

In 1962, John Glenn became the first U.S. citizen to orbit Earth. In 1998, Glenn returned to space aboard the space shuttle *Discovery.* Visit the Glencoe Science Web Site at **www. glencoe.com/sec/ science** for more information about the historical significance of Glenn's *Discovery* flight.

Mini Lab

Modeling Gravity

Procedure

1. Locate a stereo record album and turntable you can use for this activity.
2. Fold 8-cm-wide strips of construction paper in half, then unfold them.
3. Wrap the strips along the fold around the circumference of the record so there is a 4-cm wall around the outside edge of the disc.
4. Securely tape the rest underneath the record.
5. Place the record on a turntable and place three marbles at its center.
6. Switch on the turntable.

Analysis

1. What did you observe about the movements of the marbles?
2. Hypothesize how what you've observed could be useful for simulating the effects of gravity on a space station.

Crews from the former Soviet Union have spent the most time in space aboard the space station *Mir*. Cosmonaut Dr. Valery Polyakov returned to Earth after 438 days in space studying the long-term effects of weightlessness.

Cooperation in Space

In 1995, the United States and Russia began an era of cooperation and trust in exploring space. Early in the year, Dr. Norman Thagard was launched into orbit aboard the Russian *Soyuz* spacecraft, along with two Russian cosmonaut crewmates. Dr. Thagard was the first U.S. astronaut launched into space by a Russian booster and the first American resident of the Russian space station *Mir*.

In June 1995, Russian cosmonauts rode into orbit aboard the space shuttle *Atlantis*, America's 100th crewed launch. The mission of *Atlantis* involved, among other studies, a rendezvous and docking with space station *Mir*. The cooperation that existed on this mission continued through

Figure 20-12 The proposed International Space Station is scheduled for completion in 2003.

eight more space shuttle-*Mir* docking missions. Each was an important step toward building and operating the International Space Station.

The International Space Station

The International Space Station (ISS) will be a permanent laboratory designed to use in long-term research. Diverse topics will be studied, such as researching the growth of protein crystals. This project will help scientists determine protein structure and function. This could enhance work on drug design and the treatment of diseases.

The space station will draw on the resources of more than 16 nations. Various nations will build units for the space station, which will then be transported into space aboard the space shuttle and Russian launch rockets. The station will be constructed in space. **Figure 20-12** shows what the completed station will look like. ☑

NASA is planning the space station program in three phases. Phase One, now concluded, involved the space shuttle-*Mir* docking missions. Phase Two began in 1998 with the launch of the Russian-built Functional Cargo Block, and will end with the delivery of a U.S. laboratory aboard the space shuttle. During Phase Two, a crew of three people will be delivered to the space station. This is expected to occur by January 2000.

Reading Check ☑

How many nations are involved in the space station program?

Figure 20-13 Using the space shuttle, scientists have already performed extensive experiments in the weightlessness of space.

Living in Space

The project will continue with Phase Three when the Japanese Experiment Module, the European Columbus Orbiting Facility, and another Russian lab will be delivered.

The U.S. hopes to deliver its Habitation module in 2003, although this date may be delayed. This will end Phase Three and make the International Space Station fully operational and ready for its permanent six- or seven-person crew. A total of 45 separate launches are required to take all components of ISS into space. NASA plans for crews of astronauts to stay on board the station for several months at a time. As shown in **Figure 20-13,** NASA has already conducted numerous tests to prepare astronauts for extended space missions. One day, the station could be a construction site for ships that will go to the moon and Mars.

Exploring Mars

Two of the most successful missions in recent years were the 1996 launchings of the Mars *Global Surveyor* and Mars *Pathfinder*. *Surveyor* orbited Mars, taking high-quality photos of the planet's surface. *Pathfinder* descended to the Martian surface, using rockets and a parachute system to slow its descent. Large balloons were used to absorb the shock of landing. *Pathfinder* carried technology to study the surface of the planet, including a remote-controlled robot rover called *Sojourner.* Using information gathered by the rover and photographs taken by *Surveyor*, scientists determined that areas of the planet's surface were once covered with water during Mars's distant past.

Exploring the Moon

Does water exist in the craters of the moon's poles? This is one question NASA intends to explore with data gathered from the *Lunar Prospector* spacecraft. Launched in 1998, the *Lunar Prospector's* one-year mission was to orbit the moon, taking photographs of the moon's surface for mapping purposes. Early data obtained from the spacecraft indicate that hydrogen is present in the rocks of the moon's poles. Hydrogen is one of the elements found in water. Scientists now theorize that ice on the floors of the moon's polar craters may be the source of this hydrogen.

Cassini

In October 1997, NASA launched the space probe *Cassini.* Destination: Saturn. *Cassini* will not reach its goal until 2004. At that time, the space probe will explore Saturn and surrounding areas for four years. One part of its mission is to deliver the European Space Agency's *Huygens* probe to Saturn's largest moon, Titan, as shown in **Figure 20-14.** Some scientists theorize that Titan's atmosphere may be similar to the atmosphere of early Earth.

Figure 20-14 *Cassini* will reach Saturn in 2004.

Section Assessment

1. What is the main advantage of the space shuttle?
2. Why were the space shuttle-*Mir* docking missions so important?
3. Describe Phase Three of the International Space Station program.
4. Recent space missions have been characterized by a spirit of cooperation. How does this compare and contrast with early space missions?
5. **Think Critically:** Why is the space shuttle more versatile than earlier spacecraft?
6. **Skill Builder**
   Making and Using Graphs *Lunar Prospector* was placed in lunar orbit to photograph the moon's surface. Do the **Chapter 20 Skill Activity** on page 761 to learn more about satellites placed in orbit around Earth.

Science Journal
Suppose you're in charge of assembling a crew for a new space station. Select 50 people you want for the station. Remember, you will need people to do a variety of jobs, such as farming, maintenance, scientific experimentation, and so on. In your Science Journal, explain whom you would select and why.

For a **preview** of this chapter, study this Reviewing Main Ideas before you read the chapter. After you have studied this chapter, you can use the Reviewing Main Ideas to **review** the chapter.

The Glencoe MindJogger, Audiocassettes, and CD-ROM provide additional opportunities for review.

Section

20-1 RADIATION FROM SPACE

Electromagnetic waves are arranged in the electromagnetic spectrum according to their wavelengths. Optical telescopes produce magnified images of objects. A **refracting telescope** bends light to form an image. A **reflecting telescope** uses mirrors to focus light to produce an image. **Radio telescopes** collect and record radio waves given off by some space objects. *Why can radio telescopes be used during the day or night and in all types of weather?*

Section

20-2 EARLY SPACE MISSIONS

A **satellite** is an object that revolves around another object. The moons of planets are natural satellites. Artificial satellites are those made by people. An artificial satellite collects data as it **orbits** a planet. A **space probe** travels into the solar system, gathers data, and sends the information back to Earth. Some space probes become artificial satellites of the planet or other object they are sent to study. *Why can the Galileo spacecraft be referred to both as a probe and as an artificial satellite of Jupiter?*

Reading Check ✓

Review the space missions discussed in the chapter. Then, create a timeline that shows these discoveries in chronological order.

Section

20-3 RECENT AND FUTURE SPACE MISSIONS

The **space shuttle** is a reusable spacecraft that carries astronauts, satellites, and other equipment to and from space. **Space stations,** such as *Mir* and *Skylab,* provide the opportunity to conduct research not possible on Earth. The International Space Station will be constructed in Earth orbit with the cooperation of 16 different nations. Completion of the ISS should occur in the year 2003, if all goes as planned. *What advantage does the space shuttle have over other launch vehicles?*

Chapter 20 Assessment

Using Vocabulary

a. electromagnetic spectrum
b. observatory
c. orbit
d. Project Apollo
e. Project Gemini
f. Project Mercury
g. radio telescope
h. reflecting telescope
i. refracting telescope
j. satellite
k. space probe
l. space shuttle
m. space station

The sentences below include italicized terms that have been used incorrectly. Change the incorrect terms so that the sentences read correctly. Underline your change.

1. A *reflecting telescope* uses lenses to bend light toward a focal point.
2. A *space probe* is an object that revolves around another object.
3. *Project Apollo* was the first piloted U.S. space program.
4. A *space station* carries people and tools to and from space.
5. In an *observatory*, electromagnetic waves are arranged according to their wavelengths.

Checking Concepts

Choose the word or phrase that best answers the question.

6. Which spacecraft has sent back images of Venus?
   A) *Voyager*   C) *Apollo 11*
   B) *Viking*   D) *Magellan*
7. Which telescope uses mirrors to collect light?
   A) radio   C) refracting
   B) electromagnetic D) reflecting
8. *Sputnik I* was the first what?
   A) telescope   C) observatory
   B) artificial satellite D) U.S. space probe

9. Which telescope can be used during day or night and during bad weather?
   A) radio   C) refracting
   B) electromagnetic D) reflecting
10. When fully operational, the International Space Station will be crewed by up to how many people?
    A) 3   C) 15
    B) 7   D) 50
11. Which space mission had the goal to put a spacecraft in orbit and bring it back safely?
    A) Project Mercury C) Project Gemini
    B) Project Apollo   D) *Viking I*
12. The space shuttle reuses which of the following?
    A) liquid-fuel tanks C) booster engines
    B) *Gemini* rockets   D) *Saturn* rockets
13. What does the space shuttle use to place a satellite into space?
    A) liquid-fuel tank C) mechanical arm
    B) booster rocket   D) cargo bay
14. What was *Skylab?*
    A) space probe   C) space shuttle
    B) space station D) optical telescope
15. Which of the following is a natural satellite of Earth?
    A) *Skylab*   C) the sun
    B) the space shuttle D) the moon

Thinking Critically

16. How would a moon-based telescope have advantages over the Earth-based telescopes being used today?
17. Would a space probe to the sun's surface be useful? Explain.
18. Which would you choose—space missions with people aboard or robotic space probes? Why?

19. Suppose two astronauts were outside the space shuttle, orbiting Earth. The audio speaker in the helmet of one astronaut quits working. The other astronaut is 1 m away, so she shouts a message to him. Can he hear her? Explain.

20. No space probes have visited the planet Pluto. Nevertheless, probes have crossed Pluto's orbit. How?

Developing Skills

If you need help, refer to the Skill Handbook.

21. Measuring in SI: Explain whether or not the following pieces of equipment could be used aboard the space shuttle as it orbits Earth: a balance, a meterstick, and a thermometer.

22. Making and Using Tables: Copy the table below. Use information in the chapter as well as news articles and other resources to complete your table.

U.S. Space Probes			
Probe	Launch Date	Destinations	Planets or Objects Visited
Vikings 1 & 2			
Galileo			
Lunar Prospector			
Mars Pathfinder & Sojourner			

23. Classifying: Classify the following as a satellite or a space probe: *Cassini, Sputnik I, Hubble Space Telescope, space shuttle,* and *Voyager 2.*

THE PRINCETON REVIEW

Test-Taking Tip

Best Times If your test is going to be timed, then practice under timed conditions. Try timing yourself on specific sections to see if you can improve your overall speed while maintaining accuracy.

Test Practice

Use these questions to test your Science Proficiency.

1. Large telescopes are usually reflectors. Which of the following statements **BEST** explains why this is true?
A) Reflecting telescopes are easier to use and carry around.
B) Reflecting telescopes have greater magnifying power.
C) Reflecting telescopes are less expensive to build and maintain.
D) In reflecting telescopes, the objective mirror can be supported from beneath and, therefore, can be made larger.

2. The *Lunar Prospector* was classified as a space probe when launched but is now classified as a satellite. What does this illustrate about this spacecraft's flight?
A) The *Lunar Prospector* is in orbit around Earth.
B) The *Lunar Prospector* was a space probe on its flight to the moon and became a satellite when it went into orbit around the moon.
C) The *Lunar Prospector* is moving out of our solar system.
D) The *Lunar Prospector* was launched from Earth, went into orbit around the moon, and landed on the moon.

CHAPTER

21 The Sun-Earth-Moon System

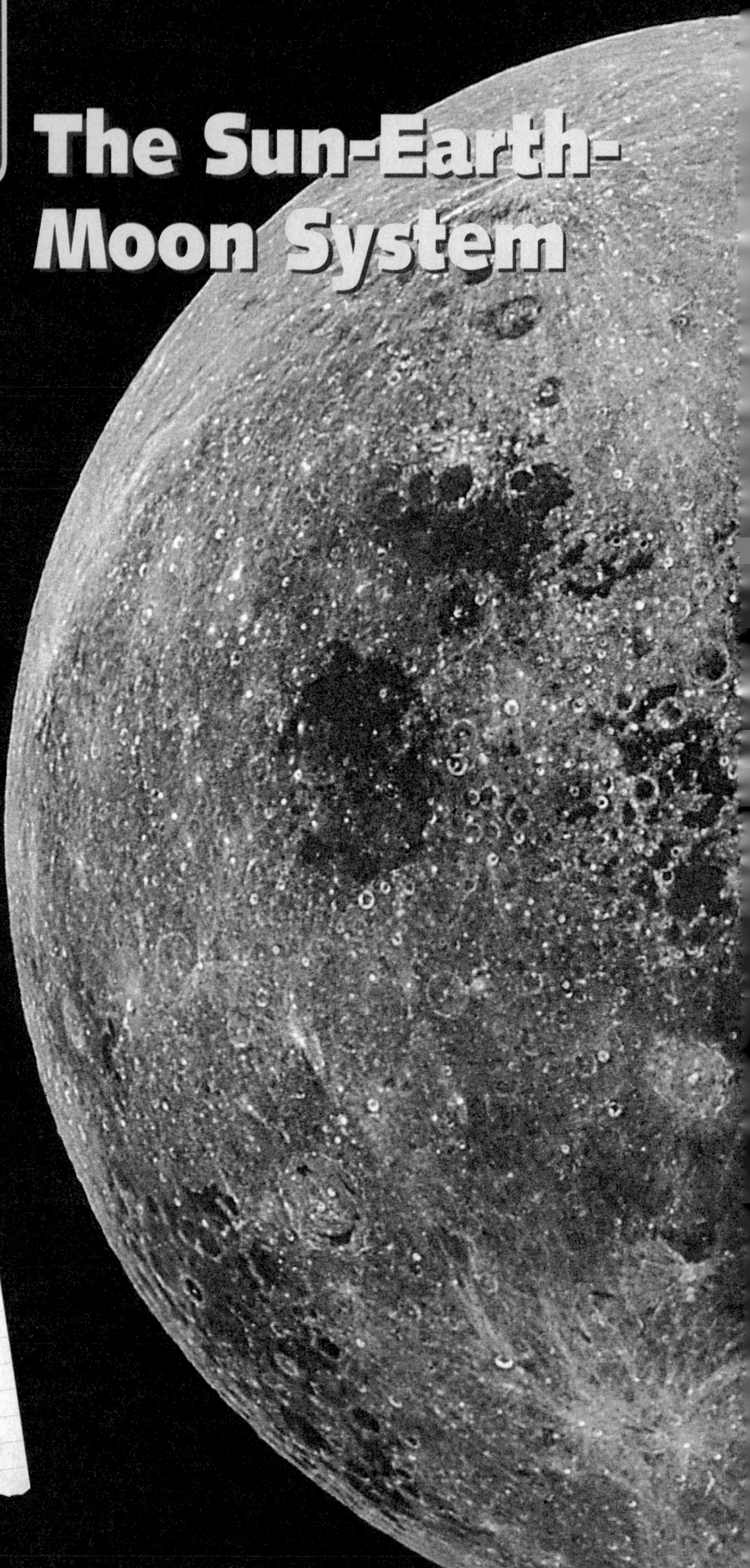

Chapter Preview

Skills Preview

Skill Builders

- Sequence

Activities

- Make a Model
- Interpret Data

MiniLabs

- Compare and Contrast
- Use Numbers

Reading Check ✔

As you read about the phases of the moon and other topics in this chapter, write down the signal words that indicate a sequence, such as *shortly after* and *just before.*

Explore Activity

Earth, the moon, and the sun are constantly moving through space. That's why one night you may see a shining full moon and weeks later see no moon at all. Is the appearance of the moon the only thing that changes because of these movements? No, seasons change, too, because of Earth's tilted axis as it moves around the sun. Let's explore how this happens.

Model Seasons

1. Use a lamp without a shade to represent the sun.

2. Turn on the lamp and hold a globe of Earth about 2 m from the lamp.

3. Tilt the globe slightly so the northern half points toward the sun.

4. Keeping the globe tilted in the same direction, walk halfway around the sun. Be careful not to turn or twist the globe as you walk.

Science Journal

In which direction is the northern hemisphere pointing relative to the sun in step 3? In step 4? In your Science Journal, describe which seasons these positions represent for the northern hemisphere.

Planet Earth Data

You rise early in the morning, while it's still dark outside. You sit by the window and watch the sun come up. Finally, day breaks, and the sun begins its journey across the sky. But, is the sun moving, or are you?

Today, we know that the sun appears to move across the sky because Earth is spinning as it travels around the sun. But, it wasn't long ago that people believed Earth was the center of the universe. They believed Earth stood still and the sun traveled around it.

As recently as the days of Christopher Columbus, some people also believed Earth was flat. They thought that if you sailed far out to sea, you eventually would fall off the edge of the world. How do you know this isn't true? How have scientists determined Earth's shape?

Earth's Shape

Space probes and artificial satellites have sent back images that show Earth is sphere-shaped. A **sphere** (SFIHR) is a round, three-dimensional object. Its surface at all points is the same distance from its center. Tennis balls and basketballs are examples of spheres. But, people had evidence of Earth's true shape long before cameras were sent into space.

Around 350 B.C., the Greek astronomer and philosopher Aristotle reasoned that Earth was spherical because it always casts a round shadow on the moon during an eclipse, as shown in **Figure 21-1.** Only a spherical object always produces a round shadow. If Earth were flat, it would cast a straight shadow.

Other evidence of Earth's shape was observed by early sailors. They watched as ships approached from across the ocean and saw that the top of the ship would come into view first. As they continued to watch the ship, more and more of it

Figure 21-1 If Earth were flat, its shadow during an eclipse would be straight on the moon, not curved, as shown.

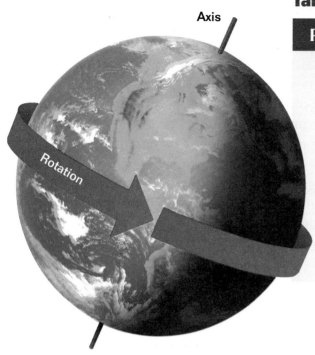

Axis

Rotation

Table 21-1

Physical Properties of Earth	
Diameter (pole to pole)	12 714 km
Diameter (equator)	12 756 km
Circumference (poles)	40 008 km
Circumference (equator)	40 075 km
Mass	5.98×10^{27} g
Density	5.52 g/cm^3
Average distance to the sun	149 600 000 km
Period of rotation (1 day)	23 hr, 56 min
Period of revolution (1 year)	365 days, 6 hr, 9 min

would appear until they could see all of it. This was possible only if Earth was a sphere.

Today, we know that Earth is sphere-shaped, but it is not a perfect sphere. It bulges slightly at the equator and is some-what flattened at the poles. The poles are located at the north and south ends of Earth's axis. Earth's **axis** is the imaginary line around which Earth spins. The spin-ning of Earth on its axis, called **rotation,** causes day and night to occur.

Earth's Rotation

As Earth rotates, the sun comes into view at daybreak. Earth continues to spin, mak-ing it seem as if the sun moves across the sky until it sets at night. During night, your area of Earth has spun away from the sun. Because of this, the sun is no longer visible. Earth continues to rotate steadily, and the sun eventually comes into view the next morning. One complete rotation takes about 24 hours, or one day. How many rotations does Earth complete during one year? As you can see in **Table 21-1,** it com-pletes about 365 rotations during its jour-ney around the sun.

Try at Home

Mini Lab

Comparing Spheres

Procedure

1. Use a long piece of string to measure the circumference of a basketball or volleyball.
2. Measure the circumference of the ball at a right angle to your first measurement.
3. Determine the roundness ratio by dividing the larger measurement by the smaller one.
4. Compare these data with the roundness ratio data about Earth's circumference provided in **Table 21-1.**

Analysis

1. How round is Earth compared with the ball?
2. Is Earth larger through the equator or through the poles?
3. Explain how your observations support your answer.

Earth's Magnetic Field

Convection currents inside Earth's mantle power the movement of tectonic plates. Scientists hypothesize that movement of material inside Earth along with Earth's rotation generates a magnetic field, as shown in **Figure 21-2.**

The magnetic field of Earth is much like that of a bar magnet. Earth has a north and a south magnetic pole, just as a bar magnet has opposite magnetic poles at its ends. **Figure 21-3** illustrates the effects of sprinkling iron shavings over a bar magnet. The shavings align with the magnetic field of the magnet. Earth's magnetic field is similar, almost as if Earth had a giant bar magnet in its core.

Magnetic North

When you observe a compass needle pointing toward the north, you are seeing evidence of Earth's magnetic field. Earth's magnetic axis, the line joining its north and south magnetic poles, does not align with its rotational axis. The magnetic axis is inclined at an angle of 11.5° to the rotational axis. If you followed a compass needle pointing north, you would end up at the magnetic north pole rather than the geographic (rotational) north pole.

Earth's magnetic field and other physical properties affect us every day. What occurrences can you explain in terms of Earth's physical properties and movement in space?

Figure 21-2 Heat and pressure within Earth cause the liquid outer core to move continuously. Driven by Earth's rotation and convection currents deep within Earth, the molten liquid forms spiraling columns. These spirals generate mechanical energy, which in turn generates electricity that creates the magnetic field.

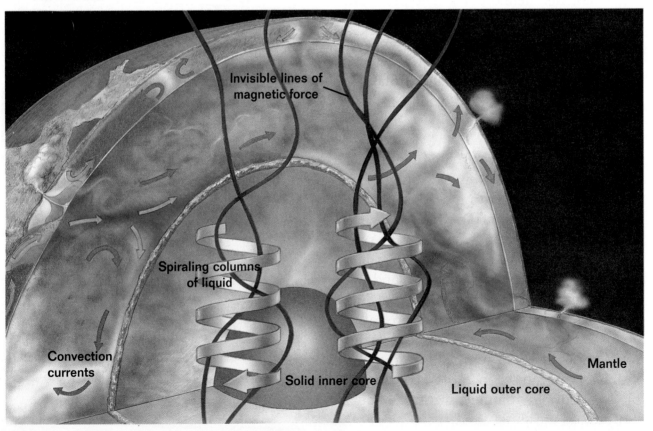

Invisible lines of magnetic force

Spiraling columns of liquid

Convection currents

Solid inner core

Liquid outer core

Mantle

Figure 21-3 Particles in the solar wind streaming through space from the sun distort Earth's magnetic field. As a result, Earth's magnetic field isn't symmetrical. It doesn't have the same shape as a magnetic field surrounding a bar magnet, which is symmetrical.

Seasons

Autumn is coming, and each day it gets colder outside. Dawn comes later each morning, and the sun appears lower in the sky. A month ago, it was light enough to ride your bike at 8:00 P.M. Now, it's dark at 8:00 P.M. What is causing this change?

Earth's Revolution

You learned earlier that Earth's rotation causes day and night. Another important motion of Earth is its **revolution,** or yearly orbit around the sun. Just as the moon is a satellite of Earth, Earth is a satellite of the sun. If Earth's orbit were a circle and the sun were at the center of the circle, Earth would maintain a constant distance from the sun. However, this is not the case. Earth's orbit is an **ellipse** (ee LIHPS), which is an elongated, closed curve. As **Figure 21-4** shows, the sun is offset from the center of the ellipse. Because of this, the distance between Earth and the sun changes during Earth's yearlong orbit. Earth gets closest to the sun—about 147 million km away—around January 3. The farthest point in Earth's orbit is about 152 million km away from the sun and is reached around July 4. ✔

Does this elliptical orbit cause seasonal temperatures on Earth? If it did, you would expect the warmest days in January. You know this isn't the case in the northern hemisphere. Something else causes the change.

Even though Earth is closest to the sun in January, the overall amount of energy Earth receives from the sun changes little throughout the year. However, the amount of energy any one place on Earth receives can vary greatly.

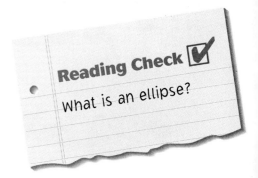

Reading Check ✔

What is an ellipse?

Figure 21-4 The northern hemisphere experiences summer when Earth is farthest from the sun. It experiences winter when Earth is closest to the sun. **Is the change of seasons caused by Earth's elliptical orbit? Explain your answer.**

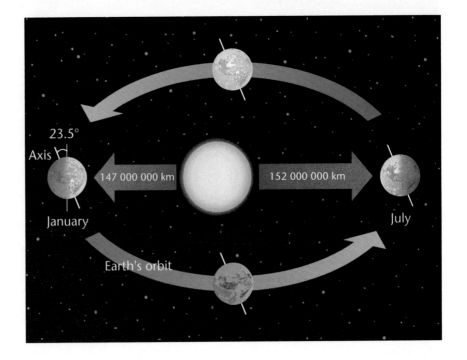

Earth's Tilted Axis

Earth's axis is tilted 23.5° from a line perpendicular to its orbit. This tilt causes the seasons. Daylight hours are longer for the hemisphere tilted toward the sun. Think of how early it gets dark in the winter compared to the summer. As shown in **Figure 21-4,** the hemisphere tilted toward the sun receives more hours of sunlight than the hemisphere tilted away from the sun.

Earth's tilt also causes the sun's radiation to strike the hemisphere tilted toward it at a higher angle than it does the other hemisphere. Because of this, the hemisphere tilted toward the sun receives more electromagnetic radiation per unit area than the hemisphere tilted away. In other words, if you measured the amount of radiation received in a 1-km^2 area in the northern hemisphere and, at the same time, measured it for 1 km^2 in the southern hemisphere, you would find a difference. The hemisphere tilted toward the sun would be receiving more energy.

A summer season results when the sun's electromagnetic radiation strikes Earth at a higher angle. Just the opposite occurs during winter. **Figure 21-5** shows scenes from winter and summer.

Figure 21-5 Temperatures during summer are warmer than those during winter. **Why?**

Equinoxes and Solstices

Because of the tilt of Earth's axis, the sun's position relative to Earth's equator constantly changes. Most of the time, the sun is north or south of the equator. Two times during the year, however, the sun is directly over the equator.

Equinox

Look at **Figure 21-6.** When the sun reaches an **equinox** (EE kwuh nahks), it is directly above Earth's equator, and the number of daylight hours equals the number of nighttime hours all over the world. At that time, neither the northern nor the southern hemisphere is tilted toward the sun. In the northern hemisphere, the sun reaches the spring equinox on March 20 or 21 and the fall equinox on September 22 or 23. In the southern hemisphere, the equinoxes are reversed. Spring occurs in September and fall occurs in March.

Solstice

The **solstice** is the point at which the sun reaches its greatest distance north or south of the equator. In the northern hemisphere, the sun reaches the summer solstice on June 21 or 22, and the winter solstice occurs on December 21 or 22. Just the opposite is true for the southern hemisphere. When the sun is at the summer solstice, there are more daylight

*inter***NET**
CONNECTION

Visit the Glencoe Science Web Site at **www.glencoe.com/ sec/science** for more information about seasons.

Figure 21-6 At summer solstice in the northern hemisphere, the sun is directly over the Tropic of Cancer, 23.5° north latitude at noon. At winter solstice, the sun is directly over the Tropic of Capricorn, 23.5° south latitude at noon. At both fall and spring equinoxes, the sun is directly over the equator at noon.

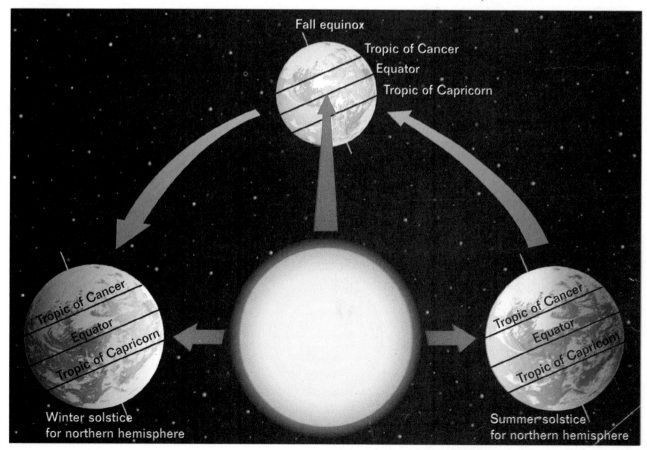

hours than during any other day of the year. When it's at the winter solstice, on the shortest day of the year, the most nighttime hours occur.

Earth Data Review

Earth, shown in **Figure 21-7,** is an imperfect sphere that bulges very slightly at the equator and is somewhat flattened at the poles. The rotation of Earth causes day and night. Earth's tilted axis is responsible for the seasons you experience, and our revolution around the sun marks the passing of a year. In the next section, you will read how Earth's nearest neighbor, the moon, is also in constant motion and how you observe this motion each day.

Figure 21-7 In this photo, Earth appears to be nearly a perfect sphere. In reality, its diameter is 42 km larger at the equator than at the poles.

Section Assessment

1. Which Earth motion causes night and day?
2. Why does summer occur in Earth's northern hemisphere when Earth's north pole is tilted toward the sun?
3. **Think Critically: Table 21–1** lists Earth's distance from the sun as an average. Why isn't there one exact measurement of this distance?
4. **Skill Builder**
   Recognizing Cause and Effect
   Answer these questions about the sun-Earth-moon relationship. If you need help, refer to Recognizing Cause and Effect in the **Skill Handbook** on page 721.
   a. What causes seasons on Earth?
   b. What causes winter?
   c. Earth is closest to the sun in January. What effect does this have on seasons?

Using Computers

Spreadsheet Using the table or spreadsheet capabilities of a computer program, generate a table of Earth's physical data showing its diameter, mass, period of rotation, and other data. Then, write a description of the planet based on the table you have created. If you need help, refer to page 738.

A Brave and Startling Truth
by Maya Angelou

In this chapter, you have learned some of the physical characteristics of our planet. Now, find out how one poet, Maya Angelou, uses Earth-science imagery to describe the human race and the quest for world peace. Below are several excerpts, or parts, from her poem "A Brave and Startling Truth."

We, this people, on a small and lonely planet
Traveling through casual space
Past aloof stars, across the way of indifferent suns
To a destination where all signs tell us
It is possible and imperative that we learn
A brave and startling truth...

When we come to it
Then we will confess that not the Pyramids
With their stones set in mysterious perfection
Nor the Gardens of Babylon
Hanging as eternal beauty
In our collective memory
Not the Grand Canyon
Kindled into delicious color
By Western sunsets
These are not the only wonders of the world...

When we come to it
We, this people, on this wayward, floating body
Created on this earth, of this earth
Have the power to fashion for this earth
A climate where every man and every woman
Can live freely without sanctimonious piety
And without crippling fear

When we come to it
We must confess that we are the possible
We are the miraculous, the true wonder of this world
That is when, and only when
We come to it.

interNET CONNECTION

Visit the Glencoe Science Web Site at **www.glencoe.com/sec/ science** to learn more about Maya Angelou and her works. Do her other books and poems also contain Earth-science imagery? Using your knowledge of Earth science, write a short poem that uses Earth-science imagery to describe a social issue important to you.

Tilt and Temperature

Possible Materials

- Tape
- Black construction paper (one sheet)
- Gooseneck lamp with 75-watt bulb
- Celsius thermometer
- Watch
- Protractor

Have you ever noticed how hot the surface of a blacktop driveway can get during the day? The sun's rays hit Earth more directly as the day progresses. Now, consider the fact that Earth is tilted on its axis. How does this affect the amount of heat an area on Earth receives from the sun?

Recognize the Problem

How is the angle at which light strikes an area on Earth related to the changing of the seasons?

Form a Hypothesis

State a hypothesis about how the angle at which light strikes an area affects the amount of heat energy received by that area.

Goals

- **Measure** the amount of heat generated by a light as it strikes a surface at different angles.

- **Describe** how light striking a surface at different angles is related to the changing of the seasons on Earth.

Safety Precautions

Do not touch the lamp without safety gloves. The lightbulb and shade can be hot even when the lamp has been turned off. Handle the thermometer carefully. If it breaks, do not touch anything. Inform your teacher immediately.

Test Your Hypothesis

Plan

1. As a group, agree upon and write out your hypothesis statement.

2. As a group, **list the steps** you need to take to test your hypothesis. Be specific, describing exactly what you will do at each step. List your materials.

3. **Make a list** of any special properties you expect to observe or test.

4. Read over your entire experiment to make sure that all steps are in a logical order.

5. **Identify** any constants, variables, and controls in the experiment.

6. Will you **summarize** data in a graph, table, or some other format?

7. How will you **determine** whether the length of time the light is turned on affects heat energy?

8. How will you **determine** whether the angle at which light strikes an area causes changes in heat and energy?

Do

1. Make sure your teacher approves your plan before you proceed.

2. **Carry out** the experiment as planned.

3. **Complete** the data table in your Science Journal.

Analyze Your Data

1. **Describe** your experiment, including how you used independent variables to test your hypothesis.

2. What happened to the temperature of the area being measured as you modified your variables?

3. **Identify** the dependent variable in your experiment.

Draw Conclusions

1. Did your experiment support your hypothesis? **Explain.**

2. If not, **determine** how you might change the experiment in order to retest your hypothesis. How might you change your hypothesis?

21·2 Earth's Moon

Motions of the Moon

You have probably noticed how the moon's apparent shape changes from day to day. Sometimes, just after sunset, you can see a full, round moon low in the sky. Other times, only half of the moon is visible, and it's high in the sky at sunset. Sometimes, the moon is visible during the day. Why does the moon look the way it does? What causes it to change its appearance and position in the sky?

The Moon's Rotation and Revolution

Just as Earth rotates on its axis and revolves around the sun, the moon rotates on its axis and revolves around Earth. The moon's revolution causes changes in its appearance. If the moon rotates on its axis, why don't we see it spin around in space? The moon rotates on its axis once every 27.3 days. It takes the same amount of time to revolve once around Earth. As **Figure 21-8** shows, because these two motions take the same amount of time, the same side of the moon always faces Earth.

What **You'll Learn**

► How the moon's phases depend on the relative positions of the sun, the moon, and Earth

► Why eclipses occur and how solar and lunar eclipses compare

► What the surface features of the moon may tell us about its history

Vocabulary

moon phase	waning
new moon	third quarter
waxing	solar eclipse
first quarter	lunar eclipse
full moon	maria

Why **It's Important**

► The moon is our closest neighbor in space.

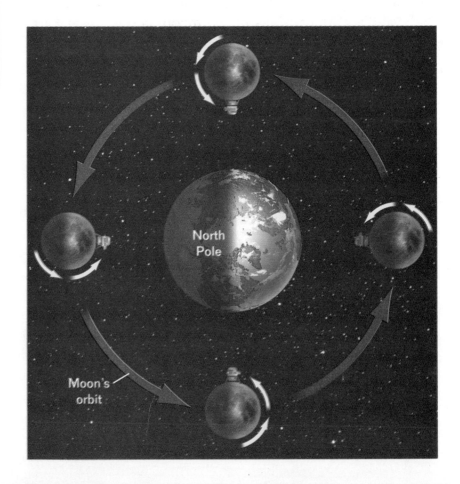

Figure 21-8 In about one month, the moon orbits Earth. It also completes one rotation on its axis during the same period. **Does this affect which side of the moon faces Earth? Explain.**

You can show this by having a friend hold a ball in front of you. Instruct your friend to move the ball around you while keeping the same side of it facing you. Everyone else in the room will see all sides of the ball. You will see only one side.

Why the Moon Shines

The moon shines because it reflects sunlight from its surface. Just as half of Earth experiences day as the other half experiences night, half of the moon is lighted while the other half is dark. As the moon revolves around Earth, you see different portions of its lighted side, causing the moon's appearance to change. **Moon phases,** as shown in **Figure 21-9,** are the changing appearances of the moon as seen from Earth. The phase you see depends on the relative positions of the moon, Earth, and the sun.

Phases of the Moon

A new moon occurs when the moon is between Earth and the sun. During a **new moon,** the lighted half of the moon is facing the sun and the dark side faces Earth. The moon is in the sky, but it cannot be seen.

Waxing Phases

Shortly after a new moon, more and more of the moon's lighted side becomes visible—the phases are **waxing.** About 24 hours after a new moon, you can see a thin slice of the side of the moon that is lighted by the sun. This phase is called the waxing crescent. About a week after a new moon, you can see half of the lighted side, or one-quarter of the moon's surface. This phase is **first quarter.**

The phases continue to wax. When more than one-quarter is visible, it is called waxing gibbous. A **full moon** occurs when all of the moon's surface that faces Earth is lit up.

Figure 21-9 The phases of the moon are: (A) new moon, (B) waxing crescent, (C) first quarter, (D) waxing gibbous, (E) full moon, (F) waning gibbous, (G) third quarter, and (H) waning crescent.

Using Math

Earth rotates through an angle of 360° in one day. How many degrees does Earth rotate in one hour?

Mini Lab

Comparing the Sun and Moon

Procedure

1. Find an area where you can make a chalk mark on pavement or another surface.
2. Tie a piece of chalk to one end of a string that's 400 cm long.
3. Hold the other end of the string to the pavement.
4. Have a friend pull the string tight and walk around you, leaving a mark on the pavement as he or she circles you.
5. Draw a circle with a 1-cm diameter in the middle of the large circle.

Analysis

1. The small circle represents the moon, and the larger circle represents the sun. How big is the sun compared to the moon?
2. The diameter of the sun is 1.39 million km. The diameter of the Earth is 12 756 km. Draw two new circles modeling the sizes of the sun and Earth.
3. What are the diameters of your two new circles?

Figure 21-10 The orbit of the moon is not in the same plane as Earth's orbit around the sun. If it were, we would experience a solar eclipse each month during the new moon. The plane of the moon's orbit is tilted about 5° to the plane of Earth's orbit.

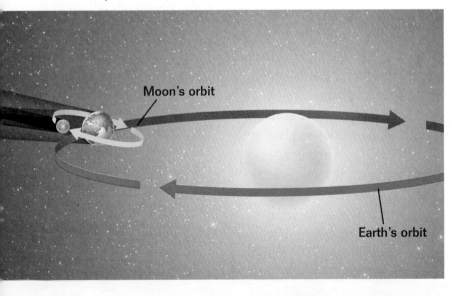

Moon's orbit

Earth's orbit

Waning Phases

After a full moon, the amount of the moon's lighted side that can be seen becomes smaller. The phases are said to be **waning.** Waning gibbous begins just after a full moon. When you can see only half of the lighted side, the **third-quarter** phase occurs. The amount of the moon that can be seen continues to become smaller. Waning crescent occurs just before another new moon. Once again, you can see a small slice of the lighted side of the moon.

The complete cycle of the moon's phases takes about 29.5 days. Recall that it takes about 27.3 days for the moon to revolve around Earth. The discrepancy between these two numbers is due to Earth's revolution. It takes the moon about two days to "catch up" with Earth's advancement around the sun.

Eclipses

Imagine yourself as one of your ancient ancestors, living 10 000 years ago. You are out foraging for nuts and other fruit in the bright afternoon sun. Gradually, the sun disappears from the sky, as if being swallowed by a giant creature. The darkness lasts only a short time, and the sun soon returns to full brightness. You realize something unusual has happened, but you don't know what caused it. It will be almost 8000 years before anyone can explain the event that you just experienced.

The event just described was a total solar eclipse (ih KLIPS). Today, we know what causes such eclipses, but for our early ancestors, they must have been terrifying events. Many animals act as if night has come. Cows return to their barns, and chickens go to sleep. What causes the day to suddenly change into night and then back into day?

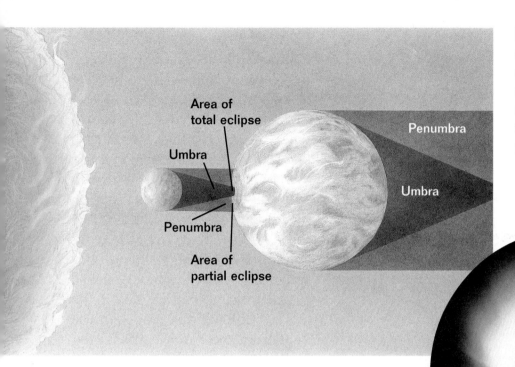

Area of
total eclipse

Umbra

Penumbra

Area of
partial eclipse

Penumbra

Umbra

Figure 21-11 Only a small area of Earth experiences a total solar eclipse during the eclipse event. Only the outer portion of the sun's atmosphere is visible during a total solar eclipse. Distances are not drawn to scale.

The Cause of Eclipses

Revolution of the moon causes eclipses. Eclipses occur when Earth or the moon temporarily blocks the sunlight reaching the other. Sometimes, during a new moon, a shadow cast by the moon falls on Earth and causes a solar eclipse. During a full moon, a shadow of Earth can be cast on the moon, resulting in a lunar eclipse.

Eclipses can occur only when the sun, the moon, and Earth are lined up perfectly. Look at **Figure 21-10.** Because the moon's orbit is not in the same plane as Earth's orbit around the sun, eclipses happen only a few times each year.

Solar Eclipses

A **solar eclipse,** such as the one in **Figure 21-11,** occurs when the moon moves directly between the sun and Earth and casts a shadow on part of Earth. The darkest portion of the moon's shadow is called the umbra (UM bruh). A person standing within the umbra experiences a total solar eclipse. The only portion of the sun that is visible is part of its atmosphere, which appears as a pearly white glow around the edge of the eclipsing moon.

Surrounding the umbra is a lighter shadow on Earth's surface called the penumbra (puh NUM bruh). Persons standing in the penumbra experience a partial solar eclipse. **CAUTION:** *Regardless of where you are standing, never look directly at a solar eclipse. The light can permanently damage your eyes.*

LIFE SCIENCE
INTEGRATION

Changing Seasons
Suppose that Earth's rotation took twice the time that it presently does. Write a report on how conditions such as global temperatures, work schedules, plant growth, and other factors might be different.

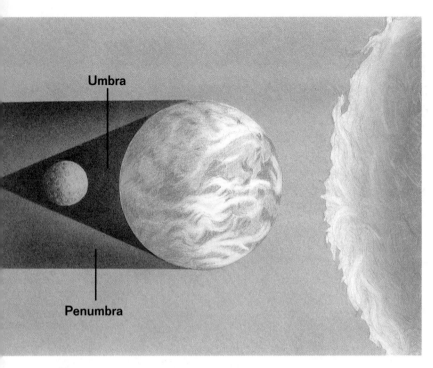

Lunar Eclipses

When Earth's shadow falls on the moon, a **lunar eclipse** like the one shown in **Figures 21-12** and **21-13** occurs. A lunar eclipse begins when the moon moves into Earth's penumbra. As the moon continues to move, it enters Earth's umbra and you see a curved shadow on the moon's surface. It was from this shadow that Aristotle concluded that Earth's shape was spherical. When the moon moves completely into Earth's umbra, the moon becomes dark red because light from the sun is refracted by Earth's atmosphere onto the moon. A total lunar eclipse has occurred.

Figure 21-12 During a total lunar eclipse, Earth's shadow blocks light coming from the sun.

A partial lunar eclipse occurs when only a portion of the moon moves into Earth's umbra. The remainder of the moon is in Earth's penumbra and, therefore, receives some direct sunlight.

A total solar eclipse occurs up to two times every year, yet most people live their entire lives without witnessing one. You may not be lucky enough to see a total solar eclipse, but it is almost certain you will have a chance to see a total lunar eclipse in your lifetime. The reason it is so difficult to view a total solar eclipse is that only those people in the small region where the moon's umbra strikes Earth can witness one. In contrast, anyone on the nighttime side of Earth can see a total lunar eclipse.

Figure 21-13 These photographs show the moon moving from right to left into Earth's umbra, then out again.

Structure of the Moon

When you look at the moon, you can see many of its larger surface features. The dark-colored, relatively flat regions are called **maria.** Maria formed when ancient lava flows from the moon's interior filled large basins on the moon's surface. The basins formed early in the moon's history.

Craters

Many depressions on the moon were formed by meteorites, asteroids, and comets, which strike the surfaces of planets and their satellites. These depressions are called craters. During impact, cracks may have formed in the moon's crust, allowing lava to reach the surface and fill in the large craters, forming maria. The igneous rocks of the maria are 3 to 4 billion years old. They are the youngest rocks found on the moon thus far.

The Moon's Interior

Seismographs left on the moon by *Apollo* astronauts have enabled scientists to study moonquakes. The study of earthquakes allows scientists to map Earth's interior. Likewise, the study of moonquakes has led to a model of the moon's interior. One model of the moon shows that its crust is about 60 km thick on the side facing Earth and about 150 km thick on the far side. Below the crust, a solid mantle may extend to a depth of 1000 km. A partly molten zone of the mantle extends farther down. Below this may be an iron-rich, solid core.

*inter*NET
CONNECTION

Visit the Glencoe Science Web Site at **www.glencoe.com/ sec/science** to learn more about the *Apollo* space missions.

Problem Solving

Survival on the Moon

You and your crew have crash-landed on the moon, far from your intended landing site at the moon colony. It will take one day to reach the colony on foot. The side of the moon that you are on will be facing away from the sun during your entire trip back. You manage to salvage the following items from your wrecked ship: food, rope, solar-powered heating unit, battery-operated heating unit, three 70-kg oxygen tanks, map of the constellations, magnetic compass, oxygen-burning signal flares, matches, 8 L of water, solar-powered radio receiver and transmitter, three flashlights and extra batteries, signal mirror, and binoculars. Keep in mind that the moon's gravity is about one-sixth that of Earth's, and it lacks a magnetic field. Determine which items will be of no use to you. Determine which items to take with you on your journey to the colony.

Think Critically: Based on what you have learned about the moon, describe why each of the salvaged items is useful or not useful.

1. How did the moon's physical properties affect your decisions?

2. How did the lack of sunlight affect your decisions?

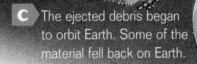
A The impact theory states that the moon was formed around 4.6 billion years ago when a Mars-sized object collided with Earth.

B The intense heat and pressure of the blast melted part of Earth's mantle and the impacting object. Materials from both bodies were ejected into space, including molten iron from the core of the impacting object.

C The ejected debris began to orbit Earth. Some of the material fell back on Earth.

VISUALIZING
Moon Formation

Figure 21-14 Evidence suggests that the impact theory may be the best explanation of the moon's origin.

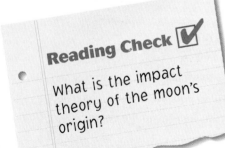

Reading Check

What is the impact theory of the moon's origin?

Origin of the Moon

Prior to the data obtained from the *Apollo* space missions, there were three theories about the moon's origin. The first was that the moon was captured by Earth's gravity. It had formed elsewhere and wandered into Earth's vicinity. The second theory was that the moon condensed from loose material surrounding Earth during the early formation of the solar system. The last theory was that a blob of molten material was ejected from Earth while Earth was still in its early molten stage.

Impact Theory

The data gathered by the *Apollo* missions have led many scientists to support a new impact theory. According to the impact theory, the moon was formed about 4.6 billion years ago when a Mars-sized object collided with Earth, throwing gas and debris into orbit. The gas and debris then condensed into one large mass, forming the moon. **Figure 21-14** illustrates the impact theory. ✔

Regardless of the moon's true origin, it has played an important role in our history. It was a source of curiosity for many early astronomers. Studying the phases of the moon and eclipses led people to conclude that Earth and the moon were in motion around the sun. Earth's shadow on the moon proved that Earth's shape was spherical. When Galileo first turned his telescope to the moon, he found a surface scarred by craters

E Within roughly 100 years, particles from the ring began to join together, eventually forming the moon. Some particles fell to Earth.

D The remaining material in orbit formed a ring of hot dust and gas around Earth. This began to occur only a few hours after impact.

F Over the course of many years, the moon spiraled out to its present position.

and maria. Before that time, many people believed that all planetary bodies were perfect, without surface features.

By studying the moon, we can learn about ourselves and the planet we live on. As you will read in the next section, not only is the moon important as an object from our past, but it is important to our future, as well.

Section Assessment

1. What are the relative positions of the sun, the moon, and Earth during a full moon?

2. Why does a lunar eclipse occur only during a full moon?

3. Compare and contrast umbra and penumbra.

4. **Think Critically:** What provides the force necessary to form craters on the moon?

5. **Skill Builder**
   Interpreting Scientific Illustrations By tracking the changing positions of the sun, Earth, and the moon, scientists can predict solar eclipses. Do the **Chapter 21 Skill Activity** on page 762 to see when and where future solar eclipses will occur.

Science Journal
Research the moon's origin in astronomy books and magazines. In your Science Journal, write a report about the various theories, including the theory about a Mars-sized object colliding with Earth. Make a drawing of each theory.

Early Moon Missions

For centuries, astronomers have studied the moon for clues to its makeup and origin. In 1958, the former Soviet Union took studies of the moon into space with the launching of the *Luna* spacecraft. Three years later, the United States launched the first *Ranger* spacecraft, beginning its own lunar space exploration program.

Early U.S. moon missions, such as those involving the uncrewed *Ranger* and later the *Lunar Orbiter* spacecraft, focused on taking detailed photographs of the moon's surface. The *Lunar Orbiter* missions were followed by the *Surveyor* missions, wherein seven *Surveyor* spacecraft landed on the moon in preparation for the ultimate goal: to land astronauts on the moon. In 1969, this goal was realized with the launching of *Apollo 11*. By 1972 when the *Apollo* missions ended, 12 U.S. astronauts had walked on the moon.

Return to the Moon

More than 20 years passed before the United States resumed its studies of the moon from space. In 1994, the *Clementine* spacecraft was placed into lunar orbit to conduct a two-month survey of the moon's surface. *Clementine's* mission was to test new sensors for tracking cold objects, such as satellites, in space.

Figure 21-15 This false-color photograph, taken by cameras on the *Clementine* spacecraft, shows the moon, the sun, and the planet Venus.

In addition, *Clementine* was placed in lunar orbit to take high-resolution photographs in order to compile a detailed map of the moon's surface. **Figure 21-15** shows a photograph taken by *Clementine*. *Clementine's* four cameras were able to resolve features as small as 200 m across, enhancing our knowledge of the moon's surface. ☑

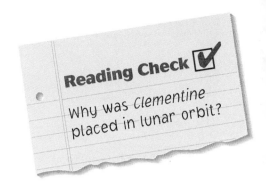

Reading Check ☑

Why was *Clementine* placed in lunar orbit?

The Moon's South Pole

The South Pole-Aitken Basin is the oldest identifiable impact feature on the moon's surface. It is also the largest and deepest impact basin or depression found thus far anywhere in the solar system, measuring 12 km in depth and 2500 km in diameter. Data returned by *Clementine* gave scientists the first set of high-resolution photographs of this area of the moon. Much of this depression stays in shadow throughout the moon's rotation, forming a cold area where ice deposits from impacting comets may have collected. Radio signals reflected from *Clementine* to Earth indicated the presence of ice at the moon's south pole. Also, a large plateau that is always in sunlight was discovered in this area. If there truly is ice near the plateau, this would be an ideal location for a moon colony powered by solar energy.

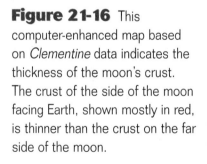

Figure 21-16 is a global map showing the moon's crustal thickness based on *Clementine* data. According to the data, the moon's crust thins under impact basins. Also, the moon's crust on the side facing Earth is much thinner than on the far side. Such maps show the location of **mascons,** which are concentrations of mass. Mascons are located under impact basins. Data collected by *Clementine* also provided information on the mineral content of moon rocks. In fact, this part of its mission was instrumental in naming the spacecraft. Clementine was the daughter of a miner in the ballad "My Darlin' Clementine."

Figure 21-16 This computer-enhanced map based on *Clementine* data indicates the thickness of the moon's crust. The crust of the side of the moon facing Earth, shown mostly in red, is thinner than the crust on the far side of the moon.

The Lunar Prospector

The success of *Clementine* at a relatively low cost opened the door for further moon missions. In 1998, NASA launched the *Lunar Prospector* spacecraft. Its mission was to orbit the moon, taking photographs of the lunar surface for mapping purposes. These maps confirmed the *Clementine* data. The

Lunar Prospector also was scheduled to conduct a detailed study of the moon's surface, searching for clues as to the origin and makeup of the moon.

Icy Poles

Early data obtained from the *Lunar Prospector* indicate that hydrogen is present in the rocks found in the craters at the moon's poles, as shown in **Figure 21-17.** Hydrogen is one of the elements that make up water. These data, combined with data from *Clementine,* have led scientists to theorize that ice may exist in the floors of the craters at both of the moon's poles. These craters are deep and cold. Sunlight never reaches their floors, where temperatures are as low as –233°C— definitely cold enough to have preserved any ice that may have collected in the craters from colliding comets or meteorites.

Based on the *Lunar Prospector* data, scientists estimate that 6 billion tons of ice lie under the surface of the moon's poles. The ice may be buried under about 40 cm of crushed rock. Data from *Lunar Prospector* also have enabled scientists to conclude that the moon has a small, iron-rich core about 600 km across.

Figure 21-17 Data from *Lunar Prospector* indicate the presence of twice as much ice at the moon's north pole as at its south pole.

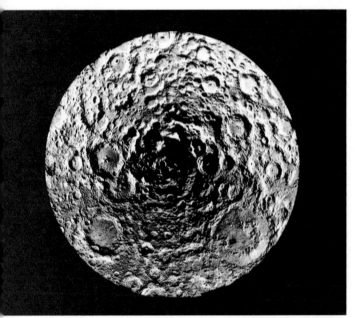

Section Assessment

1. List two discoveries about the moon made by the *Clementine* spacecraft.

2. What was the main mission of the *Lunar Prospector?*

3. How did studies of the moon change after the 1950s?

4. **Think Critically:** Why would the discovery of ice at the moon's poles be important to future space flights?

5. **Skill Builder**
   Sequencing Sequence the following moon missions in the order in which they occurred: *Surveyor, Lunar Prospector, Apollo, Lunar Orbiter, Ranger,* and *Clementine.* If you need help, refer to Sequencing in the **Skill Handbook** on page 714.

Using Math

The moon's orbit is tilted at an angle of about 5° to Earth's orbit around the sun. Using a protractor, draw an angle of 5°. Draw a model of the moon's orbit around Earth.

Moon Phases and Eclipses

Materials
- Light source (unshaded)
- Polystyrene ball on pencil
- Globe

You know that moon phases and eclipses result from the relative positions of the sun, the moon, and Earth. In this activity, you will demonstrate the positions of these bodies during certain phases and eclipses. You also will see why only people on a small portion of Earth's surface see a total solar eclipse.

What You'll Investigate

Can a model be devised to show the positions of the sun, the moon, and Earth during various phases and eclipses?

Goals
- **Model** moon phases.
- **Model** solar and lunar eclipses.

Procedure

1. Review the illustrations of moon phases and eclipses shown in Section 21-2.

2. **Use** the light source as a model sun and a polystyrene ball on a pencil as a model moon. **Move** the model moon around the globe to duplicate the exact position that would have to occur for a lunar eclipse to take place.

3. **Move** the model moon to the position that would cause a solar eclipse.

4. **Place** the model moon at each of the following phases: first quarter, full moon, third quarter, and new moon. **Identify** which, if any, type of eclipse could occur during each phase. Record your data.

5. **Place** the model moon at the location where a lunar eclipse could occur. **Move** it slightly toward Earth, then away from Earth. Note the amount of change in the size of the shadow causing the eclipse. Record this information.

6. **Repeat** step 5 with the model moon in a position where a solar eclipse could occur.

Conclude and Apply

1. During which phase(s) of the moon is it possible for an eclipse to occur?

2. **Describe** the effect that a small change in the distance between Earth and the moon has on the size of the shadow causing the eclipse.

3. As seen from Earth, how does the apparent size of the moon **compare** with the apparent size of the sun? How can an eclipse be used to confirm this?

4. **Infer** why a lunar and solar eclipse do not occur every month.

5. Suppose you wanted to more accurately model the movement of the moon around Earth. **Explain** how your model moon moves around the globe. Would it always be in the same plane as the light source and the globe?

6. Why have only a few people seen a total solar eclipse?

Moon Phase Observations	
Moon Phase	**Observations**
first quarter	
full	
third quarter	
new	

For a **preview** of this chapter, study this Reviewing Main Ideas before you read the chapter. After you have studied this chapter, you can use the Reviewing Main Ideas to **review** the chapter.

 The Glencoe MindJogger, Audiocassettes, and CD-ROM provide additional opportunities for review.

Section

21-1 PLANET EARTH

Earth is a **sphere** that is slightly flattened at its poles. Earth **rotates** once each day and **revolves** around the sun in a little more than 365 days. Seasons on Earth are due to the amount of solar radiation received by a hemisphere at a given time. The tilt of Earth on its **axis** causes the amount of solar energy to vary. *How does Earth's interior act like an electromagnet?*

Section

21-2 EARTH'S MOON

Earth's moon goes through **phases** that depend on the relative positions of the sun, the moon, and Earth. Eclipses occur when Earth or the moon temporarily blocks sunlight from the other. A **solar eclipse** occurs when the moon moves directly between the sun and Earth. A **lunar eclipse** occurs when Earth's shadow falls on the moon. The moon's **maria** are the result of ancient volcanism. Craters on the moon's surface formed from impacts with meteorites, asteroids, and comets. *If the moon is between Earth and the sun for each new moon, why are there only one or two solar eclipses each year?*

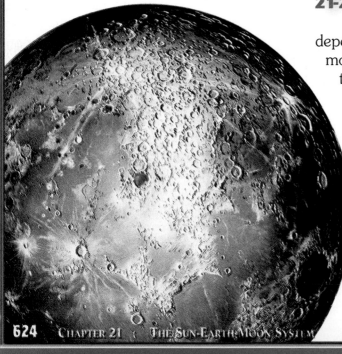

Reading Check ✔

Use these words in sentences that do not relate to the sun, Earth, or moon: *sphere, axis, rotation, revolution, ellipse, waxing,* and *waning.*

Section

21-3 EXPLORATION OF THE MOON

The *Clementine* spacecraft took detailed, high-resolution photographs of the moon's surface. Data from *Clementine* indicate that the moon's South Pole-Aitken Basin may contain ice deposits that could supply water for a moon colony. The *Clementine* spacecraft also noted that **mascons** occur beneath impact basins on the moon. NASA has returned to exploring the moon with its latest spacecraft, the *Lunar Prospector.* Data from *Lunar Prospector* seem to support the ice theory and also indicate that the moon's north pole may contain twice as much ice as the south pole. *How did the* Clementine *spacecraft get its name?*

Career
CONNECTION

Gibor Barsi, Astronomer

Gibor Barsi is an astronomer who works with the Keck Telescopes on Mauna Kea, Hawaii. The summit of Mauna Kea is considered the world's premier site for astronomical observation. Gibor is interested in answering the questions, "How many planets are there around other stars, what are they like, and how do they form?" He feels that the next generation of astronomers and technology will answer these questions. *Why do you suppose astronomers are interested in finding new planets?*

Using Vocabulary

a. axis
b. ellipse
c. equinox
d. first quarter
e. full moon
f. lunar eclipse
g. maria
h. mascon
i. moon phase

j. new moon
k. revolution
l. rotation
m. solar eclipse
n. solstice
o. sphere
p. third quarter
q. waning
r. waxing

Each phrase below describes a science term from the list. Write the term that matches the phrase describing it.

1. causes day and night to occur on Earth
2. occurs when the sun's position is directly above the equator
3. moon phase in which all of the lighted side of the moon is seen
4. eclipse that occurs when the moon is between Earth and the sun
5. concentration of mass on the moon located under an impact basin

Checking Concepts

Choose the word or phrase that completes the sentence.

6. How long does it take for the moon to rotate?
   A) 24 hours   C) 27.3 hours
   B) 365 days   D) 27.3 days

7. Where is Earth's circumference greatest?
   A) equator   C) poles
   B) mantle   D) axis

8. During an equinox, the sun is directly over what part of Earth?
   A) southern hemisphere
   B) northern hemisphere
   C) equator
   D) pole

9. Why does the sun appear to rise and set?
   A) Earth revolves.
   B) The sun moves around Earth.
   C) Earth rotates.
   D) Earth orbits the sun.

10. How long does it take for the moon to revolve?
    A) 24 hours   C) 27.3 hours
    B) 365 days   D) 27.3 days

11. As the lighted portion of the moon appears to get larger, what is it said to be?
    A) waning   C) rotating
    B) waxing   D) crescent shaped

12. During what kind of eclipse is the moon directly between the sun and Earth?
    A) solar   C) full
    B) new   D) lunar

13. What is the darkest part of the shadow during an eclipse?
    A) waxing gibbous C) waning gibbous
    B) umbra   D) penumbra

14. What are depressions on the moon called?
    A) eclipses   C) phases
    B) moonquakes   D) craters

15. What fact do data gathered from the *Clementine* spacecraft support?
    A) The moon rotates once in 29.5 days.
    B) The moon has a thinner crust on the side facing Earth.
    C) The moon revolves once in 29.5 days.
    D) The moon has a thicker crust on the side facing Earth.

Thinking Critically

16. How would the moon appear to an observer in space during its revolution? Would phases be observable? Explain.

17. Would you weigh more at Earth's equator or at the north pole? Explain.

18. Tides occur due to the gravitational attraction among the sun, the moon, and Earth. During which phases of the moon are tides the highest? Explain.

19. If you were lost on the moon's surface, why would it be more beneficial to have a star chart rather than a compass?

20. Which of the moon's motions are real? Which are apparent? Explain.

Developing Skills

If you need help, refer to the **Skill Handbook**.

21. Hypothesizing: Why do locations near Earth's equator travel faster during one rotation than places near the poles?

22. Using Variables, Constants, and Controls: Describe a simple activity to show how the moon's rotation and revolution work to keep one side facing Earth at all times.

23. Comparing and Contrasting: Compare and contrast a waning moon with a waxing moon.

24. Concept Mapping: Copy and complete the cycle map shown on this page. Show the sequences of the moon's phases.

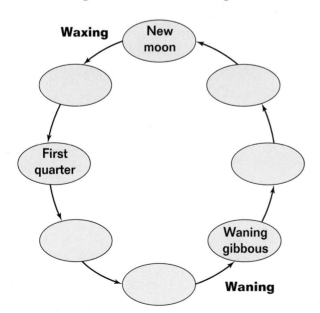

Test-Taking Tip

Practice, Practice, Practice Practice to improve *your* performance. Don't compare yourself with anyone else.

Test Practice

Use these questions to test your Science Proficiency.

1. As the moon revolves around Earth, it keeps the same side facing Earth. Which of the following statements **BEST** explains why this is so?
  A) The moon rotates once on its axis as it makes one complete revolution around Earth.
  B) The moon does not rotate as it revolves.
  C) The speed of rotation for the moon exactly equals its speed of revolution.
  D) The speed of revolution for the moon is constant and therefore keeps one side facing Earth at all times.

2. More craters are on the far side of the moon than on the side facing Earth. Which of the following statements would **BEST** explain this fact?
  A) A greater number of volcanoes occur on the far side of the moon.
  B) Earth's gravity attracts more of the objects that would produce craters on the side of the moon facing Earth.
  C) Earth blocks the paths of any objects that would collide with the side of the moon facing Earth.
  D) The far side of the moon is always facing away from the sun.

CHAPTER

22 The Solar System

Chapter Preview

Skills Preview

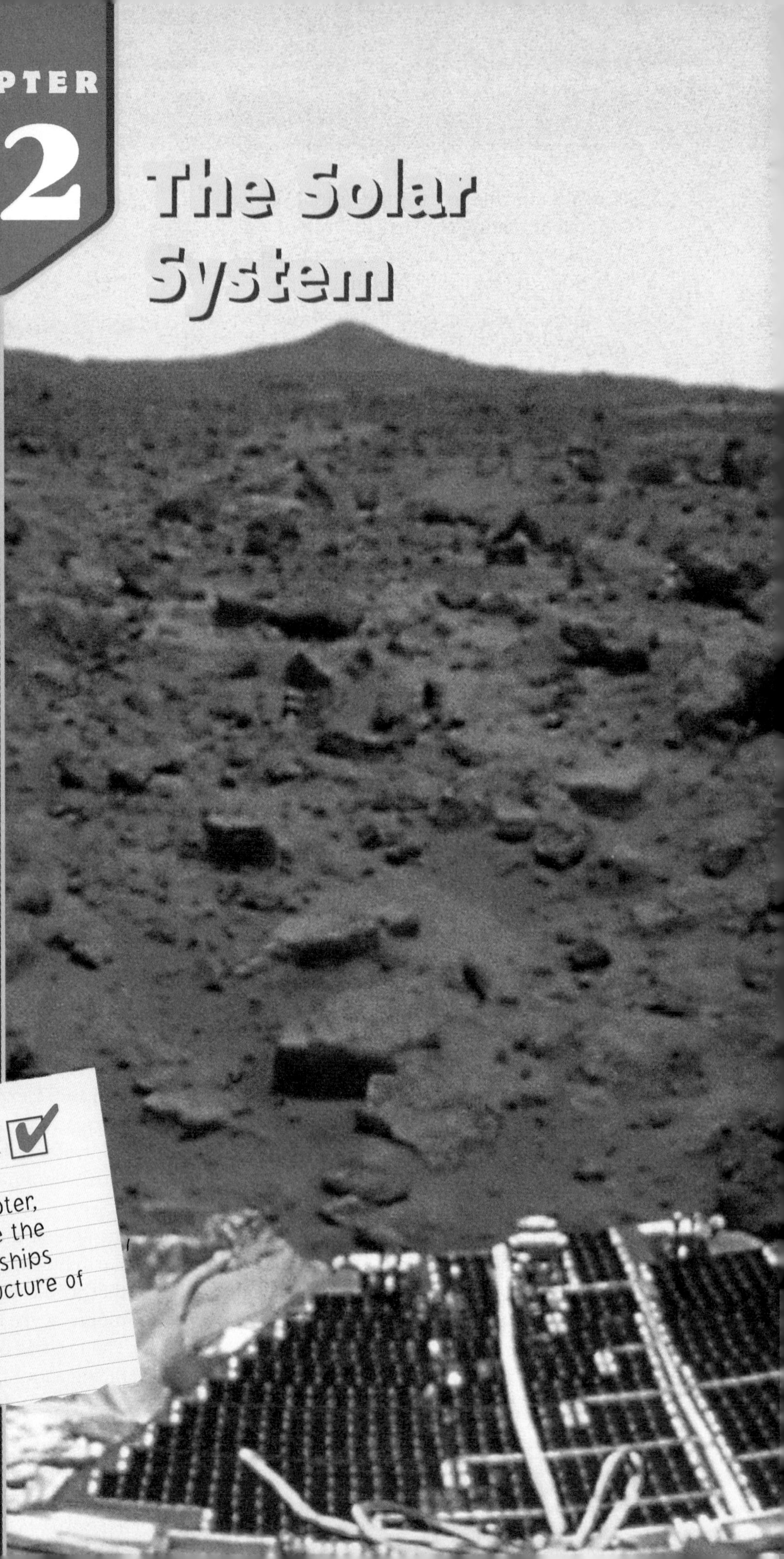

Skill Builders
- Map Concepts

Activities
- Make a Model

MiniLabs
- Observe and Infer

Reading Check ✓

As you read this chapter, identify and describe the cause-effect relationships that control the structure of the solar system.

Explore Activity

The planets of our solar system are our neighbors in space. But to us on Earth, they look like tiny points of light among the thousands of others visible on a clear night. With the help of telescopes and space probes, the points of light become giant colorful spheres, some with rings, others pitted with countless craters. This false-color image of Mars shows the space rover *Sojourner* exploring the planet's surface. Mars has two heavily cratered moons. In this activity, you'll explore how craters are made on the surfaces of planets and moons.

Model Comet Collisions

1. Place fine white flour into a cake pan to a depth of 3 cm, completely covering the bottom of the pan.

2. Cover the flour with 1 cm of fine, gray, dry cement mix, or try different colors of gelatin powder.

3. From different heights ranging from 10 cm to 25 cm, drop various-sized objects into the pan. Use marbles, lead weights, bolts, and nuts.

In your Science Journal, draw what happened to the surface of the powder in the pan when each object was dropped from different heights.

22•1 The Solar System

Early Ideas About the Solar System

Imagine yourself on a warm, clear summer night lying in the grass and gazing at the stars and the moon. The stars and the moon seem so still and beautiful. You may even see other planets in the solar system, thinking they are stars. Although the planets are different from the stars, they blend in with the stars and are usually hard to pick out.

Earth-Centered Model

It is generally known today that the sun and the stars appear to move through the sky because Earth is moving. This wasn't always an accepted fact. Many early Greek scientists thought the planets, the sun, and the moon were embedded in separate spheres that rotated around Earth. The stars were thought to be embedded in another sphere that also rotated around Earth. Early observers described moving objects in the night sky using the term *planasthai*, which means "to wander." The word *planet* comes from this term.

This model is called the Earth-centered model of the solar system. It included Earth, the moon, the sun, five planets—Mercury, Venus, Mars, Jupiter, and Saturn—and the sphere of stars.

What You'll Learn

► The sun-centered and Earth-centered models of the solar system
► Current models of the formation of the solar system

Vocabulary
solar system
inner planet
outer planet

Why It's Important

► You'll learn how views of the solar system have changed over time.

Figure 22-1 Each of the nine planets in the solar system is unique. The sizes of the planets and sun are drawn to scale but the distances between the planets and sun are not to scale.

Pluto

Neptune

Uranus

Saturn

Sun-Centered Model

The idea of an Earth-centered solar system was held for centuries until the Polish astronomer Nicholas Copernicus published a different view in 1543. Using an idea proposed by an early Greek scholar, Copernicus stated that the moon revolved around Earth, which was a planet. Earth, along with the other planets, revolved around the sun. He also stated that the daily movement of the planets and the stars was due to Earth's rotation. This is the sun-centered model of the solar system.

Using his telescope, the Italian astronomer Galileo Galilei found evidence that supported the ideas of Copernicus. He discovered that Venus went through phases like the moon's. These phases could be explained only if Venus were orbiting the sun. From this, he concluded that Venus revolves around the sun and that the sun is the center of the solar system.

Modern View of the Solar System

We now know that the **solar system** is made up of the nine planets, including Earth, and many smaller objects that orbit the sun. The sizes of the nine planets and the sun are shown to scale in **Figure 22-1.** However, the distances between the planets are not to scale. The dark areas on the sun are sunspots, which you will learn about later. Notice how small Earth is compared with some of the other planets and the sun, which is much larger than any of the planets.

The solar system includes a vast territory extending billions of kilometers in all directions from the sun. The sun contains 99.86 percent of the mass of the whole solar system. Because of its gravitational pull, the sun is the central object around which other objects of the solar system revolve.

Jupiter

Sun

Mercury

Venus

Earth

Mars

Figure 22-2 Through careful observations, astronomers have found clues that help explain how our solar system may have formed.

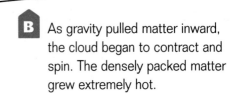

B As gravity pulled matter inward, the cloud began to contract and spin. The densely packed matter grew extremely hot.

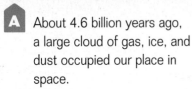

A About 4.6 billion years ago, a large cloud of gas, ice, and dust occupied our place in space.

How the Solar System Formed

Scientists hypothesize that the sun and the solar system formed from a cloud of gas, ice, and dust about 4.6 billion years ago. **Figure 22-2** illustrates how this may have happened. This cloud was slowly rotating in space. A nearby star may have exploded, and the shock waves from this event may have caused the cloud to start contracting. At first, the cloud was rotating slowly. As it contracted, the matter in the cloud was squeezed into less space. The cloud's density became greater and the increased attraction of gravity pulled more gas and dust toward the cloud center. This caused the cloud to rotate faster, which in turn caused it to flatten into a disk with a dense center. ☑

As the cloud contracted, the temperature began to increase. Eventually, the temperature in the core of the cloud reached about 10 million °C and nuclear fusion began. A star was born—this was the beginning of our sun. Nuclear fusion occurs when atoms with low mass, such as hydrogen, combine to form heavier elements, such as helium. The new, heavy element contains slightly less mass than the sum of the light atoms that formed it. The lost mass is converted into energy.

Not all of the nearby gas, ice, and dust were drawn into the core of the cloud. Remaining gas, ice, and dust particles

Reading Check

When did the solar system begin to form?

C The center of the rotating disk continued to heat. Meanwhile, gas and dust particles in the outer rim clumped together, forming larger objects.

D The larger clumps continued to grow as more objects collided.

collided and stuck together, forming larger objects that in turn attracted more particles because of the stronger pull of gravity. Close to the sun, the temperature was hot, and the easily vaporized elements could not condense into solids. This is why light elements are more scarce in the planets closer to the sun than in planets farther out in the solar system. Instead, the inner solar system is dominated by small, rocky planets with iron cores.

The **inner planets**—Mercury, Venus, Earth, and Mars—are the solid, rocky planets closest to the sun. The **outer planets**—Jupiter, Saturn, Uranus, Neptune, and Pluto—are those farthest from the sun. Except for Pluto, which is made of rock and ice, the outer planets are made mostly of lighter elements such as hydrogen, helium, methane, and ammonia.

E Eventually, the larger clumps gathered enough matter to become planets. The core of the disk grew even denser and hotter.

F Nuclear fusion began in the core, and the sun became a star. Some of the smaller objects became moons and rings around the planets.

Motions of the Planets

PHYSICS INTEGRATION

When Nicholas Copernicus developed his sun-centered model of the solar system, he thought that the planets orbited the sun in circles. In the early 1600s, the German mathematician Johannes Kepler began studying the orbits of the planets. He discovered that the shapes of the orbits are not circular, but elliptical. He also calculated that the sun is not at the center of the ellipse but is offset from the center.

Kepler also discovered that the planets travel at different speeds in their orbits around the sun. By studying these speeds, you can see that the planets closer to the sun travel faster than planets farther away from the sun. As a result, the outer planets take much longer to orbit the sun than the inner planets do.

Copernicus's ideas, considered radical at the time, led to the birth of modern astronomy. Early scientists didn't have technology such as space probes to learn about the planets. They used instruments such as the one shown in **Figure 22-3.** Nevertheless, they developed theories about the solar system that we still use today. In the next section, you'll learn about the inner planets—our nearest neighbors in space.

Figure 22-3 This instrument, called an astrolabe, was used for a variety of astronomical calculations.

Section Assessment

1. What is the difference between the sun-centered and the Earth-centered models of the solar system?

2. How do scientists hypothesize the solar system formed?

3. The outer planets are rich in water, methane, and ammonia—the materials needed for life. Yet life is unlikely on these planets. Explain.

4. **Think Critically:** Would a year on the planet Uranus be longer or shorter than an Earth year? Explain.

5. **Skill Builder**
   Concept Mapping Make a concept map that compares and contrasts the Earth-centered model with the sun-centered model of the solar system. If you need help, refer to Concept Mapping in the **Skill Handbook** on page 714.

Using Math

Assuming that the planets travel in nearly circular orbits, research their value of average orbital speeds to determine how much faster (in km/s) Mercury travels in its orbit than Earth travels in its orbit.

Planetary Orbits

Planets travel around the sun along fixed paths called orbits. Early theories about the solar system stated that planetary orbits were perfect circles. As you construct a model of a planetary orbit, you will observe that the shape of planetary orbits is an ellipse, not a circle.

Materials

- Thumbtacks or pins
- Metric ruler
- String (25 cm)
- Pencil
- Cardboard (23 cm × 30 cm)
- Paper (21.5 cm × 28 cm)

What You'll Investigate

How can a model be constructed that will show planetary orbits to be elliptical?

Goals

- **Model** planetary orbits.
- **Calculate** changes in ellipses.

Procedure

1. **Place** a blank sheet of paper on top of the cardboard and insert two thumbtacks or pins about 3 cm apart.

2. **Tie** the string into a circle with a circumference of 15 to 20 cm. **Loop** the string around the thumbtacks. With someone holding the tacks or pins, **place** your pencil inside the loop and **pull** it tight.

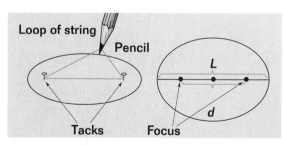

Loop of string
Pencil
L
Tacks
Focus
d

3. **Move** the pencil around the tacks, keeping the string tight, until you have completed a smooth, closed curve, called an ellipse.

4. **Repeat** steps 1 through 3 several times. First, **vary** the distance between the tacks, then **vary** the length of the string. However, change only one of these each time. Make a data table to record the changes in the sizes and shapes of the ellipses.

5. Orbits usually are described in terms of eccentricity (e). The eccentricity of any ellipse is determined by dividing the distance (d) between the foci (fixed points—here, the tacks) by the length of the major axis (L). See the diagram at left.

6. **Calculate** and **record** the eccentricity of the ellipses that you constructed.

7. **Research** the eccentricities of planetary orbits.

8. **Construct** an ellipse with the same eccentricity as Earth's orbit. **Repeat** this step with the orbit of either Pluto or Mercury.

Conclude and Apply

1. **Analyze** the effect a change in the length of the string or the distance between the tacks has on the shape of the ellipse.

2. **Hypothesize** what must be done to the string or placement of tacks to decrease the eccentricity of a constructed ellipse.

3. **Describe** the shape of Earth's orbit. Where is the sun located within the orbit?

4. **Identify** the planets that have the most eccentric orbits.

5. **Describe** the path of an orbit with an eccentricity of zero.

The Inner Planets

Inner Planets

What You'll Learn

▶ The inner planets in their relative order from the sun
▶ Important characteristics of each inner planet
▶ How Venus and Earth compare and contrast

Vocabulary

Mercury	astronomical
Venus	unit
Earth	Mars

Why It's Important

▶ Other planets have characteristics that are different from those of Earth.

We have learned much about the solar system since the days of Copernicus and Galileo. Advancements in telescopes allow astronomers to observe the planets from Earth. In addition, space probes have explored much of our solar system, adding greatly to the knowledge we have about the planets. Let's take a tour of the solar system through the "eyes" of the space probes.

Mercury

The closest planet to the sun is **Mercury.** It is also the second-smallest planet. The first and only American spacecraft mission to Mercury was in 1974-1975 by *Mariner 10,* which flew by the planet and sent pictures back to Earth. *Mariner 10* photographed only 45 percent of Mercury's surface—we do not know what the other 55 percent looks like. What we do know is that the surface of Mercury has many craters and looks much like our moon. It also has cliffs as high as 3 km on its surface, as seen in **Figure 22-4.** These cliffs may have formed when Mercury apparently shrank about 2 km in diameter.

Why did Mercury apparently shrink? Scientists think the answer may lie inside the planet. *Mariner 10* detected a weak magnetic field around Mercury, indicating that the planet has a large iron core. Some scientists hypothesize that the crust of Mercury solidified while the iron core was still hot and

Figure 22-4 Giant cliffs on Mercury, like the one marked by the arrow, suggest that the planet might have shrunk.

Mercury

molten. Then, as the core cooled and solidified, it contracted, causing the planet to shrink. The large cliffs may have resulted from breaks in the crust caused by this contraction, similar to what happens when an apple dries out and shrivels up.

Because of Mercury's small size and low gravitational pull, most gases that could form an atmosphere escape into space. Mercury's thin atmosphere is composed of hydrogen, helium, sodium, and potassium. The sodium and potassium may diffuse upward through the crust. The thin atmosphere and the nearness of Mercury to the sun cause this planet to have large extremes in temperature. Mercury's surface temperature can reach 450°C during the day and drop to –170°C at night.

Using Math

The average distance from the sun to Earth is 150 million km. How many minutes does it take light traveling at 300 000 km/s to reach Earth? Use the equation

$$\text{Time} = \frac{\text{distance}}{\text{speed}}$$

Venus

The second planet outward from the sun is **Venus.** Venus is sometimes called Earth's twin because its size and mass are similar to Earth's. One major difference is that the entire surface of Venus is blanketed by a dense atmosphere. The atmosphere of Venus, which has 96 times the surface pressure of Earth's at sea level, is mostly carbon dioxide. The clouds in the atmosphere contain droplets of sulfuric acid, which gives them a slightly yellow color.

Clouds on Venus are so dense that only two percent of the sunlight that strikes the top of the clouds reaches the planet's surface. The solar energy that reaches the surface is trapped by the carbon dioxide gas and causes a greenhouse effect similar to but more intense than Earth's greenhouse effect. Due to this intense greenhouse effect, the temperature on the surface of Venus is 470°C.

The former Soviet Union led the exploration of Venus. Beginning in 1970 with the first *Venera* probe, the Russians have photographed and mapped the surface of Venus using radar and surface probes. Between 1990 and 1994, the *U.S. Magellan* probe used its radar to make the most detailed maps yet of Venus's surface. *Magellan* revealed huge craters, faultlike cracks, and volcanoes with visible lava flows, as seen in **Figure 22-5.**

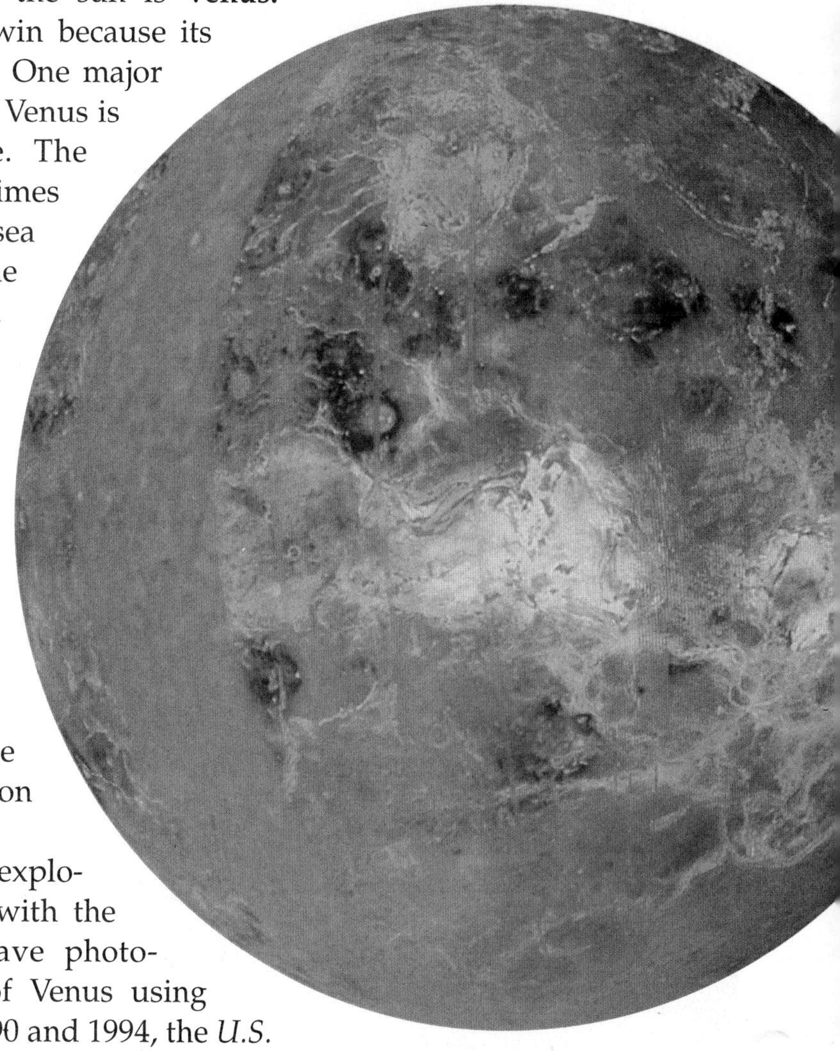

Figure 22-5 Although Venus is similar to Earth, there are important differences. **How could studying Venus help us learn more about Earth?**

Earth

Earth, shown in **Figure 22-6,** is the third planet from the sun. The average distance from Earth to the sun is 150 million km, or one astronomical unit (AU). **Astronomical units** are used to measure distances to objects in the solar system.

Unlike other planets, surface temperatures on Earth allow water to exist as a solid, liquid, and gas. Earth's atmosphere causes most meteors to burn up before they reach the surface. The atmosphere also protects life from the sun's intense radiation.

Mars

Mars, the fourth planet from the sun, is called the red planet because iron oxide in the weathered rocks on its surface gives it a reddish color, as seen in **Figure 22-7.** Other features of Mars visible from Earth are its polar ice caps, which get larger during the Martian winter and shrink during the summer. The ice caps are made mostly of frozen carbon dioxide and frozen water.

Most of the information we have about Mars came from the *Mariner 9, Viking* probes, *Mars Global Surveyor,* and *Mars Pathfinder. Mariner 9* orbited Mars in 1971–1972. It revealed long channels on the planet that may have been carved by

Figure 22-6 More than 70 percent of Earth's surface is covered by liquid water. **What is unique about surface temperatures on Earth?**

Problem Solving

Interpret Planetary Data

Your teacher asks you to determine which planet's surface is hotter, Mercury or Venus. You must also explain the temperature difference. You decide that this assignment is going to be easy. Of course, Mercury has to be hotter than Venus because it is much closer to the sun. Venus is almost twice as far away as Mercury. You write your answer and turn in your paper. Later, when you receive your paper back, you find out that your assumptions were evidently wrong. Your teacher suggests that you research the question further, using the table on this page as a guide. As a further hint, your teacher tells you to consider how a greenhouse works to keep it warmer inside than outside and to relate this to what might happen to a planet with a thick atmosphere.

Data for Mercury and Venus		
	Mercury 0.39 AU from sun	**Venus 0.72 AU from sun**
Surface Temperature (High)		
Atmosphere Density		
Atmosphere Compostion		

Think Critically: What causes Venus to have a higher surface temperature than Mercury? Explain.

flowing water. *Mariner 9* also discovered the largest volcano in the solar system, Olympus Mons. Like all Mars's volcanoes, Olympus Mons is extinct. Large rift zones that formed in the Martian crust were also discovered. One such rift, Valles Marineris, is shown in **Figure 22-7.**

The Viking probes

In 1976, the *Viking 1* and *2* probes arrived at Mars. Each spacecraft consisted of an orbiter and a lander. The *Viking 1* and *2* orbiters photographed the entire surface of Mars from orbit, while the *Viking 1* and *2* landers touched down on the planet's surface to conduct meteorological, chemical, and biological experiments. The biological experiments found no evidence of life in the soil. The *Viking* landers also sent back pictures of a reddish-colored, barren, rocky, and windswept surface.

Try at Home

Mini Lab

Inferring Effects of Gravity

Procedure

1. Suppose you are a crane operator who is sent to Mars to help build a Mars colony.

2. You know that your crane can lift 44 500 N on Earth, but the gravity on Mars is only 40 percent of Earth's gravity.

3. Using Appendix B, determine how much mass your crane could lift on Mars.

Analysis

1. How can what you have discovered be an advantage over construction on Earth?

2. In what ways might construction advantages change the overall design of the Mars colony?

Mars

Figure 22-7 Valles Marineris is more than 4000 km long, up to 240 km wide, and more than 6 km deep.

Reading Check

In what way is Valles Marineris similar to the Grand Canyon?

CHEMISTRY
INTEGRATION

Mars has always been known as the red planet. Research the composition of surface rocks on Mars. Describe the chemical reaction in the Martian soil responsible for the planet's red color.

Global Surveyor and Pathfinder

The *Mars Pathfinder*, shown in **Figure 22-8,** gathered data that indicated that iron in Mars's crust may have been leached out by groundwater. In addition, high-quality cameras on board *Global Surveyor* showed that the walls of Valles Marineris have distinct layers similar to the Grand Canyon on Earth. *Global Surveyor* also noticed that a vast flat region, similar to a dried-up seabed or mudflat, covers a large area of Mars's northern hemisphere. This evidence, combined with evidence gathered from *Mariner 9,* indicates that large amounts of water were once present on the planet. Where has all the water gone? Many believe it is frozen into Mars's crust at the poles, shown in **Figure 22-9,** or has soaked into the ground.

The Martian atmosphere is much thinner than Earth's and is composed mostly of carbon dioxide, with some nitrogen and argon. The thin atmosphere does not filter out harmful rays from the sun as Earth's atmosphere does. Surface temperatures range from 35°C to –170°C. The temperature difference between day and night sets up strong winds on the planet, which can cause global dust storms during certain seasons.

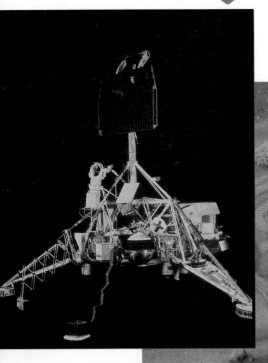

Figure 22-8 *Mars Pathfinder* (A) arrived at Mars in 1997. Upon landing, the craft opened its three petal-shaped doors, and the robot rover *Sojourner* began exploring the planet's surface (B).

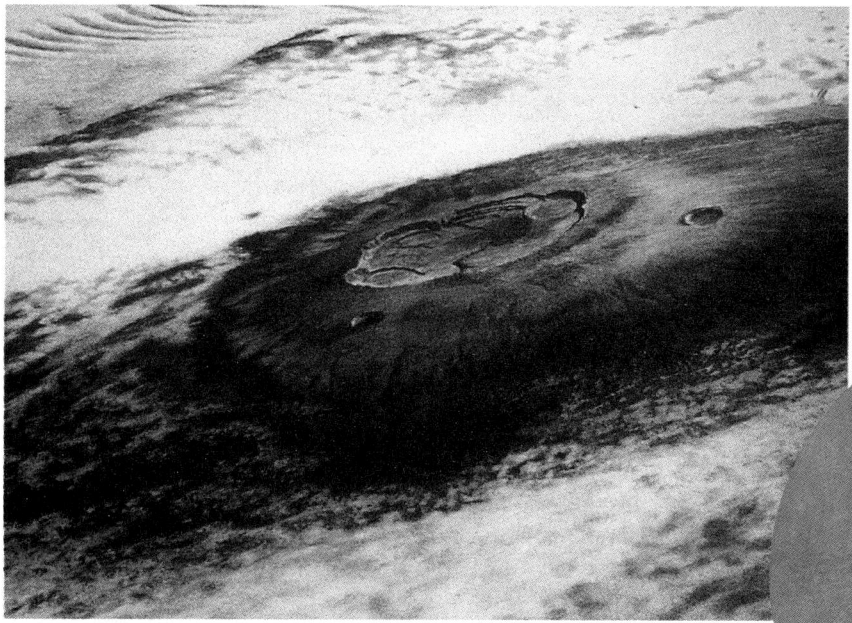

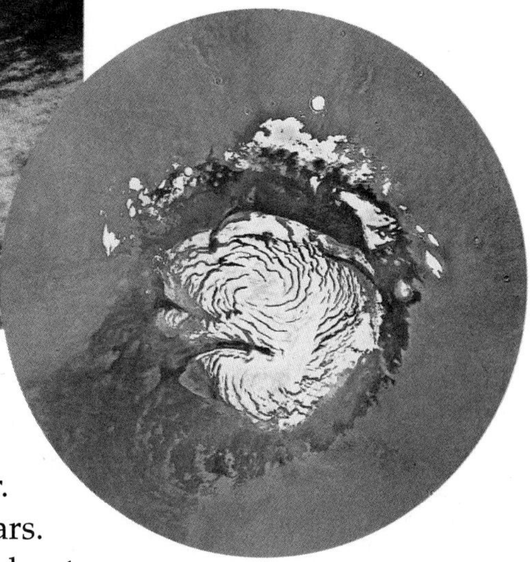

Figure 22-9 These photos show two features of Mars.

A Olympus Mons is the largest volcano in the solar system.

B Water that flowed on Mars long ago may now be frozen in polar ice caps.

Martian Moons

Mars has two small, heavily cratered moons. Phobos is 25 km in diameter, and Deimos is 13 km in diameter. Phobos's orbit is slowly spiraling inward toward Mars. Phobos is expected to impact the Martian surface in about 50 million years.

As you toured the inner planets using the "eyes" of the space probes, you saw how each planet is unique. Mercury, Venus, Earth, and Mars are different from the outer planets, which you'll explore in the next section.

Section Assessment

1. How are Mercury and Earth's moon similar?

2. List one important characteristic of each inner planet.

3. Although Venus is often called Earth's twin, why would life as we know it be unlikely on Venus?

4. Name the inner planets in order from the sun.

5. **Think Critically:** Do the closest planets to the sun always have the hottest surface temperatures? Explain your answer.

6.  **Skill Builder**
   Interpreting Data Using the information in this section, explain how Mars is like Earth. How are they different? If you need help, refer to Interpreting Data in the **Skill Handbook** on page 724.

Science Journal Use textbooks and NASA materials to investigate NASA's missions to Mars. In your Science Journal, report on the possibility of life on Mars and the tests that have been conducted to see whether life is there.

22•3 The Outer Planets

Outer Planets

You have learned that the inner planets are small, solid, rocky bodies in space. By contrast, the outer planets, except for Pluto, are large, gaseous objects.

You may have heard or read about the *Voyager* and *Galileo* spacecraft. Although they were not the first probes to the outer planets, they have uncovered a wealth of new information about Jupiter, Saturn, Uranus, and Neptune. Let's follow the spacecraft on their journeys to the outer planets of the solar system.

Jupiter

In 1979, *Voyager 1* and *Voyager 2* flew past **Jupiter,** the largest planet and the fifth planet from the sun. *Galileo* reached Jupiter in 1995. The major discoveries of the probes include new information about the composition and motion of Jupiter's atmosphere and the discovery of three new moons. *Voyager* probes also discovered that Jupiter has faint dust rings around it and that one of its moons has volcanoes on it.

Jupiter is composed mostly of hydrogen and helium, with some ammonia, methane, and water vapor as well. Scientists theorize that the atmosphere of hydrogen and helium gradually changes to a planetwide ocean of liquid hydrogen and helium toward the middle of the planet. Below this liquid layer may be a solid rocky core. The extreme pressure and temperature, however, make the core different from any rock on Earth.

You've probably seen pictures from the probes of Jupiter's colorful clouds. Its atmosphere has bands of white, red, tan, and brown clouds, as shown in **Figure 22-10.** Continuous storms of swirling, high-pressure gas have been observed on Jupiter. The **Great Red Spot** is the most spectacular of these storms. Lightning also has been observed within Jupiter's clouds.

What You'll Learn

▶ The major characteristics of Jupiter, Saturn, Uranus, and Neptune

▶ How Pluto differs from the other outer planets

Vocabulary

Jupiter	Uranus
Great Red Spot	Neptune
	Pluto
Saturn	

Why It's Important

▶ You'll learn about the planets in our solar system that differ most from Earth.

Jupiter

A

B

Figure 22-10 Jupiter (A) is the largest planet in our solar system, containing more mass than all of the other planets combined. The Great Red Spot (B) is a giant storm about 12 000 km from top to bottom.

Moons of Jupiter

Sixteen moons orbit Jupiter. The four largest, shown in **Table 22-1,** were discovered by Galileo in 1610. Io is the closest large moon to Jupiter. Jupiter's tremendous gravitational force and the gravity of Europa pull on Io. This force heats up Io, causing it to be the most volcanically active object in the solar system. The next large moon is Europa. It is composed mostly of rock with a thick, smooth crust of ice, which may indicate the presence of an ocean under the ice. Next is Ganymede, which is the largest moon in the solar system. It's larger than the planet Mercury. Callisto, the last of the large moons, is composed of ice and rock. Studying these moons and events such as the comet collision shown in **Figure 22-11** further our knowledge of the solar system.

Saturn

The next planet surveyed by the *Voyager* probes was Saturn, in 1980 and 1981. **Saturn** is the sixth planet from the sun and is also known as the ringed planet. Saturn is the second-largest planet in the solar system but has the lowest density. Its density is so low that the planet would float on water.

Table 22-1

Large Moons of Jupiter

Io The most volcanically active object in the solar system; sulfur lava gives it its distinctive red and orange color; has a thin oxygen, sulfur, and sulfur dioxide atmosphere.

Europa Rocky interior is covered by a 100-km-thick ice crust, which has a network of cracks, indicating tectonic activity; has a thin oxygen atmosphere.

Ganymede Has an ice crust about 100 km thick, covered with grooves; crust may surround a mantle of water or slushy ice; has a rocky core and a thin hydrogen atmosphere.

Callisto Has a heavily cratered, ice-rock crust several hundred kilometers thick; crust may surround a salty ocean around a rock core; has a thin atmosphere of hydrogen, oxygen, and carbon dioxide.

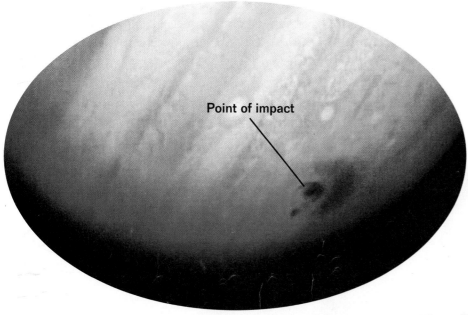

Point of impact

Figure 22-11 In 1994, comet Shoemaker-Levy 9 collided into Jupiter causing a series of spectacular explosions. Information from this impact gives us clues about what might happen if such an impact occurred on Earth.

Figure 22-12 Saturn's rings are composed of pieces of rock and ice.

Similar to Jupiter, Saturn is a large, gaseous planet with a thick outer atmosphere composed mostly of hydrogen and helium. Saturn's atmosphere also contains ammonia, methane, and water vapor. As you go deeper into Saturn's atmosphere, the gases gradually change to liquid hydrogen and helium. Below its atmosphere and liquid ocean, Saturn may have a small rocky core.

The *Voyager* probes gathered new information about Saturn's ring system and its moons. The *Voyager* probes showed that Saturn has several broad rings, each of which is composed of thousands of thin ringlets. Each ring is composed of countless ice and rock particles ranging in size from a speck of dust to tens of meters across, as shown in **Figure 22-12.** This makes Saturn's ring system the most complex of all the outer gaseous planets.

At least 20 moons orbit Saturn. That's more than any other planet in our solar system. The largest of these, Titan, is larger than Mercury. It has an atmosphere of nitrogen, argon, and methane. Thick clouds prevent us from seeing the surface of Titan.

Try at Home

Mini Lab

Modeling Planets

Procedure

1. Research the planets to determine how the sizes of the planets in the solar system compare with each other.
2. Select a scale for the diameter of Earth based on the size of your paper.
3. Make a model by drawing a circle with this diameter on paper.
4. Using Earth's diameter as 1.0, draw each of the other planets to scale.

Analysis

1. At this scale, how far would your model Earth need to be located from the sun?
2. What would 1 AU be equal to in this model?
3. Using a scale of 1 AU = 2 m, how large would the sun and Earth models have to be to remain in scale?

Uranus

After touring Saturn, *Voyager 2* flew by Uranus in 1986. **Uranus,** shown in **Figure 22-13,** is the seventh planet from the sun and wasn't discovered until 1781. It is a large, gaseous planet with 17 satellites and a system of thin, dark rings.

Voyager revealed numerous thin rings and ten moons that had not been seen earlier. *Voyager* also detected that the planet's magnetic field is tilted 55 degrees from its rotational poles.

The atmosphere of Uranus is composed of hydrogen, helium, and some methane. The methane gives the planet its blue-green color. Methane absorbs the red and yellow light, and the clouds reflect the green and blue. No cloud bands and few storm systems are seen on Uranus. Evidence suggests that under its atmosphere, Uranus has a mantle of liquid water, methane, and ammonia surrounding a rocky core.

One of the most unique features of Uranus is that its axis of rotation is tilted on its side compared with the other planets. The axes of rotation of the other planets, except Pluto, are nearly perpendicular to the planes of their orbits. Uranus, however, has a rotational axis nearly parallel to the plane of its orbit, as shown in **Figure 22-14.** Some scientists believe a collision with another object turned Uranus on its side.

Figure 22-13 The atmosphere of Uranus gives the planet its distinct blue-green color.

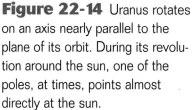

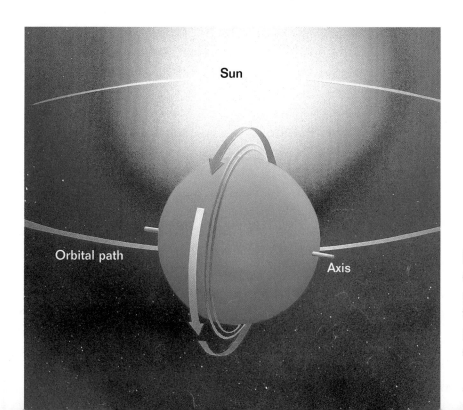

Sun

Orbital path

Axis

Figure 22-14 Uranus rotates on an axis nearly parallel to the plane of its orbit. During its revolution around the sun, one of the poles, at times, points almost directly at the sun.

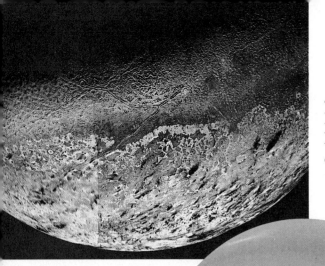

Neptune

From Uranus, *Voyager 2* traveled on to Neptune, a large, gaseous planet. Discovered in 1846, **Neptune** is usually the eighth planet from the sun. However, Pluto's orbit crosses inside Neptune's during part of its voyage around the sun. Between 1979 and 1998, Pluto was closer to the sun than Neptune. In 1999, Pluto once again became the farthest planet from the sun.

Figure 22-15

Triton, above, is Neptune's largest moon.

Neptune's atmosphere is similar to that of Uranus. The methane content gives Neptune, shown in **Figure 22-15,** its distinctive blue-green color, just as it does for Uranus.

Neptune has dark-colored, stormlike features in its atmosphere that are similar to the Great Red Spot on Jupiter. One discovered by *Voyager* is called the Great Dark Spot.

Under its atmosphere, Neptune is thought to have liquid water, methane, and ammonia. Neptune probably has a rocky core.

Neptune

Voyager 2 detected six new moons, so the total number of Neptune's known moons is now eight. Of these, Triton is the largest. Triton, shown in **Figure 22-15,** has a diameter of 2700 km and a thin atmosphere composed mostly of nitrogen. *Voyager* detected methane geysers erupting on Triton. *Voyager* also detected that Neptune has rings that are thin in some places and thick in other places. Neptune's magnetic field is tilted 47 degrees from its rotational axis. In comparison, Earth's magnetic field is tilted only 11.5 degrees from its rotational axis.

Voyager ended its tour of the solar system with Neptune. Both *Voyager* probes are now beyond the orbits of Pluto and Neptune. They will continue into space, studying how far the sun's power reaches into the outer limits of our solar system.

Reading Check ✔

Voyager's tour ended with what planet?

Pluto

The smallest planet in our solar system, and the one we know the least about, is Pluto. Because **Pluto** is farther from the sun than Neptune during most of its orbit around the sun, it is considered the ninth planet from the sun. Pluto is not like the other outer planets. It's surrounded by only a thin atmosphere, and it's the only outer planet with a solid, icy-rock surface.

Pluto's only moon, Charon, has a diameter about half the size of Pluto's. Charon orbits close to Pluto. Pluto and Charon are shown in **Figure 22-16.** Because of their close size and orbit, they are sometimes considered to be a double planet.

Recent data from the *Hubble Space Telescope* indicate the presence of a vast disk of icy comets near Neptune's orbit, called the Kuiper belt. Some of the ice comets are hundreds of kilometers in diameter. Are Pluto and Charon members of this belt? Are they escaped moons of one of the larger gaseous giants, or did they simply form at the distance they are? Maybe planets at that distance from the sun should be small and composed of icy rock. We may not find out until we send a probe to Pluto.

With the *Voyager* probes, we entered a new age of knowledge about the solar system. The space probe *Galileo*, which arrived at Jupiter in 1995, and the *Cassini* probe, which will arrive at Saturn in 2004, will continue to extend our understanding of the solar system.

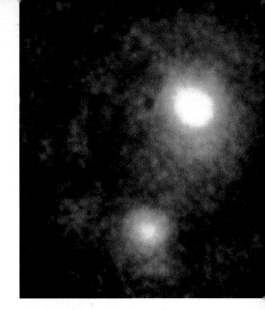

Figure 22-16 The *Hubble Space Telescope* gave astronomers their first clear view of Pluto and Charon as distinct objects.

Section Assessment

1. What are the differences between the outer planets and the inner planets?

2. Are any moons in the solar system larger than planets? If so, which ones?

3. How does Pluto differ from the other outer planets?

4. **Think Critically:** Why is Neptune sometimes the farthest planet from the sun?

5. **Skill Builder**
   Recognizing Cause and Effect
   Answer the following questions about Jupiter. If you need help, refer to Recognizing Cause and Effect in the **Skill Handbook** on page 721.

   a. What causes Jupiter's surface color?

   b. How is the Great Red Spot affected by Jupiter's atmosphere?

   c. How does Jupiter's mass affect its gravitational force?

Using Computers

Spreadsheet Design a table using spreadsheet software of the nine planets. Compare their characteristics, such as size, distance from the sun, orbital speed, and number of satellites. If you need help, refer to page 738.

Solar System Distance Model

Distances between the planets of the solar system are large. Can you design a model that will demonstrate the large distances between and among the sun and planets in the solar system?

Possible Materials

- Meterstick
- Scissors
- Pencil
- String (several meters)
- Paper (several sheets of notebook paper)

Recognize the Problem

How can a model be designed that will show the relative distances between and among the sun and planets of the solar system?

Form a Hypothesis

State a hypothesis about how a model with scale dimensions of the solar system can be constructed.

Goals

- **Make a table** of scale distances that will represent planetary distances to be used in a model of the solar system.
- **Research** planetary distances.

- **Make a model** of the distances between the sun and planets of the solar system.

Safety Precautions

Take care when handling scissors.

Planetary Distances				
Planet	Distance to Sun (km)	Distance to Sun (AU)	Scale Distance (1 AU = 10 cm)	Scale Distance (1 AU = 2 m)
Mercury	5.8×10^7			
Venus	1.08×10^8			
Earth	1.50×10^8			
Mars	2.28×10^8			
Jupiter	7.80×10^8			
Saturn	1.43×10^9			
Uranus	2.88×10^9			
Neptune	4.51×10^9			
Pluto	5.92×10^9			

Test Your Hypothesis

Plan

1. As a group, **agree** upon and write out your hypothesis statement.

2. **List** the steps that you need to take in making your model to **test** your hypothesis. Be specific, describing exactly what you will do at each step.

3. **Make** a list of the materials that you will need to complete your model.

Do

1. Make sure your teacher approves your plan before you proceed.

2. **Construct the model** as planned using your scale distances.

3. While constructing the model, **write** down any observations that you or other members of your group make and complete

4. **Make a table** of scale distances you will use in your model.

5. **Write** a description of how you will **build** your model, **explaining** how it will demonstrate relative distances between and among the sun and planets of the solar system.

the data table in your Science Journal.

4. **Calculate** the scale distance that would be used in your model if 1 AU = 2 m.

Analyze Your Data

1. **Explain** how a scale distance is determined.

2. How much string would be

required to construct a model with a scale distance 1 AU = 2 m?

Draw Conclusions

1. Was it possible to work with your scale? **Explain** why or why not.

2. Proxima Centauri, the closest star to our sun, is about

270 000 AU from the sun. Based on your scale, how much string would you need to place this star on your model?

Comets

Although the planets and their moons are the most noticeable members of the sun's family, many other objects orbit the sun. Comets, meteoroids, and asteroids are other objects in the solar system.

You've probably heard of Halley's comet. A **comet** is composed of dust and rock particles mixed in with frozen water, methane, and ammonia. Halley's comet was last seen from Earth in 1986. English astronomer Edmund Halley realized that comet sightings that had taken place about every 76 years were really sightings of the same comet. This comet, which takes about 76 years to orbit the sun, was named after him. Halley's comet is just one example of the many other objects in the solar system besides the planets. The Dutch astronomer Jan Oort proposed the idea that a large collection of comets lies in a cloud that completely surrounds the solar

Figure 22-17 Comet Hale-Bopp was visible in March and April 1997.

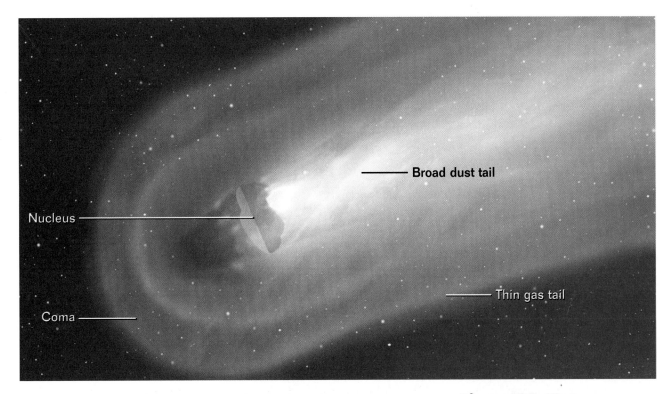

Nucleus

Broad dust tail

Thin gas tail

Coma

Figure 22-18 A comet consists of a nucleus, a coma, and a tail.

system. This cloud is located beyond the orbit of Pluto and is called the **Oort Cloud.** Evidence suggests that the gravity of the sun and nearby stars interacts with comets in the Oort Cloud. Comets either escape from the solar system or get captured into much smaller orbits. As mentioned earlier, another belt of comets, called the Kuiper belt, may exist near the orbit of Neptune.

On July 23, 1995, two backyard astronomers made an exciting discovery—a new comet was headed toward the sun. This comet, Comet Hale-Bopp, is larger than most that approach the sun and was the brightest comet visible from Earth in 20 years. Shown in **Figure 22-17,** it was at its brightest in March and April 1997.

Structure of Comets

The structure of a comet, shown in **Figure 22-18,** is like a large, dirty snowball or a mass of frozen ice and rock. But as the comet approaches the sun, it develops a distinctive structure. Ices of water, methane, and ammonia begin to vaporize because of the heat from the sun. Dust and bits of rock are released. The vaporized gases and released dust form a bright cloud called a coma around the nucleus, or solid part, of the comet. The solar wind pushes on the gases and released dust in the coma. These particles form a tail that always points away from the sun.

After many trips around the sun, most of the frozen ice in a comet has vaporized. All that is left are small particles that spread throughout the orbit of the original comet.

*inter*NET
CONNECTION

Visit the Glencoe Science Web Site at **www.glencoe.com/ sec/science** for more information about comets.

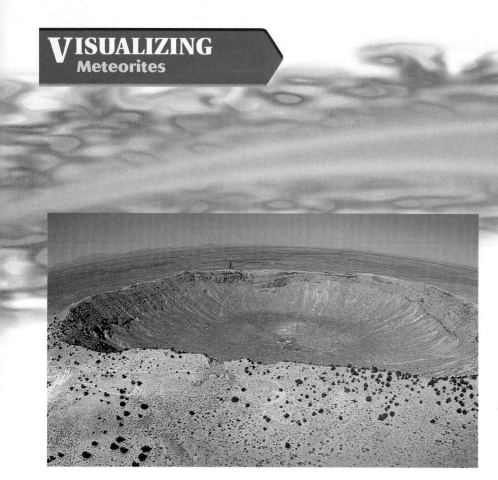

Figure 22-19 Meteorites strike the surface of a moon or planet.

A A large meteorite struck Arizona 50 000 years ago.

*inter***NET**
C O N N E C T I O N

Visit the Glencoe Science Web Site at **www.glencoe.com/ sec/science** for more information about meteor craters.

Meteoroids, Meteors, and Meteorites

You learned that comets tend to break up after they have passed close to the sun several times. The small pieces of the comet nucleus spread out into a loose group within the original orbit of the broken comet. These small pieces of rock moving through space are then called meteoroids.

When the path of a meteoroid crosses the position of Earth, it enters our atmosphere at between 15 and 70 km/s. Most meteoroids are so small that they are completely vaporized in Earth's atmosphere. A meteoroid that burns up in Earth's atmosphere is called a **meteor.** People often see these and call them shooting stars.

Each time Earth passes through the loose group of particles within the old orbit of a comet, many small particles of rock and dust enter the atmosphere. Because more meteors than usual are seen, this is called a meteor shower.

If the meteoroid is large enough, it may not completely burn up in Earth's atmosphere. When it strikes Earth, it is called a **meteorite.** Meteor Crater in Arizona, shown in **Figure 22-19A,** was formed when a large meteorite struck Earth about 50 000 years ago. Most meteorites are probably debris from asteroid collisions or broken-up comets, but some are from the moon and Mars.

Reading Check ☑
What is a meteorite?

This crater made by a meteorite is on the moon.

C A meteoroid that burns up in Earth's atmosphere is called a meteor.

Asteroids

An **asteroid** is a piece of rock similar to the material that formed into the planets. Most asteroids are located in an area between the orbits of Mars and Jupiter called the asteroid belt, shown in **Figure 22-20.** Why are they located there? The gravity of Jupiter may have kept a planet from forming in the area where the asteroid belt is now located.

Other asteroids are scattered throughout the solar system—they may have been thrown out of the belt by gravity. Some may have since been captured as moons around other planets.

Figure 22-20 The asteroid belt lies between the orbits of Mars and Jupiter.

Asteroid belt

Earth

Mars

Jupiter

Asteroid Size

The sizes of the asteroids in the asteroid belt range from tiny particles to 940 km. Ceres is the largest and the first one discovered. The next three in size are Pallas (523 km), Vesta (501 km), and Juno (244 km). Two asteroids, Gaspra and Ida, were photographed by *Galileo* on its way to Jupiter, as shown in **Figure 22-21.**

Comets, meteoroids, and asteroids are probably composed of material that formed early in the history of the solar system. Scientists study the structure and composition of these space objects in order to better understand what the solar system may have been like long ago. Understanding what the early solar system was like could help scientists to better understand the formation of Earth and its relationship to other objects in the solar system.

Figure 22-21 The asteroid Ida (A) is about 56 km long. Gaspra (B) is about 20 km long.

Section Assessment

1. How does a comet's tail form as it approaches the sun?
2. What type of feature might be formed on Earth if a large meteorite reached its surface?
3. Describe differences among comets, meteoroids, and asteroids.
4. **Think Critically:** What is the chemical composition of comets? Are comets more similar to the inner or the outer planets?
5. **Skill Builder**

   Inferring Scientists can learn a lot about a planet's history by studying its impact craters. Do the **Chapter 22 Skill Activity** on page 763 to infer how scientific illustrations can be used to determine the ages of impact craters.

Science **Journal** The asteroid belt contains many objects—from tiny particles to objects 940 km in diameter. In your Science Journal, describe how mining the asteroids for valuable minerals might be accomplished.

Mission to Mars

Scientists are currently developing plans for further exploration of Mars. But even at its closest, Mars is 55 million km away from Earth, a distance that would take astronauts three years to travel round-trip. Given the long flight, not to mention conditions astronauts would face living on Mars, a journey to the Red Planet would be full of risks. This raises a question: Should humans or robots be sent to explore Mars?

Risks to Humans

Getting to and from Mars would take a toll on the human body. In the near-zero gravity of outer space, bones lose calcium and gradually become weaker. Muscles lose their strength as well, because they don't have to work against gravity to support and move body parts. Furthermore, in a weightless environment, body fluids don't flow downward as they do on Earth. Unusual circulation of body fluids can interfere with kidney function and lead to dehydration.

Assuming humans survived the long flight to Mars in good health, they would face other challenges upon arrival. To explore Mars properly, a team of astronauts would probably have to live on the planet for months, even years. The NASA painting, left, shows a module that could house explorers. Such a structure would have to withstand the Martian environment and protect astronauts from high levels of solar radiation.

The Case for Robots

Because of the many risks a Mars mission would pose for humans, some scientists suggest sending specialized robots that could operate equipment and carry out scientific experiments. These robots would be equipped with artificial senses that would allow researchers on Earth to experience the planet's surface in a way second only to being there in person. However, radio signals sent back and forth between robots on Mars and operators on Earth would take up to 20 minutes to travel each way. Scientists are working to solve this problem in the hope that extensive exploration of Mars will soon be a reality—by people or by machines.

Science JOURNAL ▶

How do you think Mars should be further explored? Write a proposal to your class explaining how you would explore Mars.

For a **preview** of this chapter, study this Reviewing Main Ideas before you read the chapter. After you have studied this chapter, you can use the Reviewing Main Ideas to **review** the chapter.

The Glencoe MindJogger, Audiocassettes, and CD-ROM provide additional opportunities for review.

Section

22-1 THE SOLAR SYSTEM

Early astronomers thought that the planets, the moon, the sun, and the stars were embedded in separate spheres that rotated around Earth. The sun-centered model of the **solar system** states that the sun is the center of the solar system. Using a telescope, Galileo discovered evidence that supported the sun-centered model. Later, Kepler discovered that the planets orbit the sun in elliptical orbits, not circles. *What type of evidence did Galileo discover that indicated the sun-centered model was correct?*

Section

22-2 THE INNER PLANETS

The **inner planets,** in increasing distance from the sun are Mercury, Venus, Earth, and Mars. The moonlike **Mercury** has craters and cliffs on its surface. **Venus** has a dense atmosphere of carbon dioxide and sulfuric acid. On **Earth,** water exists in three states. **Mars** appears red due to the iron oxide content of its weathered rocks. Recent studies by *Pathfinder* indicate that Mars's surface once had large amounts of water flowing over it. *Venus and Earth are similar in size and mass. Why, then, are their surface characteristics so different?*

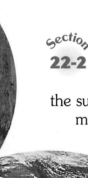

Reading Check ✓

Locate a legend, myth, or folktale from another culture that explains the origin of all or part of the solar system. Share it with the class.

Section

22-3 THE OUTER PLANETS

Faint rings and 16 moons orbit the gaseous **Jupiter.** Jupiter's Great Red Spot is a high-pressure storm generated by huge thunderstorms in Jupiter's atmosphere. **Saturn** is made mostly of gas and has pronounced rings. **Uranus** is a large, gaseous planet with many moons and several rings. **Neptune** is similar to Uranus in size, composition, and stormlike features. **Pluto** has a thin, changing atmosphere, and its surface is icy rock. *Why would the average densities of the four large, outer planets be so low when compared with the average densities of the inner planets?*

Section

22-4 OTHER OBJECTS IN THE SOLAR SYSTEM

As a **comet** approaches the sun, vaporized gases form a bright coma around the comet's nucleus and solar wind forms a tail that points away from the sun. Meteoroids form when asteroids collide, when comets break up, or when **meteorites** collide with the moon or other planets. An **asteroid** is a piece of rock usually found in the asteroid belt. *Why does the tail of a comet always point away from the sun?*

Using Vocabulary

a. asteroid
b. astronomical unit
c. comet
d. Earth
e. Great Red Spot
f. inner planet
g. Jupiter
h. Mars
i. Mercury
j. meteor
k. meteorite
l. Neptune
m. Oort Cloud
n. outer planet
o. Pluto
p. Saturn
q. solar system
r. Uranus
s. Venus

Distinguish between the terms in each of the following pairs.

1. asteroid, comet
2. inner planet, outer planet
3. meteor, meteorite
4. Great Red Spot, Oort Cloud
5. Neptune, Uranus

Checking Concepts

Choose the word or phrase that best answers the question.

6. Who proposed a sun-centered solar system?
   A) Ptolemy
   B) Copernicus
   C) Galileo
   D) Oort

7. How does the sun produce energy?
   A) magnetism
   B) nuclear fission
   C) nuclear fusion
   D) the greenhouse effect

8. What is the shape of planetary orbits?
   A) circles
   B) ellipses
   C) squares
   D) rectangles

9. Which planet has extreme temperatures because it has essentially no atmosphere?
   A) Earth
   B) Jupiter
   C) Mars
   D) Mercury

10. Water is a solid, liquid, and gas on which planet?
    A) Pluto
    B) Uranus
    C) Saturn
    D) Earth

11. Where is the largest known volcano in the solar system?
    A) Earth
    B) Jupiter
    C) Mars
    D) Uranus

12. What do scientists call a rock that strikes Earth's surface?
    A) asteroid
    B) comet
    C) meteorite
    D) meteoroid

13. Which planet has a complex ring system made of hundreds of ringlets?
    A) Pluto
    B) Saturn
    C) Uranus
    D) Mars

14. Which planet has a magnetic pole tilted 60 degrees?
    A) Uranus
    B) Earth
    C) Jupiter
    D) Pluto

15. How does the tail of a comet always point?
    A) toward the sun
    B) away from the sun
    C) toward Earth
    D) away from the Oort Cloud

Thinking Critically

16. Why is the surface temperature on Venus so much higher than that on Earth?

17. Describe the relationship between the mass of a planet and the number of satellites it has.

18. Why are probe landings on Jupiter or Saturn unlikely events?

19. What evidence suggests that water is or once was present on Mars?

20. An observer on Earth can watch Venus go through phases much like Earth's moon does. Explain why this is so.

Developing Skills

If you need help, refer to the **Skill Handbook.**

21. Concept Mapping: Complete the concept map on this page to show how a comet changes as it travels through space.

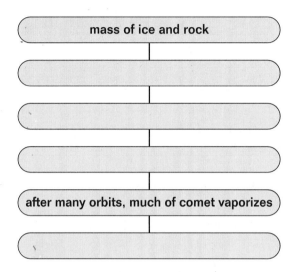

mass of ice and rock

after many orbits, much of comet vaporizes

22. Hypothesizing: Mercury is the closest planet to the sun, yet it does not reflect much of the sun's light. What can you say about Mercury's color?

23. Sequencing: Arrange the following planets in order from the planet with the most natural satellites to the one with the fewest: Earth, Jupiter, Saturn, Neptune, Uranus, and Mars.

24. Making and Using Tables: Make a table that summarizes the main characteristics of each planet in the solar system.

25. Measuring in SI: The Great Red Spot of Jupiter is about 40 000 km long and about 12 000 km wide. What is its approximate area in km^2?

THE PRINCETON REVIEW

Test-Taking Tip

Get to the Root of Things If you don't know a word's meaning, you can still get an idea of its meaning if you focus on its roots, prefixes, and suffixes. For instance, words that start with *non-, un-, a-, dis-,* and *in-* generally reverse what the rest of the word means.

Test Practice

Use these questions to test your Science Proficiency.

1. Earth is probably the only planet in our solar system on which life exists. Which of the following statements **BEST** explains why this is true?
A) Earth is the only planet on which water exists in all three states.
B) Earth has frozen ice caps at its poles.
C) Earth has carbon dioxide in its atmosphere.
D) Earth has an atmosphere.

2. Both Copernicus and Kepler proposed a model of the solar system. What was the major difference between the two models?
A) Copernicus's model had the sun in the center. Kepler's model had Earth in the center.
B) Copernicus's model included Saturn. Kepler's model did not.
C) Copernicus's model included circular orbits for the planets. Kepler's model included elliptical orbits for the planets.
D) Copernicus's model showed the moon as a planet. Kepler's model showed the moon as a satellite of Earth.

CHAPTER

23 Stars and Galaxies

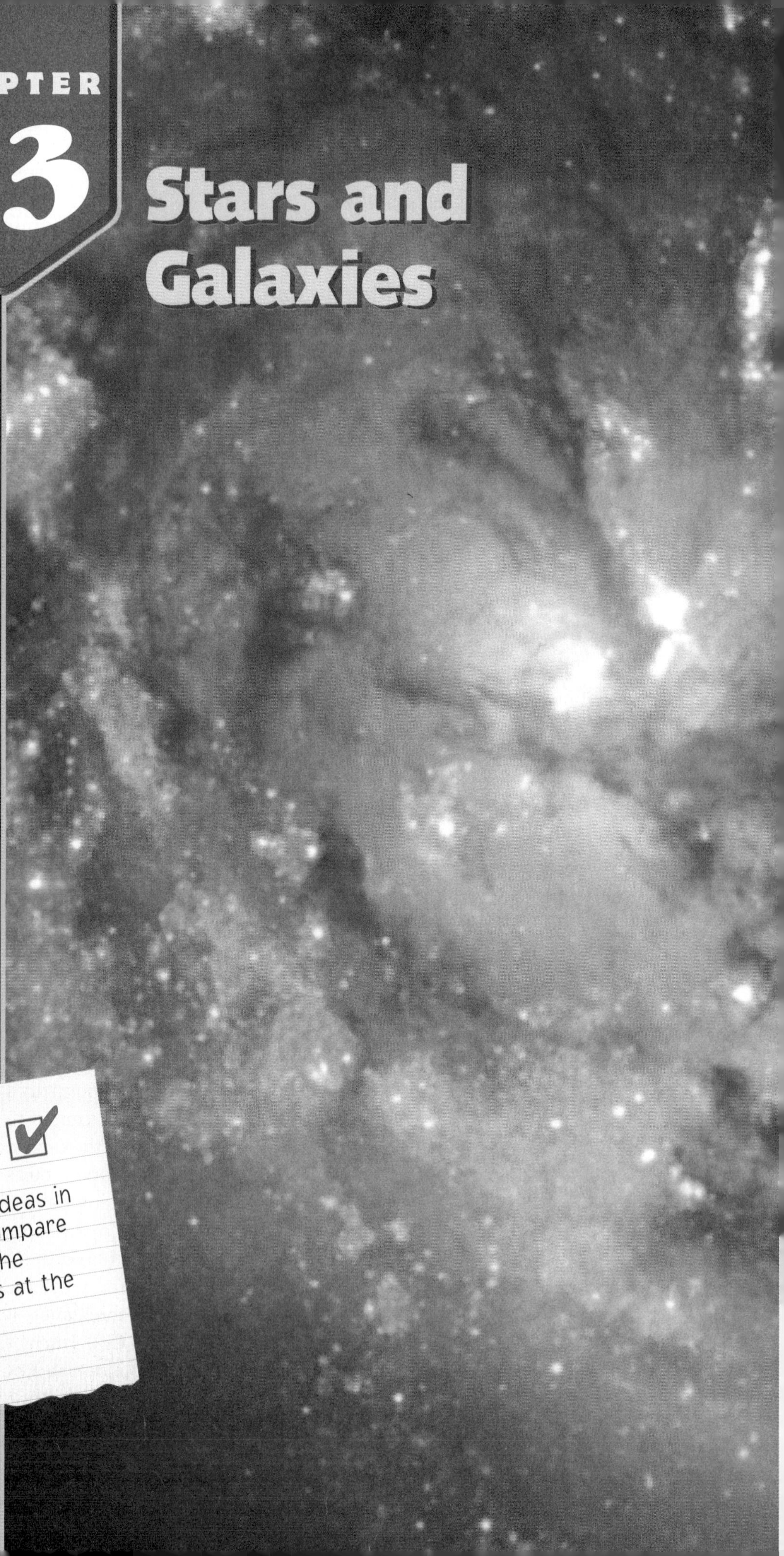

Chapter Preview

Skills Preview

Skill Builders
- Predict

Activities
- Measure in SI

MiniLabs
- Make a Model

Reading Check

Summarize the main ideas in Section 23-1. Then, compare your summary with the Reviewing Main Ideas at the end of the chapter.

Explore Activity

This photo may look like science fiction, but it shows a real event. It is a photo of two galaxies colliding. Other galaxies are moving away from each other. The universe is full of billions of galaxies, each containing billions of stars. By studying deep space, astronomers have observed that the universe is expanding in all directions. In the following activity, you can model how the universe might be expanding.

Model the Universe

1. Partially inflate a balloon. Clip the neck shut with a clothespin.

2. Draw six evenly spaced dots on the balloon with a felt-tip marker. Label the dots A through F.

3. Use a string and ruler to measure the distance, in millimeters, from dot A to each of the other dots.

4. Remove the clothespin and inflate the balloon some more.

5. Measure the distance of each dot from A again.

6. Inflate the balloon again, tie the neck shut, and take new measurements.

Science Journal

If each dot represents a galaxy and the balloon represents the universe, describe the motion of the galaxies relative to one another. Is the universe expanding? Explain.

Constellations

Have you ever watched clouds drift by on a summer day? It's fun to look at the clouds and imagine they have shapes familiar to you. One may look like a face. Another might resemble a rabbit or a bear. People long ago did much the same thing with patterns of stars in the sky. They named certain groups of stars, called **constellations,** after animals, characters in mythology, or familiar objects.

From Earth, a constellation looks like a group of stars that are relatively close to one another. In most cases, the stars in a constellation have no relationship to each other in space.

The position of a star in the sky can be given as a specific location within a constellation. For example, you can say that the star Betelgeuse (BEE tul jooz) is in the shoulder of the mighty hunter Orion. Orion's faithful companion is his dog, Canis Major. The brightest star in the sky, Sirius, is in the constellation Canis Major. Orion and Canis Major are shown in **Figure 23-1.**

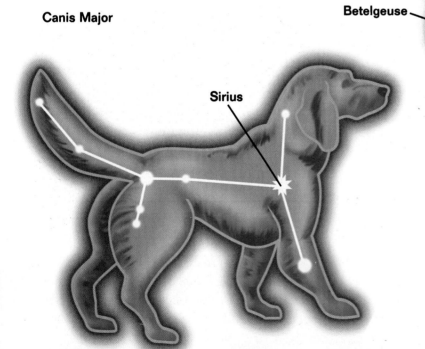

Canis Major

Sirius

Betelgeuse

Orion

Figure 23-1 Groups of stars can form patterns that look like familiar objects or characters.

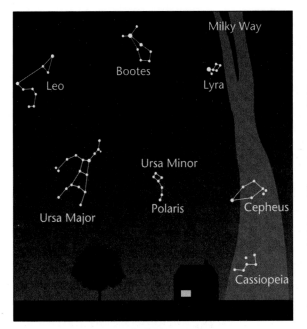

Summer

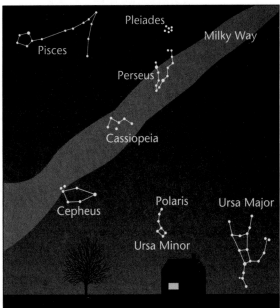

Winter

Early Greek astronomers named many constellations. Modern astronomers used many of these names to divide the sky into 88 constellations. You may already know some of them. Have you ever tried to find the Big Dipper? It's part of the constellation Ursa Major, shown in **Figure 23-2.** Notice how the front two stars of the Big Dipper point directly at the star Polaris. Polaris, also known as the North Star, is located at the end of the Little Dipper in the constellation Ursa Minor. Polaris is almost directly over Earth's north pole. You'll learn how to locate Polaris and constellations in the **Field Guide to Backyard Astronomy** at the end of this chapter.

Figure 23-2 Some constellations are visible only during certain seasons of the year. Others, such as those close to Polaris, are visible year-round.

Circumpolar Constellations

As Earth rotates, you can watch Ursa Major, Ursa Minor, and other constellations in the northern sky circle around Polaris. Because these constellations circle Polaris, they are called circumpolar constellations.

All of the constellations appear to move because Earth is moving. Look at **Figure 23-3.** The stars appear to complete one full circle in the sky in just under 24 hours as Earth rotates on its axis. The stars also appear to change positions in the sky throughout the year as Earth revolves around the sun.

Circumpolar constellations are visible all year long, but other constellations are not. As Earth orbits the sun, different constellations come into view while others disappear. Orion, which is visible in the winter in the northern hemisphere, can't be seen in the summer because the daytime side of Earth is facing it.

Figure 23-3 This photograph shows the path of circumpolar stars over several hours. Polaris is almost directly over the north pole. **Does Polaris appear to move as Earth rotates? Explain.**

Absolute and Apparent Magnitudes

When you look at constellations, you'll notice that some stars are brighter than others. Sirius looks much brighter than Rigel. But is Sirius actually a brighter star, or is it just closer to Earth, which makes it appear to be brighter? As it turns out, Sirius is 100 times closer to Earth than Rigel. If Sirius and Rigel were the same distance from Earth, Rigel would appear much brighter in the night sky than would Sirius.

When you refer to the brightness of a star, you can refer to either its absolute magnitude or its apparent magnitude. The **absolute magnitude** of a star is a measure of the amount of light it actually gives off. A measure of the amount of light received on Earth is called the **apparent magnitude.** A star that's actually rather dim can appear bright in the sky if it's close to Earth. A star that's actually bright can appear dim if it's far away. If two stars are the same distance away, what factors might cause one of them to be brighter than the other? ☑

You can experience the effect of distance on apparent magnitude when driving in a car at night. Observe the other cars' headlights as they approach. Which cars' headlights are brighter—those that are closer to you or those that are farther away?

Reading Check ☑

What is absolute magnitude?

Problem Solving

Star Light, Star Bright

Mary conducted an experiment to determine the relationship between distance and the brightness of stars. She used a meterstick, a light meter, and a lightbulb. The bulb was mounted at the zero end of the meterstick. Mary placed the light meter at the 20-cm mark on the meterstick and recorded the distance and the light-meter reading in the data table below. Readings are in luxes, which are units for measuring light intensity. Mary doubled and tripled the distance and took more readings.

Think Critically: What happened to the amount of light recorded when the distance was increased from 20 cm to 40 cm? From 20 cm to 60 cm? What does this indicate about the relationship between light intensity and distance? What would the light intensity be at 100 cm?

Effect of Distance on Light	
Distance (cm)	Meter Reading (luxes)
20	4150.0
40	1037.5
60	461.1
80	259.4

How far are stars?

How do we know when a star is close to our solar system? One way is to measure its parallax. **Parallax** is the apparent shift in the position of an object when viewed from two different positions. You are already familiar with parallax. Hold your hand at arm's length and look at one finger first with your left eye closed and then with your right eye closed. Your finger appears to change position with respect to the background. Now, try the same experiment with your finger closer to your face. What do you observe? The nearer an object is to the observer, the greater its parallax.

We can measure the parallax of relatively close stars to determine their distances from Earth, as shown in **Figure 23-4.** When astronomers first realized how far away stars actually are, it became apparent that a new unit of measure would be needed to record their distances. Measuring star distances in kilometers would be like measuring the distance between cities in millimeters.

Distances in space are measured in light-years. A **light-year** is the distance that light travels in one year. Light travels at 300 000 km/s, or about 9.5 trillion km in one year. The nearest star to Earth, other than the sun, is Proxima Centauri. Proxima Centauri is 4.2 light-years away, or about 40 trillion km.

Try at Home

Mini Lab

Observing Star Patterns

Procedure

1. On a clear night, go outside after dark and study the stars. Take an adult with you and see if you can help each other find constellations.

2. Let your imagination go to work and try to see any patterns of stars in the sky that look like something with which you are familiar.

3. Draw the stars you see, where they are in the sky, and include a drawing of what you think the star pattern resembles.

Analysis

1. How do your constellations compare with those observed by your classmates?

2. How do you think recognizing star patterns could be useful?

Figure 23-4 Parallax can be seen if you observe the same star while Earth is at two different points during its orbit around the sun (A). The star's position relative to more-distant background stars will appear to change (B and C).

As seen in January

As seen in July

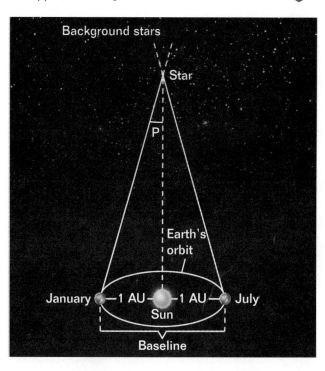

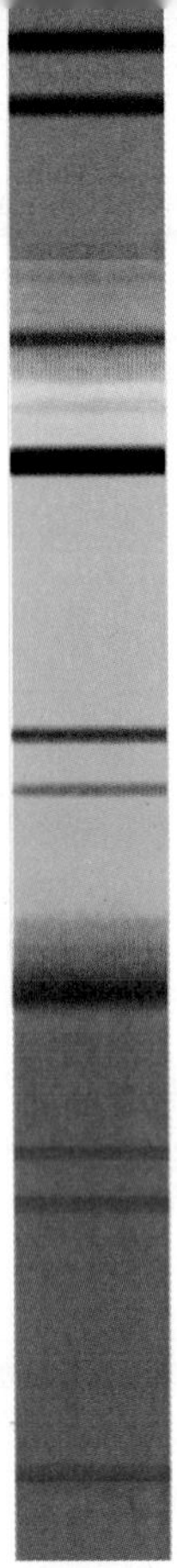

How hot are stars?

The color of a star indicates its temperature. For example, hot stars are a blue-white color. A relatively cool star looks orange or red. Stars the temperature of our sun have a yellow color.

Astronomers learn about other properties of stars by studying their spectra. They use spectrographs to break visible light from a star into its component colors. If you look closely at the spectrum of a star, such as the ones shown in **Figure 23-5,** you will see dark lines in it. The lines are caused by elements in the star's atmosphere.

As light radiated from a star passes through the star's atmosphere, some of it is absorbed by elements in the atmosphere. The wavelengths of visible light that are absorbed appear as dark lines in the spectrum. Each element absorbs certain wavelengths, producing a certain pattern of dark lines. The patterns of lines can be used to identify which elements are in a star's atmosphere.

Figure 23-5
These star spectra were made by placing a prism over a telescope's objective lens. **What causes the lines in spectra?**

Section Assessment

1. Explain how Earth's revolution affects constellations that are visible throughout the year.

2. If two stars give off the same amount of light, what might cause one to look brighter than the other?

3. If the spectrum of another star shows the same absorption lines as the sun, what can be said about its composition?

4. **Think Critically:** Only about 700 stars can be studied using parallax. Most stars are invisible to the naked eye. What does this indicate about their apparent magnitudes?

5. **Skill Builder**
   Recognizing Cause and Effect
   Suppose you viewed Proxima Centauri through a telescope. How old were you when the light that you see left Proxima Centauri? Why might Proxima Centauri look dimmer than the star Betelgeuse, a large star 310 light-years away? If you need help, refer to Recognizing Cause and Effect in the **Skill Handbook** on page 721.

Using Computers

Graphics Use drawing software on a computer to make a star chart of major constellations visible from your home during the current season. Include reference points to help others find the charted constellations. If you need help, refer to page 734.

The Sun

Layers of the Sun

More than 99 percent of all of the matter in our solar system is in the sun. The sun is the center of our solar system, and it makes life possible on Earth. But in the grand scheme of the universe, our sun is just another star in the sky.

The sun is an average, middle-aged star. Its absolute magnitude is about average and it shines with a yellow light. Like other stars, the sun is an enormous ball of gas, producing energy by fusing hydrogen into helium in its core. **Figure 23-6** is a model of the sun's interior and atmosphere.

The Sun's Atmosphere

The lowest layer of the sun's atmosphere and the layer from which light is given off is the **photosphere.** The photosphere is often called the surface of the sun. Temperatures there are around 6000 K. Above the photosphere is the **chromosphere.** This layer extends upward about 2000 km above the photosphere. A transition zone occurs between 2000 and 10 000 km above the photosphere. Above the transition zone is the **corona.** This is the largest layer of the sun's atmosphere and extends millions of kilometers into space. Temperatures in the corona are as high as 2 million K. Charged particles continually escape from the corona and move through space as solar wind.

What You'll Learn

► How energy is produced in the sun
► That sunspots, prominences, and solar flares are related
► Why our sun is considered an average star and how it differs from stars in binary systems

Vocabulary
photosphere
chromosphere
corona
sunspot
binary system

Why It's Important

► The sun is the source of most energy on Earth.

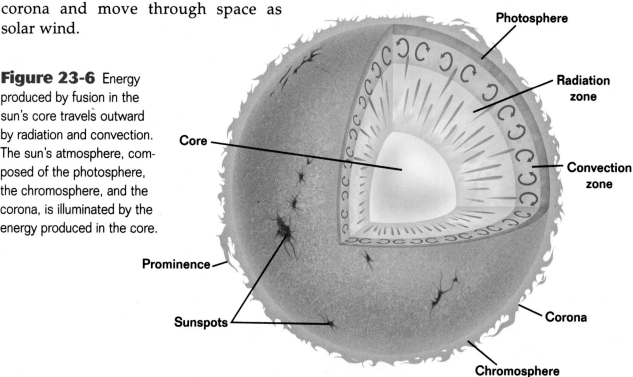

Figure 23-6 Energy produced by fusion in the sun's core travels outward by radiation and convection. The sun's atmosphere, composed of the photosphere, the chromosphere, and the corona, is illuminated by the energy produced in the core.

Photosphere

Radiation zone

Convection zone

Core

Corona

Prominence

Chromosphere

Sunspots

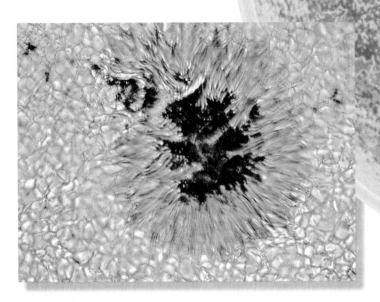

Figure 23-7 Sunspots are bright, but when viewed against the rest of the photosphere, they appear dark. The small photo is a close-up of a sunspot.

Surface Features of the Sun

Because the sun is a ball of hot gas, it's hard to imagine its surface as anything but a smooth layer. In reality, the sun's surface has many features, including sunspots, prominences, and flares.

Sunspots

Areas of the sun's surface that appear to be dark because they are cooler than surrounding areas are called **sunspots.** Ever since Galileo identified sunspots like those in **Figure 23-7,** scientists have been studying them. One thing we've learned by studying sunspots is that the sun rotates. We can observe the movement of individual sunspots as they move with the sun's rotation. The sun doesn't rotate as a solid body, as does Earth. It rotates faster at its equator than at its poles. Sunspots near the equator take about 27 days to go around the sun. At higher latitudes, they take 31 days. ☑

Reading Check ☑
What are sunspots?

Sunspots aren't permanent features on the sun. They appear and disappear over a period of several days, weeks, or months. Also, there are times when there are many large sunspots—a sunspot maximum—and times when there are only a few small sunspots or none at all—a sunspot minimum. Periods of sunspot maximum occur about every 11 years.

Prominences and Flares

Sunspots are related to several features on the sun's surface. The intense magnetic field associated with sunspots may cause prominences, which are huge arching columns of gas. Some prominences blast material from the sun into space at speeds ranging from 600 km/s to more than 1000 km/s.

Gases near a sunspot sometimes brighten up suddenly, shooting gas outward at high speed. These violent eruptions from the sun, shown in **Figure 23-8,** are called solar flares.

Ultraviolet light and X rays from solar flares can reach Earth and cause disruption of radio signals. Solar flares make communication by radio and telephone difficult at times. High-energy particles emitted by solar flares are captured by Earth's magnetic field, disrupting communication equipment. These particles also interact with Earth's atmosphere near the polar regions and create light. This light is called the aurora borealis, or northern lights, when it occurs in the northern hemisphere. In the southern hemisphere, it is called the aurora australis.

*inter*NET
CONNECTION

Visit the Glencoe Science Web Site at **www.glencoe.com/ sec/science** for more information about sunspots, solar flares, and prominences.

Figure 23-8 Features such as solar flares (A) and solar prominences (B) can reach hundreds of thousands of kilometers into space. **How big is this compared with the size of Earth?**

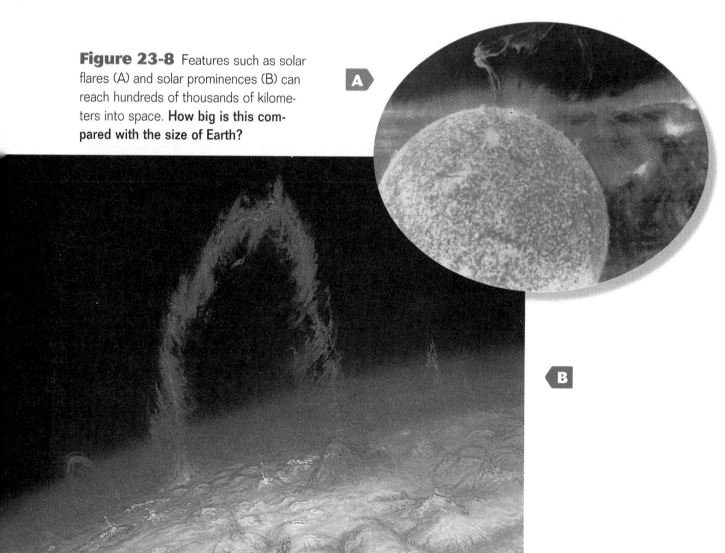

Our Sun—A Typical Star?

Figure 23-9 Pleiades is a cluster of stars that are gravitationally bound to each other.

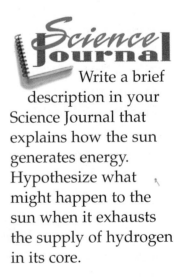

Although our sun is an average star, it is somewhat unusual in one way. Most stars are in systems in which two or more stars orbit each other. When two stars orbit each other, they make up a **binary system.**

In some cases, astronomers can detect binary systems because one star occasionally eclipses the other. The total amount of light from the star system becomes dim and then bright again on a regular cycle. Algol in Perseus is an example of this.

In many cases, stars move through space together as a cluster. In a star cluster, many stars are relatively close to one another and are gravitationally attracted to each other. The Pleiades star cluster, shown in **Figure 23-9,** can be seen in the constellation of Taurus in the winter sky. On a clear, dark night, you may be able to see seven of the stars of this cluster. Most star clusters are far from our solar system and appear as a fuzzy patch in the night sky.

Section Assessment

1. How are sunspots, prominences, and solar flares related?

2. What properties does the sun have in common with other stars? What property makes it different from most other stars?

3. **Think Critically:** Because most stars are found in multiple-star systems, what might explain why the sun is a single star?

4. **Skill Builder**
   Interpreting Scientific Illustrations Use **Figure 23-6** to answer the questions below. If you need help, refer to Interpreting Scientific Illustrations in the **Skill Handbook** on page 726.

   a. Which layers make up the sun's atmosphere?

   b. What process occurs in the sun's convection zone that enables energy produced in the core to reach the surface?

Science Journal Write a brief description in your Science Journal that explains how the sun generates energy. Hypothesize what might happen to the sun when it exhausts the supply of hydrogen in its core.

Sunspots

Sunspots are dark, relatively cool areas on the surface of the sun. They can be observed moving across the face of the sun as it rotates. Do this activity to measure the movement of sunspots, and use your data to determine the sun's period of rotation.

What You'll Investigate

Can sunspot motion be used to determine the sun's period of rotation?

Goals

- **Observe** sunspots.
- **Estimate** sunspot size and rate of apparent motion.

Procedure

1. **Find** a location where the sun may be viewed at the same time of day for a minimum of five days. **CAUTION:** *Do not look directly at the sun. Do not look through the telescope at the sun. You could damage your eyes.*

2. **Set up** the telescope with the eyepiece facing away from the sun, as shown below. Align the telescope so that the shadow it casts on the ground is the smallest size possible. **Cut** and **attach** the cardboard as shown in the photo.

3. **Use** books to prop the clipboard upright. Point the eyepiece at the drawing paper.

4. If the telescope has a small finder scope attached, **remove** the finder scope or keep it covered.

5. **Move** the clipboard back and forth until you have the largest possible image of the sun on the paper. Adjust the telescope to form a clear image. **Trace** the outline of the sun on the paper.

6. **Trace** any sunspots that appear as dark areas on the sun's image. Repeat this step at the same time each day for a week.

Materials

- Several books
- Cardboard (about 8 cm × 12 cm)
- Clipboard
- Drawing paper (5 sheets)
- Small refracting telescope
- Small tripod
- Scissors

7. Using the sun's diameter (approximately 1 390 000 km), **estimate** the size of the largest sunspots that you observed.

8. **Calculate** how many kilometers any observed sunspots appear to move each day.

9. At the rate determined in step 8, **predict** how many days it will take for the same group of sunspots to return to about the same position in which you first observed them.

Conclude and Apply

1. What was the average number of sunspots observed each day?

2. What was the estimated size and rate of apparent motion of the largest sunspots?

3. **Infer** how sunspots can be used to determine that the sun's surface is not solid like Earth's.

The H-R Diagram

In the early 1900s, Ejnar Hertzsprung and Henry Russell noticed that for most stars, the higher their temperatures, the brighter their absolute magnitudes. They developed a graph to show this relationship.

Hertzsprung and Russell placed the temperatures of stars across the bottom of the graph and the absolute magnitudes of stars up one side. A graph that shows the relationship of a star's temperature to its absolute magnitude is called a Hertzsprung-Russell (H-R) diagram. **Figure 23-10** shows a variation of an H-R diagram.

The Main Sequence

As you can see, stars seem to fit into specific areas of the chart. Most stars fit into a diagonal band that runs from the upper left to the lower right of the chart. This band, called the **main sequence,** contains hot, blue, bright stars in the upper left and cool, red, dim stars in the lower right. Yellow, medium-temperature, medium-brightness stars fall in between. The sun is a yellow main sequence star.

About 90 percent of all stars are main sequence stars, most of which are small, red stars found in the lower right of the H-R diagram. Among main sequence stars, the hottest stars generate the most light and the coolest generate the least. But,

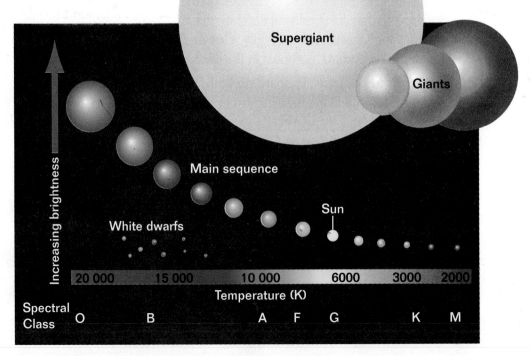

Figure 23-10 This variation of a Hertzsprung-Russell diagram shows the relationships among a star's color, temperature, and brightness. Stars in the main sequence run from hot, bright stars in the upper-left corner of the diagram to cool, faint stars in the lower-right corner. **What type of star shown in the diagram is the coolest, brightest star?**

what about the remaining ten percent? Some of these stars are hot but not bright. These small stars are located on the lower left of the H-R diagram and are called white dwarfs. Other stars are extremely bright but not hot. These large stars on the upper right of the H-R diagram are called giants, or red giants because they are usually red in color. The largest giants are called supergiants. The relative sizes of stars are shown in **Figure 23-11.**

Fusion

When the H-R diagram was developed, scientists didn't know what caused stars to shine. Hertzsprung and Russell developed their diagram without knowing what produced the light and heat of stars.

For centuries, people had been puzzled by the question of what stars were and what made them shine. It wasn't until the early part of the twentieth century that scientists began to understand how a star could shine for billions of years. Until that time, many had estimated that Earth was only a few thousand years old. The sun could have been made of coal and shined for that long. But what material could possibly burn for billions of years?

Generating Energy

In 1920, one scientist hypothesized that temperatures in the center of the sun must be high. Another scientist then suggested that with these high temperatures, hydrogen could fuse to make helium in a reaction that would release tremendous amounts of energy. **Figure 23-12** on the next page illustrates how four hydrogen nuclei could combine to create one helium nucleus. The mass of one helium nucleus is less than the mass of four hydrogen nuclei, so some mass is lost in the reaction. In the 1930s, scientists hypothesized that carbon could be used as a catalyst in fusion reactions. This explained the energy production in hotter stars.

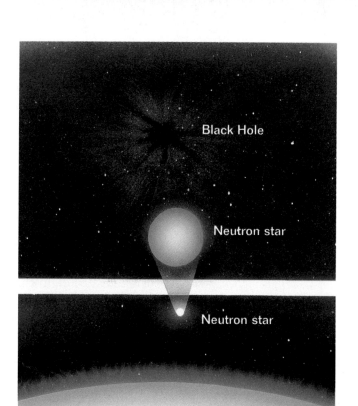
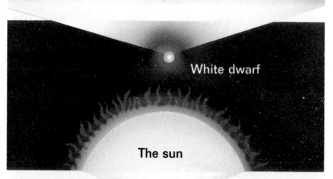
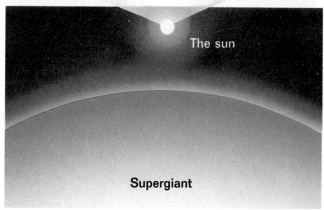

Figure 23-11 The relative sizes of stars range from supergiants as much as 800 times larger than the sun to neutron stars and black holes possibly 30 km or less across. The relative sizes of a supergiant, the sun, a white dwarf, a neutron star, and a black hole are shown.

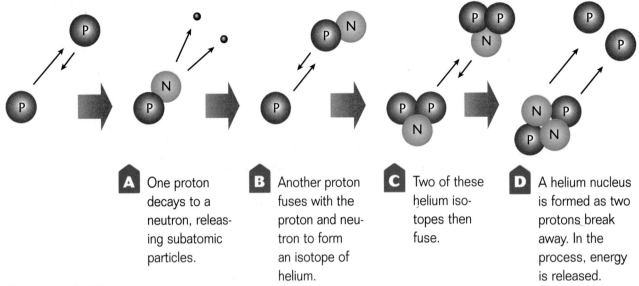

A One proton decays to a neutron, releasing subatomic particles.

B Another proton fuses with the proton and neutron to form an isotope of helium.

C Two of these helium isotopes then fuse.

D A helium nucleus is formed as two protons break away. In the process, energy is released.

Figure 23-12 In a star's core, fusion begins as two hydrogen nuclei (protons) are forced together. **What happens to the "lost" mass during this process?**

Years earlier, in 1905, Albert Einstein had proposed a theory stating that mass can be converted into energy. This was stated as the famous equation $E = mc^2$, where E is the energy produced, m is the mass, and c is the speed of light. The small amount of mass "lost" when hydrogen atoms fuse to form a helium atom is converted to a large amount of energy.

Fusion occurs in the cores of stars. Only in the core are temperatures and pressures high enough to cause atoms to fuse. Normally, they would repel each other, but in the core of a star, atoms are forced close enough together that their nuclei fuse together.

PHYSICS
INTEGRATION▶

The Evolution of Stars

The H-R diagram and other theories explained a lot about stars. But they also led to more questions. Many wondered why some stars didn't fit in the main sequence group and what happened when a star exhausted its supply of hydrogen fuel. Today, we have a theory of how stars evolve, what makes them different from one another, and what happens when they die. **Figure 23-13** illustrates the lives of different types of stars.

Nebula

Stars begin as a large cloud of gas and dust called a **nebula.** The particles of gas and dust exert a gravitational force on each other, and the nebula begins to contract. Gravitational forces cause instability within the nebula. The nebula can fragment into smaller pieces. Each will eventually collapse to form a star. ☑

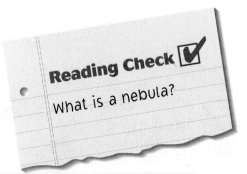
Reading Check ☑
What is a nebula?

As the particles in the smaller clouds move closer together, the temperatures in each nebula increase. When temperatures inside each nebula reach 10 millionK, fusion begins. The energy released radiates outward through the condensing ball of gas. As the energy radiates into space, stars are born.

Main Sequence to Giant Stars

In the newly formed star, the heat from fusion causes pressure that balances the attraction due to gravity, and the star becomes a main sequence star. It continues to use up its hydrogen fuel.

When hydrogen in the core of the star is exhausted, there is no longer a balance between pressure and gravity. The core contracts, and temperatures inside the star increase. This causes the outer layers of the star to expand. In this late stage of its life cycle, a star is called a **giant.**

Once the core temperature reaches 100 millionK, helium nuclei fuse to form carbon in the giant's core. By this time, the star has expanded to an enormous size, and its outer layers are much cooler than they were when it was a main sequence star. In about 5 billion years, our sun will become a giant.

CHEMISTRY
INTEGRATION

Star Spectrum
The spectrum of a star shows absorption lines of helium and hydrogen and is bright in the blue end. Describe as much as you can about the star's composition and surface temperature.

Figure 23-13 The life of a star depends greatly on its mass. Massive stars eventually become neutron stars, or possibly black holes. **What happens to stars the size of our sun?**

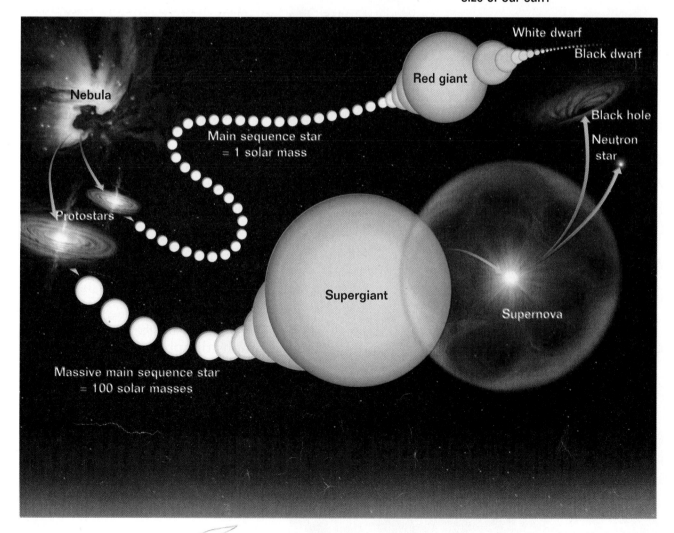

White dwarf

Black dwarf

Red giant

Nebula

Black hole

Neutron star

Main sequence star = 1 solar mass

Protostars

Supergiant

Supernova

Massive main sequence star = 100 solar masses

White Dwarfs

After the star's core uses up its supply of helium, it contracts even more. As the core of a star like the sun runs out of fuel, its outer layers escape into space. This leaves behind the hot, dense core. The core contracts under the force of gravity. At this stage in a star's evolution, it is a **white dwarf.** A white dwarf is about the size of Earth.

Supergiants and Supernovas

In stars that are over ten times more massive than our sun, the stages of evolution occur more quickly and more violently. The core heats up to much higher temperatures. Heavier and heavier elements form by fusion. The star expands into a **supergiant.** Eventually, iron forms in the core. Fusion can no longer occur once iron forms. The core collapses violently, sending a shock wave outward through the star. The outer portion of the star explodes, producing a supernova like the one shown in **Figure 23-14.** A supernova can be billions of times brighter than the original star.

Figure 23-14 This photo shows a supernova, the explosion of a star. **Explain why a supernova occurs.**

Neutron Stars

The collapsed core of a supernova shrinks to about 10 km to 15 km in diameter. Only neutrons can exist in the dense core, and the supernova becomes a **neutron star.**

If the remaining dense core is more than two times more massive than the sun, probably nothing can stop the core's collapse. It quickly evolves into a **black hole**—an object so dense that nothing can escape its gravity field.

Black Holes

If you could shine a flashlight on a black hole, the light wouldn't illuminate the black hole. The light would simply disappear into it. So, how do scientists locate black holes? Matter being pulled into a black hole can collide with other material, generating X rays. Astronomers have located X-ray sources around possible black holes. Extremely massive black holes probably exist in the centers of galaxies.

What are nebulas?

A star begins its life as a nebula, shown in **Figure 23-15**. But where does the matter in a nebula come from? Nebulas form partly from the matter that was once in other stars. A star ejects enormous amounts of matter during its lifetime. This matter can be incorporated into other nebulas, which can evolve into new stars. The matter in stars is recycled many times.

What about the matter created in the cores of stars? Are elements such as carbon and iron recycled also? Some of these elements do become parts of new stars. In fact, spectrographs have shown that our sun contains some carbon, iron, and other such elements. Because the sun is a main sequence star, it is too young to have created these elements itself. Our sun condensed from material that was created in stars that died many billions of years ago.

Some elements condense to form planets and other bodies rather than stars. In fact, your body contains many atoms that were fused in the cores of ancient stars. Evidence suggests that the first stars formed from hydrogen and helium and that all the other elements have formed in the cores of stars.

Figure 23-15 Stars are forming in the Crescent Nebula.

Section Assessment

1. Explain why giants are not in the main sequence on the H-R diagram. How do their temperatures and absolute magnitudes compare with those of main sequence stars?

2. What can be said about the absolute magnitudes of two equal-sized stars whose colors are blue and yellow?

3. Outline the history and probable future of our sun.

4. **Think Critically:** Why doesn't the helium currently in the sun's core undergo fusion?

5. **Skill Builder**
   Sequencing Sequence the following in order of most evolved to least evolved: *main sequence star, supergiant, neutron star,* and *nebula.* If you need help, refer to Sequencing in the **Skill Handbook** on page 714.

Using Math

Assume that a star's core has shrunk to a diameter of 12 km. What would be the circumference of the shrunken stellar core? Use the equation $C = \pi d$. How does this compare with the circumference of Earth with a diameter of 12 756 km?

Dreamtime Down Under

The Aborigines of Australia believe that the world began long ago—before anyone can remember—when Dreamtime began. At first, Earth was cold and dark, and the spirit Ancestors slept underground.

When the Ancestors awoke, they moved to Earth's surface and created the sun for warmth and light. Some Ancestors became people. Others became plants, animals, clouds, or stars. As the Ancestors moved over Earth, they sang, and their singing created hills, rivers, and other features.

Leaving a Path

The movement of the Ancestors left Dreaming Tracks that the Aborigines still treasure. When the Ancestors tired, they returned underground. The bodies of some Ancestors remain on Earth's surface as rock outcroppings, trees, islands, and other natural features, such as the formation in the inset, below right.

Ancient Aborigines drew maps to show where the Ancestors came out, walked, and returned underground. Drawings with traditional dot patterns (see bark painting, far right) form the basis of Aboriginal art.

Dreaming the Big Bang

Some compare the Dreamtime forces that shaped Earth to the big bang theory—huge fields of energy interacting and forming planets. Later, more energy—more Dreaming—created today's continents, including Australia.

Today, Aborigines are struggling to maintain ancient traditions while living in modern Australia. They believe that the Ancestors still live in the land and that Dreamtime continues with no foreseeable end.

Science JOURNAL ▶

In your Science Journal, write a poem that expresses your own view of our relationship to nature and to the land.

Galaxies and the Universe

Galaxies

One reason to study astronomy is to learn about your place in the universe. Long ago, people thought they were at the center of the universe and everything revolved around Earth. Today, you know this isn't the case. But, do you know where you are in the universe?

You are on Earth, and Earth orbits the sun. But does the sun orbit anything? How does it interact with other objects in the universe? The sun is one star among many in a galaxy. A **galaxy** is a large group of stars, gas, and dust held together by gravity. Our galaxy, called the Milky Way, is shown in **Figure 23-16.** It contains about 200 billion stars, including the sun. Galaxies are separated by huge distances—often millions of light-years.

Just as stars are grouped together within galaxies, galaxies are grouped into clusters. The cluster the Milky Way belongs to is called the Local Group. It contains about 30 galaxies of various types and sizes.

What **You'll Learn**

► The three main types of galaxies
► Several characteristics of the Milky Way Galaxy
► How the big bang theory explains the observed Doppler shifts of galaxies

Vocabulary
galaxy
big bang theory

Why **It's Important**

► You'll explore theories about how the universe may have formed.

Figure 23-16 The Milky Way Galaxy is usually classified as a normal spiral galaxy. Its spiral arms, composed of stars and gas, radiate out from an area of densely packed stars called the nucleus.

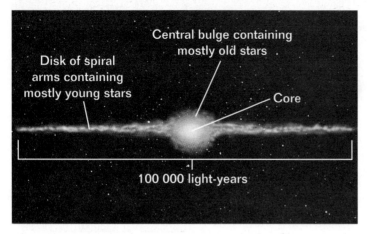

Core

Central bulge containing mostly old stars

Disk of spiral arms containing mostly young stars

Core

100 000 light-years

Location of the solar system

Figure 23-17 These illustrations show a side view and an overhead view of the Milky Way. **The Milky Way is part of what group of galaxies?**

Spiral Galaxies

The three major types of galaxies are elliptical, spiral, and irregular. Spiral galaxies have spiral arms that wind outward from inner regions. The Milky Way is a spiral galaxy, as shown in **Figure 23-17.** Its spiral arms are made up of bright stars and dust. The fuzzy patch you can see in the constellation of Andromeda is actually a spiral galaxy. It's so far away that you can't see its individual stars. Instead, it appears as a hazy spot in our sky. The Andromeda Galaxy is a member of the Local Group. It is about 2.2 million light-years away.

Arms in a normal spiral start close to the center of the galaxy. Barred spirals have spiral arms extending from a large bar of stars and gas that passes through the center of the galaxy.

Elliptical Galaxies

Probably the most common type of galaxy is the elliptical galaxy, shown in **Figure 23-18.** These galaxies are shaped like large, three-dimensional ellipses. Many are football-shaped, but others are round. Some elliptical galaxies are small, while some are so large that the entire Local Group of galaxies would fit inside one of them. **Figure 23-19** shows the Local Group and its relation to the solar system, the Milky Way, and large galaxy clusters. ☑

Reading Check ☑
Describe an elliptical galaxy.

Figure 23-18 This photo shows an example of an elliptical galaxy. **What are the two other types of galaxies?**

The Local Supercluster

The Local Cluster (Coma-Sculptor Cloud)

The Solar System

The Local Group

The Milky Way Galaxy

Irregular Galaxies

The third type of galaxy, irregular, includes most of those galaxies that don't fit into the other classifications. Irregular galaxies have many different shapes and are smaller and less common than the other types. Two irregular galaxies called the Clouds of Magellan orbit the Milky Way. The Large Magellanic Cloud is shown in **Figure 23-20**.

The Milky Way Galaxy

The Milky Way contains more than 200 billion stars. The visible disk of stars is about 100,000 light-years across, and the sun is located about 30,000 light-years out from its center. In our galaxy, all stars orbit around a central region. Based on a distance of 30,000 light-years and a speed of 235 km/s, the sun orbits around the center of the Milky Way once every 240 million years.

The Milky Way is usually classified as a normal spiral galaxy. However, recent evidence suggests that it might be a barred spiral. It is difficult to know for sure because we can never see our galaxy from the outside.

You can't see the normal spiral or barred shape of the Milky Way because you are

Figure 23-19 There may be more than 100 billion galaxies in the universe, and nearly all of them seem to be organized into clusters.

Figure 23-20 The Large Magellanic Cloud is an irregular galaxy. It's a member of the Local Group, and it orbits our own galaxy.

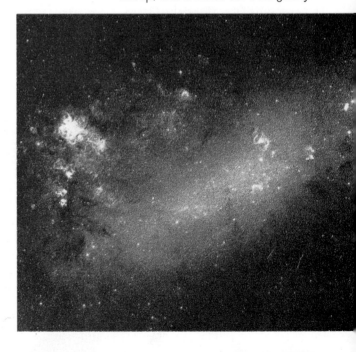

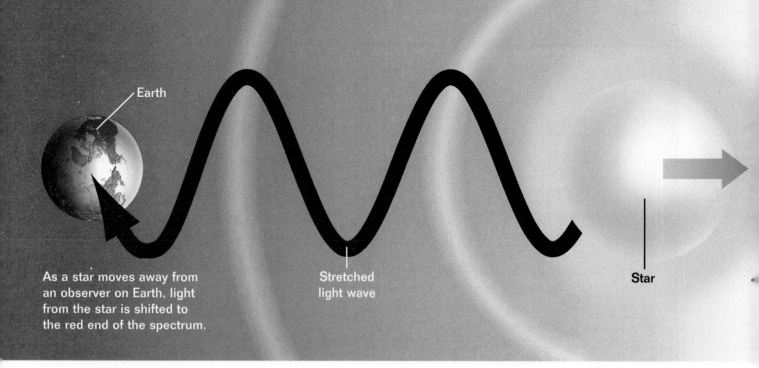

As a star moves away from an observer on Earth, light from the star is shifted to the red end of the spectrum.

Earth

Stretched light wave

Star

Figure 23-21 The Doppler shift causes the wavelengths of light coming from stars and galaxies to be compressed or stretched.

located within one of its spiral arms. You can see the Milky Way stretching across the sky as a faint band of light. All of the stars you can see in the night sky belong to the Milky Way Galaxy.

Mini Lab

Measuring Distance in Space

Procedure

1. On a large sheet of paper, draw an overhead view of the Milky Way Galaxy. If necessary, refer to **Figure 23–17.** Choose a scale to show distance in light-years.

2. Mark the approximate location of our solar system, about two-thirds of the way out on one of the spiral arms.

3. Draw a circle around the sun indicating the 4.2 light-year distance of the next closest star to the sun, Proxima Centauri.

Analysis

1. What scale did you use to represent distance on your model?

2. At this scale, interpret how far away the next closest spiral galaxy—the Andromeda Galaxy—would be located.

Expansion of the Universe

What does it sound like when a car is blowing its horn while it drives past you? The horn has a high pitch as the car approaches you, then the horn seems to drop in pitch as the car drives away. This effect is called the Doppler shift. The Doppler shift occurs with light as well as with sound. **Figure 23-21** shows how the Doppler shift causes changes in the light coming from distant stars and galaxies. If a star is moving toward us, its wavelengths of light are pushed together. If a star is moving away from us, its wavelengths of light are stretched.

The Doppler Shift

Look at the spectrum of a star in **Figure 23-22A.** Note the position of the dark lines. How do they compare with the lines in **Figures 23-22B** and **C?** They have shifted in position. What caused this shift? As you just learned, when a star is moving toward Earth, its wavelengths of light are

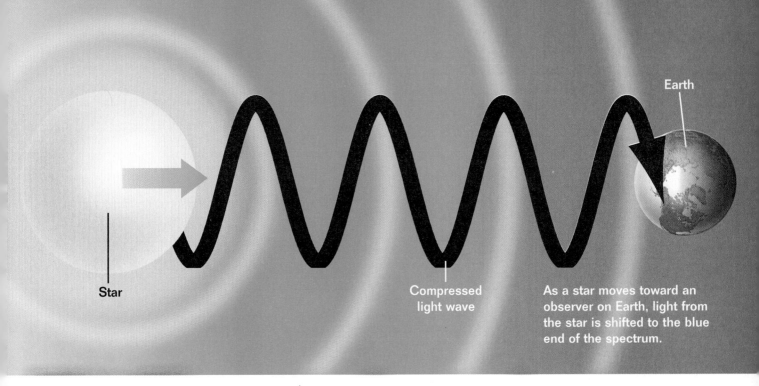

Star

Compressed
light wave

As a star moves toward an
observer on Earth, light from
the star is shifted to the blue
end of the spectrum.

Earth

pushed together, just as the sound waves from the car's horn are. This causes the dark lines in the spectrum to shift toward the blue-violet end of the spectrum. A red shift in the spectrum occurs when a star is moving away from Earth. In a red shift, the dark lines shift toward the red end of the spectrum.

In the early twentieth century, scientists noticed an interesting fact about the light coming from most galaxies. When a spectrograph is used to study light from galaxies beyond the Local Group, there is a red shift in the light. What does this red shift tell you about the universe?

Because all galaxies beyond the Local Group show a red shift in their spectra, they must be moving away from Earth. If all galaxies outside the Local Group are moving away from Earth, this indicates that the entire universe must be expanding. Think of the Explore Activity at the beginning of the chapter. The dots on the balloon moved apart as the model universe expanded. Regardless of which dot you picked, all the other dots moved away from it. Galaxies beyond the Local Group move away from us just as the dots moved apart on the balloon.

*inter*NET
CONNECTION

Visit the Glencoe Science Web Site at **www.glencoe.com/ sec/science** for more information about the Doppler shift.

A

B

C

Figure 23-22 The dark lines in the spectra (A) are shifted toward the blue-violet end when a star is moving toward Earth (B). A red shift (C) indicates that a star is moving away from Earth.

VISUALIZING The Big Bang Theory

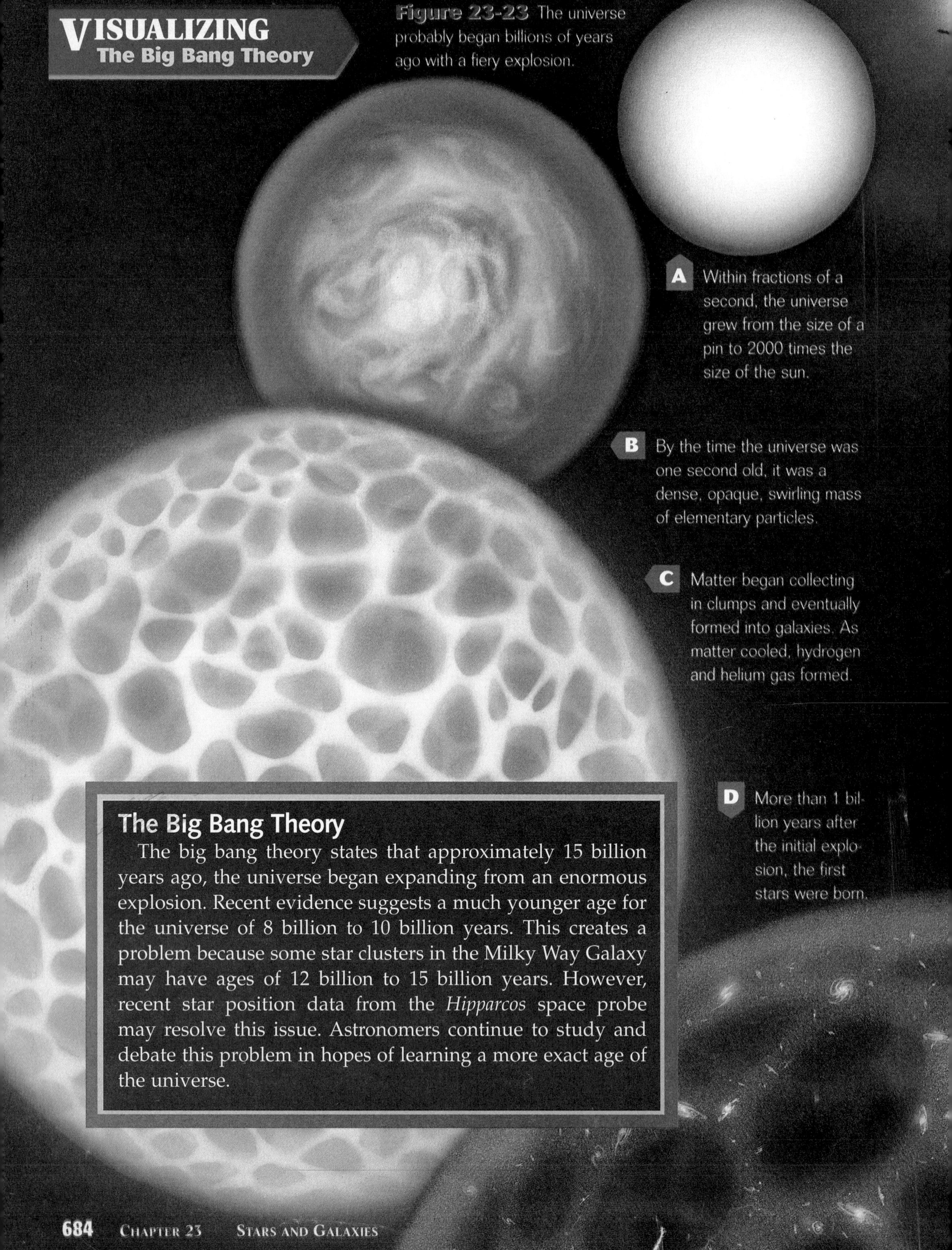

Figure 23-23 The universe probably began billions of years ago with a fiery explosion.

A Within fractions of a second, the universe grew from the size of a pin to 2000 times the size of the sun.

B By the time the universe was one second old, it was a dense, opaque, swirling mass of elementary particles.

C Matter began collecting in clumps and eventually formed into galaxies. As matter cooled, hydrogen and helium gas formed.

D More than 1 billion years after the initial explosion, the first stars were born.

The Big Bang Theory

The big bang theory states that approximately 15 billion years ago, the universe began expanding from an enormous explosion. Recent evidence suggests a much younger age for the universe of 8 billion to 10 billion years. This creates a problem because some star clusters in the Milky Way Galaxy may have ages of 12 billion to 15 billion years. However, recent star position data from the *Hipparcos* space probe may resolve this issue. Astronomers continue to study and debate this problem in hopes of learning a more exact age of the universe.

The Big Bang Theory

When scientists determined that the universe was expanding, they realized that galaxy clusters must have been closer together in the past. The leading theory about the formation of the universe, called the big bang theory, is based on this explanation. **Figure 23-23** illustrates the **big bang theory,** which states that approximately 15 billion years ago, the universe began with an enormous explosion.

The time-lapse photograph shown in **Figure 23-24** was taken in December 1995 by the *Hubble Space Telescope.* It shows more than 1500 galaxies at a distance of more than 10 billion light-years. These galaxies may date back to when the universe was no more than 1 billion years old. The galaxies are in various stages of development. One astronomer indicates that we may be looking back to a time when our own galaxy was forming. Studies of this nature will eventually enable astronomers to determine the approximate age of the universe.

Whether the universe expands forever or stops depends on how much matter is in the universe. All matter exerts a gravitational force. If there's enough matter, gravity will halt the expansion, and the universe will contract until everything comes to one point.

Figure 23-24 The light from these galaxies in this photo mosaic took billions of years to reach Earth.

Section Assessment

1. List the three major classifications of galaxies. What do they have in common?

2. What is the name of the galaxy that you live in? What motion do the stars in this galaxy exhibit?

3. **Think Critically:** All galaxies outside the Local Group show a red shift in their spectra. Within the Local Group, some galaxies show a red shift and some show a blue shift. What does this tell you about the galaxies in the Local Group and outside the Local Group?

4. **Skill Builder**
   Predicting Astronomical distances are measured in light-years, the distance light travels in one year. It takes light from the star Betelgeuse 310 light-years to reach Earth. Do the **Chapter 23 Skill Activity** on page 764 to predict what was happening on Earth when light from distant stars began traveling toward our solar system.

Science Journal Research and write a report in your Science Journal about the most recent evidence supporting or disputing the big bang theory. Describe how the big bang theory explains observations of galaxies made with spectrometers.

Design Your Own Experiment

Measuring Parallax

Possible Materials

- Meterstick
- Metric ruler
- Masking tape
- Pencil

Parallax is the apparent shift in the position of an object when viewed from two locations. The nearer an object is to the observer, the greater its parallax. Do this activity to design a model and use it in an experiment that will show how distance affects the amount of observed parallax.

Recognize the Problem

How can you build a model to show the relationship between distance and parallax?

Form a Hypothesis

State a hypothesis about how a model must be built in order for it to be used in an experiment to show how distance affects the amount of observed parallax.

Goals

- **Design a model** to show how the distance from an observer to an object affects the object's parallax shift.
- **Design an experiment** that shows how distance affects the amount of observed parallax.

Safety Precautions

 **CAUTION:** *Be sure to wear goggles to protect your eyes.*

Test Your Hypothesis

Plan

1. As a group, agree upon and write out your hypothesis statement.

2. List the steps that you need to take to build your model. Be specific, describing exactly what you will do at each step.

3. Devise a method to test how distance from an observer to an object, such as a pencil, affects the relative position of the object.

4. List the steps you will take to test your hypothesis. Be specific, describing exactly what you will do at each step.

5. Read over your plan for the model to be used in this experiment.

6. How will you determine changes in observed parallax? Remember, these changes should occur when the distance from the observer to the object is changed.

7. You should measure shifts in parallax from several different positions. How will these positions differ?

8. How will you measure distances accurately and compare relative position shift?

Do

1. Make sure your teacher approves your plan before you proceed.

2. Construct the model your team has planned.

3. Carry out the experiment as planned.

4. While conducting the experiment, write down any observations that you or other members of your group make in your Science Journal.

Analyze Your Data

1. **Compare** what happened to the object when it was viewed with one eye closed, then the other.

2. At what distance from the observer did the object appear to shift the most?

Draw Conclusions

1. **Infer** what happened to the apparent shift of the object's location as the distance from the observer was increased or decreased.

2. How might astronomers use parallax to study stars?

FIELD GUIDE

to Backyard Astronomy

FIELD *ACTIVITY*

Study the star maps included in this field guide. Each night for a week, about one hour after sundown, observe the stars and identify at least three constellations. Draw and label the constellations in your Science Journal. Then, using the key of constellations visible in the northern hemisphere, make drawings of the objects, animals, or characters your constellations represent.

To help them study the night sky, early astronomers developed ways to organize stars into recognizable patterns. We call these patterns constellations. Think of constellations as drawings in the sky. They represent objects, animals, or characters in stories—things that were familiar to ancient stargazers. Using this field guide, you can observe the stars year-round.

Early astronomers saw the shape of a lion in the constellation Leo.

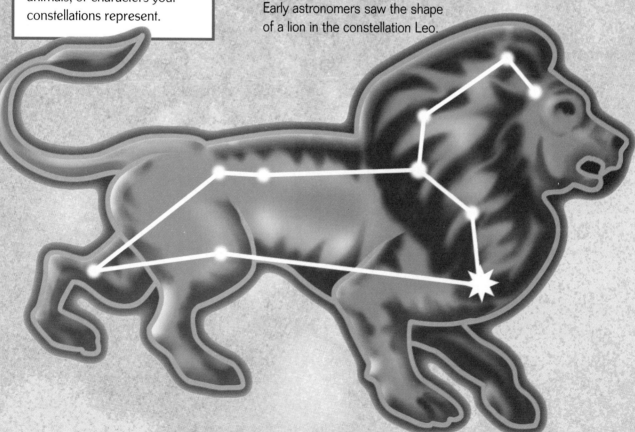

Major Constellations Visible in the Northern Hemisphere

Name	Represents	Name	Represents
Andromeda	Princess	Lyra	Harp
Aquila	Eagle	Orion	Hunter
Bootes	Herdsman	Pegasus	Winged Horse
Canis Major	Big Dog	Sagittarius	Archer
Canis Minor	Little Dog	Scorpius	Scorpion
Cygnus	Swan (Northern Cross)	Taurus	Bull
Gemini	Twins	Ursa Major	Great Bear (Big Dipper)
Hercules	Hercules	Ursa Minor	Little Bear (Little Dipper)
Leo	Lion	Virgo	Virgin (Maiden)

This map shows the constellations that appear to circle the North Star, also known as Polaris. Because these constellations appear to circle Polaris, which is located almost directly over the north pole, they are called circumpolar constellations. Look toward the north to locate these constellations. To orient yourself, first locate Polaris, which is found by looking directly north, then up at an angle of roughly 35° to 45°.

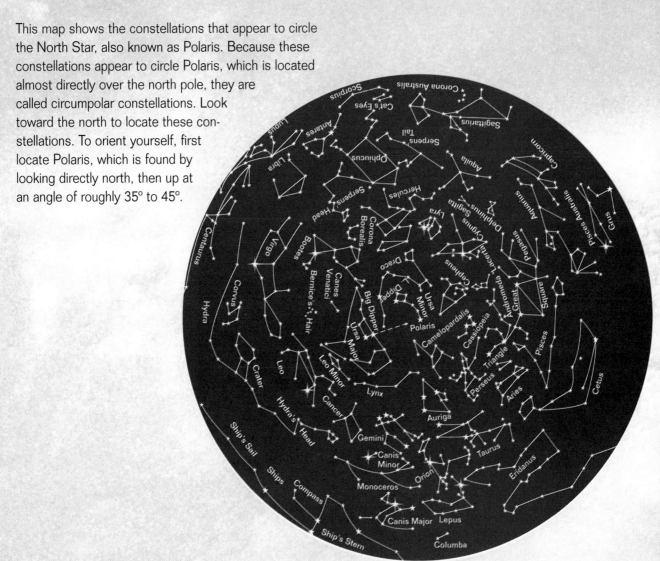

Different constellations are visible during different seasons, so this guide includes four star maps—one for each season. Choose the correct seasonal map, and face south. Hold the sky map above you, with the north part of the map pointing north (behind you). Look toward the southern sky between your zenith (the highest point above you) and the horizon to locate these constellations.

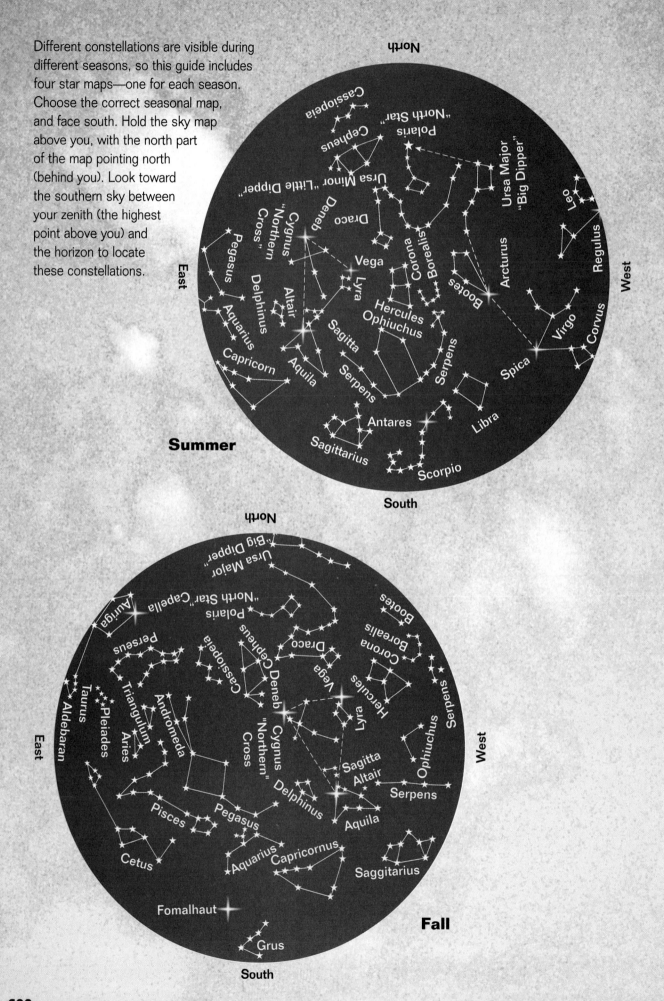

Summer

Fall

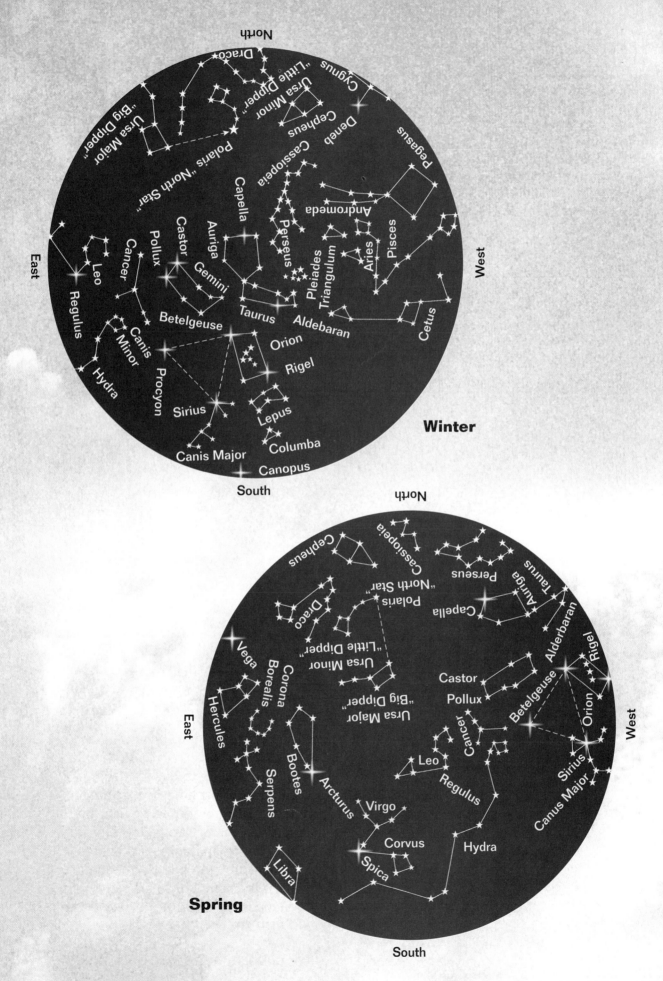

Winter

Spring

For a **preview** of this chapter, study this Reviewing Main Ideas before you read the chapter. After you have studied this chapter, you can use the Reviewing Main Ideas to **review** the chapter.

The Glencoe MindJogger, Audiocassettes, and CD-ROM provide additional opportunities for review.

Section
23-1 STARS

The magnitude of a star is a measure of the star's brightness. **Absolute magnitude** is a measure of the light emitted. **Apparent magnitude** is a measure of the amount of light received on Earth. **Parallax** is the apparent shift in the position of an object when viewed from two different positions. The closer to Earth a star is, the greater its shift in parallax. A star's temperature and composition can be determined from the star's spectrum. *What term describes how bright a star looks from Earth?*

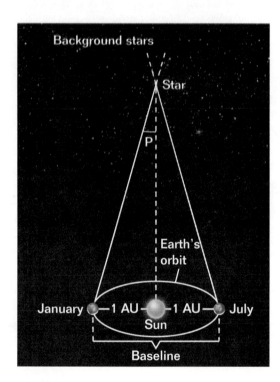

Section
23-2 THE SUN

The sun produces energy by fusing hydrogen into helium in its core. Light is given off from the photosphere, which is the lowest layer of the sun's atmosphere. **Sunspots** are areas of the sun that are cooler and less bright than surrounding areas. Sunspots, prominences, and flares are caused by the intense magnetic field of the sun, which is a main sequence star. *Why is the sun considered an average star?*

Reading Check ☑

The big bang theory is still controversial. What part of this theory is supported by evidence? What part is opinion?

Section 23-3 EVOLUTION OF STARS

When hydrogen is used up in a **main sequence** star, the star's core collapses and its temperature increases. The star becomes a **giant** or a **supergiant,** which uses helium as fuel. As the star evolves, its outer layers escape into space and the star becomes a **white dwarf.** Stars containing high amounts of mass can explode. During a supernova explosion, the outer layers of a star are blown away and the remaining core evolves into a **neutron star** or **black hole.** *At what temperature does fusion begin inside a nebula?*

Section 23-4 GALAXIES AND THE UNIVERSE

A **galaxy** is a large group of stars, gas, and dust held together by gravity. Galaxies can be elliptical, spiral, or irregular in shape. The galaxy that our sun belongs to, the Milky Way, contains about 200 billion stars. There may be more than 100 billion galaxies in the universe. The most accepted theory about the origin of the universe is the **big bang theory.** *What is the Local Group of galaxies?*

Chapter 23 Assessment

Using Vocabulary

a. absolute magnitude
b. apparent magnitude
c. big bang theory
d. binary system
e. black hole
f. chromosphere
g. constellation
h. corona
i. galaxy
j. giant
k. light-year
l. main sequence
m. nebula
n. neutron star
o. parallax
p. photosphere
q. sunspot
r. supergiant
s. white dwarf

Explain the differences in the terms given below. Then explain how the terms are related.

1. absolute magnitude, apparent magnitude
2. black hole, neutron star
3. chromosphere, photosphere
4. binary system, constellation
5. light-year, parallax

Checking Concepts

Choose the word or phrase that best answers the question.

6. What do constellations form?
   A) clusters
   B) giants
   C) black holes
   D) patterns
7. What is a measure of the amount of a star's light received on Earth?
   A) absolute magnitude
   B) apparent magnitude
   C) fusion
   D) parallax
8. What increases as an object comes closer to an observer?
   A) absolute magnitude
   B) red shift
   C) parallax
   D) size

9. What begins once a nebula contracts and temperatures increase to 10 millionK?
   A) main sequencing
   B) a supernova
   C) fusion
   D) a white dwarf
10. What is about 10 km in size?
   A) giant
   B) white dwarf
   C) black hole
   D) neutron star
11. Our sun fuses hydrogen into what?
   A) carbon
   B) oxygen
   C) iron
   D) helium
12. What are loops of matter flowing from the sun?
   A) sunspots
   B) auroras
   C) coronas
   D) prominences
13. What are groups of galaxies called?
   A) clusters
   B) supergiants
   C) giants
   D) binary systems
14. Which galaxies are sometimes shaped like footballs?
   A) spiral
   B) elliptical
   C) barred
   D) irregular
15. What do scientists study to determine shifts in wavelengths of light?
   A) spectrum
   B) surface
   C) corona
   D) chromosphere

Thinking Critically

16. What is significant about the 1995 discovery by the *Hubble Space Telescope* of more than 1500 galaxies at a distance of more than 10 billion light-years?

17. How do scientists know that black holes exist if these objects don't emit any visible light?

18. Use the autumn star chart in Appendix K to determine which constellation is directly overhead at 8 P.M. on November 23 for an observer in North America.

19. How are radio waves used to detect objects in space?

20. What kinds of reactions produce the energy emitted by stars?

Developing Skills

If you need help, refer to the Skill Handbook.

21. **Concept Mapping:** Complete the concept map on this page that shows the evolution of a main sequence star with a mass similar to that of the sun.

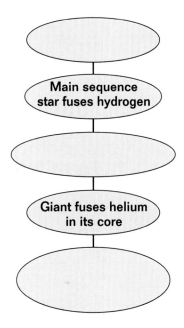

22. **Comparing and Contrasting:** Compare and contrast the sun with other stars on the H-R diagram.

23. **Measuring in SI:** The Milky Way Galaxy is 100 000 light-years in diameter. What scale would you use if you were to construct a model of the Milky Way with a diameter of 20 cm?

24. **Designing an Experiment:** Design and carry out an experiment that uses sunspot locations to compare rotational periods of different latitudes of the sun.

25. **Making a Model:** Design and construct scale models of a spiral and a barred spiral Milky Way Galaxy. Show the approximate position of the sun in each.

Test-Taking Tip

Read the Label No matter how many times you've taken a particular test or practiced for an exam, it's always a good idea to skim through the instructions provided at the beginning of each section.

Test Practice

Use these questions to test your Science Proficiency.

1. A white dwarf star is located in the lower-left-hand corner of an H-R diagram. Which of the following statements **BEST** explains why it is positioned there?
   A) White dwarf stars have low absolute magnitudes and high surface temperatures.
   B) White dwarf stars have low absolute magnitudes and low surface temperatures.
   C) White dwarf stars have high absolute magnitudes and high surface temperatures.
   D) White dwarf stars have high absolute magnitudes and low surface temperatures.

2. Sunspots are dark areas of the sun's surface. Which of the following statements **BEST** explains why this is true?
   A) Sunspots are areas of the sun's surface that do not give off light.
   B) Sunspots appear dark because they give off more energy than surrounding areas of the sun's surface.
   C) Sunspots are hotter than surrounding areas of the sun's surface.
   D) Sunspots are cooler than surrounding areas of the sun's surface.

Appendices

Appendix A

Safety in the Science Classroom

1. Always obtain your teacher's permission to begin an investigation.

2. Study the procedure. If you have questions, ask your teacher. Be sure you understand any safety symbols shown on the page.

3. Use the safety equipment provided for you. Goggles and a safety apron should be worn during an investigation.

4. Always slant test tubes away from yourself and others when heating them.

5. Never eat or drink in the lab, and never use lab glassware as food or drink containers. Never inhale chemicals. Do not taste any substances or draw any material into a tube with your mouth.

6. If you spill any chemical, wash it off immediately with water. Report the spill immediately to your teacher.

7. Know the location and proper use of the fire extinguisher, safety shower, fire blanket, first aid kit, and fire alarm.

8. Keep all materials away from open flames. Tie back long hair and loose clothing.

9. If a fire should break out in the classroom, or if your clothing should catch fire, smother it with the fire blanket or a coat, or get under a safety shower. NEVER RUN.

10. Report any accident or injury, no matter how small, to your teacher.

Follow these procedures as you clean up your work area.

1. Turn off the water and gas. Disconnect electrical devices.

2. Return all materials to their proper places.

3. Dispose of chemicals and other materials as directed by your teacher. Place broken glass and solid substances in the proper containers. Never discard materials in the sink.

4. Clean your work area.

5. Wash your hands thoroughly after working in the laboratory.

Table A-1

First Aid	
Injury	**Safe Response**
Burns	Apply cold water. Call your teacher immediately.
Cuts and bruises	Stop any bleeding by applying direct pressure. Cover cuts with a clean dressing. Apply cold compresses to bruises. Call your teacher immediately.
Fainting	Leave the person lying down. Loosen any tight clothing and keep crowds away. Call your teacher immediately.
Foreign matter in eye	Flush with plenty of water. Use eyewash bottle or fountain.
Poisoning	Note the suspected poisoning agent and call your teacher immediately.
Any spills on skin	Flush with large amounts of water or use safety shower. Call your teacher immediately.

Appendix
B

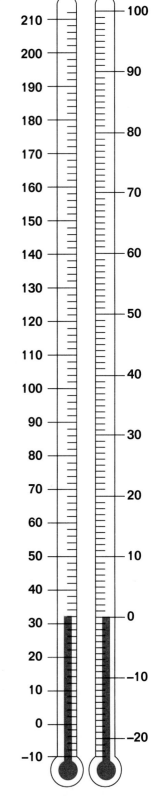

SI/Metric to English Conversions			
	When you want to convert:	**To:**	**Multiply by:**
Length	inches	centimeters	2.54
	centimeters	inches	0.39
	feet	meters	0.30
	meters	feet	3.28
	yards	meters	0.91
	meters	yards	1.09
	miles	kilometers	1.61
	kilometers	miles	0.62
Mass and Weight*	ounces	grams	28.35
	grams	ounces	0.04
	pounds	kilograms	0.45
	kilograms	pounds	2.2
	tons (short)	tonnes (metric tons)	0.91
	tonnes (metric tons)	tons (short)	1.10
	pounds	newtons	4.45
	newtons	pounds	0.23
Volume	cubic inches	cubic centimeters	16.39
	cubic centimeters	cubic inches	0.06
	cubic feet	cubic meters	0.03
	cubic meters	cubic feet	35.30
	liters	quarts	1.06
	liters	gallons	0.26
	gallons	liters	3.78
Area	square inches	square centimeters	6.45
	square centimeters	square inches	0.16
	square feet	square meters	0.09
	square meters	square feet	10.76
	square miles	square kilometers	2.59
	square kilometers	square miles	0.39
	hectares	acres	2.47
	acres	hectares	0.40
Temperature	Fahrenheit	$5/9 \, (°F - 32)$ =	Celsius
	Celsius	$9/5 \, (°C) + 32$ =	Fahrenheit

*Weight as measured in standard Earth gravity

Appendix C

SI Units of Measurement

Table C-1

SI Base Units					
Measurement	**Unit**	**Symbol**	**Measurement**	**Unit**	**Symbol**
length	meter	m	temperature	kelvin	K
mass	kilogram	kg	amount of substance	mole	mol
time	second	s			

Table C-2

Units Derived from SI Base Units		
Measurement	**Unit**	**Symbol**
energy	joule	J
force	newton	N
frequency	hertz	Hz
potential difference	volt	V
power	watt	W
pressure	pascal	Pa

100,000 cm

Table C-3

Common SI Prefixes					
Prefix	**Symbol**	**Multiplier**	**Prefix**	**Symbol**	**Multiplier**
	Greater than 1			Less than 1	
mega-	M	1 000 000	*deci-*	d	0.1
kilo-	k	1 000	*centi-*	c	0.01
hecto-	h	100	*milli-*	m	0.001
deca-	da	10	*micro-*	μ	0.000 001

Appendix
D

Care and Use of a Microscope

Eyepiece Contains a magnifying lens you look through

Arm Supports the body tube

Low-power objective Contains the lens with low-power magnification

Stage clips Hold the microscope slide in place

Coarse adjustment Focuses the image under low power

Fine adjustment Sharpens the image under high and low magnification

Body tube Connects the eyepiece to the revolving nosepiece

Revolving nosepiece Holds and turns the objectives into viewing position

High-power objective Contains the lens with the highest magnification

Stage Supports the microscope slide

Light source Allows light to reflect upward through the diaphragm, the specimen, and the lenses

Base Provides support for the microscope

Care of a Microscope

1. Always carry the microscope holding the arm with one hand and supporting the base with the other hand.

2. Don't touch the lenses with your fingers.

3. Never lower the coarse adjustment knob when looking through the eyepiece lens.

4. Always focus first with the low-power objective.

5. Don't use the coarse adjustment knob when the high-power objective is in place.

6. Store the microscope covered.

Using a Microscope

1. Place the microscope on a flat surface that is clear of objects. The arm should be toward you.

2. Look through the eyepiece. Adjust the diaphragm so that light comes through the opening in the stage.

3. Place a slide on the stage so that the specimen is in the field of view. Hold it firmly in place by using the stage clips.

4. Always focus first with the coarse adjustment and the low-power objective lens. Once the object is in focus on low power, turn the nosepiece until the high-power objective is in place. Use ONLY the fine adjustment to focus with the high-power objective lens.

Making a Wet-Mount Slide

1. Carefully place the item you want to look at in the center of a clean, glass slide. Make sure the sample is thin enough for light to pass through.

2. Use a dropper to place one or two drops of water on the sample.

3. Hold a clean coverslip by the edges and place it at one edge of the drop of water. Slowly lower the coverslip onto the drop of water until it lies flat.

4. If you have too much water or a lot of air bubbles, touch the edge of a paper towel to the edge of the coverslip to draw off extra water and force out air.

Diversity of Life: Classification of Living Organisms

Scientists use a six-kingdom system of classification of organisms. In this system, there are two kingdoms of organisms, Kingdoms Archaebacteria and Eubacteria, which contain organisms that do not have a nucleus and lack membrane-bound structures in the cytoplasm of their cells. The members of the other four kingdoms have cells which contain a nucleus and structures in the cytoplasm that are surrounded by membranes. These kingdoms are Kingdom Protista, Kingdom Fungi, the Kingdom Plantae, and the Kingdom Animalia.

Kingdom Archaebacteria

One-celled prokaryotes; absorb food from surroundings or make their own food by chemosynthesis; found in extremely harsh environments including salt ponds, hot springs, swamps, and deep-sea hydrothermal vents.

Kingdom Eubacteria

Cyanobacteria one-celled prokaryotes; make their own food; contain chlorophyll; some species form colonies; most are blue-green

Bacteria one-celled prokaryotes; most absorb food from their surroundings; some are photosynthetic; many are parasites; round, spiral, or rod-shaped

Kingdom Protista

Phylum Euglenophyta one-celled; can photosynthesize or take in food; most have one flagellum; euglenoids

Phylum Bacillariophyta one-celled; make their own food through photosynthesis; have unique double shells made of silica; diatoms

Phylum Dinoflagellata one-celled; make their own food through photosynthesis; contain red pigments; have two flagella; dinoflagellates

Phylum Chlorophyta one-celled, many-celled, or colonies; contain chlorophyll; make their own food; live on land, in fresh water, or salt water; green algae

Phylum Rhodophyta most are many-celled; photosynthetic; contain red pigments; most live in deep saltwater environments; red algae

Phylum Phaeophyta most are many-celled; photosynthetic; contain brown pigments; most live in saltwater environments; brown algae

Phylum Foraminifera many-celled; take in food; primarily marine; shells constructed of calcium carbonate, or made from grains of sand; forams

Phylum Myxomycota
Slime Mold
Magnification: 5×

Phylum Chlorophyta
Desmids Magnification: 50×

Phylum Rhizopoda one-celled; take in food; move by means of pseudopods; free-living or parasitic; amoebas

Phylum Zoomastigina one-celled; take in food; have one or more flagella; free-living or parasitic; zoomastigotes

Phylum Ciliophora one-celled; take in food; have large numbers of cilia; ciliates

Phylum Sporozoa one-celled; take in food; no means of movement; parasites in animals; sporozoans

Phylum Myxomycota and Acrasiomycota: one- or many-celled; absorb food; change form during life cycle; cellular and plasmodial slime molds

Phylum Oomycota many-celled; live in fresh or salt water; are either parasites or decomposers; water molds, rusts and downy mildews

Kingdom Fungi

Phylum Zygomycota many-celled; absorb food; spores are produced in sporangia; zygote fungi; bread mold

Phylum Ascomycota one- and many-celled; absorb food; spores produced in asci; sac fungi; yeast

Phylum Basidiomycota many-celled; absorb food; spores produced in basidia; club fungi; mushrooms

Phylum Deuteromycota: members with unknown reproductive structures; imperfect fungi; penicillin

Lichens organisms formed by symbiotic relationship between an ascomycote or a basidiomycote and green alga or cyanobacterium

Kingdom Plantae
Non-seed Plants

Division Bryophyta nonvascular plants; reproduce by spores produced in capsules; many-celled; green; grow in moist land environments; mosses and liverworts

Division Lycophyta many-celled vascular plants; spores produced in conelike structures; live on land; are photosynthetic; club mosses

Division Sphenophyta vascular plants; ribbed and jointed stems; scalelike leaves; spores produced in conelike structures; horsetails

Division Pterophyta vascular plants; leaves called fronds; spores produced in clusters of sporangia called sori; live on land or in water; ferns

Division Bryophyta
Liverwort

Lichens
British soldier lichen × 3

Appendix E

Seed Plants

Division Ginkgophyta: deciduous gymnosperms; only one living species; fan-shaped leaves with branching veins; reproduces with seeds; ginkgos

Division Cycadophyta: palmlike gymnosperms; large featherlike leaves; produce seeds in cones; cycads

Division Coniferophyta: deciduous or evergreen gymnosperms; trees or shrubs; needlelike or scalelike leaves; seeds produced in cones; conifers

Division Gnetophyta: shrubs or woody vines; seeds produced in cones; division contains only three genera; gnetum

Division Anthophyta: dominant group of plants; ovules protected in an ovary; sperm carried to ovules by pollen tube; produce flowers and seeds in fruits; flowering plants

Kingdom Animalia

Phylum Porifera: aquatic organisms that lack true tissues and organs; they are asymmetrical and sessile; sponges

Phylum Cnidaria: radially symmetrical organisms; have a digestive cavity with one opening; most have tentacles armed with stinging cells; live in aquatic environments singly or in colonies; includes jellyfish, corals, hydra, and sea anemones

Phylum Platyhelminthes: bilaterally symmetrical worms; have flattened bodies; digestive system has one opening; parasitic and free-living species; flatworms

Phylum Cnidaria
Jellyfish

Phylum Arthopoda
Orb Weaver Spider

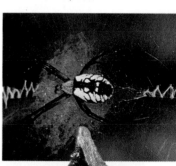

Division Coniferophyta
Pine cone

Division Anthophyta
Strawberry Blossoms

Phylum Arthropoda
Hermit Crab

Phylum Mollusca
Florida Fighting Conch

Division Anthophyta
Strawberries

Phylum Annelida
Sabellid Worms Feather Duster

Phylum Nematoda: round, bilaterally symmetrical body; digestive system with two openings; some free-living forms but mostly parasitic; roundworms

Phylum Mollusca: soft-bodied animals, many with a hard shell; a mantle covers the soft body; aquatic and terrestrial species; includes clams, snails, squid, and octopuses

Phylum Annelida: bilaterally symmetrical worms; have round, segmented bodies; terrestrial and aquatic species; includes earthworms, leeches, and marine polychaetes

Phylum Arthropoda: largest phylum of organisms; have segmented bodies; pairs of jointed appendages; have hard exoskeletons; terrestrial and aquatic species; includes insects, crustaceans, spiders, and horseshoe crabs

Phylum Echinodermata: marine organisms; have spiny or leathery skin; water-vascular system with tube feet; radial symmetry; includes sea stars, sand dollars, and sea urchins

Phylum Chordata: organisms with internal skeletons; specialized body systems; paired appendages; all at some time have a notochord, dorsal nerve cord, gill slits, and a tail; include fish, amphibians, reptiles, birds, and mammals

Phylum Arthropoda
Giant Swallowtail Butterfly

Phylum Echinodermata
Blood Sea Star and Red Sea Urchin

Phylum Chordata
Eastern Box Turtle

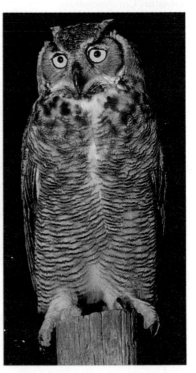

Phylum Chordata
Lemon Butterfly fish

Phylum Chordata
Great Horned Owl

Appendix

F

Minerals

Mineral (formula)	Color	Streak	Hardness	Breakage pattern	Uses and other properties
graphite (C)	black to gray	black to gray	1–1.5	basal cleavage (scales)	pencil lead, lubricants for locks, rods to control some small nuclear reactions, battery poles
galena (PbS)	gray	gray to black	2.5	cubic cleavage perfect	source of lead, used in pipes, shields for X rays, fishing equipment sinkers
hematite (Fe_2O_3)	black or reddish brown	reddish brown	5.5–6.5	irregular fracture	source of iron; converted to "pig" iron, made into steel
magnetite (Fe_3O_4)	black	black	6	conchoidal fracture	source of iron, naturally magnetic, called lodestone
pyrite (FeS_2)	light, brassy, yellow	greenish black	6–6.5	uneven fracture	source of iron, "fool's gold"
talc ($Mg_3Si_4O_{10}(OH)_2$)	white greenish	white	1	cleavage in one direction	used for talcum powder, sculptures, paper, and tabletops
gypsum ($CaSO_4 \cdot 2H_2O$)	colorless, gray, white brown	white	2	basal cleavage	used in plaster of paris and dry wall for building construction
sphalerite (ZnS)	brown, reddish brown, greenish	light to dark brown	3.5–4	cleavage in six directions	main ore of zinc; used in paints, dyes and medicine
muscovite ($KAl_3Si_3O_{10}(OH)_2$)	white, light gray, yellow, rose, green	colorless	2–2.5	basal cleavage	occurs in large flexible plates; used as an insulator in electrical equipment, lubricant
biotite ($K(Mg, Fe)_3(AlSi_3O_{10})(OH)_2$)	black to dark brown	colorless	2.5–3	basal cleavage	occurs in large flexible plates
halite (NaCl)	colorless, red, white, blue	colorless	2.5	cubic cleavage	salt; soluble in water; a preservative

Appendix F

Minerals

Mineral (formula)	Color	Streak	Hardness	Breakage pattern	Uses and other properties
calcite $(CaCO_3)$	colorless, white, pale blue	colorless, white	3	cleavage in three directions	fizzes when HCl is added; used in cements and other building materials
dolomite $(CaMg (CO_3)_2)$	colorless, white, pink green, gray black	white	3.5–4	cleavage in three directions	concrete and cement; used as an ornamental building stone
fluorite (CaF_2)	colorless, white, blue green, red yellow, purple	colorless	4	cleavage in four directions	used in the manufacture of optical equipment; glows under ultraviolet light
hornblende $(CaNa)_{2\text{-}3}(Mg, Al,Fe)_5(Al,Si)_2 Si_6O_{22}(OH)_2)$	green to black	gray to white	5–6	cleavage in two directions	will transmit light on thin edges; 6-sided cross section
feldspar $(KAlSi_3O_8)$ $(NaAlSi_3O_8)$ $(CaAl_2Si_2O_8)$	colorless, white to gray, green	colorless	6	two cleavage planes meet at ~90° angle	used in the manufacture of ceramics
augite $((Ca, Na) (Mg, Fe, Al) (Al, Si)_2O_6)$	black	colorless	6	cleavage in two directions	square or 8-sided cross section
olivine $((Mg, Fe)_2 SiO_4)$	olive, green	none	6.5–7	conchoidal fracture	gemstones, refractory sand
quartz (SiO_2)	colorless, various color	none	7	conchoidal fracture	used in glass manufacture, electronic equipment, radios, computers, watches, gemstones

Appendix
G

Rocks

Rock Type	Rock Name	Characteristics
Igneous (intrusive)	Granite	Large mineral grains of quartz, feldspar, hornblende, and mica. Usually light in color.
	Diorite	Large mineral grains of feldspar, hornblende, mica. Less quartz than granite. Intermediate in color.
	Gabbro	Large mineral grains of feldspar, hornblende, augite, olivine, and mica. No quartz. Dark in color.
Igneous (extrusive)	Rhyolite	Small mineral grains of quartz, feldspar, hornblende, and mica or no visible grains. Light in color.
	Andesite	Small mineral grains of feldspar, hornblende, mica or no visible grains. Less quartz than rhyolite. Intermediate in color.
	Basalt	Small mineral grains of feldspar, hornblende, augite, olivine, mica or no visible grains. No quartz. Dark in color.
	Obsidian	Glassy texture. No visible grains. Volcanic glass. Fracture looks like broken glass.
	Pumice	Frothy texture. Floats. Usually light in color.
Sedimentary (detrital)	Conglomerate	Coarse-grained. Gravel or pebble-sized grains.
	Sandstone	Sand-sized grains 1/16 to 2 mm in size.
	Siltstone	Grains are smaller than sand but larger than clay.
	Shale	Smallest grains. Usually dark in color.
Sedimentary (chemical or biochemical)	Limestone	Major mineral is calcite. Usually forms in oceans, lakes, rivers, and caves. Often contains fossils.
	Coal	Occurs in swampy. low-lying areas. Compacted layers of organic material, mainly plant remains.
Sedimentary (chemical)	Rock Salt	Commonly forms by the evaporation of seawater.
Metamorphic (foliated)	Gneiss	Well-developed banding because of alternating layers of different minerals, usually of different colors. Common parent rock is granite.
	Schist	Well-defined parallel arrangement of flat, sheet-like minerals, mainly micas. Common parent rocks are shale, phyllite.
	Phyllite	Shiny or silky appearance. May look wrinkled. Common parent rocks are shale, slate.
	Slate	Harder, denser, and shinier than shale. Common parent rock is shale.
Metamorphic (non-foliated)	Marble	Interlocking calcite or dolomite crystals. Common parent rock is limestone.
	Soapstone	Composed mainly of the mineral talc. Soft with a greasy feel.
	Quartzite	Hard and well cemented with interlocking quartz crystals. Common parent rock is sandstone.

Topographic Map Symbols

Primary highway, hard surface	
Secondary highway, hard surface	
Light-duty road, hard or Improved surface	
Unimproved road	
Railroad: single track and multiple track	
Railroads in juxtaposition	
Buildings	
Schools, church, and cemetery	cem
Buildings (barn, warehouse, etc)	
Wells other than water (labeled as to type)	o oil o gas
Tanks: oil, water, etc. (labeled only if water)	water
Located or landmark object; windmill	
Open pit, mine, or quarry; prospect	

Marsh (swamp)	
Wooded marsh	
Woods or brushwood	
Vineyard Land subject to controlled inundation	
Submerged marsh	
Mangrove	
Orchard	
Scrub	
Urban area	

Spot elevation	×7369
Water elevation	670

Index contour	
Supplementary contour	
Intermediate contour	
Depression contours	
Boundaries: National	
State	
County, parish, municipal	
Civil township, precinct, town, barrio	
Incorporated city, village, town, hamlet	
Reservation, National or State	
Small park, cemetery, airport, etc.	
Land grant	
Township or range line, United States land survey	
Township or range line, approximate location	

Perennial streams	
Elevated aqueduct	
Water well and spring	o Ov
Small rapids	
Large rapids	
Intermittent lake	
Intermittent streams Aqueduct tunnel	
Glacier Small falls	
Large falls	
Dry lake bed	

Appendix
I

Weather Map Symbols

Sample Plotted Report at Each Station

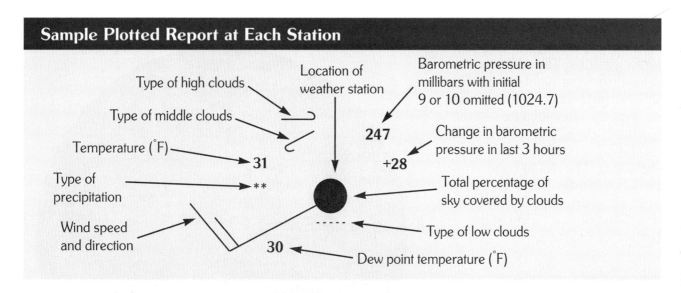

Type of high clouds

Type of middle clouds

Temperature (°F) → **31**

Type of precipitation → ******

Wind speed and direction

Location of weather station

Barometric pressure in millibars with initial 9 or 10 omitted (1024.7)

247

Change in barometric pressure in last 3 hours

+28

Total percentage of sky covered by clouds

Type of low clouds

30 ← Dew point temperature (°F)

Sample Plotted Report at Each Station

Precipitation		Wind speed and direction		Sky coverage		Some types of high clouds	
☰	Fog	○	0 calm	○	No cover		Scattered cirrus
★	Snow		1-2 knots	◍	1/10 or less		Dense cirrus in patches
●	Rain		3-7 knots	◔	2/10 to 3/10		
			8-12 knots	◑	4/10		Veil of cirrus covering entire sky
	Thunder-storm		13-17 knots	◐	1/2		
			18-22 knots		6/10		
,	Drizzle		23-27 knots	●	7/10		Cirrus not covering entire sky
			48-52 knots	◍	Overcast with openings		
▽	Showers	1 knot = 1.852 km/h		●	Complete overcast		

Some types of middle clouds		Some types of low clouds		Fronts and pressure systems	
∕	Thin altostratus layer	⌒	Cumulus of fair weather	(H) or High	Center of high-or
⫽	Thick altostratus layer	⌣	Stratocumulus	(L) or Low	low-pressure system
	Thin altostratus in patches	-----	Fractocumulus of bad weather	▲▲▲▲	Cold front
	Thin altostratus in bands	──	Stratus of fair weather	●●●●	Warm Front
				▲▲▲	Occluded front
				▲●▲●	Stationary front

Star Charts

Shown here are star charts for viewing stars in the Northern Hemisphere during the four different seasons. These charts are drawn from the night sky at about 35° North Latitude, but they can be used for most locations in the Northern Hemisphere. The lines on the charts outline major constellations. The dense band of stars is the milky Way. To use, hold the chart vertically, with the direction you are facing at the bottom of the map.

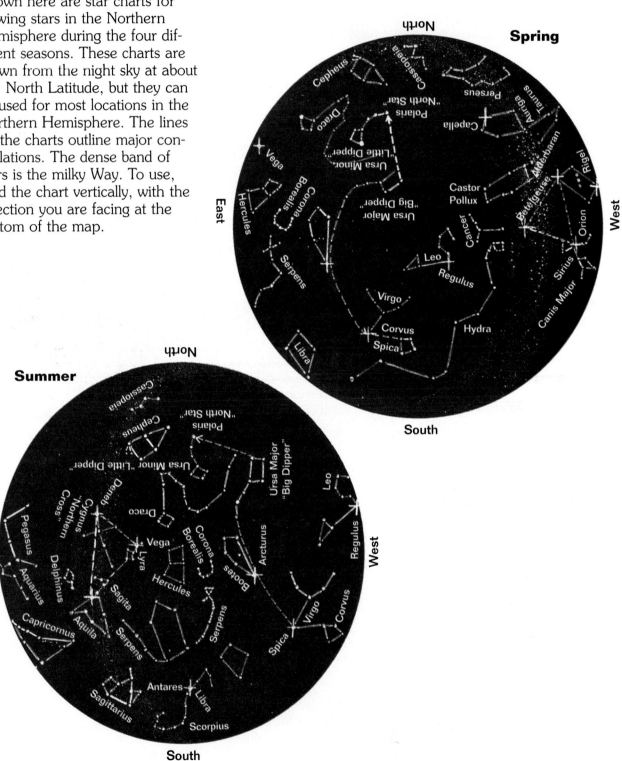

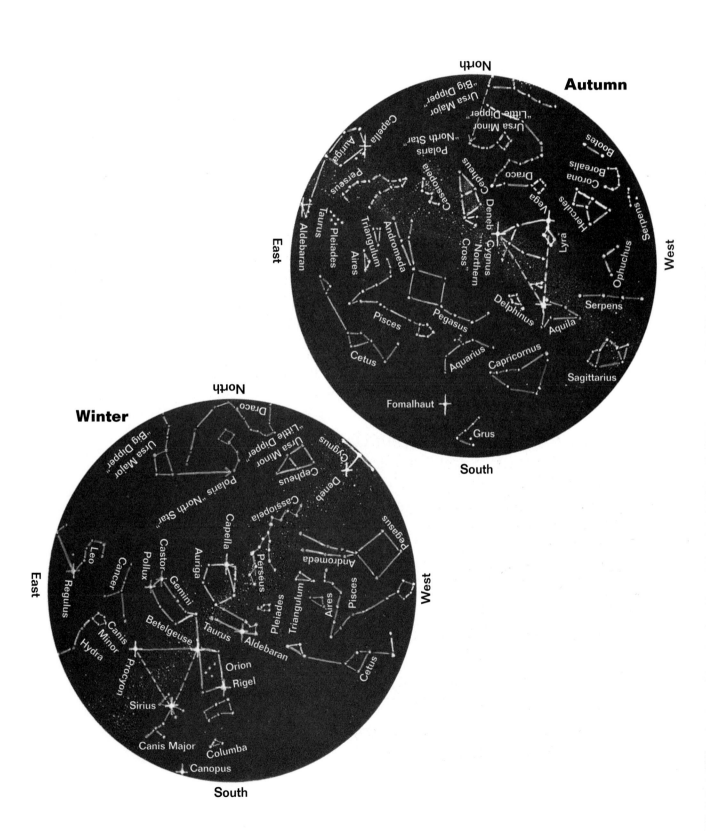

Skill Handbook

Table of Contents

Science Skill Handbook

Technology Skill Handbook

Organizing Information

Communicating

The communication of ideas is an important part of our everyday lives. Whether reading a book, writing a letter, or watching a television program, people everywhere are expressing opinions and sharing information with one another. Writing in your Science Journal allows you to express your opinions and demonstrate your knowledge of the information presented on a subject. When writing, keep in mind the purpose of the assignment and the audience with which you are communicating.

Examples Science Journal assignments vary greatly. They may ask you to take a viewpoint other than your own; perhaps you will be a scientist, a TV reporter, or a committee member of a local environmental group. Maybe you will be expressing your opinions to a member of Congress, a doctor, or to the editor of your local newspaper, as shown in **Figure 1.** Sometimes, Science Journal writing may allow you to summarize information in the form of an outline, a letter, or in a paragraph.

Figure 1 A Science Journal entry

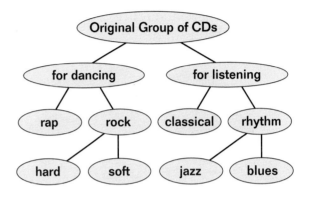

Figure 2 Classifying CDs

Classifying

You may not realize it, but you make things orderly in the world around you. If you hang your shirts together in the closet or if your favorite CDs are stacked together, you have used the skill of classifying.

Classifying is the process of sorting objects or events into groups based on common features. When classifying, first observe the objects or events to be classified. Then, select one feature that is shared by some members in the group, but not by all. Place those members that share that feature into a subgroup. You can classify members into smaller and smaller subgroups based on characteristics.

Remember, when you classify, you are grouping objects or events for a purpose. Keep your purpose in mind as you select the features to form groups and subgroups.

Example How would you classify a collection of CDs? As shown in **Figure 2,** you might classify those you like to dance to in one subgroup and CDs you like to listen to in the next subgroup. The CDs you like to dance to could be subdivided into a rap subgroup and a rock subgroup. Note that for each feature selected, each CD fits into only one subgroup. You would keep selecting features until all the CDs are classified. **Figure 2** shows one possible classification.

Figure 3 A recipe for bread contains sequenced instructions

Sequencing

A sequence is an arrangement of things or events in a particular order. When you are asked to sequence objects or events within a group, figure out what comes first, then think about what should come second. Continue to choose objects or events until all of the objects you started out with are in order. Then, go back over the sequence to make sure each thing or event in your sequence logically leads to the next.

Example A sequence with which you are most familiar is the use of alphabetical order. Another example of sequence would be the steps in a recipe, as shown in **Figure 3.** Think about baking bread. Steps in the recipe have to be followed in order for the bread to turn out right.

Concept Mapping

If you were taking an automobile trip, you would probably take along a road map. The road map shows your location, your destination, and other places along the way. By looking at the map and finding where you are, you can begin to understand where you are in relation to other locations on the map.

A concept map is similar to a road map. But, a concept map shows relationships among ideas (or concepts) rather than places. A concept map is a diagram that visually shows how concepts are related. Because the concept map shows relationships among ideas, it can make the meanings of ideas and terms clear, and help you understand better what you are studying.

There is usually not one correct way to create a concept map. As you construct one type of map, you may discover other ways to construct the map that show the

Figure 4 Network tree describing U.S. currency

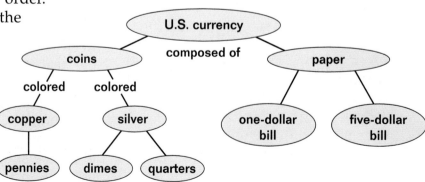

relationships between concepts in a better way. If you do discover what you think is a better way to create a concept map, go ahead and use the new one. Overall, concept maps are useful for breaking a big concept down into smaller parts, making learning easier.

Examples

Network Tree Look at the concept map about U.S. currency in **Figure 4.** This is called a network tree. Notice how some words are in ovals while others are written across connecting lines. The words inside the ovals are science concepts. The lines in the map show related concepts. The words written on the lines describe the relationships between concepts.

When you are asked to construct a network tree, write down the topic and list the major concepts related to that topic on a piece of paper. Then look at your list and begin to put them in order from general to specific. Branch the related concepts from the major concept and describe the relationships on the lines. Continue to write the more specific concepts. Write the relationships between the concepts on the lines until all concepts are mapped. Examine the concept map for relationships that cross branches, and add them to the concept map.

Events Chain An events chain is another type of concept map. An events chain map, such as the one describing a typical morning routine in **Figure 5,** is used to describe ideas in order. In science, an events chain can be used to describe a sequence of events, the steps in a procedure, or the stages of a process.

When making an events chain, first find the one event that starts the chain. This

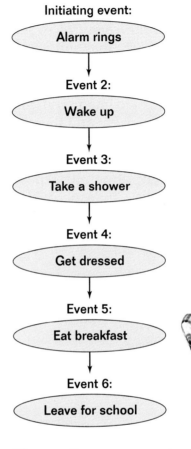

Initiating event:

Alarm rings

Event 2:

Wake up

Event 3:

Take a shower

Event 4:

Get dressed

Event 5:

Eat breakfast

Event 6:

Leave for school

Figure 5 Events chain of a typical morning routine

event is called the initiating event. Then, find the next event in the chain and continue until you reach an outcome. Suppose you are asked to describe what happens when your alarm rings. An events chain map describing the steps might look like **Figure 5.** Notice that connecting words are not necessary in an events chain.

Science Skill Handbook

Cycle Map A cycle concept map is a special type of events chain map. In a cycle concept map, the series of events does not produce a final outcome. Instead, the last event in the chain relates back to the initiating event.

As in the events chain map, you first decide on an initiating event and then list each event in order. Because there is no outcome and the last event relates back to the initiating event, the cycle repeats itself. Look at the cycle map describing the relationship between day and night in **Figure 6.**

Figure 6 Cycle map of day and night.

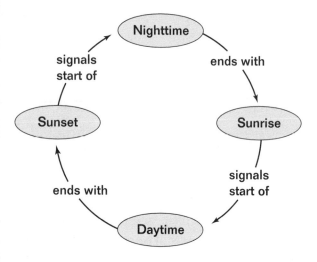

Spider Map A fourth type of concept map is the spider map. This is a map that you can use for brainstorming. Once you have a central idea, you may find you have a jumble of ideas that relate to it, but are not necessarily clearly related to each other. As illustrated by the homework spider map in **Figure 7,** by writing these ideas outside the main concept, you may begin to separate and group unrelated terms so that they become more useful.

Figure 7 Spider map about homework.

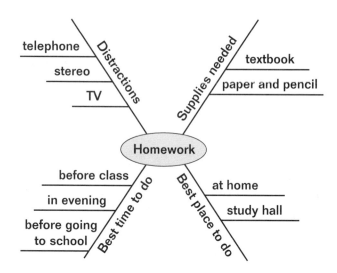

Making and Using Tables

Browse through your textbook and you will notice tables in the text and in the activities. In a table, data or information is arranged in a way that makes it easier for you to understand. Activity tables help organize the data you collect during an activity so that results can be interpreted.

Examples Most tables have a title. At a glance, the title tells you what the table is about. A table is divided into columns and rows. The first column lists items to be compared. In **Figure 8,** the collection of recyclable materials is being compared in a table. The row across the top lists the specific characteristics being compared. Within the grid of the table, the collected data are recorded.

What is the title of the table in **Figure 8?** The title is "Recycled Materials." What is being compared? The different materials being recycled and on which days they are recycled.

Making Tables To make a table, list the items to be compared down in columns and the characteristics to be compared across in rows. The table in

Figure 8 Table of recycled materials

Recycled Materials			
Day of Week	Paper (kg)	Aluminum (kg)	Plastic (kg)
Mon.	4.0	2.0	0.5
Wed.	3.5	1.5	0.5
Fri.	3.0	1.0	1.5

Figure 8 compares the mass of recycled materials collected by a class. On Monday, students turned in 4.0 kg of paper, 2.0 kg of aluminum, and 0.5 kg of plastic. On Wednesday, they turned in 3.5 kg of paper, 1.5 kg of aluminum, and 0.5 kg of plastic. On Friday, the totals were 3.0 kg of paper, 1.0 kg of aluminum, and 1.5 kg of plastic.

Using Tables How much plastic, in kilograms, is being recycled on Wednesday? Locate the column labeled "Plastic (kg)" and the row "Wed." The data in the box where the column and row intersect is the answer. Did you answer "0.5"? How much aluminum, in kilograms, is being recycled on Friday? If you answered "1.0," you understand how to use the parts of the table.

Making and Using Graphs

After scientists organize data in tables, they may display the data in a graph. A graph is a diagram that shows the relationship of one variable to another. A graph makes interpretation and analysis of data easier. There are three basic types of graphs used in science—the line graph, the bar graph, and the circle graph.

Examples

Line Graphs A line graph is used to show the relationship between two variables. The variables being compared go on two axes of the graph. The independent variable always goes on the horizontal axis, called the *x*-axis. The dependent variable always goes on the vertical axis, called the *y*-axis.

Suppose your class started to record the amount of materials they collected in one week for their school to recycle. The collected information is shown in **Figure 9.**

You could make a graph of the materials collected over the three days of the school week. The three weekdays are the independent variables and are placed on the *x*-axis of your graph. The amount of materials collected is the dependent variable and would go on the *y*-axis.

After drawing your axes, label each with a scale. The *x*-axis lists the three weekdays. To make a scale of the amount of materials collected on the *y*-axis, look at the data values. Because the lowest amount collected was 1.0 and the highest was 5.0, you will have to start numbering at least at 1.0 and go through 5.0. You decide to start numbering at 0 and number by ones through 6.0, as shown in **Figure 10.**

Next, plot the data points for collected paper. The first pair of data you want to plot is Monday and 5.0 kg of paper.

Figure 9 Amount of recyclable materials collected during one week

Materials Collected During Week		
Day of Week	Paper (kg)	Aluminum (kg)
Mon.	5.0	4.0
Wed.	4.0	1.0
Fri.	2.5	2.0

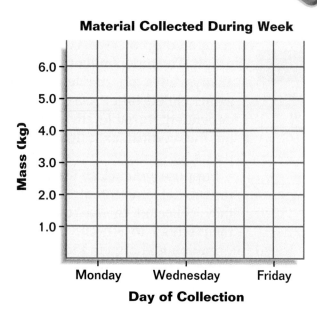

Figure 10 Graph outline for material collected during week

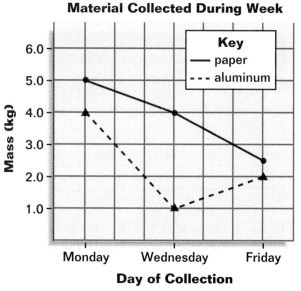

Figure 11 Line graph of materials collected during week

Locate "Monday" on the x-axis and locate "5.0" on the y-axis. Where an imaginary vertical line from the x-axis and an imaginary horizontal line from the y-axis would meet, place the first data point. Place the other data points the same way. After all the points are plotted, connect them with the best smooth curve. Repeat this procedure for the data points for aluminum. Use continuous and dashed lines to distinguish the two line graphs. The resulting graph should look like **Figure 11.**

Bar Graphs Bar graphs are similar to line graphs. They compare data that do not continuously change. In a bar graph, vertical bars show the relationships among data.

To make a bar graph, set up the x-axis and y-axis as you did for the line graph. The data is plotted by drawing vertical bars from the x-axis up to a point where the y-axis would meet the bar if it were extended.

Look at the bar graph in **Figure 12** comparing the mass of aluminum collected over three weekdays. The x-axis is the days on which the aluminum was collected. The y-axis is the mass of aluminum collected, in kilograms.

Circle Graphs A circle graph uses a circle divided into sections to display data. Each section represents part of the whole. All the sections together equal 100 percent.

Suppose you wanted to make a circle graph to show the number of seeds that germinated in a package. You would count the total number of seeds. You find that there are 143 seeds in the package. This represents 100 percent, the whole circle.

You plant the seeds, and 129 seeds germinate. The seeds that germinated will make up one section of the circle graph, and the seeds that did not germinate will make up the remaining section.

To find out how much of the circle each section should take, divide the number of seeds in each section by the total number of seeds. Then, multiply your answer by 360, the number of degrees in a circle, and round to the nearest whole number. The

Aluminum Collected During Week

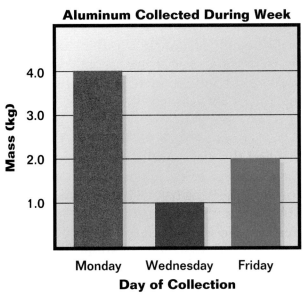

Figure 12 Bar graph of aluminum collected during week

section of the circle graph in degrees that represents the seeds germinated is figured below.

$$\frac{129}{143} \times 360 = 324.75 \text{ or } 325 \text{ degrees (or } 325°)$$

Plot this group on the circle graph using a compass and a protractor. Use the compass to draw a circle. It will be easier to

measure the part of the circle representing the non-germinating seeds, so subtract 325° from 360° to get 35°. Draw a straight line from the center to the edge of the circle. Place your protractor on this line and use it to mark a point at 325°. Use this point to draw a straight line from the center of the circle to the edge. This is the section for the group of seeds that did not germinate. The other section represents the group of 129 seeds that did germinate. Label the sections of your graph and title the graph as shown in **Figure 13.**

Figure 13 Circle graph of germinated seeds

Seeds Germinated

Not germinating (35°)

Germinating (325°)

Thinking Critically

Observing and Inferring

Observing Scientists try to make careful and accurate observations. When possible, they use instruments such as microscopes, thermometers, and balances to make observations. Measurements with a balance or thermometer provide numerical data that can be checked and repeated.

When you make observations in science, you'll find it helpful to examine the entire object or situation first. Then, look carefully for details. Write down everything you observe.

Example Imagine that you have just finished a volleyball game. At home, you open the refrigerator and see a jug of orange juice on the back of the top shelf. The jug, shown in **Figure 14,** feels cold as you grasp it. Then, you drink the juice, smell the oranges, and enjoy the tart taste in your mouth.

Figure 14 Why is this jug of orange juice cold?

As you imagined yourself in the story, you used your senses to make observations. You used your sense of sight to find the jug in the refrigerator, your sense of touch when you felt the coldness of the jug, your sense of hearing to listen as the liquid filled the glass, and your senses of smell and taste to enjoy the odor and tartness of the juice. The basis of all scientific investigation is observation.

Inferring Scientists often make inferences based on their observations. An inference is an attempt to explain or interpret observations or to say what caused what you observed.

When making an inference, be certain to use accurate data and observations. Analyze all of the data that you've collected. Then, based on everything you know, explain or interpret what you've observed.

Example When you drank a glass of orange juice after the volleyball game, you observed that the orange juice was cold as well as refreshing. You might infer that the juice was cold because it had been made much earlier in the day and had been kept in the refrigerator, or you might infer that it had just been made, using both cold water and ice. The only way to be sure which inference is correct is to investigate further.

Comparing and Contrasting

Observations can be analyzed by noting the similarities and differences between two or more objects or events that you observe. When you look at objects or events to see how they are similar, you are comparing them. Contrasting is looking for differences in similar objects or events.

Figure 15 Table comparing the nutritional value of *Cereal A* and *Cereal B*

Nutritional Value		
	Cereal A	**Cereal B**
Serving size	103 g	105 g
Calories	220	160
Total Fat	10 g	10 g
Protein	2.5 g	2.6 g
Total Carbohydrate	30 g	15 g

Example Suppose you were asked to compare and contrast the nutritional value of two kinds of cereal, *Cereal A* and *Cereal B.* You would start by looking at what is known about these cereals. Arrange this information in a table, like the one in **Figure 15.**

Similarities you might point out are that both cereals have similar serving sizes, amounts of total fat, and protein. Differences include *Cereal A* having a higher calorie value and containing more total carbohydrates than *Cereal B.*

Recognizing Cause and Effect

Have you ever watched something happen and then made suggestions about why it happened? If so, you have observed an effect and inferred a cause. The event is an effect, and the reason for the event is the cause.

Example Suppose that every time your teacher fed the fish in a classroom aquarium, she or he tapped the food container on the edge of the aquarium. Then, one day your teacher just happened to tap the edge of the aquarium with a pencil while making a point. You observed the fish swim to the surface of the aquarium to feed, as shown in **Figure 16.** What is the effect, and what would you infer to be the cause? The effect is the fish swimming to the surface of the aquarium. You might infer the cause to be the teacher tapping on the edge of the aquarium. In determining cause and effect, you have made a logical inference based on your observations.

Perhaps the fish swam to the surface because they reacted to the teacher's waving hand or for some other reason. When scientists are unsure of the cause of a certain event, they design controlled experiments to determine what causes the event. Although you have made a logical conclusion about the behavior of the fish, you would have to perform an experiment to be certain that it was the tapping that caused the effect you observed.

Figure 16 What cause-and-effect situations are occurring in this aquarium?

Science Skill Handbook

Practicing Scientific Processes

You might say that the work of a scientist is to solve problems. But when you decide how to dress on a particular day, you are doing problem solving, too. You may observe what the weather looks like through a window. You may go outside and see whether what you are wearing is heavy or light enough.

Scientists use an orderly approach to learn new information and to solve problems. The methods scientists may use include observing to form a hypothesis, designing an experiment to test a hypothesis, separating and controlling variables, and interpreting data.

Forming Operational Definitions

Operational definitions define an object by showing how it functions, works, or behaves. Such definitions are written in terms of how an object works or how it can be used; that is, what is its job or purpose?

Example Some operational defini-

Figure 17 What observations can be made about this dog?

tions explain how an object can be used.
- A ruler is a tool that measures the size of an object.
- An automobile can move things from one place to another.

Or such a definition may explain how an object works.
- A ruler contains a series of marks that can be used as a standard when measuring.
- An automobile is a vehicle that can move from place to place.

Forming a Hypothesis

Observations You observe all the time. Scientists try to observe as much as possible about the things and events they study so they know that what they say about their observations is reliable.

Some observations describe something using only words. These observations are called qualitative observations. Other observations describe how much of something there is. These are quantitative observations and use numbers, as well as words, in the description. Tools or equipment are used to measure the characteristic being described.

Example If you were making qualitative observations of the dog in **Figure 17,** you might use words such as *furry, yellow,* and *short-haired.* Quantitative observations of this dog might include a mass of 14 kg, a height of 46 cm, ear length of 10 cm, and an age of 150 days.

Hypotheses Hypotheses are tested to help explain observations that have been made. They are often stated as *if* and *then* statements.

Examples Suppose you want to make a perfect score on a spelling test. Begin by thinking of several ways to accomplish this. Base these possibilities on past observations. If you put each of these possibilities into sentence form, using the words *if* and *then*, you can form a hypothesis. All of the following are hypotheses you might consider to explain how you could score 100 percent on your test:

If the test is easy, then I will get a perfect score.

If I am intelligent, then I will get a perfect score.

If I study hard, then I will get a perfect score.

Perhaps a scientist has observed that plants that receive fertilizer grow taller than plants that do not. A scientist may form a hypothesis that says: If plants are fertilized, then their growth will increase.

Designing an Experiment to Test a Hypothesis

In order to test a hypothesis, it's best to write out a procedure. A procedure is the plan that you follow in your experiment. A procedure tells you what materials to use and how to use them. After following

the procedure, data are generated. From this generated data, you can then draw a conclusion and make a statement about your results.

If the conclusion you draw from the data supports your hypothesis, then you can say that your hypothesis is reliable. *Reliable* means that you can trust your conclusion. If it did not support your hypothesis, then you would have to make new observations and state a new hypothesis—just make sure that it is one that you can test.

Example Super premium gasoline costs more than regular gasoline. Does super premium gasoline increase the efficiency or fuel mileage of your family car? Let's figure out how to conduct an experiment to test the hypothesis, "*if* premium gas is more efficient, *then* it should increase the fuel mileage of our family car." Then a procedure similar to **Figure 18** must be written to generate data presented in **Figure 19** on the next page.

These data show that premium gasoline is less efficient than regular gasoline. It took more gasoline to travel one mile (0.064) using premium gasoline than it does to travel one mile using regular gasoline (0.059). This conclusion does not support the original hypothesis made.

PROCEDURE

1. Use regular gasoline for two weeks.

2. Record the number of miles between fill-ups and the amount of gasoline used.

3. Switch to premium gasoline for two weeks.

4. Record the number of miles between fill-ups and the amount of gasoline used.

Figure 18 Possible procedural steps

Figure 19 Data generated from procedure steps

Gasoline Data			
	Miles traveled	Gallons used	Gallons per mile
Regular gasoline	762	45.34	0.059
Premium gasoline	661	42.30	0.064

Separating and Controlling Variables

In any experiment, it is important to keep everything the same except for the item you are testing. The one factor that you change is called the *independent variable*. The factor that changes as a result of the independent variable is called the *dependent variable*. Always make sure that there is only one independent variable. If you allow more than one, you will not know what causes the changes you observe in the independent variable. Many experiments have *controls*—a treatment or an experiment that you can compare with the results of your test groups.

Example In the experiment with the gasoline, you made everything the same except the type of gasoline being used. The driver, the type of automobile, and the weather conditions should remain the same throughout. The gasoline should also be purchased from the same service station. By doing so, you made sure that at the end of the experiment, any differences were the result of the type of fuel being used—regular or premium. The type of gasoline was the *independent factor* and the gas mileage achieved was the *dependent factor*. The use of regular gasoline was the *control*.

Interpreting Data

The word *interpret* means "to explain the meaning of something." Look at the problem originally being explored in the gasoline experiment and find out what the data show. Identify the control group and the test group so you can see whether or not the variable has had an effect. Then, you need to check differences between the control and test groups.

Figure 20 Which gasoline type is most efficient?

These differences may be qualitative or quantitative. A qualitative difference would be a difference that you could observe and describe, while a quantitative difference would be a difference you can measure using numbers. If there are differences, the variable being tested may have had an effect. If there is no difference between the control and the test groups, the variable being tested apparently has had no effect.

Example Perhaps you are looking at a table from an experiment designed to test the hypothesis: If premium gas is more efficient, then it should increase the fuel mileage of our family car. Look back at **Figure 19** showing the results of this experiment. In this example, the use of regular gasoline in the family car was the control, while the car being fueled by premium gasoline was the test group.

Data showed a quantitative difference in efficiency for gasoline consumption. It took 0.059 gallons of regular gasoline to travel one mile, while it took 0.064 gallons of the premium gasoline to travel the same distance. The regular gasoline was more efficient; it increased the fuel mileage of the family car.

What are data? In the experiment described on these pages, measurements were taken so that at the end of the experiment, you had something concrete to interpret. You had numbers to work with. Not every experiment that you do will give you data in the form of numbers. Sometimes, data will be in the form of a description. At the end of a chemistry experiment, you might have noted that

Figure 21

one solution turned yellow when treated with a particular chemical, and another remained colorless, as water, when treated with the same chemical. Data, therefore, are stated in different forms for different types of scientific experiments.

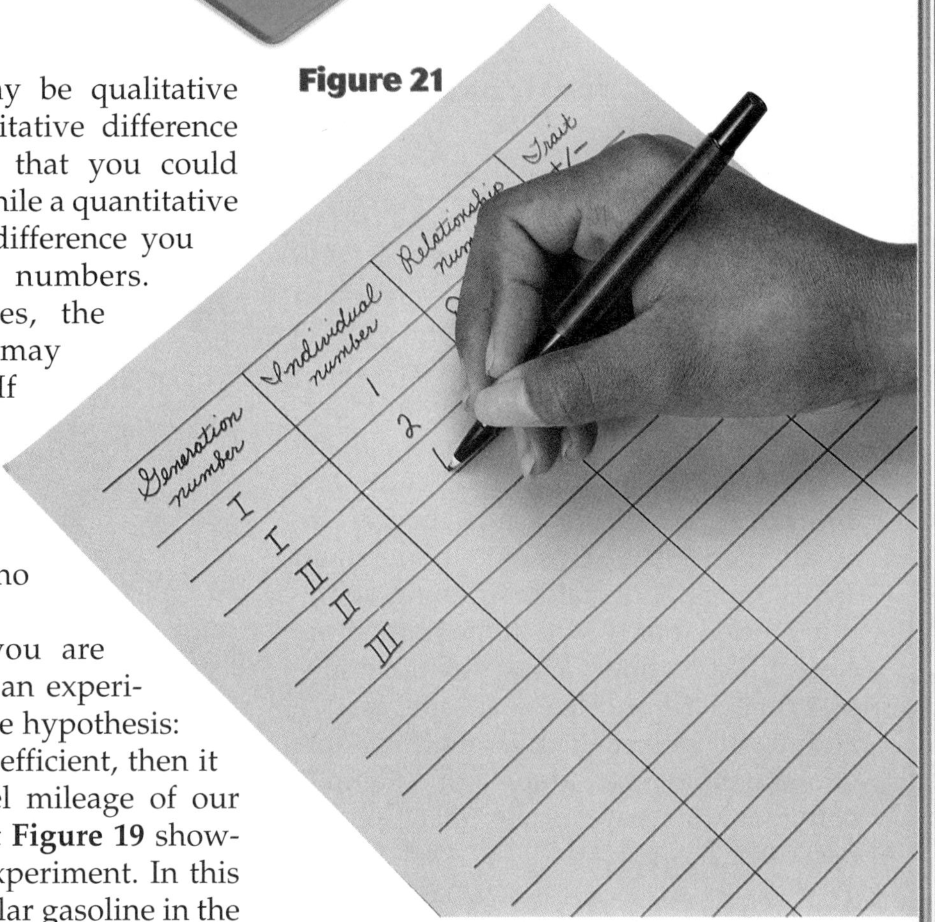

Are all experiments alike? Keep in mind as you perform experiments in science that not every experiment makes use of all of the parts that have been described on these pages. For some, it may be difficult to design an experiment that will always have a control. Other experiments are complex enough that it may be hard to have only one dependent variable. Real scientists encounter many variations in the methods that they use when they perform experiments. The skills in this handbook are here for you to use and practice. In real situations, their uses will vary.

Representing and Applying Data

Interpreting Scientific Illustrations

As you read a science textbook, you will see many drawings, diagrams, and photographs. Illustrations help you to understand what you read. Some illustrations are included to help you understand an idea that you can't see easily by yourself. For instance, we can't see atoms, but we can look at a diagram of an atom and that helps us to understand some things about atoms. Seeing something often helps you remember more easily. Illustrations also provide examples that clarify difficult concepts or give additional information about the topic you are studying. Maps, for example, help you to locate places that may be described in the text.

Examples

Captions and Labels Most illustrations have captions. A caption is a comment that identifies or explains the illustration. Diagrams, such as **Figure 22,** often have

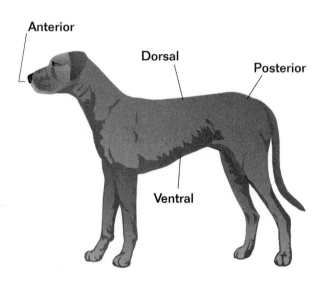

Figure 23 The orientation of a dog is shown here.

labels that identify parts of the organism or the order of steps in a process.

Learning with Illustrations An illustration of an organism shows that organism from a particular view or orientation. In order to understand the illustration, you may need to identify the front (anterior) end, tail (posterior) end, the underside (ventral), and the back (dorsal) side, as shown in **Figure 23.**

You might also check for symmetry. A shark in **Figure 24** has bilateral symmetry. This means that drawing an imaginary line through the center of the animal from the anterior to posterior end forms two mirror images.

Radial symmetry is the arrangement of similar parts around a central point. An object or organism, such as a hydra, can be divided anywhere through the center into similar parts.

Some organisms and objects cannot be divided into two similar parts. If an

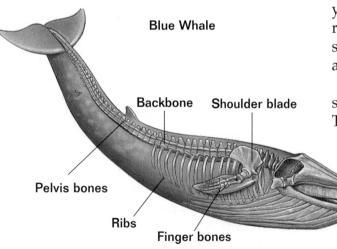

Figure 22 A labeled diagram of a blue whale

Figure 24 A shark (A) illustrating bilateral symmetry and a pear (B) illustrating a longitudinal section and a cross section

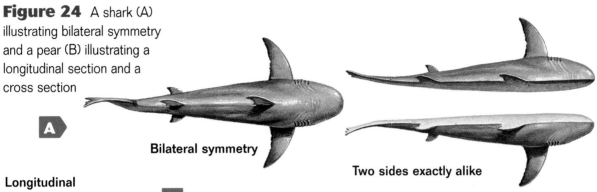

Bilateral symmetry

Two sides exactly alike

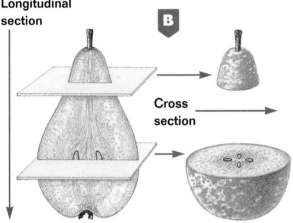

Longitudinal section

B

Cross section

organism or object cannot be divided, it is asymmetrical. Regardless of how you try to divide a natural sponge, you cannot divide it into two parts that look alike.

Some illustrations enable you to see the inside of an organism or object. These illustrations are called sections. **Figure 24** also illustrates some common sections.

Look at all illustrations carefully. Read captions and labels so that you understand exactly what the illustration is showing you.

Making Models

Have you ever worked on a model car, plane, or rocket? These models look, and sometimes work, much like the real thing, but they are often on a different scale than the real thing. In science, models are used to help simplify large or small processes or structures that otherwise would be dif-

ficult to see and understand. Your understanding of a structure or process is enhanced when you work with materials to make a model that shows the basic features of the structure or process.

Example In order to make a model, you first have to get a basic idea about the structure or process involved. You decide to make a model to show the differences in size of arteries, veins, and capillaries. First, read about these structures. All three are hollow tubes. Arteries are round and thick. Veins are flat and have thinner walls than arteries. Capillaries are small.

Now, decide what you can use for your model. Common materials are often most useful and cheapest to work with when making models. As illustrated in **Figure 25** on the next page, different kinds and sizes of pasta might work for these models. Different sizes of rubber tubing might do just as well. Cut and glue the different noodles or tubing onto thick paper so the openings can be seen. Then label each. Now you have a simple, easy-to-understand model showing the differences in size of arteries, veins, and capillaries.

What other scientific ideas might a model help you to understand? A model of a molecule can be made from balls of modeling clay (using different colors for the different elements present) and toothpicks (to show different chemical bonds).

Figure 25 Different types of pasta may be used to model blood vessels

A working model of a volcano can be made from clay, a small amount of baking soda, vinegar, and a bottle cap. Other models can be devised on a computer. Some models are mathematical and are represented by equations.

Measuring in SI

The metric system is a system of measurement developed by a group of scientists in 1795. It helps scientists avoid problems by providing standard measurements that all scientists around the world can understand. A modern form of the metric system, called the International System, or SI, was adopted for worldwide use in 1960.

The metric system is convenient because unit sizes vary by multiples of 10. When changing from smaller units to larger units, divide by 10. When changing

from larger units to smaller, multiply by 10. For example, to convert millimeters to centimeters, divide the millimeters by 10. To convert 30 millimeters to centimeters, divide 30 by 10 (30 millimeters equal 3 centimeters).

Prefixes are used to name units. Look at **Figure 26** for some common metric prefixes and their meanings. Do you see how the prefix *kilo-* attached to the unit *gram* is *kilogram*, or 1000 grams? The prefix *deci-* attached to the unit *meter* is *decimeter*, or one-tenth (0.1) of a meter.

Examples

Length You have probably measured lengths or distances many times. The meter is the SI unit used to measure length. A baseball bat is about one meter long. When measuring smaller lengths, the meter is divided into smaller units called centimeters and millimeters. A centimeter is one-hundredth (0.01) of a meter, which is about the size of the width of the fingernail on your ring finger. A millimeter is one-thousandth of a meter (0.001), about the thickness of a dime.

Most metric rulers have lines indicating centimeters and millimeters, as shown in

Figure 26 Common metric prefixes

Metric Prefixes			
Prefix	Symbol	Meaning	
kilo-	k	1000	thousand
hecto-	h	200	hundred
deca-	da	10	ten
deci-	d	0.1	tenth
centi-	c	0.01	hundredth
milli-	m	0.001	thousandth

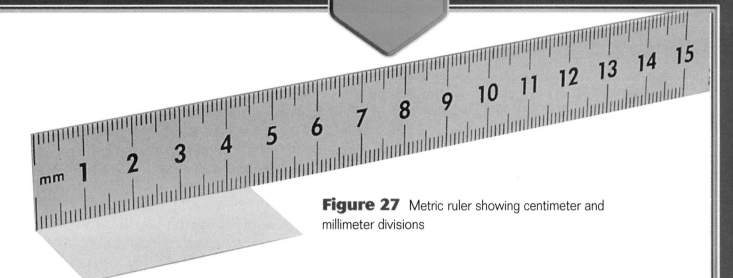

Figure 27 Metric ruler showing centimeter and millimeter divisions

Figure 27. The centimeter lines are the longer, numbered lines; the shorter lines are millimeter lines. When using a metric ruler, line up the 0-centimeter mark with the end of the object being measured, and read the number of the unit where the object ends, in this instance 4.5 cm.

Surface Area Units of length are also used to measure surface area. The standard unit of area is the square meter (m²). A square that's one meter long on each side has a surface area of one square meter. Similarly, a square centimeter, (cm²), shown in **Figure 28,** is one centimeter long on each side. The surface area of an object is determined by multiplying the length times the width.

Volume The volume of a rectangular solid is also calculated using units of length. The cubic meter (m³) is the standard SI unit of volume. A cubic meter is a cube one meter on each side. You can determine the volume of rectangular solids by multiplying length times width times height.

Liquid Volume During science activities, you will measure liquids using beakers and graduated cylinders marked in milliliters, as illustrated in **Figure 29.** A graduated cylinder is a cylindrical container marked with lines from bottom to top.

Liquid volume is measured using a unit called a liter. A liter has the volume of 1000 cubic centimeters. Because the prefix *milli-* means thousandth (0.001), a milliliter equals one cubic centimeter. One milliliter of liquid would completely fill a cube measuring one centimeter on each side.

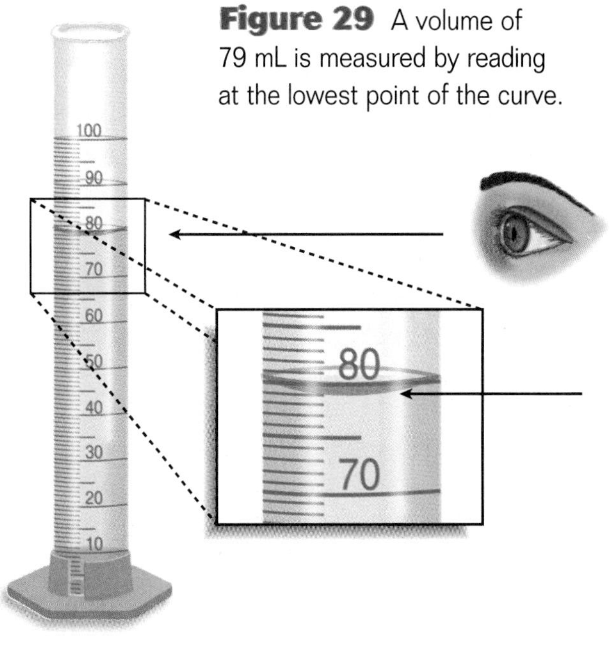

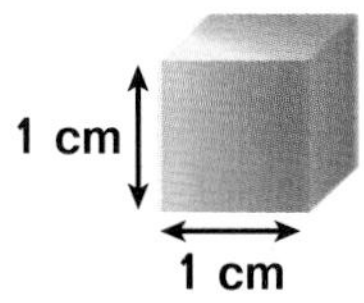

Figure 29 A volume of 79 mL is measured by reading at the lowest point of the curve.

Figure 28 A square centimeter

1 cm

1 cm

Mass Scientists use balances to find the mass of objects in grams. You might use a beam balance similar to **Figure 30.** Notice that on one side of the balance is a pan and on the other side is a set of beams. Each beam has an object of a known mass called a *rider* that slides on the beam.

Before you find the mass of an object, set the balance to zero by sliding all the riders back to the zero point. Check the pointer on the right to make sure it swings an equal distance above and below the zero point on the scale. If the swing is unequal, find and turn the adjusting screw until you have an equal swing.

Place an object on the pan. Slide the rider with the largest mass along its beam until the pointer drops below zero. Then move it back one notch. Repeat the process on each beam until the pointer swings an equal distance above and below the zero point. Add the masses on each beam to find the mass of the object.

You should never place a hot object or pour chemicals directly onto the pan. Instead, find the mass of a clean beaker or a glass jar. Place the dry or liquid chemicals in the container. Then find the combined mass of the container and the chemicals. Calculate the mass of the chemicals by subtracting the mass of the empty container from the combined mass.

Predicting

When you apply a hypothesis, or general explanation, to a specific situation, you predict something about that situation. First, you must identify which hypothesis fits the situation you are considering.

Examples People use prediction to make everyday decisions. Based on previous observations and experiences, you may form a hypothesis that if it is wintertime, then temperatures will be lower. From past experience in your area, temperatures are lowest in February. You may then use this hypothesis to predict specific temperatures and weather for the month of February in advance. Someone could use these predictions to plan to set aside more money for heating bills during that month.

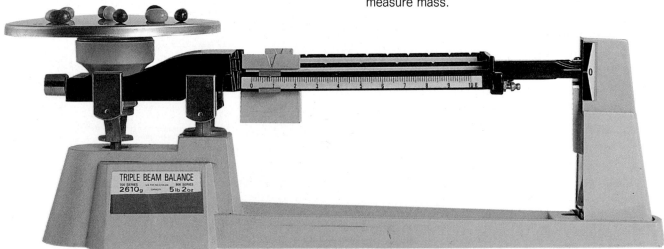

Figure 30 A beam balance is used to measure mass.

Using Numbers

When working with large populations of organisms, scientists usually cannot observe or study every organism in the population. Instead, they use a sample or a portion of the population. To sample is to take a small representative portion of organisms of a population for research. By making careful observations or manipulating variables within a portion of a group, information is discovered and conclusions are drawn that might then be applied to the whole population.

Scientific work also involves estimating. To estimate is to make a judgment about the size of something or the number of something without actually measuring or counting every member of a population.

Examples Suppose you are trying to determine the effect of a specific nutrient on the growth of black-eyed Susans. It would be impossible to test the entire population of black-eyed Susans, so you would select part of the population for your experiment. Through careful experimentation and observation on a sample of the population, you could generalize the effect of the chemical on the entire population.

Here is a more familiar example. Have you ever tried to guess how many beans were in a sealed jar? If you did, you were estimating. What if you knew the jar of beans held one liter (1000 mL)? If you knew that 30 beans would fit in a 100-milliliter jar, how many beans would you estimate to be in the one-liter jar? If you said about 300 beans, your estimate would be close to the actual number of beans. Can you estimate how many jelly beans are on the cookie sheet in **Figure 31**?

Scientists use a similar process to estimate populations of organisms from bacteria to buffalo. Scientists count the actual number of organisms in a small sample and then estimate the number of organisms in a larger area. For example, if a scientist wanted to count the number of bacterial colonies in a petri dish, a microscope could be used to count the number of organisms in a one-square-centimeter sample. To determine the total population of the culture, the number of organisms in the square-centimeter sample is multiplied by the total number of square centimeters in the culture.

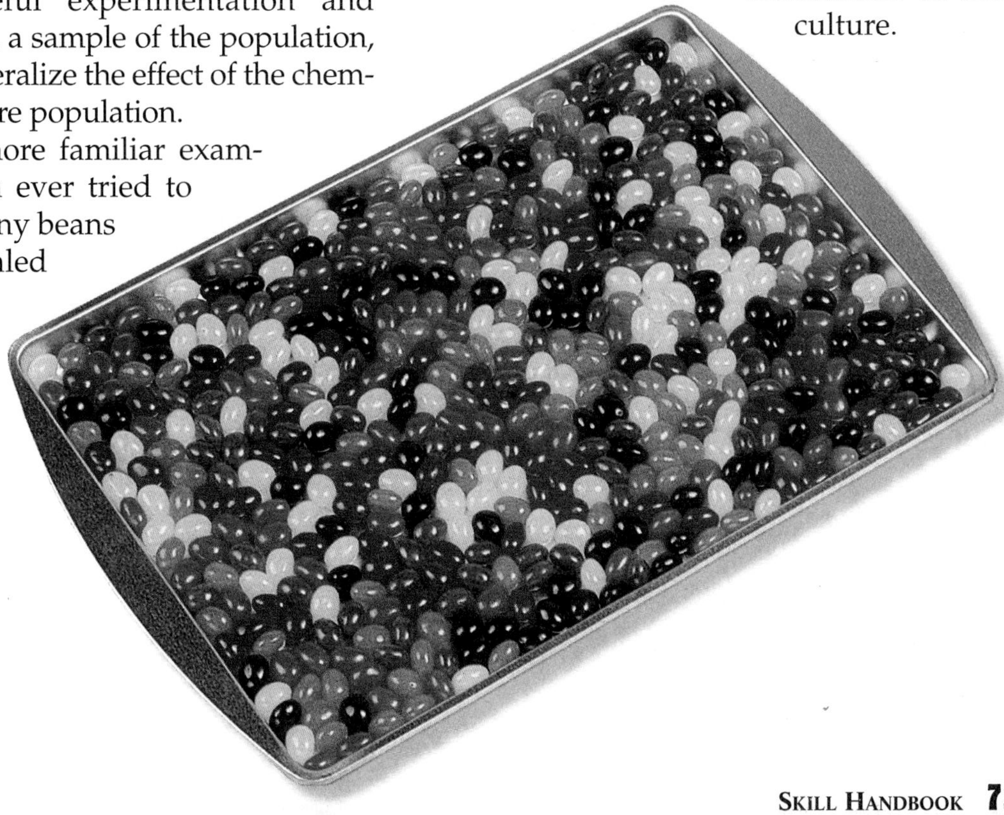

Figure 31
Sampling a group of jelly beans allows for an estimation of the total number of jelly beans in the group.

Technology Skill Handbook

Using a Word Processor

Suppose your teacher has assigned you to write a report. After you've done your research and decided how you want to write the information, you need to put all that information on paper. The easiest way to do this is with a word processor.

A word processor is a computer program in which you can write your information, change it as many times as you need to, and then print it out so that it looks neat and clean. You can also use a word processor to create tables and columns, add bullets or cartoon art, include page numbers, and even check your spelling.

Example Last week in Science class, your teacher assigned a report on the history of the atom. It has to be double spaced and include at least one table. You've collected all the facts, and you're ready to write your report. Sitting down at your computer, you decide you want to begin by explaining early scientific ideas about the atom and then talk about what scientists think about the atom now.

After you've written the two parts of your report, you decide to put a heading or subtitle above each part and add a title to the paper. To make each of these look different from the rest of your report, you can use a word processor to make the words bigger and bolder. The word processor also can double space your entire report, so that you don't have to add an extra space between each line.

You decide to include a table that lists each scientist that contributed to the theory of the atom along with his or her contribution. Using your word processor, you can create a table with as many rows and columns as you need. And, if you forget to include a scientist in the middle, you can go back and insert a row in the middle of your table without redoing the entire table.

When you've finished with your report, you can tell the word processor to check your spelling. If it finds misspelled words, it often will suggest a word you can use to replace the misspelled word. But, remember that the word processor may not know how to spell all the words in your report. Scan your report and double check your spelling with a dictionary if you're not sure if a word is spelled correctly.

After you've made sure that your report looks just the way you want it on the screen, the word processor will print your report on a printer. With a word processor, your report can look like it was written by a real scientist.

Helpful Hints

- If you aren't sure how to do something using your word processor, look under the help menu. You can look up how to do something, and the word processor will tell you how to do it. Just follow the instructions that the word processor puts on your screen.

- Just because you've spelled checked your report doesn't mean that the spelling is perfect. The spell check can't catch misspelled words that look like other words. So, if you've accidentally typed *mind* instead of *mine*, the spell checker won't know the difference. Always reread your report to make sure you didn't miss any mistakes.

Technology Skill Handbook

Using a Database

Imagine you're in the middle of research project. You are busily gathering facts and information. But, soon you realize that its becoming harder and harder to organize and keep track of all the information. The tool to solve "information overload" is a database. A database is exactly what it sounds like—a base on which to organize data. Similar to how a file cabinet organizes records, a database also organizes records. However, a database is more powerful than a simple file cabinet because at the click of a mouse, the entire contents can be reshuffled and reorganized. At computer-quick speeds, databases can sort information by any characteristic and filter data into multiple categories. Once you use a database, you will be amazed at how quickly all those facts and bits of information become manageable.

Example For the past few weeks, you have been gathering information on living and extinct primates. A database would be ideal to organize your information. An entry for gorillas might contain fields (categories) for fossil locations, brain size, average height, earliest fossil, and so on. Later on, if you wanted to know which primates have been found in Asia, you could quickly filter all entries using Asia in the field that listed locations. The database will scan all the entries and select the entries containing Asia. If you wanted to rank all the primates by arm length, you would sort all the entries by arm length. By using different combinations of sorting and filtering, you can discover relationships between the data that otherwise might remain hidden.

Helpful Hints

- Before setting up your own database, it's easier to learn the features of your database software by practicing with an established database.

- Entering the data into a database can be time consuming. Learn shortcuts such as tabbing between entry fields and automatic formatting of data that your software may provide.

- Get in the habit of periodically saving your database as you are entering data. That way, if something happens and your computer locks up or the power goes out, you won't lose all of your work.

Most databases have specific words you can use to narrow your search.

- AND: If you place an AND between two words in your search, the database will look for any entries that have both the words. For example, "blood AND cell" would give you information about both blood and cells.

- OR: If you place an OR between two words, the database will show entries that have at least one of the words. For example, "bird OR fish" would show you information on either birds or fish.

- NOT: If you place a NOT between two words, the database will look for entries that have the first word but do not have the second word. For example, "reproduction NOT plant" would show you information about reproduction but not about plant reproduction.

Technology Skill Handbook

Using Graphics Software

Having trouble finding that exact piece of art you're looking for? Do you have a picture in your mind of what you want but can't seem to find the right graphic to represent your ideas? To solve these problems, you can use graphics software. Graphics software allows you to change and create images and diagrams in almost unlimited ways. Typical uses for graphics software include arranging clip-art, changing scanned images, and constructing pictures from scratch. Most graphics-software applications work in similar ways. They use the same basic tools and functions. Once you master one graphics application, you can use any other graphics application relatively easily.

Example For your report on bird adaptations, you want to make a poster displaying a variety of beak and foot types. You have acquired many photos of birds, scanned from magazines and downloaded off the Internet. Using graphics software, you separate the beaks and feet from the birds and enlarge them. Then, you use arrows and text to diagram the particular features that you want to highlight. You also highlight the key features in color, keeping the rest of the graphic in black and white. With graphics software, the possibilities are endless. For the final layout, you place the picture of the bird next to enlarged graphics of the feet and beak. Graphics software allows you to integrate text into your diagrams, which makes your bird poster look clean and professional.

Helpful Hints

- As with any method of drawing, the more you practice using the graphic software, the better your results.
- Start by using the software to manipulate existing drawings. Once you master this, making your own illustrations will be easier.
- Clip art is available on CD-ROMs, and on the Internet. With these resources, finding a piece of clip art to suit your purposes is simple.
- As you work on a drawing, save it often.
- Often you can learn a lot from studying other people's art. Look at other computer illustrations and try to figure out how the artist created it.

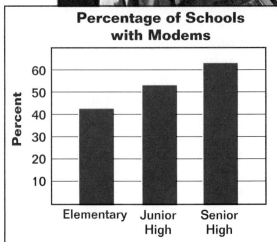

Percentage of Schools with Modems

Technology Skill Handbook

Using a Computerized Card Catalog

When you have a report or paper to research, you go to the library. To find the information, skill is needed in using a computerized card catalog. You use the computerized card catalog by typing in a subject, the title of a book, or an author's name. The computer will list on the screen all the holdings the library has on the subject, title, or author requested.

A library's holdings include books, magazines, databases, videos, and audio materials. When you have chosen something from this list, the computer will show whether an item is available and where in the library to find it.

Example You have a report due on dinosaurs, and you need to find three books on the subject. In the library, follow the instructions on the computer screen to select the "Subject" heading. You could start by typing in the word *dinosaurs*. This will give you a list of books on that subject. Now you need to narrow your search to the kind of dinosaur you are interested in, for example, *Tyrannosaurus rex*. You can type in *Tyrannosaurus rex* or just look through the list to find titles that you think would have information you need. Once you have selected a short list of books, click on each selection to find out if the library has the books. Then, check on where they are located in the library.

Helpful Hints

- Remember that you can use the computer to search by subject, author, or title. If you know a book's author, but not the title, you can search for all the books the library has by that author.

- When searching by subject, it's often most helpful to narrow your search by using specific search terms. If you don't find enough, you can then broaden your search.

- Pay attention to the type of materials found in your search. If you need a book, you can eliminate any videos or other resources that come up in your search.

- Knowing how your library is arranged can save a lot of time. The librarian will show you where certain types of material are kept and how to find something.

Developing Multimedia Presentations

It's your turn—you have to present your science report to the entire class. How do you do it? You can use many different sources of information to get the class excited about your presentation. Posters, videos, photographs, sound, computers, and the Internet can help show our ideas. First, decide the most important points you want your presentation to make. Then, sketch out what materials and types of media would be best to illustrate those points. Maybe you could start with an outline on an overhead projector, then show a video, followed by something from the Internet or a slide show accompanied by music or recorded voices. Make sure you don't make the presentation too complicated, or you will confuse yourself and the class. Practice your presentation a few times for your parents or brothers and sisters before you present it to the class.

Example Your assignment is to give a presentation on bird-watching. You could have a poster that shows what features you use to identify birds, with a sketch of your favorite bird. A tape of the calls of your favorite bird or a video of birds in your area would work well with the poster. If possible, include an Internet site with illustrations of birds that the class can look at.

Helpful Hints

- Carefully consider what media will best communicate the point you are trying to make.
- Keep your topic and your presentation simple.
- Make sure you learn how to use any equipment you will be using in your presentation.
- Practice the presentation several times.
- If possible, set up all of the equipment ahead of time. Make sure everything is working correctly.

Using E-Mail

It's science fair time and you want to ask a scientist a question about your project, but he or she lives far away. You could write a letter or make a phone call. But you can also use the computer to communicate. You can do this using electronic mail (E-mail). You will need a computer that is connected to an E-mail network. The computer is usually hooked up to the network by a device called a *modem*. A modem works through the telephone lines. Finally, you need an address for the person you want to talk with. The E-mail address works just like a street address to send mail to that person.

Example There are just a few steps needed to send a message to a friend on an E-mail network. First, select Message from the E-mail software menu. Then, enter the E-mail address of your friend. Next, type your message. Make sure you check it for spelling and other errors. Finally, click the Send button to mail your message and off it goes! You will get a reply back in your electronic mailbox. To read your reply, just click on the message and the reply will appear on the screen.

Helpful Hints
- Make sure that you have entered the correct address of the person you're sending the message to.
- Reread your message to make sure it says what you want to say, and check for spelling and grammar.
- If you receive an E-mail message, respond to it as soon as possible.
- If you receive frequent email messages, keep them organized by either deleting them, or saving them in folders according to the subject or sender.

Technology Skill Handbook

Using an Electronic Spreadsheet

Your science fair experiment has produced lots of numbers. How do you keep track of all the data, and how can you easily work out all the calculations needed? You can use a computer program called a *spreadsheet* to keep track of data that involve numbers. A spreadsheet is an electronic worksheet. Type in your data in rows and columns, just as in a data table on a sheet of paper. A spreadsheet uses some simple math to do calculations on the data. For example, you could add, subtract, divide, or multiply any of the values in the spreadsheet by another number. Or you can set up a series of math steps you want to apply to the data. If you want to add 12 to all the numbers and then multiply all the numbers by 10, the computer does all the calculations for you in the spreadsheet. Below is an example of a spreadsheet that is a schedule.

Example Let's say that to complete your project, you need to calculate the speed of the model cars in your experiment. Enter the distance traveled by each car in the rows of the spreadsheet. Then enter the time you recorded for each car to travel the measured distance in the column across from each car. To make the formula, just type in the equation you want the computer to calculate; in this case, *speed = distance ÷ time*. You must make sure the computer knows what data are in the rows and what data are in the

columns so the calculation will be correct. Once all the distance and time data and the formula have been entered into the spreadsheet program, the computer will calculate the speed for all the trials you ran. You can even make graphs of the results.

Helpful Hints

- Before you set up the spreadsheet, sketch out how you want to organize the data. Include any formulas you will need to use.
- Make sure you have entered the correct data into the correct rows and columns.
- As you experiment with your particular spreadsheet program you will learn more of its features.
- You can also display your results in a graph. Pick the style of graph that best represents the data you are working with.

Test Run Data

	A	B	C	D
1	Test Runs	Time	Distance	Speed
2	Car 1	5 mins.	5 miles	60 mph
3	Car 2	10 mins.	4 miles	24 mph
4	Car 3	6 mins.	3 miles	30 mph

Technology Skill Handbook

Using a CD-ROM

What's your favorite music? You probably listen to your favorite music on compact discs (CDs). But, there is another use for compact discs, called CD-ROM. CD-ROM means Compact Disc-Read Only Memory. CD-ROMs hold information. Whole encyclopedias and dictionaries can be stored on CD-ROM discs. This kind of CD-ROM and others are used to research information for reports and papers. The information is accessed by putting the disc in your computer's CD-ROM drive and following the computer's installation instructions. The CD-ROM will have words, pictures, photographs, and maybe even sound and video on a range of topics.

Example Load the CD-ROM into the computer. Find the topic you are interested in by clicking on the Search button. If there is no Search button, try the Help button. Most CD-ROMs are easy to use, but refer to the Help instructions if you have problems. Use the arrow keys to move down through the list of titles on your topic. When you double-click on a title, the article will appear on the screen. You can print the article by clicking on the Print button. Each CD-ROM is different. Click the Help menu to see how to find what you want.

Helpful Hints

- Always open and close the CD-ROM drive on your computer by pushing the button next to the drive. Pushing on the tray to close it will stress the opening mechanism over time.
- Place the disc in the tray so the side with no printing is facing down.
- Read through the installation instructions that come with the CD-ROM.
- Remember to remove the CD-ROM before you shut your computer down.

Using Probeware

Data collecting in an experiment sometimes requires that you take the same measurement over and over again. With probeware, you can hook a probe directly to a computer and have the computer collect the data about temperature, pressure, motion, or pH. Probeware is a combination sensor and software that makes the process of collecting data easier. With probes hooked to computers, you can make many measurements quickly, and you can collect data over a long period of time without needing to be present. Not only will the software record the data, most software will graph the data.

Example Suppose you want to monitor the health of an enclosed ecosystem. You might use an oxygen and a carbon dioxide sensor to monitor the gas concentrations or humidity or temperature. If the gas concentrations remain stable, you could predict that the ecosystem is healthy. After all the data is collected, you can use the software to graph the data and analyze it. With probeware, experimenting is made efficient and precise.

Helpful Hints

- Find out how to properly use each probe before using it.
- Make sure all cables are solidly connected. A loose cable can interrupt the data collection and give you inaccurate results.
- Because probeware makes data collection so easy, do as many trials as possible to strengthen your data.

Technology Skill Handbook

Using a Graphing Calculator

Science can be thought of as a means to predict the future and explain the past. In other language, if x happens, can we predict y? Can we explain the reason y happened? Simply, is there a relationship between x and y? In nature, a relationship between two events or two quantities, x and y, often occur. However, the relationship is often complicated and can only be readily seen by making a graph. To analyze a graph, there is no quicker tool than a graphing calculator. The graphing calculator shows the mathematical relationship between two quantities.

Example If you have collected data on the position and time for a migrating whale, you can use the calculator to graph the data. Using the linear regression function on the calculator, you can determine the average migration speed of the whale. The more you use the graphing calculator to solve problems, the more you will discover its power and efficiency.

Graphing calculators have some keys that other calculators do not have. The keys on the bottom half of the calculator are those found on all scientific calculators. The keys located just below the screen are the graphing keys. You will also notice the up, down, left, and right arrow keys. These allow you to move the cursor around on the screen, to "trace" graphs that have been plotted, and to choose items from the menus. The other keys located on the top of the calculator access the special features such as statistical computations and programming features.

A few of the keystrokes that can save you time when using the graphing calculator are listed below.

- The commands above the calculator keys are accessed with the [2nd] or [ALPHA] key. The [2nd] key and its commands are yellow and the [ALPHA] and its commands are green.
- [2nd] [ENTRY] copies the previous calculation so you can edit and use it again.
- Pressing [ON] while the calculator is graphing stops the calculator from completing the graph.
- [2nd] [QUIT] will return you to the home (or text) screen.
- [2nd] [A-LOCK] locks the [ALPHA] key, which is like pressing "shift lock" or "caps lock" on a typewriter or computer. The result is that all letters will be typed and you do not have to repeatedly press the [ALPHA] key. (This is handy for programming.) Stop typing letters by pressing [ALPHA] again.
- [2nd] [OFF] turns the calculator off.

Helpful Hints

- Mastering the graphing calculator takes practice. Don't expect to learn it all in an afternoon.
- Programming a graphing calculator takes a plan. Write out all of the steps before entering them.
- It's easiest to learn how to program the calculator by first using programs that have already been written. As you enter them, figure out what each step is telling the calculator to do.

Skill Activities

Table of Contents

Sequencing

Background

A complex project, such as a crewed mission to Mars, requires a great deal of planning over many years. The sequence of the plan is important because many of the steps cannot be done until a previous item is completed. The people responsible for the project have an overall planning sequence required for a crewed mission to Mars.

One of the recent ideas for a Mars mission involves building a spacecraft at a space station orbiting Earth. A space shuttle would ferry materials and people between Earth's surface and the space station. Then, the astronauts would travel in the spacecraft to Mars and return again to the space station.

Procedure

1. Read through the steps, which are out of order, listed in the table for a crewed mission to Mars.

2. Decide in what order the steps need to be completed.

3. On a separate sheet of paper, list the letters of the steps in what you consider to be the most logical sequence.

Steps for a Mission to Mars	
a. Plan second Mars mission	**k.** Estimate cost of mission
b. Spacecraft leaves Mars orbit for Earth	**l.** Spacecraft leaves Earth orbit for Mars
c. Study Mars data and samples	**m.** Astronauts explore Mars
d. Space shuttle meets returning spacecraft	**n.** Construct spacecraft
e. Mars Rover returns to spacecraft	**o.** Design spacecraft
f. Spacecraft enters orbit around Earth	**p.** Select astronauts
g. Make any necessary course adjustments	**q.** Astronauts receive hero's welcome
h. Select a company to build spacecraft	**r.** Space shuttle carries astronauts to Earth
i. Astronauts send television viewers greetings from Mars	**s.** Space shuttle carries astronauts to space station
j. Study future positions of Earth and Mars and select launch date	**t.** Space shuttle carries building materials into orbit

Practicing the SKILL

1. This mission plan is very brief and some details are left out. A real plan for a Mars mission would be many, many pages long. Read over your plan sequence. Add at least three more details to your plan and indicate where they should be placed in the sequence.

2. Think about how you would go about planting a vegetable or flower garden. Write down in the most logical sequence the steps you would take to plant a garden.

For more skill practice, do the Chapter 1 Interactive Exploration on the **Science Voyages Level Blue CD-ROM.**

GLENCOE TECHNOLOGY

Making Models

Background

You can use a model to help you better understand the structure of an atom. A model can be a drawing or something you build, like a model car. A model isn't exactly like the real object. It is often a simplified picture of a more complex object. For example, a diagram of an atom shows only a two-dimensional representation of a three-dimensional object. However, it gives you a simple picture of how the particles in an atom are arranged, and it helps you understand how matter behaves.

Procedure

1. Copy the Subatomic Particles table in your Science Journal.

2. Use the periodic table to find the number of protons, neutrons, and electrons in a lithium-7 atom. The number 7 in lithium-7 means that this is the isotope of lithium with mass number 7. In a neutral atom, the number of protons is the atomic number. The number of neutrons is the mass number minus the atomic number. The number of electrons is the same as the number of protons.

3. In the table, list the number of each particle in lithium-7.

4. Draw a circle about 2 cm in diameter. See the example in the figure at the right.

5. Write the number of protons in the circle next to a p^+ symbol.

6. Write the number of neutrons in the circle next to an n symbol.

7. Draw another circle around the circle you already drew. On this circle, write next to an e^- symbol the number of electrons that are in the atom's electron cloud.

Subatomic Particles			
Atoms	Protons	Neutrons	Electrons
Lithium-7			
Boron-10			
Boron-11			
Carbon-12			
Carbon-14			

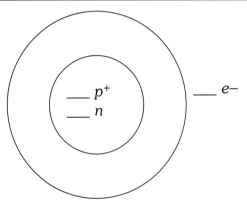

Practicing the SKILL

1. Refer to the periodic table and list the numbers of protons, neutrons, and electrons in the isotopes of boron and carbon listed in the Subatomic Particles table.

2. Using the steps given in the procedure, make models for the boron and carbon isotopes.

For more skill practice, do the Chapter 2 Interactive Exploration on the **Science Voyages Level Blue CD-ROM.**

GLENCOE TECHNOLOGY

Classifying

Background

You classify objects every day. You may put all your socks in one drawer and your sweaters in another. You store soaps, detergents, and other cleaners separately from food. You may store canned vegetables and soups on one shelf and spices on another. Putting similar objects together is classification.

By classifying objects into groups, scientists can organize information. Classifying helps them compare and contrast properties of different groups. For example, scientists classify some substances as metals, nonmetals, or metalloids. Once classified, these substances can be more easily studied.

Procedure

Use the periodic table and what you have learned to classify the following elements into categories. Label each category. Write your answers on a separate sheet of paper.

F	Li	B	Cl	Si	Na
Br	Po	Cs	Al	He	Ni

Practicing the SKILL

1. Classify the following elements into two categories. Label each category.

hydrogen	aluminum
silver	gold
iron	oxygen
fluorine	copper
zinc	bromine
mercury	helium
radon	tungsten
bismuth	actinium

2. In what other ways can these elements be classified?

For more skill practice, do the Chapter 3 Interactive Exploration on the **Science Voyages Level Blue CD-ROM.**

GLENCOE TECHNOLOGY

H																	He
Li	Be											B	C	N	O	F	Ne
Na	Mg											Al	Si	P	S	Cl	Ar
K	Ca	Sc	Ti	V	Cr	Mn	Fe	Co	Ni	Cu	Zn	Ga	Ge	As	Se	Br	Kr
Rb	Sr	Y	Zr	Nb	Mo	Tc	Ru	Rh	Pd	Ag	Cd	In	Sn	Sb	Te	I	Xe
Cs	Ba	La	Hf	Ta	W	Re	Os	Ir	Pt	Au	Hg	Tl	Pb	Bi	Po	At	Rn
Fr	Ra	Ac	Rf	Db	Sg	Bh	Hs	Mt	Uun	Uuu	Uub						

Metal

Metalloid

Nonmetal

Predicting

Background

Any time you apply a hypothesis to a specific situation, you are making a prediction. Predictions can be made using tables, graphs, and other tools that give information. They also can be made based upon previous experience.

Electrons are more strongly attracted to some atoms. You can think of the sharing of electrons in a bond as a tug-of-war between two atoms. Electronegativity is a measure of the ability of an atom in a bond to attract electrons. When there is little difference in the electronegativities of two atoms, the bond is covalent. The bond has a small percentage of ionic character. As the difference between their electronegativities gets larger, the electrons are more attracted to one of the atoms. The bond has a greater percent ionic character. If the difference is large enough, one atom will lose an electron and the other atom will gain one. An ionic bond forms.

Chemists often use graphs to predict whether two atoms will form an ionic or covalent bond. The difference in the electronegativities of potassium and chlorine is 2.2. Use the graph to predict the type of bond that they will form.

Procedure

1. Notice that the difference in electronegativity is plotted on the x-axis.

2. When reading the y-axis, the larger the percent ionic character, the more certain you can be that the bond will be ionic.

3. Locate 2.2 on the x-axis. Go straight up from 2.2 to the curve.

4. Go straight from the point on the curve to the y-axis. Read that the percent ionic character is 69 percent.

5. The bond between potassium and chlorine will be ionic.

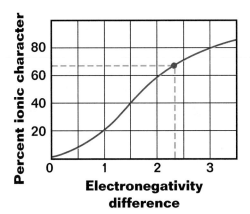

Practicing the SKILL

1. Predict the type of bond that will form between carbon and nitrogen. The difference in electronegativity is 0.5.

2. Predict the type of bond that will form between lithium and fluorine. The difference in electronegativity is 3.0.

3. What is the difference in electronegativity for a bond with 40 percent ionic character?

For more skill practice, do the Chapter 4 Interactive Exploration on the **Science Voyages Level Blue CD-ROM.**

GLENCOE TECHNOLOGY

Observing and Inferring

Background

Many prescription drugs come with detailed instructions on how to take them. If you don't follow the instructions carefully, the drug may not work well. It could also make you seriously ill. Over-the-counter medications have instructions, too. You can buy medication for heartburn, indigestion, upset stomach, and a cold from almost any grocery or drug store.

How do scientists determine the best way to take a drug so that it gives the patient the relief he or she needs? Before any drug is given to a patient, it is tested many times. Scientists have to observe how the chemicals in a drug react with the chemicals in the body. In some cases, scientists recommend that the drug be taken in a certain way. The label on the bottle or box may say to take the medication with food, water, on an empty stomach, or with milk. It is always important to follow the directions so the medication can work properly. In this activity, you will observe how water temperature affects the reaction time of an effervescent tablet.

Procedure

1. Copy the data table.

2. Use masking tape to label three beakers A, B, and C.

3. Write a hypothesis stating the effect of temperature on the decomposition of an effervescent tablet.

4. Pour exactly 150 mL of ice water into beaker A. Measure the temperature of the water. Record the temperature in the data table.

5. Carefully drop one effervescent tablet into the beaker. Measure and record the number of seconds needed for the tablet to completely dissolve.

6. Pour 150 mL of water at room temperature into beaker B. Measure and record the temperature of the water.

7. Repeat step 5 using the room-temperature water.

8. Pour 150 mL of warm water into beaker C. Measure and record the temperature of the water.

9. Repeat step 5 using the warm water.

Dissolving an Effervescent Tablet

Beaker	Temperature of Water	Time to Dissolve
A		
B		
C		

Practicing the SKILL

1. In which beaker did the reaction occur most rapidly?

2. In which beaker was the reaction slowest?

3. What effect did temperature have on the reaction time of an effervescent tablet?

For more skill practice, do the Chapter 5 Interactive Exploration on the **Science Voyages Level Blue CD-ROM.**

GLENCOE TECHNOLOGY

Using Numbers

Background

Scientists often use formulas to solve problems. Suppose you are asked: How does the average velocity of a ball change during flight? You could use the formula that says the average velocity equals displacement over time. It is written below.

$$v = \frac{d}{t}$$

Procedure

1. The figure shows a ball in motion. The time interval between each position of the ball is 1/30 of a second.

2. Place a piece of paper on top of the drawing.

3. Mark each position of the ball with a dot.

4. Remove the paper. Draw a straight line connecting the first four positions of the ball (three intervals). The time between three intervals of the ball is 0.1 s. Why?

5. Measure and record the length of the straight line. The length of the line can be used to show the distance traveled during the first 0.1 s of flight.

6. Repeat steps 4 and 5 for the next four positions of the ball, and so on. The length of each line shows the distance traveled during each 0.1 s of flight.

Practicing the SKILL

At what interval is the average velocity smallest? Largest?

For more skill practice, do the Chapter 6 Interactive Exploration on the **Science Voyages Level Blue CD-ROM.**

Making and Using Tables

Background

Scientists collect and interpret data as a part of their investigations. They often organize the data into a data table. Data tables help the scientists to arrange information so it is easier for them to understand. Scientists interpret the data by looking for patterns that may lead to general conclusions.

Suppose the class decides to see how far a ball will travel over a period of time.

Procedure

1. Look at the Rolling Distance table.

2. Notice that the time, in seconds, that the ball rolled is listed in the first column.

3. The distance, in meters, that the ball traveled in that amount of time is listed in the second column.

4. Now, see if there is a pattern between the time allowed for the ball to roll and the distance it traveled.

5. By looking at the table, you can see that the longer the ball rolled, the further it traveled.

6. You can also see that the distance traveled was double the time allowed each time.

7. Look at the Planetary Weight Factors table.

8. To figure out what you would weigh on different planets, multiply your weight on Earth by the factor listed next to each planet in the Planetary Weight Factors table.

Rolling Distance

Time (s)	Distance (m)
0.0	0.0
1.0	2.0
2.0	4.0
3.0	6.0

Sample Data

Planetary Weight Factors

Planet	Factor	Your Weight on Earth (lb)	Your Weight on Planet (lb)
Venus	0.91		
Mars	0.38		
Jupiter	2.5		
Saturn	1.1		
Neptune	1.1		

Practicing the SKILL

Use the Planetary Weight Factors table to answer the following questions.

1. On which planet(s) do you weigh more than you do on Earth? Less than Earth?

2. On which planet(s) would you weigh nearly the same as you do on Earth?

For more skill practice, do the Chapter 7 Interactive Exploration on the **Science Voyages Level Blue CD-ROM.**

GLENCOE TECHNOLOGY

Using Numbers

Background

What do people need to survive? What is the difference between a necessity and a luxury? An earthquake can make the answers to these questions clear to people. During a damaging earthquake, basic services such as water, power, communication, and roads may be unavailable. Disaster relief experts advise that you should be prepared to be self-sufficient for 72 hours. An earthquake survival pack is a good way to be prepared.

Procedure

1. Study the list of items in the Survival Kit Items table. Decide which items are necessities and which are luxuries.

2. Using prices in your area, calculate the total cost of items you have chosen for your survival pack.

Survival Kit Items

Item	Cost ($)	Item	Cost ($)	Item	Cost ($)
aspirin or acetaminophen	1.49	prescription medicines (insulin, etc.)	varies	water-purification tablets	2.69
ipecac*	2.69	latex gloves	1.39	crackers	3.19
adhesive bandages	1.59	gauze pads 4" × 4"	2.89	canned beans	0.69
tweezers	0.99	flashlight	5.79	dried fruit	4.79
thermometer	4.29	batteries	8.49	blankets	7.99
rubbing alcohol	0.49	radio	9.99	plastic tarp	6.49
tissues	0.89	bottled water 4 liters/person	2.16	first aid handbook	4.99
pocketknife	12.99	canned tuna	2.79	matches	0.39
adhesive tape	2.19	canned juice	1.19	candles	1.99
scissors	3.19	pet food	3.00	can opener	2.39
canned heat	1.89	paper and pencil	2.00	ax	15.89
disposable dishes	2.39	antibiotic ointment	2.59	disposable utensils	2.19
bucket	3.99	chlorine bleach	0.25	eye dropper	1.99
clothing	varies	cotton swabs	0.89	signal flare	6.19
towel	5.49	books	7.50	toilet paper	0.49
elastic bandage	2.49	peanut butter	1.19	shovel	12.98

*drug used to induce vomiting in case of accidental poisoning

Practicing the SKILL

1. Which items do you consider to be the most important? Why?

2. Are there any items not on the list that you think should be included? What are they and why do you want to include them?

3. Which items would you buy if you were restricted to a $50 budget?

For more skill practice, do the Chapter 8 Interactive Exploration on the **Science Voyages Level Blue CD-ROM.**

Making and Using Graphs

Background

You have learned that composite volcanoes can sometimes erupt violently, throwing large volumes of material into the atmosphere. Volcanologists have used various methods to rank these explosive eruptions. One of the most commonly used is to compare the volumes of erupted material. Because the amount of material is huge, scientists use cubic kilometers (km^3). A cubic kilometer is the amount of material in a cube that measures one kilometer on each side. That's a lot of rock!

Procedure

The Volcano Information table contains information about violent volcanic eruptions from around the world. Use these data to make a bar graph that compares the volume of material that was ejected by these volcanoes. Put the eruption date on the x-axis and the volume of material on the y-axis.

Practicing the SKILL

1 When was the largest eruption of Mount St. Helens? How many km^3 of material were ejected?

2 How are the data organized in the Volcano Information table?

3 What was the largest eruption of the 20th century? When did it occur?

For more skill practice, do the

GLENCOE TECHNOLOGY

Chapter 9 Interactive Exploration on the **Science Voyages Level Blue CD-ROM.**

Volcano Information		
Volcano Name and Location	**Eruption Date**	**Volume (km^3)**
Mount Pinatubo, Philippines	1991	5.0
El Chichón, Mexico	1982	0.85
Mount St. Helens, Washington	1980	1.3
Mount Katmai, Alaska	1912	12.8
Mount Pelée, Martinique	1902	0.85
Krakatau, Indonesia	1883	19.0
Mount St. Helens, Washington	1842–1857	1.5
Tambora, Indonesia	1815	32.0
Mount Fuji, Japan	1707	2.1
Mount St. Helens, Washington	1480–1482	2.6
Vesuvius, Italy (Pompeii)	A.D. 79	3.0
Mount St. Helens, Washington	1900 B.C.	3.4
Mount Mazama, Oregon (Crater Lake)	5000 B.C.	43.0

Interpreting Scientific Illustrations

Background

When a large earthquake occurs in the Pacific Ocean, the epicenter is quickly determined and a tsunami warning is issued. Scientists have created tsunami travel-time charts such as in the figure below, for the Pacific Ocean. Using these charts allows them to predict when a tsunami will reach different Pacific Ocean coastal regions.

On Friday, July 17, 1998, a magnitude 7.0 earthquake occurred on the seafloor near Papua New Guinea in the South Pacific Ocean. Within moments a 7-meter-high tsunami struck the shore and more than 3000 people were killed as coastal villages were washed away.

Procedure

Study the figure below. If you know the epicenter of an earthquake you can determine when a tsunami might reach land. For example, a tsunami caused by an earthquake in Guam would take about 8 hours to reach Hilo, Hawaii.

Practicing the SKILL

1. A large earthquake off the coast of Peru has generated a tsunami. If you live in Hilo, Hawaii, how long do you have before the tsunami reaches your beach house?

2. An underwater volcanic eruption near Midway Island has caused a tsunami. How long before this wave reaches Tokyo, Japan?

3. Why was a tsunami warning of no use to the villagers in Papua New Guinea?

For more skill practice, do the Chapter 10 Interactive Exploration on the **Science Voyages Level Blue CD-ROM.**

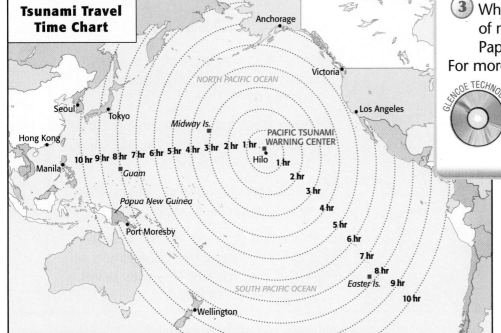

Tsunami Travel Time Chart

Observing and Inferring

Background

Throughout Earth's history, many changes have taken place. Unfortunately, there is no written record from prehistoric time. There are clues to Earth's past imbedded in rock, though. Fossils are the remains of once-living organisms that have been preserved in rock.

Scientists study fossils in order to gain knowledge about the organism. They also learn what the environment was like when the organism was alive. Scientists look at (observe) the fossil and estimate (infer) what the environment was like during the lifetime of the organism. In this skill activity, you will make observations of certain fossils and infer the type of environment that existed when the organism was alive.

Procedure

1. Look at the table above. What type of organism is fossilized in each rock in this table? Research the conditions necessary for each of these organisms to survive.

2. Read the information given about each fossil next to the picture.

Organism	Location
	• Found in California • 1 million years old
	• Found in Kansas • 1.5 million years old
	• Found in Wyoming • 5 million years old

Practicing the SKILL

1. What can you infer abut the environment of the fossil found in California?

2. What does finding a reptile fossil tell you about the climate in Wyoming 5 million years ago?

3. What can you infer about the fossil found in Kansas?

For more skill practice, do the Chapter 11 Interactive Exploration on the **Science Voyages Level Blue CD-ROM.**

Making and Using Graphs

Background

A bar graph is used to compare similar things that show variations. The numbers of each group are normally plotted on the vertical y-axis. The horizontal x-axis is used for plotting each separate group. The data are graphed within separate bars.

Procedure

1 Examine Table 12-1 of the Geologic Time Scale in Chapter 12. Observe the names listed under the heading *Period*.

2 Calculate the length of time for each period. The first two have been done for you in the table shown here.

Geologic Time	
Period	**Length of Period in Millions of Years**
Quaternary	1.6 − 0 = 1.6
Tertiary	66 − 1.6 = 64.4

3 Make a bar graph showing the length of time for each period.

4 Mark the number of years up the vertical axis. (Each block on the graph paper should represent one million years.) Make the highest number on this line the highest number of years calculated in your table. The bottom of the vertical line is 0.

5 List the periods along the horizontal axis starting with Cambrian on the left and going to Quaternary. Allow one block on the graph paper for each period.

6 Complete the graph by drawing each bar the correct height for the number of years. Color in each bar.

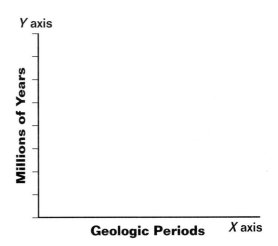

Practicing the SKILL

1 Other than Precambrian, which period lasted the longest time?

2 Which period is the shortest?

3 What kind of pattern in the lengths of periods can be seen from the graph?

4 Why is a graph more helpful than a table in comparing geologic time periods?

For more skill practice, do the Chapter 12 Interactive Exploration on the **Science Voyages Level Blue CD-ROM.**

Interpreting Data

Background

Dinosaurs were a successful group of animals. They lived on Earth for about 160 million years and became extinct about 66 million years ago. Several species of dinosaur, such as *Tyrannosaurus rex* and Stegosaurus, are well known. Many people have the misconception that these well-known dinosaurs lived at the same time. During the Jurassic and Cretaceous periods, such species of dinosaurs died out while other, new species developed. In other words, not all the dinosaurs lived at the same time. The approximate time periods for several well-known dinosaurs are listed in the Dinosaur Ranges table.

Interpret the age relationships between different dinosaurs.

Procedure

Use the information in the Dinosaur Ranges table and a geologic time scale in Chapter 13 to answer the following questions.

a. Which dinosaur species were present at the end of the Cretaceous Period?

b. Which dinosaur species lived during the Upper Jurassic Period and survived into the Lower Cretaceous?

c. Which dinosaur species lived during the Jurassic Period?

Dinosaur Ranges

Dinosaur species	Approximate time that species lived (million yrs before present)
Allosaurus	180–144
Ankylosaurus	90–66
Apatosaurus	150–145
Brachiosaurus	150–145
Diplodocus	150–145
Iguanodon	144–110
Megalosaurus	208–170
Stegosaurus	170–150
Tyrannosaurus rex	100–66
Triceratops	90–66
Velociraptor	95–66

Practicing the SKILL

Read each of the following statements and decide if it could be true or must be false. Explain your answer.

1. A Tyrannosaurus skeleton has been found with Ankylosaurus bones in the stomach region.

2. The bones of Megalosaurus, Brachiosaurus, and Iguanodon are found mixed together in a fossil bed.

3. Triceratops were frequent prey for groups of Velociraptors.

For more skill practice, do the Chapter 13 Interactive Exploration on the **Science Voyages Level Blue CD-ROM.**

Making Models

Background

Many molecules are isomers. Isomers are molecules that have the same chemical formula but different structures. Many organic compounds have isomers. Some large hydrocarbons have thousands of isomers. The different arrangements of the atoms in the isomers give them different properties. To understand the properties of a molecule, it is necessary to know the structure of the molecule. In this Skill Activity, you will make a model to show that isomers differ from one another.

Procedure

1. Use large foam balls to represent carbon atoms and small foam balls to represent hydrogen atoms. Pipe cleaners can be used to represent the bonds and attach the balls together.

2. Use four large balls and ten small balls to make a model of butane, C_4H_{10}, with the four carbon atoms in a straight chain. Place the bonds evenly around each carbon atom.

3. Draw a diagram of your model and describe it in your own words.

4. Remove the end carbon with its three hydrogen atoms.

5. You now have a three-carbon chain. Remove one hydrogen atom from the middle carbon and place it in the position from which you removed the carbon atom and its three hydrogens.

6. Attach the carbon and its three hydrogen atoms to the center carbon where the hydrogen atom was.

7. Draw a diagram of your model and describe it in your own words. The models in steps 3 and 7 are two isomers of butane.

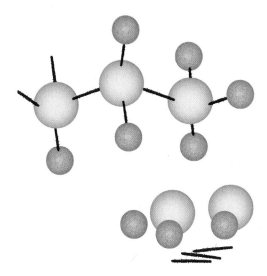

Practicing the SKILL

1. Use five large balls, twelve small balls, and 16 pieces of pipe cleaner to make a model of pentane, C_5H_{12}.

2. Rearrange the same set of materials to form an isomer of pentane.

For more skill practice, do the Chapter 14 Interactive Exploration on the **Science Voyages Level Blue CD-ROM.**

GLENCOE TECHNOLOGY

Observing and Inferring

Background

One of the best tools for learning science is having good observation skills. You can learn by simply watching things happen. This was the main tool that Aristotle used when he made many of his discoveries. He kept detailed records of his observations. Over time, he collected much information about the living things in his surroundings. He made many inferences from his observations. Some have been proven to be true, but others have been shown not to be true. Other scientists used many of his recorded observations for further study.

Procedure

1. Your teacher will tape to your back a card with the name of a plant, flower, fruit, or vegetable written on it.

2. For thirty minutes, move around the classroom and have other students act out clues to the name on your card. No one should speak during the observation time.

3. Keep a list of the clues then make an inference about the name written on your card.

Practicing the SKILL

1. Were you able to infer the correct name on your card?

2. How many clues did you observe before you knew the name on your card?

3. How many of your classmates correctly inferred the names on their cards?

For more skill practice, do the Chapter 15 Interactive Exploration on the **Science Voyages Level Blue CD-ROM.**

GLENCOE TECHNOLOGY

Sequencing

Background

Sequence diagrams illustrate in a simple way series of events in the order in which they occur. The events in the life cycle of a plant are represented by a series of diagrams that show how the separate stages of the life cycle pass from one to the other.

What are the stages and events in the life cycle of a fern?

Each stage in the life cycle of a plant, such as a fern, occurs in a particular order. This order is indicated by the use of arrows that are placed between the stages. The drawings in a sequence diagram are labeled to identify each stage and the important structures of each drawing.

Fern Observations	
Gametophyte Stage	Sporophyte Stage
1.	
2.	
3.	

Pine Observations	
Gametophyte Stage	Sporophyte Stage
pollen grains	
fertilization	
pollen cone	
embryo forms	
seed dispersal	

Procedure

1. Examine **Figure 16-6** in Chapter 16. This diagram shows drawings of the individual stages in the life cycle of a fern.

2. Observe the number and direction of the arrows that are drawn between each stage of the life cycle.

3. Copy the Fern Observations table on this page. Record three events in the fern gametophyte stage and three in the sporophyte stage on the table.

4. Examine **Figure 16-9** in Chapter 16. Copy the Pine Observations table on this page. Number the items listed in the correct order as they occur in a pine's life cycle.

Practicing the SKILL

1. How many stages are there in the life cycle of a fern?

2. In which stage are spores formed?

3. In which stage are sex organs formed?

4. What structure begins the sporophyte stage?

For more skill practice, do the Chapter 16 Interactive Exploration on the **Science Voyages Level Blue CD-ROM.**

GLENCOE TECHNOLOGY

Predicting

Background

Large populations of organisms need to be counted to determine the overall health of the species. However, counting each individual in a population can be time consuming and confusing. Therefore, scientists have developed methods for estimating the number of individuals in a population in order to save time. In this activity, you will predict the number of beetles by estimating the total number.

Ladybird Numbers		
Predicted number _____ Time _____		
Number in top left square	Total number of squares	Estimated total number
×	=	
_____	_____	_____
Actual number _____ Time _____		

Procedure

① Estimate the number of ladybird beetles in the figure to the right and record the number in a table like the one shown.

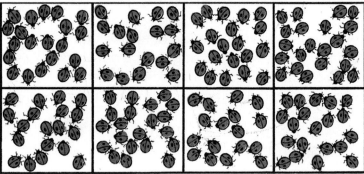

② Place tracing paper over the diagram. Make a population count by placing a checkmark next to each ladybird beetle. Record the actual number of beetles in the table. Next to this number, record the amount of time it took to make the count.

③ Count the ladybird beetle population a second time by sampling. A sample is made by selecting and counting only a portion of the population. Count the number of ladybird beetles in the top left square and record this number in the table.

④ Enter the total number of squares in the table. Multiply the number of ladybird beetles in the top left square by the total number of squares. Record this estimated total number in the table.

⑤ At the top of the table, record the amount of time it took to make the sample count.

Practicing the SKILL

① How many ladybird beetles did you estimate were shown?

② Which way was faster—making an actual count or sampling?

③ Were the results exactly the same?

For more skill practice, do the Chapter 17 Interactive Exploration on the **Science Voyages Level Blue CD-ROM.**

GLENCOE TECHNOLOGY

Observing and Inferring

Background

Living things survive in their environments because they have behavioral and physical adaptations that allow them to live. For example, a jackrabbit will run when it sees a coyote. This is a behavioral adaptation. The jackrabbit also has strong legs. This is a physical adaptation. Both adaptations, working together, give the jackrabbit an advantage in escaping predators. In this activity, you will observe adaptations that help living things near your classroom survive.

Procedure

① Read Section 2, Land Environments. Pay special attention to the Adaptations of Desert Plants and Animals.

② In a table like the one shown below, record the names of five living things you find near your classroom.

③ Briefly describe two behavioral adaptations and two physical adaptations for each. Record these in your table.

④ Write how you think each of the adaptations might give each organism an advantage that allows it to survive in the wild.

Practicing the SKILL

① Many birds, insects, and bats are able to fly. What are the advantages of this adaptation?

② Many mammals in both hot and cold climates have thick fur. What might the advantages of this adaptation be?

For more skill practice, do the Chapter 18 Interactive Exploration on the **Science Voyages Level Blue CD-ROM.**

Organism Behavior			
Organism	**Physical adaptations**	**Behavioral adaptations**	**Advantages in the wild**

Comparing and Contrasting

Background

Most of the energy humans use for power and transportation comes from the burning of fossil fuels. If humans continue to use them, fossil fuels will become more scarce, and it will be necessary to find other sources of energy. There are also concerns that fossil fuels are not clean enough and may be affecting our quality of life and the health of our planet. Every source of energy has advantages and disadvantages. In the Skill Activity, you will compare and contrast sources of energy and begin to plan what humans should do about energy today and for the future.

Procedure

1. Read Section 19-1. Pay special attention to Energy for Now and the Future.

2. On a separate piece of paper, draw and complete a table like the one shown. Much of the information for the table is in the text, but in some cases you may need to use your own ideas or go to other sources to find the information.

Fuel Observations

Energy Source	Advantages	Disadvantages
Fossil Fuels		
Solar Energy		
Solar Cells		
Water Power		
Wind Power		
Geothermal Energy		
Nuclear Energy		

Practicing the SKILL

1. Which source of energy will probably last the longest? Why?

2. If you could select one energy source to eliminate entirely, which would you choose? Why?

3. List three energy sources that you would recommend we use in the future. Give reasons for the sources you choose.

For more skill practice, do the Chapter 19 Interactive Exploration on the **Science Voyages Level Blue CD-ROM.**

GLENCOE TECHNOLOGY

Making and Using Graphs

Background

The length of time it takes for a satellite to complete one orbit is called the orbital period. The greater the altitude of a satellite, the longer its orbital period. Satellites that stay above the same spot on Earth's surface are called geostationary satellites. The orbital period of a geostationary satellite equals 24 h. Communication systems for telephone and television use geostationary satellites.

What is the altitude of a geostationary orbit? Try the following procedure to determine the altitude of a geostationary orbit.

Orbital Data			
Altitude of orbit (km)	Orbital velocity (km/hr)	Orbital circumference (km)	Orbital period (hr)
10 000	26 470	46 400	
20 000	17 770	103 000	
30 000	11 920	229 000	
40 000	10 560	292 000	
50 000	9575	354 000	

Procedure

1. The Orbital Data table lists the altitude, speed, and circumference of six different orbits. The orbital period can be calculated by dividing the circumference by the speed. Calculate the orbital periods for each altitude and record the data.

2. Make a line graph that compares the altitude and orbital period.

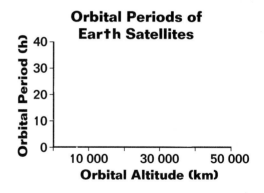

Orbital Periods of Earth Satellites

Orbital Period (h): 0, 10, 20, 30, 40

Orbital Altitude (km): 10 000, 30 000, 50 000

Practicing the SKILL

1. What is the relationship between the altitude and the orbital speed?

2. What is the approximate altitude of a satellite in a geostationary orbit?

For more skill practice, do the Chapter 20 Interactive Exploration on the **Science Voyages Level Blue CD-ROM.**

GLENCOE TECHNOLOGY

Interpreting Scientific Illustrations

Background

During a total solar eclipse, the moon's shadow falls on Earth. The darkest part of the shadow, the umbra, traces a narrow, curved path across Earth's surface. By plotting the moon's orbit and phases, scientists are able to predict the umbra's path for future total solar eclipses. The world map below shows the times and locations of all total solar eclipses until the year 2020.

When and where will future total solar eclipses occur?

Procedure

1 Study the map of future eclipses.

2 Answer the questions in the Practicing the Skill box.

Practicing the SKILL

1 When will the next total solar eclipse occur in the United States? How old will you be at this time?

2 Which eclipse path will be located mostly over the ocean?

3 How many total solar eclipses will occur between the years 1999 and 2020?

For more skill practice, do the Chapter 21 Interactive Exploration on the **Science Voyages Level Blue CD-ROM.**

GLENCOE TECHNOLOGY

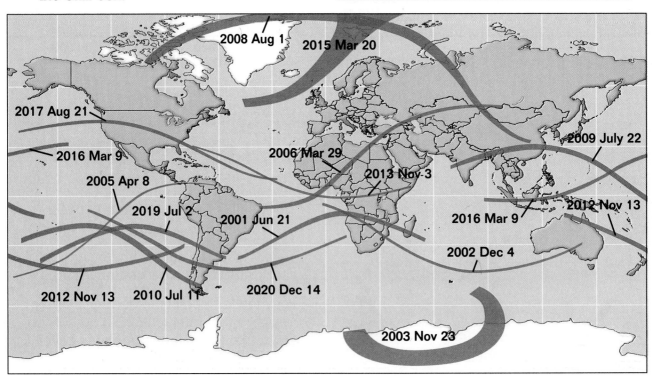

2008 Aug 1
2015 Mar 20
2017 Aug 21
2009 July 22
2016 Mar 9
2006 Mar 29
2013 Nov 3
2005 Apr 8
2019 Jul 2
2001 Jun 21
2012 Nov 13
2016 Mar 9
2002 Dec 4
2012 Nov 13
2010 Jul 11
2020 Dec 14
2003 Nov 23

Inferring

Background

The surfaces of Earth's moon, Mercury, and other planetary bodies often are covered with craters. Scientists usually are unable to determine the exact age of the craters because they do not have actual rock samples. However, photographs taken by satellites help scientists determine the rough ages of the craters. For example, if two craters overlap, the crater that appears to be underneath is the older of the two.

Procedure

1. The diagram below shows an area containing several craters. Each crater is labeled by a letter in its center. Study the relationships between the craters and determine their relative ages.

Practicing the SKILL

1. Which crater occurred first, crater A or crater C?

2. Can the rough age of crater J be determined? Why or why not?

3. What is the estimated diameter of crater D?

4. List craters A through I in order of increasing age (youngest crater first).

For more skill practice, do the Chapter 22 Interactive Exploration on the **Science Voyages Level Blue CD-ROM.**

GLENCOE TECHNOLOGY

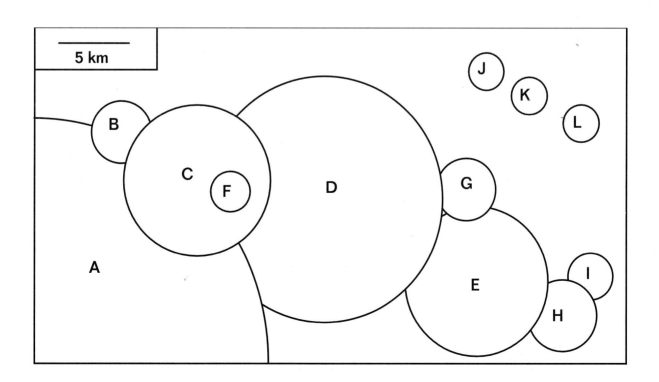

5 km

Predicting

Background

Astronomical distances are measured in light-years. A light-year is the distance that light can travel in one year. Proxima Centauri is a star that is 4.2 light-years away from Earth. When astronomers observe Proxima Centauri, they are seeing what occurred 4.2 years ago. In other words, when you look at the stars, you are looking back in time. The light astronomers observe for Proxima Centauri left the star 4.2 years ago.

What was happening on Earth when a star's light began its journey?

Star Distances

Star	Distance from Earth in light-years	Star	Distance from Earth in light-years
Sirius	8.8	Deneb	1800
Arcturus	36	Barnard's Star	5.9
Rigel	920	Wolf 359	7.6
Betelgeuse	310	Procyon	11
Antares	330	Altair	17
Vega	26	Regulus	85

Procedure

1. The Star Distances table lists the distances to several different stars. Study these distances to determine how long the light has been traveling toward Earth.

2. Using your history references, find a significant event that occurred when light from a particular star began its journey to Earth.

3. Make a data table that lists the significant historical events that occurred when light from the stars began the journey to Earth. Include the historical event, date, and the star in your table. Use at least six of the stars listed.

Practicing the SKILL

1. On July 20, 1969, astronauts landed on the moon. If a television signal showing this landing had been broadcast out to space, which stars would it have reached by the year 2000? by 2005? (Television signals travel at the speed of light, which is 300 000 km/s in a vacuum.)

2. Describe a historic event that took place when light from Rigel began traveling toward Earth.

3. How many times farther is Arcturus from Earth than Barnard's Star is?

For more skill practice, do the Chapter 23 Interactive Exploration on the **Science Voyages Level Blue CD-ROM.**

GLENCOE TECHNOLOGY

English Glossary

This glossary defines each key term that appears in **bold type** in the text. It also shows the page number where you can find the word used.

A

abiotic factors: all the nonliving, physical features of the environment, including light, soil, water, and temperature, that help determine which species can survive in an area. (ch. 17, p. 483)

absolute dating: process that uses the properties of atoms in rocks and other objects to determine their exact ages, in years. (ch. 11, p. 321)

absolute magnitude: measure of the amount of light a star actually emits. (ch. 23, p. 664)

acceleration: rate of change of velocity; can act in the direction of motion, at an angle, or opposite to the direction of motion. (ch. 6, p. 152)

acid rain: rain or snow with a pH below 5.6; results from the mixture of water vapor and air pollutants in the atmosphere. (ch. 19, p. 560)

alloy (AL oy): mixture made of two or more elements, one of which is a metal. (ch. 3, p. 74)

alternation of generations: occurs when a plant's life cycle alternates between a sex-cell–producing stage and a spore-producing stage. (ch. 16, p. 453)

amino (uh ME no) **acid:** building block of proteins; contains both an amino group and a carboxyl group substituted on the same carbon atom. (ch. 14, p. 407)

amino (uh ME no) **group:** consists of a nitrogen atom joined by covalent bonds to two hydrogen atoms; formula is $-NH_2$; when substituted for hydrogen in a hydrocarbon, forms an amine. (ch. 14, p. 406)

amphibians: animals that live on land and breathe air but return to water to reproduce. (ch. 13, p. 376)

apparent magnitude: measure of the amount of light that is received on Earth from a star. (ch. 23, p. 664)

asteroid: piece of rock usually found in the asteroid belt between the orbits of Mars and Jupiter. (ch. 22, p. 653)

asthenosphere (as THEN uh sfihr): plastic-like layer below the lithosphere. (ch. 10, p. 277)

astronomical unit: average distance from Earth to the sun (150 million km), which is used to measure distances to objects in the solar system. (ch. 22, p. 638)

atomic number: number of protons in the nucleus of an atom of a specific element. (ch. 2, p. 47)

auxin: type of plant hormone that can cause plants to show positive phototropism. (ch. 15, p. 437)

axis: imaginary line around which Earth spins. (ch. 21, p. 603)

B

balanced forces: two or more forces acting on an object that cancel each other out and do not cause a change in the object's motion. (ch. 7, p. 177)

batholiths: largest intrusive igneous rock bodies that form when magma cools underground before reaching Earth's surface. (ch. 9, p. 255)

big bang theory: states that approximately 15 billion years ago, the universe began expanding out of an enormous explosion. (ch. 23, p. 685)

binary system: system in which two stars orbit each other. (ch. 23, p. 670)

biomes (BI ohmz): large geographic areas with similar climates and ecosystems; the six most common are tundra, taiga, temperate forest, tropical rain forest, grassland, and desert. (ch. 18, p. 519)

biosphere (BI uh sfihr): part of Earth that supports organisms, is the highest level of biological organization, and is made up of all Earth's ecosystems. (ch. 17, p. 482)

biotic factors: living or once-living organisms in the environment. (ch. 17, p. 485)

black hole: remnant of a star that is so dense that nothing can escape its gravity. (ch. 23, p. 676)

C

caldera: large opening formed when the top of a volcano collapses. (ch. 9, p. 257)

carbohydrates: energy-supplying organic compounds that are broken down into simple sugars in the body; contain only carbon, hydrogen, and oxygen. (ch. 14, p. 412)

carbonaceous (kar boh NAY shus) **film:** fossil formed when the remains of a once-living organism are subjected to heat and pressure, leaving only a thin film of carbon behind. (ch. 11, p. 307)

carboxyl (kar BOX ul) **group:** consists of one carbon atom, two oxygen atoms, and one hydrogen atom; formula is –COOH; when substituted for hydrogen in a hydrocarbon, forms a carboxylic acid. (ch. 14, p. 406)

carrying capacity: largest number of individuals an environment can support and maintain over a long period of time. (ch. 17, p. 490)

cast: fossil formed when sediments fill a mold and harden into rock. (ch. 11, p. 307)

catalyst (KAT uh lihst): substance, such as an enzyme, that speeds up a chemical reaction but is not used up or permanently changed. (ch. 5, p. 136)

Cenozoic (sen uh ZOH ihk) **era:** geologic era in which we live; began with the extinction of dinosaurs and many other life-forms. (ch. 13, p. 386)

chemical bond: force that holds two atoms together. (ch. 4, p. 102)

chemical reaction: energy-requiring process in which chemical changes occur; results in the formation of new substances that have different properties than the original substances. (ch. 5, p. 122)

chromosphere: layer of the sun's atmosphere above the photosphere and below the corona. (ch. 23, p. 667)

cinder cone: steep-sided volcano made of loosely packed tephra. (ch. 9, p. 252)

climax community: community that has reached the final stage of ecological succession. (ch. 18, p. 513)

comet: mass of dust and rock particles mixed in with frozen water, ammonia, and methane; consists of a nucleus, a coma, and a tail. (ch. 22, p. 650)

community: consists of groups of populations that interact with each other in a given area and depend on each other for food, shelter, and for other needs. (ch. 17, p. 486)

composite volcano: volcano formed by alternating layers of tephra and lava and that is found mostly where Earth's plates come together. (ch. 9, p. 252)

compound: pure substance that contains two or more elements. (ch. 4, p. 107)

constant: variable that stays the same in an experiment. (ch. 1, p. 14)

constellation: group of stars that forms a pattern that looks like a familiar object, animal, or character. (ch. 23, p. 662)

continental drift: hypothesis proposed by Alfred Wegener that states that continents have moved slowly to their current locations on Earth. (ch. 10, p. 268)

control: standard used for comparison in an experiment. (ch. 1, p. 13)

convection current: cycle of heating, rising, cooling, and sinking that is thought to be the force behind plate tectonics (ch. 10, p. 282)

corona: largest layer of the sun's atmosphere that extends millions of miles into space. (ch. 23, p. 667)

covalent (koh VAY luhnt) **bond:** chemical bond that forms between atoms when they share one or more electrons. (ch. 4, p. 109)

crater: steep-walled depression around a volcano's vent. (ch. 9, p. 242)

crust: Earth's outermost layer, which varies in thickness from about 5 km to 60 km and is separated from the mantle by the Moho discontinuity. (ch. 8, p. 220)

cyanobacteria: one of the earliest life-forms on Earth; evolved during Precambrian time. (ch. 13, p. 373)

D

day-neutral plant: plant that does not have a specific photoperiod and whose flowering process can begin over a wide range of hours of darkness. (ch. 15, p. 440)

dependent variable: factor being measured or observed in a controlled experiment. (ch. 1, p. 13)

desert: driest biome on Earth; receives less than 25 cm of rain each year and supports little plant life. (ch. 18, p. 524)

dike: intrusive igneous rock body formed when magma is squeezed into a vertical crack that cuts across rock layers and hardens. (ch. 9, p. 257)

displacement: measures the change in position of an object, using the starting point and ending point and noting the direction. (ch. 6, p. 149)

E

Earth: third planet from the sun; surface temperatures allow water to exist as a solid, liquid, and gas and atmosphere protects life from the sun's radiation. (ch. 22, p. 638)

earthquakes: vibrations caused by breaking rocks along faults; most result from plates moving over, under, and past each other. (ch. 8, p. 211)

ecological pyramid: model used to describe the transfer of energy from the producers of an ecosystem through successive levels of organisms in the food chain. (ch. 17, p. 498)

ecological succession: process of gradual change from one community of organisms to another. (ch. 18, p. 510)

ecology: study of the interactions that take place among organisms and between organisms and the physical features of the environment. (ch. 17, p. 483)

ecosystem: consists of a biotic community and the abiotic factors that affect it. (ch. 17, p. 486)

electromagnetic spectrum: arrangement of electromagnetic radiation according to wavelength. (ch. 20, p. 575)

electron: tiny, negatively charged particle that is present in all atoms and that has almost no mass. (ch. 2, p. 39)

electron cloud: region surrounding the nucleus of an atom, where electrons are more likely to be found. (ch. 2, p. 45)

electron dot diagram: shows the chemical symbol for an element surrounded by as many dots as there are electrons in its outer energy level. (ch. 4, p. 102)

element: substance that cannot be broken down into simpler substances and whose atoms are exactly alike. (ch. 2, p. 37)

ellipse (ee LIHPS): elongated, closed curve that describes Earth's orbit. (ch. 21, p. 605)

embryology (em bree AHL uh jee): study of development in organisms. (ch. 12, p. 350)

endangered species: species that is in danger of becoming extinct unless action is taken to protect it. (ch. 19, p. 551)

endothermic (en duh THUR mihk) **reaction:** chemical reaction in which energy is absorbed, such as the reaction that breaks water down into hydrogen and oxygen. (ch. 5, p. 127)

energy: ability to cause change; cannot be destroyed or created, only transferred from one form to another. (ch. 6, p. 165)

epicenter (EP ih sent ur): point on Earth's surface directly above an earthquake's focus. (ch. 8, p. 217)

epoch: division of geologic time smaller than a period. (ch. 13, p. 365)

equinox (EE kwuh nahks): twice-yearly time when the sun is directly above Earth's equator and the number of nighttime hours equals the number of daylight hours worldwide. (ch. 21, p. 607)

era: major subdivision of the geologic time scale based on differences in life-forms. (ch. 13, p. 365)

erosion: wearing away of soil by wind and water. (ch. 19, p. 550)

estuary: area where a river meets the ocean that contains a mixture of freshwater and salt water and serves as nursery for many species of ocean fish. (ch. 18, p. 530)

evolution: changes in the inherited features of a species over time; can occur slowly (gradualism) or rapidly (punctu-

ated equilibrium). (ch. 12, p. 334)

exothermic (ek soh THUR mihk) **reaction:** chemical reaction that releases energy, such as occurs when propane is burned in a gas grill. (ch. 5, p. 128)

extinction: dying out of an entire species either naturally or through the actions of humans. (ch. 19, p. 550)

fault: surface along which rocks break and move. (ch. 8, p. 210)

first quarter: moon phase in which one-quarter of the moon's surface that faces Earth is lit up; occurs about a week after a new moon. (ch. 21, p. 613)

focus: in an earthquake, the point beneath Earth's surface where energy release occurs. (ch. 8, p. 215)

food chain: model that describes the feeding relationships in a community, usually has three or four links, and shows how energy in the form of food passes from one organism to another. (ch. 17, p. 497)

food web: model used to describe a series of overlapping food chains and that shows the many organisms that feed on more than one level in an ecosystem. (ch. 17, p. 498)

force: push or a pull exerted on an object. (ch. 7, p. 176)

formula: combination of chemical symbols that tells what elements are in molecules and how many atoms of each element are present. (ch. 4, p. 113)

fossil: remains or traces of a once-living organism preserved in rock. (ch. 11, p. 304)

fossil fuel: nonrenewable energy source, such as natural gas, that formed from the bodies of organisms that died hundreds of millions of years ago. (ch. 19, p. 544)

friction: rubbing force that acts against motion between two touching surfaces. (ch. 7, p. 179)

frond: leaf of a fern that grows from a rhizome. (ch. 16, p. 454)

full moon: moon phase in which all of the moon's surface that faces Earth is lit up. (ch. 21, p. 613)

G

galaxy: large group of stars, gas, and dust held together by gravity. (ch. 23, p. 679)

gametophyte (guh MEET uh fite) **stage:** plant life cycle stage in which all plant structures are made of cells with a haploid number (n) of chromosomes. (ch. 16, p. 452)

gastroliths: stones swallowed by dinosaurs and by modern birds to help with digestion. (ch. 13, p. 385)

geologic time scale: record of events in Earth's history based on major evolutionary changes and geologic events; major subdivisions are eras, periods, and epochs. (ch. 13, p. 364)

geothermal energy: heat energy from below the surface of Earth. (ch. 19, p. 546)

giant: stage in a star's life cycle where hydrogen in the core is used up, the core contracts, and temperatures inside the star increase, causing the outer layers of the star to expand. (ch. 23, p. 675)

global warming: increase in the average yearly temperature of Earth. (ch. 19, p. 561)

gradualism: model of evolution that shows a slow change of one species to another, new species through continued mutations and variations over time. (ch. 12, p. 340)

graph: diagram that shows the relationship of one variable to another variable and that makes it easier to interpret and analyze data. (ch. 1, p. 18)

grasslands: temperate and tropical regions that receive between 25 cm and 75 cm of precipitation each year and are dominated by climax communities of grasses. (ch. 18, p. 524)

gravitational potential energy: energy an object could potentially gain if it falls, depending on its mass and the height it can fall. (ch. 6, p. 167)

Great Red Spot: high-pressure storm generated by huge thunderstorms in Jupiter's atmosphere. (ch. 22, p. 642)

greenhouse effect: warming of Earth due to a blanket of gases in the atmosphere that prevents heat from radiating back into space. (ch. 19, p. 561)

groundwater: water contained in the soil or trapped in underground pockets formed by nonporous rock; comes from rainfall and runoff that soaks through the soil. (ch. 19, p. 563)

group: family of elements with similar physical or chemical properties that occupies the same column in the periodic table. (ch. 3, p. 68)

H

habitat: physical location where an organism lives. (ch. 17, p. 493)

half-life: time needed for one-half the mass of a sample of a radioactive isotope to decay; can vary from fractions of a second to billions of years. (ch. 11, p. 322; ch. 2, p. 50)

hazardous waste: waste materials, such as pesticides and nuclear waste, that are harmful to human health or poisonous to living organisms and that must be properly disposed of. (ch. 19, p. 562)

hominids: humanlike primates that walked upright on two feet and ate both meat and vegetables. (ch. 12, p. 355)

Homo sapiens: human species thought to have evolved about 400 000 years ago. (ch. 12, p. 356)

homologous (huh MAHL uh gus): body structures that are similar in origin and show that two or more species may share common ancestors. (ch. 12, p. 349)

hot spot: location in the mantle that is hotter than other areas and that melts rock, which is forced up toward the crust as magma. (ch. 9, p. 244)

hydrocarbon: compound that contains only carbon and hydrogen atoms—for example, methane, CH_4, and ethane, C_2H_6. (ch. 14, p. 399)

hydroelectric power: electricity produced by the energy of flowing water. (ch. 19, p. 546)

hydroxyl (hi DROX ul) **group:** consists of one oxygen atom and one hydrogen atom joined by a covalent bond; formula is –OH; when substituted for hydrogen in a hydrocarbon, forms an alcohol. (ch. 14, p. 405)

hypothesis: prediction about a problem that can be tested; may be based on observations, new information, and personal experience, and is often written as an if-and-then statement. (ch. 1, p. 12)

I

independent variable: factor that is changed in a controlled experiment. (ch. 1, p. 13)

index fossils: fossils of species that existed on Earth for only a short time, were abundant, and were widespread geographically; used by scientists to determine the age of rock layers. (ch. 11, p. 310)

inertia: measures an object's tendency to remain at rest or to stay in constant motion. (ch. 6, p. 158)

inference: attempt at an explanation based on observation. (ch. 1, p. 25)

inhibitor: substance, such as butyl hydroxy toluene (BHT), that doesn't totally stop a chemical reaction but slows it down. (ch. 5, p. 136)

inner core: very dense, solid center of Earth that is made mostly of iron with smaller amounts of oxygen, silicon, sulfur, or nickel. (ch. 8, p. 219)

inner planets: four solid, rocky planets that are closest to the sun—Mercury, Venus, Earth, and Mars. (ch. 22, p. 633)

intertidal zone: portion of the shoreline that is covered with water at high tide and exposed to the air at low tide. (ch. 18, p. 530)

ion (I ahn): atom that is no longer neutral because it has gained or lost an electron. (ch. 4, p. 106)

ionic bond: chemical bond that is created when one atom loses one or more electrons and another atom gains one or more electrons. (ch. 4, p. 107)

isomers (I suh murz): compounds with the same chemical formulas but different structures and different chemical and physical properties. (ch. 14, p. 402)

isotopes (I suh tohps): atoms of the same element that have different numbers of neutrons in their nuclei. (ch. 2, p. 47)

J

Jupiter: largest planet and fifth planet from the sun; composed mostly of hydrogen and helium; has continuous storms of high-pressure gas. (ch. 22, p. 642)

K

kinetic energy: energy an object has due to its motion; depends on the object's mass and velocity. (ch. 6, p. 165)

L

law: well-tested description of how something in nature works. (ch. 1, p. 12)

law of conservation of energy: states that energy cannot be destroyed or created, but it is only transformed from one form to another. (ch. 6, p. 165)

law of conservation of momentum: states that if no outside forces act on a group of objects, the momentum of the group will not change. (ch. 6, p. 161)

light-year: distance that light travels in one year (9.5 trillion km), which is used to measure distances in space. (ch. 23, p. 665)

limiting factor: any biotic or abiotic factor that restricts the number of individuals in a population. (ch. 17, p. 489)

lipids: energy-supplying and energy-storing organic compounds composed of three long-chain carboxylic acids bonded to glycerol; commonly called fats and oils and can be saturated or unsaturated. (ch. 14, p. 415)

lithosphere (LIHTH uh sfihr): rigid, outermost layer of Earth that is about 100 km thick, and is composed of the crust and part of the upper mantle. (ch. 10, p. 277)

long-day plant: plant that needs less than ten to twelve hours of darkness to begin the flowering process. (ch. 15, p. 439)

lunar eclipse: eclipse that occurs when Earth's shadow falls on the moon. (ch. 21, p. 616)

M

magnitude: measure of the energy released by an earthquake. (ch. 8, p. 226)

main sequence: in an H-R diagram, the diagonal band of stars that runs from hot, bright stars in the upper-left corner of the diagram to cool, faint stars in the lower-right corner. (ch. 23, p. 672)

mantle: largest layer inside Earth, lying directly above the outer core and that is made mostly of silicon, oxygen, magnesium, and iron. (ch. 8, p. 219)

maria: dark-colored, relatively flat areas of the moon that were formed when ancient lava filled basins on the moon's surface. (ch. 21, p. 617)

Mars: fourth planet from the sun; appears red due to the iron oxide content in its weathered rocks. (ch. 22, p. 638)

mascon: concentration of mass on the moon located beneath an impact basin. (ch. 21, p. 621)

mass: quantity of matter in an object and a measure of the object's inertia; unit is the kilogram (kg). (ch. 6, p. 158)

mass number: number of neutrons plus the number of protons in the nucleus of an atom. (ch. 2, p. 48)

Mercury: planet closest to the sun; has many craters, low gravitational pull, and is the second-smallest planet in our solar system. (ch. 22, p. 636)

Mesozoic (mez uh ZOH ihk) **era:** geologic era in which Pangaea broke up, the present-day continents were formed, and whose dominant land life-forms were reptiles and gymnosperms. (ch. 13, p. 381)

metal: element that is a good conductor of electricity and heat, is usually a solid at room temperature and usually is shiny, ductile, and malleable. (ch. 3, p. 69)

metalloid: element that shares some properties with metals and some with non-metals. (ch. 3, p. 70)

meteor: meteoroid that burns up in Earth's atmosphere. (ch. 22, p. 652)

meteorite: meteoroid that does not completely burn up in Earth's atmosphere and strikes Earth. (ch. 22, p. 652)

mold: fossil formed when an organism is buried, decays, and leaves behind a hollow place in the rock. (ch. 11, p. 307)

molecule (MAH luh kyewl): neutral particle that is formed when atoms share electrons. (ch. 4, p. 109)

momentum: product of mass and velocity; quantity of motion for an object. (ch. 6, p. 159)

moon phase: changing appearance of the moon as seen from Earth, which depends on the relative positions of the moon, Earth, and sun. (ch. 21, p. 613)

N

natural resource: material found in nature that is useful or necessary for living organisms. (ch. 19, p. 542)

natural selection: Darwin's theory of evolution, which says that organisms with traits best suited to their environments are more likely to survive and reproduce. (ch. 12, p. 337)

nebula: large cloud of gas and dust that can fragment into smaller pieces, each of which will collapse and form stars. (ch. 23, p. 674)

Neptune: large, gaseous planet similar to Uranus; is usually the eighth planet from the sun. (ch. 22, p. 646)

net force: sum of the forces acting on an object. (ch. 7, p. 176)

neutron (NEW trahn): electrically neutral particle that is present in the nucleus of all atoms; has the same mass as a proton. (ch. 2, p. 44)

neutron star: collapsed core of a supernova that shrinks to about 10 km to 15 km in diameter and has only neutrons in the dense core. (ch. 23, p. 676)

new moon: moon phase that occurs when the lighted half of the moon faces the sun and the dark side faces Earth. (ch. 21, p. 613)

Newton's first law of motion: states that an object at rest or moving at a constant speed in a straight path continues to do so until a net force acts on it. (ch. 7, p. 178)

Newton's second law of motion: states that an object acted upon by a net force will accelerate in the direction of this force according to the following equation: $a = F_{net}/m$, where a is the acceleration, F_{net} is the net force, and m is the mass. (ch. 7, p. 184)

Newton's third law of motion: states that forces always act in equal but opposite pairs. (ch. 7, p. 192)

niche: role of an organism in the ecosystem, including what it eats, how it interacts with other organisms, and how it gets its food. (ch. 17, p. 493)

nitrogen cycle: transfer of nitrogen from the atmosphere to plants and back to the atmosphere or directly into plants again. (ch. 17, p. 502)

nonmetal: element that is a poor conductor of heat and electricity and may be a gas or a brittle solid at room temperature. (ch. 3, p. 70)

nonrenewable resource: natural resource, such as petroleum, that is available in limited amounts and cannot be replaced or is only replaced slowly. (ch. 19, p. 543)

normal fault: break in rock due to tension forces, where rock above the fault surface moves downward in relation to rock below the fault surface. (ch. 8, p. 212)

normal force: outward force a surface supplies to support an object. (ch. 7, p. 185)

nuclear energy: energy produced when the nuclei of uranium atoms split apart in a nuclear fission reaction. (ch. 19, p. 547)

O

observatory: specially designed building, often with a dome-shaped roof that opens up to admit light; used to house optical telescopes. (ch. 20, p. 576)

Oort Cloud: cloud of comets that completely surrounds the solar system and that is located beyond the orbit of Pluto. (ch. 22, p. 651)

orbit: curved path of a satellite as it revolves around an object in space. (ch. 20, p. 582)

organic compound: compound that contains carbon. (ch. 14, p. 398)

outer core: liquid core that surrounds Earth's solid inner core and that is made mostly of iron. (ch. 8, p. 219)

outer planets: five planets that are farthest from the sun—Jupiter, Saturn, Uranus, Neptune, and Pluto. (ch. 22, p. 633)

ovary: in angiosperms, the swollen base of the pistil where ovules are formed (ch. 16, p. 461)

ovule: in a seed plant, the structure that contains an egg cell, food-storage tissue, and a sticky fluid. (ch. 16, p. 458)

ozone depletion: thinning of Earth's protective ozone layer, primarily from chlorofluorocarbons reacting with and destroying ozone molecules. (ch. 19, p. 561)

P

Paleozoic (pay lee uh ZOH ihk) **era:** geologic era marked by the first appearance of life-forms with hard parts. (ch. 13, p. 374)

Pangaea (pan JEE uh): single large landmass made up of all the continents connected together that broke apart about 200 million years ago. (ch. 10, p. 268)

parallax: apparent shift in position of an object when it is viewed from two different positions. (ch. 23, p. 665)

period: horizontal row of elements in the periodic table whose properties change gradually and predictably. (ch. 3, p. 65) next-smaller division of the geologic time scale after the era. (ch. 13, p. 365)

petrified (PEH truh fide) **remains:** fossils that form when some or all of the original materials that made up the organisms are replaced with minerals. (ch. 11, p. 306)

photoperiodism: response of a plant to the number of hours of daylight and darkness it receives each day. (ch. 15, p. 439)

photosphere: lowest layer of the sun's atmosphere and the layer that gives off light. (ch. 23, p. 667)

photosynthesis: food-making process that takes place in the chloroplasts of plant cells, where carbon dioxide from the air, water in the soil, and light energy react to form glucose and oxygen. (ch. 15, p. 429)

photovoltaic (PV) cell: device made of silicon that turns sunlight directly into electric current. (ch. 19, p. 545)

pioneer community: first community of organisms to move into a new environment. (ch. 18, p. 511)

pistil: female reproductive organ inside the flower of an angiosperm; consists of a sticky stigma, a style, and an ovary. (ch. 16, p. 461)

plankton: microscopic algae, plants, and other organisms that float in warm, sunlit waters near the surface of freshwater lakes and ponds. (ch. 18, p. 529)

plate tectonics: theory that Earth's crust and upper mantle are broken into sections that move around on a plasticlike layer of the mantle. (ch. 10, p. 277)

plates: sections of Earth's lithosphere that are composed of oceanic crust, continental crust, and rigid upper mantle and that move around on a plasticlike layer of the mantle. (ch. 10, p. 277)

Pluto: smallest planet and considered the ninth planet from the sun; has a thin, changing atmosphere and icy-rock surface. (ch. 22, p. 646)

pollen grains: produced by the male reproductive organs of seed plants; two sperm develop in each pollen grain. (ch. 16, p. 458)

pollination: transfer of pollen grains from the stamen to the stigma. (ch. 16, p. 462)

pollutant: any substance that contaminates the environment and causes pollution. (ch. 19, p. 559)

polymer: large natural or synthetic molecule made of many small organic molecules that link together to form a long chain. (ch. 14, p. 410)

population: all the individuals of one species that live in the same area at the same time and compete with each other for food, water, mates, and space. (ch. 17, p. 486)

population density: size of a population that occupies an area of limited size. (ch. 17, p. 489)

Precambrian (pree KAM bree un) **time:** longest geologic time unit in Earth's history; has a poor fossil record. (ch. 13, p. 372)

primary succession: ecological succession that begins in a place that does not have soil. (ch. 18, p. 511)

primary waves: waves that travel outward from an earthquake's focus and cause particles in rocks to move back and forth in the same direction the wave is moving. (ch. 8, p. 216)

primates: group of mammals that includes monkeys, apes, and humans and that shares several characteristics, such as opposable thumbs and binocular vision. (ch. 12, p. 354)

principle of superposition: states that for undisturbed layers of rocks, older rocks lie underneath younger and younger rocks. (ch. 11, p. 312)

product: substance that is formed by a chemical reaction; in a chemical equation, the product is placed on the right side of the arrow. (ch. 5, p. 124)

Project Apollo: final stage in the U.S. effort to reach the moon—on July 20, 1969, Neil Armstrong was the first human to set foot on the lunar surface. (ch. 20, p. 587)

Project Gemini: second stage in the U.S. program to reach the moon, in which a team of astronauts met and connected with another spacecraft while in orbit. (ch. 20, p. 586)

Project Mercury: first step in the U.S. effort to reach the moon, in which a piloted spacecraft successfully orbited around Earth and returned safely. (ch. 20, p. 586)

protein: polymer made of individual amino acids linked together in a chain; catalyzes many cell reactions and provides the structural material for many parts of the body. (ch. 14, p. 411)

prothallus: fern gametophyte, which can make its own food, absorb water and nutrients, and has both male and female reproductive structures. (ch. 16, p. 454)

proton: positively charged, heavy particle contained in the nucleus of all atoms. (ch. 2, p. 40)

punctuated equilibrium: model of evolution that shows the rapid change of a species caused by the mutation of just a few genes, resulting in the appearance of a new species. (ch. 12, p. 340)

R

radioactive decay: release of nuclear particles and energy from unstable atomic nuclei. (ch. 2, p. 48; ch. 11, p. 321)

radioactive element: element that gives off radiation due to an unstable nucleus. (ch. 12, p. 346)

radiometric dating: process to determine the absolute ages of rocks by measuring the amounts of parent and daughter materials in a rock and by knowing the half-life of the parent. (ch. 11, p. 323)

radio telescope: type of telescope that uses a large, curved dish to collect and record radio waves traveling through space and that can be used during the day or at night and during bad weather. (ch. 20, p. 579)

rate of reaction: measure of how quickly a chemical reaction occurs, which can be influenced by temperature, particle size, the concentration of the reactants, and the amount of activation energy that starts the reaction. (ch. 5, p. 133)

reactant (ree AK tunt): substance that exists before a chemical reaction begins; in a chemical equation, the reactant is listed on the left side of the arrow. (ch. 5, p. 124)

recycling: process that reduces the use of natural resources by reusing an item after it has been changed or reprocessed. (ch. 19, p. 553)

reflecting telescope: optical telescope that uses a mirror (or mirrors) to focus light and produce an image at the focal point. (ch. 20, p. 576)

refracting telescope: optical telescope that uses a double convex lens to focus light and form an image at the focal point. (ch. 20, p. 576)

relative dating: method to determine the order of events and relative age of the rocks by examining the position of rocks in a sequence. (ch. 11, p. 313)

renewable resource: natural resource, such as water, that is recycled or replaced by ongoing natural processes. (ch. 19, p. 542)

reptiles: egg-laying, scaly skinned animals that do not need to return to water to reproduce and probably evolved from the same ancestor as amphibians. (ch. 13, p. 376)

respiration: series of chemical reactions by which all living cells break down food to release energy. (ch. 15, p. 432)

reverse fault: break in rock due to compression forces, where rocks above the fault surface move upward and over the rocks below the fault surface. (ch. 8, p. 212)

revolution: yearly orbit of Earth around the sun. (ch. 21, p. 605)

rhizome: underground stem of a fern, from which fronds and roots grow. (ch. 16, p. 454)

rotation: spinning of Earth on its axis, which causes day and night to occur. (ch. 21, p. 603)

S

satellite: any object that revolves around another object; can be natural (Earth's moon) or artificial (*Sputnik I*). (ch. 20, p. 582)

saturated hydrocarbon: hydrocarbon with only single bonds—for example, propane, C_3H_8, and butane, C_4H_{10}. (ch. 14, p. 400)

Saturn: sixth planet from the sun; has a complex ring system made of hundreds of ringlets. (ch. 22, p. 643)

science: process used to investigate the world and provide some possible answers to scientific questions. (ch. 1, p. 8)

scientific methods: approaches taken to try and solve a problem; can include recognizing the problem, forming a hypothesis, testing the hypothesis, analyzing the data, and drawing conclusions. (ch. 1, p. 10)

seafloor spreading: theory that magma from below Earth's crust is forced upward toward the surface at a mid-ocean ridge, flows from the cracks as the seafloor spreads apart and becomes solid as it cools, forming new seafloor. (ch. 10, p. 273)

secondary succession: ecological succession that begins in a place that already has soil and was once the home of living organisms. (ch. 18, p. 512)

secondary waves: waves that travel outward from an earthquake's focus and move through Earth by causing particles in rocks to vibrate at right angles to the direction of the wave. (ch. 8, p. 216)

sedimentary rock: rock formed by compaction and cementation of sediments or when minerals precipitate out of solution or are left behind when a solution evaporates; rock type formed from particles of preexisting rocks contains the most fossils. (ch. 12, p. 345)

seismic (SIZE mihk) **waves:** energy waves that are produced at and travel outward from the earthquake focus. (ch. 8, p. 215)

seismograph: device used by seismologists to record primary, secondary, and surface waves from earthquakes. (ch. 8, p. 226)

seismologist: scientist who studies earthquakes and seismic waves. (ch. 8, p. 226)

semiconductor: element that doesn't conduct electricity as well as a metal but does conduct electricity better than a nonmetal. (ch. 3, p. 76)

sequence: arrangement of things or events in a certain order. (ch. 1, p. 25)

shield volcano: broad volcano with gently sloping sides formed when hot, fluid lava flows from one or more vents. (ch. 9, p. 251)

short-day plant: plant that needs twelve or more hours of darkness to begin the flowering process. (ch. 15, p. 439)

sill: intrusive igneous rock body that forms when magma is squeezed into a horizontal crack between rock layers and hardens. (ch. 9, p. 257)

smog: air pollution that forms when sunlight reacts with pollutant chemicals produced by burning fossil fuels. (ch. 19, p. 559)

soil depletion: removal of soil nutrients from land used for agriculture due to the replacement of native plants with crops that do not decay and replenish the soil. (ch. 19, p. 549)

soil management: use of plowing methods to prevent or reduce soil depletion and erosion. (ch. 19, p. 550)

solar eclipse (ih KLIPS): eclipse that occurs when the moon moves directly between the sun and Earth and casts a shadow on part of Earth. (ch. 21, p. 614)

solar system: system of nine planets, including Earth and many smaller objects, that orbit the sun. (ch. 22, p. 631)

solstice: point at which the sun reaches its greatest distance north or south of the equator. (ch. 21, p. 607)

sori: spore-producing structures on the undersides of fern fronds. (ch. 16, p. 454)

space probe: instrument that travels out into the solar system to gather information and sends the data back to Earth. (ch. 20, p. 583)

space shuttle: reusable spacecraft that carries astronauts, satellites, and other materials to and from space. (ch. 20, p. 590)

space station: large artificial satellite that provides support systems, living quarters, and equipment so that humans can live and work in space and conduct research not possible on Earth. (ch. 20, p. 591)

species: group of similar organisms that can successfully reproduce among themselves in their natural environment. (ch. 12, p. 334)

speed: rate of change of an object's position. (ch. 6, p. 148)

sphere (SFIHR): round, three-dimensional object whose surface at all points is the same distance from its center. (ch. 21, p. 602)

sporophyte (SPOR uh fite) **stage:** plant life-cycle stage in which all plant structures are made of cells with a diploid number ($2n$) of chromosomes. (ch. 16, p. 452)

stamen: male reproductive organ inside the flower of an angiosperm; consists of a filament and an anther. (ch. 16, p. 461)

stomata: openings on leaf surfaces or leaflike structures through which gases like carbon dioxide and water vapor may enter and leave a plant. (ch. 15, p. 426)

strike-slip fault: break in rock due to shearing forces, where rocks on either side of the fault surface move past each other with little upward or downward movement. (ch. 8, p. 213)

sunspot: dark, relatively cool area on the surface of the sun. (ch. 23, p. 668)

supergiant: late stage in the life cycle of a massive star where the core reaches very high temperatures, heavy elements form by fusion, and the star expands. (ch. 23, p. 676)

surface waves: waves of energy that reach Earth's surface during an earthquake, travel outward from the epicenter, and move rock particles up and down and side to side. (ch. 8, p. 217)

symbiosis (sihm bee OH sus): any close relationship between two or more different species. (ch. 17, p. 491)

T

taiga (TI guh): cold region of cone-bearing evergreen trees that lies just below the tundra and is the world's largest terrestrial biome. (ch. 18, p. 520)

technology: application of what has been learned through science. (ch. 1, p. 22)

temperate deciduous forest: biome that lies at latitudes below about 50° in both the northern and southern hemispheres, usually has four distinct seasons, and supports a wide variety of plants and animals. (ch. 18, p. 521)

tephra: bits of rock or solidified lava dropped from the air during an explo-sive volcanic eruption. (ch. 9, p. 251)

theory: explanation backed by results received from repeated tests or experiments. (ch. 1, p. 12)

third quarter: moon phase in which only half of the lighted side of the moon is visible. (ch. 21, p. 614)

transpiration: loss of water vapor through the stomata of a leaf. (ch. 15, p. 427)

trilobite (TRI luh bite): organism that lived hundreds of millions of years ago and is considered an index fossil of the Paleozoic era. (ch. 13, p. 367)

tropical rain forest: hot, wet, equatorial biome that contains the largest number of species. (ch. 18, p. 523)

tropism: response of a plant to an outside stimulus such as gravity or light. (ch. 15, p. 436)

tsunami (soo NAHM ee): powerful seismic sea wave that can travel thousands of kilometers in all directions and that begins over an earthquake focus. (ch. 8, p. 227)

tundra (TUN dra): cold, dry, treeless biome located at latitudes surrounding the north pole and that has winters six to nine months long. (ch. 18, p. 519)

U

unbalanced forces: two or more unequal forces acting on an object that cause the object to accelerate. (ch. 7, p. 177)

unconformities (un kun FOR mihteez): gaps in the rock layers due to erosion, nondeposition, or both. (ch. 11, p. 315)

uniformitarianism (yew nih for mih TAHR ee ah nizm): states that Earth processes happening today are similar to those that happened in the past. (ch. 11, p. 325)

unsaturated hydrocarbon: hydrocarbon that has one or more double or triple bonds—for example, ethylene, C_2H_4, and propylene, C_3H_6. (ch. 14, p. 401)

Uranus: large, gaseous planet and seventh planet from the sun; has a magnetic pole tilted 60 degrees and rotates on an axis nearly parallel to the plane of its orbit. (ch. 22, p. 645)

variation: an inherited trait that makes an individual different from other members of the same species; can be beneficial, harmful, or neutral in a population. (ch. 12, p. 338)

velocity (vel AH seh TEE): rate of change of displacement; includes both speed and direction. (ch. 6, p. 150)

vent: opening on Earth's surface where magma is forced up and flows out as lava. (ch. 9, p. 242)

Venus: second planet from the sun; has a dense atmosphere of carbon dioxide and sulfuric acid. (ch. 22, p. 637)

vestigial (veh STIHJ ee ul) structure: body structure with no obvious use, which may once have functioned in an ancestor. (ch. 12, p. 350)

volcanic neck: solid, igneous core of a volcano left behind when a volcano stops erupting and the softer cone erodes away. (ch. 9, p. 257)

volcano: opening in Earth's surface that often forms a mountain when layers of lava and volcanic ash erupt and build up; occurs where Earth's plates are moving apart or together and at hot spots. (ch. 9, p. 240)

waning: occurs after a full moon, when the amount of the moon's lighted side that can be seen becomes smaller. (ch. 21, p. 614)

water cycle: constant journey of water molecules on Earth as they rise into the atmosphere, fall to land or the ocean as rain or snow, and flow into rivers and oceans through the processes of evaporation, condensation, and precipitation. (ch. 17, p. 500)

waxing: occurs shortly after a new moon, when more and more of the moon's lighted side becomes visible. (ch. 21, p. 613)

white dwarf: late stage in a star's life cycle where its core uses up its supply of helium, it contracts, and its outer layers escape into space, leaving behind the hot dense core. (ch. 23, p. 676)

Glossary/Glosario

Este glossario define cada término clave que aparece en **negrillas** en el texto. También muestra el número de página donde se usa dicho término.

A

abiotic factors / factores abióticos: Características físicas inanimadas que a menudo determinan los organismos que pueden sobrevivir en cierto ambiente. (Cap. 17, pág. 483)

absolute dating / datación absoluta: Método utilizado para determinar la edad, en años, de una roca u otro objeto. (Cap. 11, pág. 321)

absolute magnitude / magnitud absoluta: Medida de la cantidad de luz que una estrella emite verdaderamente. (Cap. 23, pág. 664)

acceleration / aceleración: Razón de cambio de la velocidad. El acelerar, el decelerar y el voltear son formas de aceleración. (Cap. 6, pág. 152)

acid rain / lluvia ácida: Lluvia o nieve con un pH menor que 5.6; resulta de la mezcla de vapor de agua y contaminantes del aire en la atmósfera; puede conducir a la muerte de árboles y plantas. (Cap. 19, pág. 560)

alloy / aleación: Mezcla de dos o más elementos, uno de los cuales es un metal. (Cap. 3, pág. 74)

alternation of generations / alternación de generaciones: Ciclo vital de las plantas en la cual se alternan las etapas de producción de esporas y de producción de células sexuales. (Cap. 16, pág. 453)

amino acid / aminoácido: Unidad básica de la cual están compuestas las proteínas, las cuales son una clase importante de moléculas biológicas necesarias para las células vivas. (Cap. 14, pág. 407)

amino group / grupo amino: Grupo formado por un átomo de nitrógeno unido por enlaces covalentes a dos átomos de hidrógeno. (Cap. 14, pág. 406)

amphibians / anfibios: Animales que viven en tierra y respiran aire, pero que deben regresar al agua con el fin de reproducirse. (Cap. 13, pág. 376)

apparent magnitude / magnitud aparente: Medida de la cantidad de luz de una estrella que llega a la Tierra. (Cap. 23, pág. 664)

asteroid / asteroide: Fragmento rocoso semejante al material que formó los planetas. (Cap. 22, pág. 653)

asthenosphere / astenosfera: Capa tipo plástico situada debajo de la litosfera. (Cap. 10, pág. 277)

astronomical unit / unidad astronómica: Medida que se usa para medir distancias hacia los objetos en el sistema solar; corresponde a 150 millones de kilómetros, lo cual es la distancia promedio entre la Tierra y el sol. (Cap. 22, pág. 638)

atomic number / número atómico: Número de protones en el núcleo de un átomo de un elemento. (Cap. 2, pág. 47)

auxin / auxina: Tipo de hormona vegetal. (Cap. 15, pág. 437)

axis / eje: Línea imaginaria alrededor de la cual gira la Tierra. (Cap. 21, pág. 603)

B

balanced forces / fuerzas equilibradas: Fuerzas cuyos efectos se cancelan entre sí y no causan un cambio en el movimiento del objeto. (Cap. 7, pág. 177)

batholiths / batolitos: Las masas más grandes de rocas ígneas intrusivas, las cuales pueden extenderse por cientos de kilómetros y tener varios kilómetros de profundidad. (Cap. 9, pág. 255)

big bang theory / teoría de la gran explosión: Teoría que enuncia que hace unos 15 billones de años, el universo comenzó con una enorme explosión. (Cap. 23, pág. 685)

binary system / sistema binario: Sistema en el cual dos estrellas giran una alrededor de la otra. (Cap. 23, pág. 670)

biomes / biomas: Áreas geográficas extensas que poseen climas y ecosistemas similares. (Cap. 18, pág. 519)

biosphere / biosfera: La parte de la Tierra que sostiene organismos vivos. (Cap. 17, pág. 482)

biotic factors / factores bióticos: Cualquier organismo vivo o que alguna vez estuvo vivo, en un ambiente. (Cap. 17, pág. 485)

black hole / agujero negro: Núcleo restante de una estrella de neutrones, el cual es tan denso y masivo que nada puede escapar de su campo de gravedad, ni siquiera la luz. (Cap. 23, pág. 676)

C

caldera / caldera: Gran abertura que resulta cuando la cima de un volcán se hunde. (Cap. 9, pág. 257)

carbohydrates / carbohidratos: Compuestos orgánicos que solo contienen carbono, hidrógeno y oxígeno, en una proporción de dos átomos de hidrógeno por átomo de oxígeno y de carbono. (Cap. 14, pág. 412)

carbonaceous film / película carbonácea: Tipo de fósil producido por una película fina de residuo carbonoso, la cual forma un bosquejo del organismo original. (Cap. 11, pág. 307)

carboxyl group / grupo carboxilo: Grupo formado por un átomo de carbono, dos átomos de oxígeno y un átomo de hidrógeno. (Cap. 14, pág. 406)

carrying capacity / capacidad de carga: El mayor número de individuos que un ambiente puede soportar y mantener durante un largo período de tiempo. (Cap. 17, pág. 490)

cast / impresión fósil: Se forma cuando otros sedimentos llenan el hueco que deja el molde, se endurecen y forman una roca produciendo una impresión del objeto original. (Cap. 11, pág. 307)

catalyst / catalizador: Sustancia que acelera una reacción química, pero que no aparece en la ecuación química porque dicha sustancia no sufre cambio permanente ni se agota. (Cap. 5, pág. 136)

Cenozoic era / era Cenozoica: También denominada era de vida reciente. Esta era comenzó hace unos 65 millones de años cuando los dinosaurios y muchas otras formas de vida se extinguieron. (Cap. 13, pág. 386)

chemical bond / enlace químico: Fuerza que mantiene unidos dos átomos. (Cap. 4, pág. 107)

chemical reaction / reacción química: Proceso en que ocurren cambios químicos. El óxido sobre la carrocería de un auto de acero, un huevo que se fríe y las hojas que se tornan rojas en el otoño, son ejemplos de reacciones químicas. (Cap. 5, pág. 122)

chromosphere / cromosfera: Capa que se encuentra encima de la fotosfera y que se extiende por encima de esta unos 2000 km. (Cap. 23, pág. 667)

cinder cone / cono de carbonilla: Volcán de lados empinados y ligeramente empacado que se forma cuando la tefrita llega al suelo. (Cap. 9, pág. 252)

climax community / comunidad clímax: Comunidad que ha alcanzado la etapa final de sucesión ecológica. (Cap. 18, pág. 513)

comet / cometa: Objeto compuesto de polvo y partículas rocosas mezclados con agua congelada, metano y amoníaco. (Cap. 22, pág. 650)

community / comunidad: Grupo de poblaciones que interactúan entre sí en un área determinada. (Cap. 17, pág. 486)

composite volcano / volcán compuesto: Volcán que se forma del continuo y alternado ciclo de erupciones de lava y tefrita. (Cap. 9, pág. 252)

compound / compuesto: Sustancia pura que contiene dos o más elementos. (Cap. 4, pág. 107)

constant / constante: Variable que permanece inalterada en un experimento. (Cap. 1, pág. 14)

constellation / constelación: Grupo de estrellas en el firmamento. Las constelaciones recibieron nombres de animales, figuras mitológicas u objetos cotidianos. (Cap. 23, pág. 662)

continental drift / deriva continental: Hipótesis propuesta por Alfred Wegener que dice que los continentes se han movido lentamente a sus posiciones actuales. (Cap. 10, pág. 268)

control / control: Un estándar de comparación. (Cap. 1, pág. 13)

convection current / corriente de convección: Ciclo completo de calentamiento, ascenso, enfriamiento y hundimiento. (Cap. 10, pág. 282)

corona / corona: La capa más grande de la atmósfera solar, la cual se extiende millones de kilómetros en el espacio. (Cap. 23, pág. 667)

covalent bond / enlace covalente: Enlace químico que se forma entre átomos que comparten electrones. (Cap. 4, pág. 109)

crater / cráter: Depresión de paredes empi-nadas alrededor de la chimenea de un volcán. (Cap. 9, pág. 242)

crust / corteza: La capa más externa de la Tierra y separada del manto por la discontinuidad de Moho. (Cap. 8, pág. 220)

cyanobacteria / cianobacterias: Una de las formas de vida más tempranas sobre la Tierra; evolucionaron durante la Era Precámbrica. (Cap. 13, pág. 373)

D

day-neutral plant / planta de día neutro: Planta que no requiere un fotoperíodo específico y en la cual el proceso de floración puede comenzar dentro de una gama de horas de oscuridad. (Cap. 15, pág. 440)

dependent variable / variable dependiente: Factor que se mide, o se observa, en un experimento. (Cap. 1, pág. 13)

desert / desierto: El bioma terrestre más seco; recibe menos de 25 cm de lluvia al año y tiene poca vegetación. (Cap. 18, pág. 524)

dike / dique: Magma que ha sido apretujado en una resquebrajadura, generalmente, vertical y el cual atraviesa capas rocosas y se endurece. (Cap. 9, pág. 257)

displacement / desplazamiento: Mide el cambio en la posición de un objeto, el cual incluye dirección. (Cap. 6, pág. 149)

E

Earth / la Tierra: El tercer planeta a partir del sol; tiene temperaturas superficiales que permiten que el agua exista como sólido, líquido y gas y una atmósfera que protege la vida de la radiación solar. (Cap. 22, pág. 638)

earthquakes / terremotos: Vibraciones producidas por rocas que se rompen a lo largo de fallas; la mayoría resulta del movimiento de las placas. (Cap. 8, pág. 211)

ecological pyramid / pirámide ecológica: Modelo que representa la transferencia de energía en la biosfera. (Cap. 17, pág. 498)

ecological succession / sucesión ecológica: Proceso de cambio gradual de una comunidad de organismos a otra. (Cap. 18, pág. 510)

ecology / ecología: Ciencia que estudia las interacciones entre los organismos y entre los organismos y los rasgos físicos del ambiente. (Cap. 17, pág. 483)

ecosystem / ecosistema: Está compuesto de una comunidad biótica y de los factores abióticos que la afectan. (Cap. 17, pág. 486)

electromagnetic spectrum / espectro electromagnético: Arreglo de radiación electromagnética, de acuerdo con sus longitudes de onda. (Cap. 20, pág. 575)

electron / electrón: Partícula de materia con carga negativa. (Cap. 2, pág. 39)

electron cloud / nube de electrones: Región que rodea el núcleo del átomo y en donde, posiblemente, se encuentran los electrones. (Cap. 2, pág. 45)

electron dot diagram / diagrama de puntos electrónicos: Símbolo químico de un elemento rodeado por puntos que representan los electrones en el nivel energético externo. (Cap. 4, pág. 102)

element / elemento: Sustancia que no puede ser dividida en sustancias más sencillas. (Cap. 2, pág. 37)

ellipse / elipse: Curva cerrada y alargada. La órbita de la Tierra forma un elipse. (Cap. 21, pág. 605)

embryology / embriología: El estudio del desarrollo de los organismos. (Cap. 12, pág. 350)

endangered species / especie en peligro de extinción: Especie que está en peligro de desaparecer a menos que se tomen medidas para protegerla. (Cap. 19, pág. 551)

endothermic reaction / reacción endotérmica: Reacción en la cual se absorbe energía. (Cap. 5, pág. 127)

energy / energía: La capacidad de causar cambio. (Cap. 6, pág. 165)

epicenter / epicentro: Punto en la superficie terrestre directamente encima del foco de un terremoto. (Cap. 8, pág. 217)

epoch / época: Unidad de tiempo más pequeña en que se subdividen los períodos de la escala del tiempo geológico. (Cap. 13, pág. 365)

equinox / equinoccio: Época del año cuando el sol está directamente encima del ecuador terrestre y las horas de luz solar son iguales a las horas de oscuridad. (Cap. 21, pág. 607)

era / era: Subdivisión importante de la escala del tiempo geológico que se basa en las diferencias en las formas de vida. (Cap. 13, pág. 365)

erosion / erosión: Agotamiento del suelo por acción del viento y del agua. (Cap. 19, pág. 550)

estuary / estuario: Área en donde un río desemboca en el océano y la cual contiene una mezcla de agua dulce y salada. Es un ambiente muy fértil y productivo que sirve de vivero para muchas especies de peces oceánicos. (Cap. 18, pág. 530)

evolution / evolución: Cambio en los rasgos hereditarios de una especie a lo largo del tiempo. (Cap. 12, pág. 334)

exothermic reaction / reacción exotérmica: Reacción en la cual se libera energía. (Cap. 5, pág. 128)

extinction / extinción: La desaparición de una especie completa. (Cap. 19, pág. 550)

fault / falla: Superficie a lo largo de la cual se mueven y rompen las rocas, al exceder su límite de elasticidad. (Cap. 8, pág. 210)

first quarter / cuarto creciente: Fase de la luna cuando, desde la Tierra, se puede observar la mitad de su faz iluminada o un cuarto de la superficie lunar. (Cap. 21, pág. 613)

focus / foco: Punto en el interior de la Tierra donde ocurre la liberación de energía de un terremoto. (Cap. 8, pág. 215)

food chain / cadena alimenticia: Manera simple de mostrar cómo la energía de los alimentos pasa de un organismo a otro. (Cap. 17, pág. 497)

food web / red alimenticia: Serie de cadenas alimenticias sobrepuestas. (Cap. 17, pág. 498)

force / fuerza: Empuje o fuerza de atracción sobre un objeto. (Cap. 7, pág. 176)

formula / fórmula: Combinación de símbolos químicos de elementos, la cual indica los elementos que posee una molécula y cuántos átomos de cada elemento hay. (Cap. 4, pág. 113)

fossil / fósil: Resto, impresión o huella de organismos que una vez estuvieron vivos, conservado en las rocas. (Cap. 11, pág. 304)

fossil fuel / combustible fósil: Se forma cuando los organismos mueren y son enterrados debajo de capas de roca y sedimentos. El carbón, el gas natural y los combustibles hechos a partir del petróleo, son ejemplos de combustibles fósiles. (Cap. 19, pág. 544)

friction / fricción: Fuerza desequilibrada que hace que casi todos los objetos se detengan y que causa una fuerza de roce que se opone al movimiento entre dos superficies que están en contacto una con otra. (Cap. 7, pág. 179)

frond / fronda: La hoja de un helecho. (Cap. 16, pág. 454)

full moon / luna llena o plenilunio: Fase lunar durante la cual toda la superficie lunar que da a la Tierra está totalmente iluminada. (Cap. 21, pág. 613)

G

galaxy / galaxia: Grupo inmenso de estrellas, gas y polvo que se mantiene unido gracias a la gravedad. Nuestra galaxia, la Vía Láctea contiene unos 200 billones de estrellas. (Cap. 23, pág. 679)

gametophyte stage / etapa de gametofito: Etapa en que todas las estructuras de la planta están compuestas de células con un número haploide de cromosomas. (Cap. 16, pág. 452)

gastroliths / gastrolitos: Piedras ingeridas por ciertos animales para facilitar la digestión. (Cap. 13, pág. 385)

geologic time scale / escala del tiempo geológico: División de la historia de la Tierra en unidades más pequeñas de tiempo con base en los tipos de formas de vida que vivieron durante ciertos períodos. (Cap. 13, pág. 364)

geothermal energy / energía geotérmica: Energía térmica contenida dentro de la corteza terrestre que se puede aprovechar como fuente energética. (Cap. 19, pág. 546)

giant / gigante: Etapa en el ciclo de vida de una estrella en que se agota el hidrógeno del núcleo, el núcleo estelar se contrae y las temperaturas dentro de la estrella aumentan, haciendo que sus capas externas se expandan. (Cap. 23, pág. 675)

global warming / calentamiento global: Aumento del promedio de la temperatura anual sobre la Tierra. (Cap. 19, pág. 561)

gradualism / gradualismo: Modelo que describe la evolución como un cambio lento de una especie en otra especie nueva. (Cap. 12, pág. 340)

graph / gráfica: Diagrama que muestra la relación entre variables y el cual facilita el análisis de los datos. (Cap. 1, pág. 18)

grasslands / praderas: Regiones tropicales y templadas que reciben de 25 a 75 cm de precipitación anual y en la cual dominan la comunidad clímax de hierbas. (Cap. 18, pág. 524)

gravitational potential energy / energía potencial gravitacional: La energía que un objeto ganaría al caer, la cual depende de la masa del objeto y de la altura de la caída. (Cap. 6, pág. 167)

Great Red Spot / la Gran Mancha Roja: Espectacular tormenta de gas turbulento y de alta presión que se puede observar continuamente en Júpiter. (Cap. 22, pág. 642)

greenhouse effect / efecto de invernadero: Retención en la atmósfera terrestre del calor proveniente del sol, el cual es esencial para sostener vida sobre la Tierra. (Cap. 19, pág. 561)

groundwater / agua subterránea: Agua contenida en el suelo o atrapada en espacios subterráneos formados por roca no porosa. (Cap. 19, pág. 563)

group / grupo: Familia de elementos que contiene elementos con propiedades físicas o químicas parecidas. (Cap. 3, pág. 68)

H

habitat / hábitat: Ubicación física en donde vive un organismo (Cap. 17, pág. 493)

half-life / media vida: El tiempo que se demora la mitad de los átomos de un isótopo para desintegrarse. (Cap. 2, pág. 50; Cap. 11, pág. 322)

hazardous waste / desperdicio peligroso: Material de desecho dañino para la salud de los seres humanos o venenoso para los organismos vivos. (Cap. 19, pág. 562)

hominids / homínidos: Primates que parecían humanos y que comían tanto plantas como animales y caminaban erguidos. (Cap. 12, pág. 355)

homologous / homólogo: Estructuras corporales similares en origen y estructura que indican que dos o más especies pueden haber tenido antepasados comunes. (Cap. 12, pág. 349)

Homo sapiens / Homo sapiens: El nombre de nuestra especie. Significa "humano sabio". (Cap. 12, pág. 356)

hot spot / punto cálido: Área del manto que según algunos geólogos es más caliente que otras áreas y en donde se derriten las rocas que luego brotan en forma de magma hacia la corteza terrestre. (Cap. 9, pág. 244)

hydrocarbon / hidrocarburo: Compuesto que solo contiene carbono e hidrógeno. (Cap. 14, pág. 399)

hydroelectric power / potencia hidroeléctrica: Electricidad que produce la energía del agua que fluye. Es una fuente de energía renovable. (Cap. 19, pág. 546)

hydroxyl group / grupo hidroxilo: Grupo formado por un átomo de oxígeno y un átomo de hidrógeno unidos por un enlace covalente. (Cap. 14, pág. 405)

hypothesis / hipótesis: Predicción acerca de un problema que puede probarse. (Cap. 1, pág. 12)

I

independent variable / variable independiente: Variable que se cambia en un experimento. (Cap. 1, pág. 13)

index fossils / fósiles guías: Provienen de especies que existieron abundantemente en la Tierra durante cortos períodos de tiempo y que se encontraban muy extendidas geográficamente; los científicos los usan para determinar la edad de las rocas. (Cap. 11, pág. 310)

inertia / inercia: Mide la tendencia de un objeto a permanecer en reposo o de continuar en movimiento constante. Una medida de la inercia de un objeto es su masa. (Cap. 6, pág. 158)

inference / inferencia: Intento de explicar algo, con base en la observación. (Cap. 1, pág. 25)

inhibitor / inhibidor: Sustancia que decelera una reacción química. (Cap. 5, pág. 136)

inner core / núcleo interno: Núcleo sólido, muy denso en el mismo centro de la Tierra, compuesto principalmente de hierro y pequeñas cantidades de oxígeno, sílice, azufre o níquel. (Cap. 8, pág. 219)

inner planets / planetas interiores: Planetas sólidos rocosos situados más cerca del sol: Mercurio, Venus, la Tierra y Marte. (Cap. 22, pág. 633)

intertidal zone / zona entre la marea baja y la alta: Porción de la costa cubierta de agua durante la marea alta y expuesta al aire durante la marea baja. (Cap. 18, pág. 530)

ion / ion: Átomo que ya no es neutro porque ha ganado o perdido un electrón. (Cap. 4, pág. 106)

ionic bond / enlace iónico: Fuerza de atracción que mantiene unidos los iones de carga opuesta. (Cap. 4, pág. 107)

isomers / isómeros: Compuestos que tienen fórmulas químicas idénticas, pero diferentes estructuras y diferentes propiedades químicas y físicas. (Cap. 14, pág. 402)

isotopes / isótopos: Átomos del mismo elemento que poseen diferentes números de neutrones. (Cap. 2, pág. 47)

Jupiter / Júpiter: El planeta más grande del sistema solar y está ubicado en quinto lugar a partir del sol. (Cap. 22, pág. 642)

kinetic energy / energía cinética: La energía de la materia en movimiento. (Cap. 6, pág. 165)

law / ley: Descripción probada repetidamente de cómo funciona algo en la naturaleza. Por lo general predice o describe una situación dada, pero no explica por qué se da dicha situación. (Cap. 1, pág. 12)

law of conservation of energy / ley de conservación de la energía: Establece que la energía no puede ser creada ni destruida, sino que solo es transformada de una forma de energía a otra. (Cap. 6, pág. 165)

law of conservation of momentum / ley de conservación del momento: Ley que dice que si no existe una fuerza externa que actúe sobre un grupo de objetos, el momento del grupo entero nunca cambia. (Cap. 6, pág. 161)

light-year / año luz: Distancia que viaja la luz en un año. Es también la unidad que se usa para medir distancias en el espacio. (Cap. 23, pág. 665)

limiting factor / factor limitante: Cualquier factor biótico o abiótico que limita el número de individuos en una población. (Cap. 17, pág. 489)

lipids / lípidos: Compuestos orgánicos que contienen los mismos elementos que los carbohidratos: carbono, hidrógeno y oxígeno, pero en diferentes proporciones. (Cap. 14, pág. 415)

lithosphere / litosfera: Nombre que reciben la corteza y una parte del manto superior terrestres. (Cap. 10, pág. 227)

long-day plant / planta de día largo: Planta que necesita, generalmente, menos de diez a doce horas de oscuridad para comenzar el proceso de floración. (Cap. 15, pág. 439)

lunar eclipse / eclipse lunar: Ocurre cuando la sombra de la Tierra cae sobre la luna. (Cap. 21, pág. 616)

magnitude / magnitud: Medida de la energía liberada en un terremoto. (Cap. 8, pág. 226)

main sequence / secuencia principal: En el diagrama H-R, la banda diagonal de estrellas que corre desde las estrellas calientes y brillantes, en la parte superior izquierda del diagrama, hasta las estrellas frías y tenues, en la parte inferior derecha. (Cap. 23, pág. 672)

mantle / manto: Capa más extensa de la Tierra ubicada directamente encima del núcleo externo y compuesta principalmente de sílice, oxígeno, magnesio y hierro. (Cap. 8, pág. 219)

maria / maria: Regiones oscuras y relativamente planas de la superficie lunar. (Cap. 21, pág. 617)

Mars / Marte: Denominado el planeta rojo, Marte es el cuarto planeta a partir del sol. (Cap. 22, pág. 638)

mascon / concentración de masa: Concentración de masa ubicada debajo de las cuencas de impacto en la Luna. (Cap. 21, pág. 621)

mass / masa: Medida de la cantidad de materia. (Cap. 6, pág. 158)

mass number / número de masa: Número de protones y neutrones en el núcleo de un átomo. (Cap. 2, pág. 48)

Mercury / Mercurio: El planeta más cercano al sol y es también el segundo planeta más pequeño. (Cap. 22, pág. 636)

Mesozoic era / era Mesozoica: También denominada era de vida media. Esta era comenzó hace unos 245 millones de años (Cap. 13, pág. 381)

metal / metal: Elemento que tiene lustre, es buen conductor de calor y electricidad y por lo general es sólido a temperatura ambiente. (Cap. 3, pág. 69)

metalloid / metaloide: Elemento que comparte algunas propiedades con los metales y con no metales. Por ejemplo, el boro posee lustre como un metal; pero como los no metales, es un conductor deficiente de electricidad (Cap. 3, pág. 70)

meteor / meteoro: Meteoroide que se quema en la atmósfera terrestre. (Cap. 22, pág. 652)

meteorite / meteorito: Meteoroide lo suficientemente grande como para caer sobre la superficie terrestre. (Cap. 22, pág. 652)

mold / molde: Fósil que se forma cuando un organismo es enterrado y se descompone dejando solo un espacio vacío en la roca. (Cap. 11, pág. 307)

molecule / molécula: Partícula neutra que se forma cuando los átomos comparten electrones. (Cap. 4, pág. 109)

momentum / momento: El producto de la masa y la velocidad, incluyendo dirección. (Cap. 6, pág. 159)

moon phase / fase lunar: Apariencia cambiante de la luna vista desde la Tierra. La fase que vemos depende de las posiciones relativas de la luna, la Tierra y el sol. (Cap. 21, pág. 613)

natural resource / recurso natural: Material que se encuentra en la naturaleza y que son útiles o necesarios para los seres vivos. (Cap. 19, pág. 542)

natural selection / selección natural: Teoría de la evolución según Darwin, la cual establece que los organismos cuyos rasgos los hacen más aptos para sus ambientes son los que sobreviven, se reproducen y pasan esos rasgos a la progenie. (Cap. 12, pág. 337)

nebula / nebulosa: Nube extensa de gas y polvo que corresponde a la etapa inicial de formación de una estrella. (Cap. 23, pág. 674)

Neptune / Neptuno: Planeta grande y gaseoso descubierto en 1846; por lo general es el octavo planeta a partir del sol. (Cap. 22, pág. 646)

net force / fuerza neta: Fuerza total que siente un objeto, la cual siempre hace que el objeto acelere en la dirección de la fuerza neta. (Cap. 7, pág. 176)

neutron / neutrón: Partícula neutra con la misma masa que un protón. (Cap. 2, pág. 44)

neutron star / estrella de neutrones: La etapa de una supernova cuando el núcleo denso y colapsado de la estrella se encoge hasta unos 10 a 15 km en diámetro y solo pueden existir neutrones en él. (Cap. 23, pág. 676)

new moon / luna nueva: Ocurre cuando la cara iluminada de la luna mira hacia el Sol y la cara oscura mira hacia la Tierra. La luna se encuentra en el firmamento, pero no podemos verla desde la Tierra. (Cap. 21, pág. 613)

Newton's first law of motion / primera ley de movimiento de Newton: Enuncia que un objeto en reposo, o que se mueve a una rapidez constante en una trayectoria recta, continúa en dicha posición o movimiento hasta que una fuerza neta actúe sobre él. (Cap. 7, pág. 178)

Newton's second law of motion / segunda ley de movimiento de Newton: Ley que enuncia que una fuerza neta que actúa sobre un objeto hace que el objeto acelere en dirección de la fuerza, de acuerdo con la ecuación: $a = F_{net}/m$, en que a es la aceleración, F_{net} es la fuerza neta y m es la masa. (Cap. 7, pág. 184)

Newton's third law of motion / tercera ley de movimiento de Newton: Enuncia que las fuerzas siempre actúan en pares iguales pero opuestos. Es decir, que por cada acción existe una reacción igual y opuesta. (Cap. 7, pág. 192)

niche / nicho: Papel de un organismo en el ecosistema. (Cap. 17, pág. 493)

nitrogen cycle / ciclo del nitrógeno: Transferencia de nitrógeno de la atmósfera a las plantas y de regreso a la atmósfera o directamente a las plantas nuevamente. (Cap. 17, pág. 502)

nonmetal / no metal: Por lo general, un gas o sólido quebradizo a temperatura ambiente, el cual no es buen conductor de calor y electricidad. (Cap. 3, pág. 70)

nonrenewable resource / recurso no renovable: Recurso natural, como el petróleo, accesible solo en cantidades limitadas y que no se puede reemplazar o que solo se reemplaza muy lentamente. (Cap. 19, pág. 543)

normal fault / falla normal: Falla que se forma cuando las rocas, bajo tensión sobre la superficie de la falla, se mueven hacia abajo en relación con las rocas debajo de la superficie. (Cap. 8, pág. 212)

normal force / fuerza normal: La fuerza exterior que ejerce una superficie, la cual es provista por la potencia de la superficie. Por ejemplo, si colocas un objeto pesado sobre una silla desvencijada, podría suceder que la silla no provea suficiente fuerza normal para equilibrar el peso y se rompa bajo el peso. (Cap. 7, pág. 185)

nuclear energy / energía nuclear: Energía que se produce del rompimiento de billones de núcleos de uranio en una reacción de fisión nuclear. (Cap. 19, pág. 547)

O

observatory / observatorio: Edificio que alberga la mayoría de los telescopios ópticos usados por los astrónomos profesionales. A menudo, estos edificios tienen techos, en forma de domo, los cuales se abren para permitir la entrada de la luz. (Cap. 20, pág. 576)

Oort Cloud / Nube de Oort: Nube que, según el astrónomo holandés Jan Oort, está ubicada más allá de la órbita de Plutón y la cual rodea completamente el sistema solar. (Cap. 22, pág. 651)

orbit / órbita: Trayectoria curva que sigue un objeto a medida que gira alrededor de otro objeto en el espacio. Por ejemplo, los planetas giran, en órbitas, alrededor del Sol. (Cap. 20, pág. 582)

organic compound / compuesto orgánico: Compuesto que contiene carbono. (Cap. 14, pág. 398)

outer core / núcleo externo: Núcleo líquido ubicado directamente encima del núcleo interno sólido; también compuesto principalmente de hierro. (Cap. 8, pág. 219)

outer planets / planetas exteriores: Planetas más alejados del sol: Júpiter, Neptuno, Saturno, Urano y Plutón. Excepto por Plutón que está formado de roca y hielo, todos los planetas exteriores están formados principalmente de elementos livianos tales como hidrógeno, helio, metano y amoníaco. (Cap. 22, pág. 633)

ovary / ovario: Base hinchada del pistilo donde se forman los óvulos en las angiospermas. (Cap. 16, pág. 461)

ovule / óvulo: Parte reproductora femenina de una planta de semillas. (Cap. 16, pág. 458)

ozone depletion / agotamiento de la capa de ozono: Adelgazamiento de la capa de ozono que protege la Tierra de los rayos ultravioletas dañinos del sol. Este problema lo causa principalmente el uso de clorofluorocarbonos. (Cap. 19, pág. 561)

P

Paleozoic era / era Paleozoica: Era geológica cuyo comienzo lo marca la presencia de los primeros organismos con partes duras, lo cual facilitó la formación de fósiles. (Cap. 13, pág. 374)

Pangaea / Pangaea: Inmensa extensión territorial que, según Wegener, una vez conectó a todos los continentes y que se separó hace unos 200 millones de años. (Cap. 10, pág. 268)

parallax / paralaje: Cambio aparente en la posición de un objeto cuando uno lo observa desde dos posiciones diferentes. (Cap. 23, pág. 665)

period / período: Hilera de elementos en la tabla periódica cuyas propiedades cambian paulatina y previsiblemente (Cap. 3, pág. 65); Unidad de tiempo en que se subdividen las eras de la escala del tiempo geológico. (Cap. 13, pág. 365)

petrified remains / restos petrificados: Restos duros y de consistencia parecida a la roca, en los cuales algunos o todos los materiales originales han sido reemplazados por minerales. (Cap. 11, pág. 306)

photoperiodism / fotoperiodismo: Respuesta de una planta al número de horas de luz y oscuridad que recibe diariamente. (Cap. 15, pág. 439)

photosphere / fotosfera: Capa más baja de la atmósfera del sol y desde la cual se emite la luz solar. A menudo llamada superficie solar. (Cap. 23, pág. 667)

photosynthesis / fotosíntesis: Proceso mediante el cual las plantas utilizan la energía luminosa para producir alimento. (Cap. 15, pág. 429)

photovoltaic (PV) cell / pila fotovoltaica: Disco hecho del mineral silicio cubierto con capas finas de metales. Se usa para generar electricidad utilizando la energía solar. (Cap. 19, pág. 545)

pioneer community / comunidad pionera: Primera comunidad de organismos que se mudan a un nuevo ambiente. (Cap. 18, pág. 511)

pistil / pistilo: Órgano reproductor femenino de la flor que consiste en un estigma, un estilo alargado en forma de tallo y un ovario. (Cap. 16, pág. 461)

plankton / plancton: Algas, plantas y otros organismos microscópicos que flotan cerca de la superficie en las aguas cálidas y soleadas de lagos y lagunas de agua dulce. (Cap. 18, pág. 529)

plate tectonics / tectónica de placas: Teoría que afirma que la corteza y el manto superior de la Tierra están separados en secciones que se mueven sobre una capa del manto que parece plástico. (Cap. 10, pág. 277)

plates / placas: Secciones de la litosfera terrestre compuestas de corteza oceánica, corteza continental y el manto superior rígido, las cuales se mueven sobre una capa del manto que parece plástico. (Cap. 10, pág. 277)

Pluto / Plutón: El planeta más pequeño del sistema solar y del cual tenemos menos información. Se le considera el noveno planeta a partir del sol. (Cap. 22, pág. 646)

pollen grains / granos de polen: Partes reproductoras masculinas de las plantas de semillas; dos espermatozoides se desarrollan en cada grano de polen. (Cap. 16, pág. 458)

pollination / polinización: Proceso de transferencia de granos de polen desde el estambre al estigma. (Cap. 16, pág. 462)

pollutant / contaminante: Cualquier sustancia que contamina el ambiente y causa contaminación. (Cap. 19, pág. 559)

polymer / polímero: Molécula que está compuesta de muchas moléculas orgánicas pequeñas, que se enlazan una a la otra formando una cadena larga. (Cap. 14, pág. 410)

population / población: Organismos individuales de la misma especie que viven en el mismo lugar y que pueden producir crías. (Cap. 17, pág. 486)

population density / densidad demográfica: El tamaño de una población que ocupa un área de tamaño limitado. (Cap. 17, pág. 489)

Precambrian time / Era Precámbrica: Representa la unidad de tiempo geológico más larga de la historia de la Tierra, la cual duró desde hace 4.6 billones de años hasta hace 544 millones de años. (Cap. 13, pág. 372)

primary succession / sucesión primaria: Sucesión ecológica que comienza en un lugar que no tiene suelo. (Cap. 18, pág. 511)

primary waves / ondas primarias: Ondas que hacen que las partículas en las rocas se muevan oscilatoriamente, en la misma dirección de la onda. (Cap. 8, pág. 216)

primates / primates: Grupo de mamíferos que incluye los monos, los simios y a los seres humanos, los cuales comparten varias características como pulgares oponibles, visión binocular y hombros flexibles. Los científicos consideran que todos los primates evolucionaron de un antepasado común. (Cap. 12, pág. 354)

principle of superposition / principio de sobreposición: Principio que dice que en las capas rocosas inalteradas, las rocas más antiguas se encuentran en las capas inferiores y que las rocas son más y más recientes hacia la parte superior. (Cap. 11, pág. 312)

product / producto: Sustancia que se forma al ocurrir una reacción química. (Cap. 5, pág. 124)

Project Apollo / Proyecto Apolo: Etapa final del programa americano de viajar a la luna. (Cap. 20, pág. 587)

Project Gemini / Proyecto Gemini: Segunda etapa en la meta de viajar a la luna. (Cap. 20, pág. 586)

Project Mercury / Proyecto Mercurio: Proyecto que inició el programa americano de viajar a la luna. (Cap. 20, pág. 586)

protein / proteína: Polímero que consiste en una cadena de aminoácidos individuales unidos entre sí. Las proteínas son necesarias para el funcionamiento adecuado del cuerpo humano. (Cap. 14, pág. 411)

prothallus / prótalo: Gametofito del helecho que produce células sexuales que se unen para formar el cigoto. (Cap. 16, pág. 454)

proton / protón: Partícula con carga positiva que se encuentra en todos los átomos. (Cap. 2, pág. 40)

punctuated equilibrium / equilibrio puntuado: Modelo que muestra que la evolución rápida de una especie puede resultar debido a la mutación de unos cuantos genes, resultando en una nueva especie. (Cap. 12, pág. 340)

R

radioactive decay / desintegración radiactiva: Proceso en que la descomposición de un átomo de algunos isótopos resulta en un cambio en el número de protones y en la formación de un nuevo elemento. (Cap. 2, pág. 48; Cap. 11, pág. 321)

radioactive element / elemento radiactivo: Elemento que despide radiación debido a un núcleo inestable. Al despedir radiación, los elementos radiactivos se convierten en productos más estables. (Cap. 12, pág. 346)

radiometric dating / datación radiométrica: Proceso que se usa para calcular la edad absoluta de las rocas al medir las cantidades de material original y de los productos de desintegración que hay en la roca, conociendo el período de media vida del material original. (Cap. 11, pág. 323)

radio telescope / radiotelescopio: Tipo de telescopio que se usa para estudiar ondas radiales que viajan a través del espacio. (Cap. 20, pág. 579)

rate of reaction / tasa de reacción: Es una medida de la rapidez con que ocurre una reacción. (Cap. 5, pág. 133)

reactant / reactivo: Sustancia que existe antes de que comience una reacción química y la cual reacciona durante la reacción química. (Cap. 5, pág. 124)

recycling / reciclaje: Proceso que disminuye el uso de los recursos naturales al reutilizar artículos después de cambiarlos o procesarlos nuevamente. (Cap. 19, pág. 553)

reflecting telescope / telescopio reflector: Telescopio que usa un espejo como objetivo para enfocar la luz del objeto bajo observación. (Cap. 20, pág. 576)

refracting telescope / telescopio refractor: Telescopio en que la luz del objeto pasa a través de una lente convexa doble, en donde la luz se dobla formando una imagen sobre el punto focal. Luego el ocular magnifica la imagen. (Cap. 20, pág. 576)

relative dating / datación relativa: Se utiliza en geología para determinar el orden de los sucesos y la edad relativa de las rocas al examinar sus posiciones en una secuencia. (Cap. 11, pág. 313)

renewable resource / recurso renovable: Recurso natural, como el agua, que se puede reemplazar o reciclar mediante procesos naturales. (Cap. 19, pág. 542)

reptiles / reptiles: Animales con piel escamosa que ponen huevos y que no necesitan regresar al agua para reproducirse; probablemente evolucionaron de los mismos antepasados que los anfibios. (Cap. 13, pág. 376)

respiration / respiración: Serie de reacciones químicas que llevan a cabo todos los organismos para descomponer el alimento y liberar energía. (Cap. 15, pág. 432)

reverse fault / falla invertida: Falla en que las rocas sobre la superficie son forzadas hacia arriba y sobre las rocas debajo de la superficie de la falla. (Cap. 8, pág. 212)

revolution / revolución: Órbita anual de la Tierra alrededor del sol. (Cap. 21, pág. 605)

rhizome / risoma: Tallo subterráneo de donde crecen las hojas y las raíces de los helechos. (Cap. 16, pág. 454)

rotation / rotación: Movimiento de la Tierra alrededor de su eje, el cual causa el día y la noche. (Cap. 21, pág. 603)

S

satellite / satélite: Cualquier objeto que gira alrededor de otro objeto. (Cap. 20, pág. 582)

saturated hydrocarbon / hidrocarburo saturado: Hidrocarburo cuyos átomos solo contienen enlaces sencillos. (Cap. 14, pág. 400)

Saturn / Saturno: Conocido como el planeta anular, es el sexto planeta a partir del sol. (Cap. 22, pág. 643)

science / ciencia: Proceso que se usa para investigar el mundo a tu alrededor y el cual te provee algunas posibles respuestas. (Cap. 1, pág. 8)

scientific methods / métodos científicos: Procedimientos que se usan para tratar de resolver un problema. (Cap. 1, pág. 10)

seafloor spreading / expansión del suelo marino: Teoría que dice que el magma proveniente de debajo de la superficie terrestre es forzado a ascender a la superficie a través de la dorsal medioceánica, en donde fluye de las grietas a medida que el suelo marino se esparce, y se solidifica al enfriarse, formando nuevo suelo marino. (Cap. 10, pág. 273)

secondary succession / sucesión secundaria: Sucesión que comienza en un lugar que ya tiene suelo y el cual fue la morada de organismos vivos. (Cap. 18, pág. 512)

secondary waves / ondas secundarias: Ondas que se mueven a través de la Tierra haciendo que las partículas en las rocas vibren formando un ángulo recto a la dirección de la onda. (Cap. 8, pág. 216)

sedimentary rock / roca sedimentaria: Tipo de roca formada de barro, arena y otras partículas finas que quedan al secárseles el líquido. (Cap. 12, pág. 345)

seismic waves / ondas sísmicas: Ondas generadas por un terremoto. (Cap. 8, pág. 215)

seismograph / sismógrafo: Instrumento que registra las ondas primarias, secundarias y de superficie que producen los terremotos por todo el mundo. (Cap. 8, pág. 226)

seismologist / sismólogo: Científico que estudia los terremotos y las ondas sísmicas. (Cap. 8, pág. 226)

semiconductor / semiconductor: Elemento que no conduce electricidad tan bien como un metal, pero que sí la conduce mejor que un no metal. (Cap. 3, pág. 76)

sequence / sucesión: Arreglo de cosas o eventos en cierto orden. (Cap. 1, pág. 25)

shield volcano / volcán de escudo: Volcán amplio con suaves pendientes formado por la acumulación de capas llanas de lava basáltica. (Cap. 9, pág. 251)

short-day plant / planta de día corto: Planta que necesita doce o más horas de oscuridad para comenzar el proceso de floración. (Cap. 15, pág. 439)

sill / intrusión: Magma que después de ser apretujado formando una resquebrajadura horizontal entre capas rocosas se endurece. (Cap. 9, pág. 257)

smog / smog: Tipo de contaminante del aire que se forma cuando la luz solar reacciona con los contaminantes químicos que se producen de la quema de combustibles fósiles. (Cap. 19, pág. 559)

soil depletion / desgaste del suelo: Eliminación de nutrientes del suelo. (Cap. 19, pág. 549)

soil management / manejo del suelo: Uso de métodos de arado del terreno para disminuir su erosión. (Cap. 19, pág. 550)

solar eclipse / eclipse solar: Ocurre cuando la luna se mueve directamente entre el sol y la Tierra y proyecta una sombra sobre parte de la Tierra. (Cap. 21, pág. 614)

solar system / sistema solar: Está compuesto de nueve planetas, incluyendo la Tierra, y muchos objetos más pequeños que giran alrededor del sol. (Cap. 22, pág. 631)

solstice / solsticio: Punto en que el sol alcanza su mayor distancia al norte o al sur del ecuador. (Cap. 21, pág. 607)

sori / soros: Estructuras productoras de esporas que se encuentran en los lados inferiores de las frondas maduras de los helechos. (Cap. 16, pág. 454)

space probe / sonda espacial: Instrumento que viaja por el sistema solar; reúne información y la envía a la Tierra. (Cap. 20, pág. 583)

space shuttle / transbordador espacial: Nave espacial reutilizable que transporta a astronautas, satélites y otros materiales hacia el espacio y desde el mismo. (Cap. 20, pág. 590)

space station / estación espacial: Estación en el espacio que posee viviendas, áreas de trabajo y de ejercicio, y todo el equipo y sistemas auxiliares que necesitan los seres humanos para vivir y trabajar en el espacio. (Cap. 20, pág. 591)

species / especie: Grupo de organismos cuyos miembros pueden aparearse entre sí en su ambiente natural. (Cap. 12, pág. 334)

speed / rapidez: Razón del cambio en posición. (Cap. 6, pág. 148)

sphere / esfera: Objeto redondo tridimensional cuya superficie en cualquiera de sus puntos está a la misma distancia de su centro. (Cap. 21, pág. 602)

sporophyte stage / etapa de esporofito: Etapa en que todas las estructuras de la planta están compuestas de células con un número diploide de cromosomas. (Cap. 16, pág. 452)

stamen / estambre: Órgano reproductor masculino de la flor que consiste en un filamento y una antera. (Cap. 16, pág. 461)

stomata / estomas: Aberturas en la superficie de las hojas de las plantas, o en la superficie de estructuras que parecen hojas, las cuales permiten que el dióxido de carbono, el agua y el oxígeno entren y salgan de la planta. (Cap. 15, pág. 426)

strike-slip fault / falla transformante: Falla en la cual las rocas en cualquiera de los dos lados de la falla se alejan unas de otras, sin mucho movimiento ascendente o descendente. (Cap. 8, pág. 213)

sunspot / mancha solar: Área de la superficie solar que parece oscura porque es más fría que las áreas que la rodean. (Cap. 23, pág. 668)

supergiant / supergigante: Etapa en la formación de una estrella en la cual se forman elementos cada vez más pesados por medio de la fusión, haciendo que a la larga, se forme hierro en su núcleo. (Cap. 23, pág. 676)

surface waves / ondas de superficie: Ondas que viajan hacia afuera del epicentro y mueven las partículas de arriba hacia abajo y de un lado a otro, en un movimiento oscilatorio. Estas ondas causan la mayor parte de la destrucción durante un terremoto. (Cap. 8, pág. 217)

symbiosis / simbiosis: Cualquier relación estrecha entre dos o más especies diferentes. (Cap. 17, pág. 491)

taiga / taiga: Región fría de árboles coníferos siempre verdes. (Cap. 18, pág. 520)

technology / tecnología: La aplicación del conocimiento aprendido a través de la ciencia. (Cap. 1, pág. 22)

temperate deciduous forest / bosque deciduo de zonas templadas: Comunidad clímax de árboles deciduos, los cuales pierden sus hojas en el otoño. (Cap. 18, pág. 521)

tephra / tefrita: Pedazos de roca o lava solidificada que cae del aire después de ser expulsados en una erupción explosiva. (Cap. 9, pág. 251)

theory / teoría: Explicación basada en los resultados obtenidos al hacer pruebas o experimentos repetidamente. (Cap. 1, pág. 12)

third quarter / cuarto menguante: Cuando se ve solo la mitad de la faz iluminada de la luna. (Cap. 21, pág. 614)

transpiration / transpiración: Pérdida de agua a través de los estomas de la hoja. (Cap. 15, pág. 427)

trilobites / trilobites: Organismos que vivieron hace cientos de millones de años; aparecieron primero durante el período Cámbrico y existieron en la Tierra a través de la era Paleozoica y finalmente se extinguieron a finales del período Pérmico. (Cap. 13, pág. 367)

tropical rain forest / bosque pluvial tropical: La comunidad clímax más importante en las regiones ecuatoriales del mundo y que posee una vegetación frondosa. (Cap. 18, pág. 523)

tropism / tropismo: Respuesta de una planta a un estímulo exterior. Puede ser positivo o negativo. (Cap. 15, pág. 436)

tsunami / tsunami: Onda oceánica sísmica causada por un terremoto. (Cap. 8, pág. 227)

tundra / tundra: Región fría, seca y sin árboles, que a veces se denomina desierto gélido porque tiene inviernos que duran de seis a nueve meses. (Cap. 18, pág. 519)

unbalanced forces / fuerzas desequilibradas: Fuerzas cuya fuerza neta es cero y que provocan la aceleración de un objeto. (Cap. 7, pág. 177)

unconformities / discordancias: Brechas entre las capas rocosas. (Cap. 11, pág. 315)

uniformitarianism / uniformitarianismo: Dice que los procesos terrestres que tienen lugar actualmente son similares a los del pasado. (Cap. 11, pág. 325)

unsaturated hydrocarbon / hidrocarburo no saturado: Hidrocarburo cuyos átomos de carbono forman enlaces dobles o triples. (Cap. 14, pág. 401)

Uranus / Urano: El séptimo planeta a partir del sol, descubierto en 1781. Es un planeta grande y gaseoso con 17 satélites y un sistema de anillos oscuros y delgados. (Cap. 22, pág. 645)

variation / variación: Rasgo heredado que diferencia a un individuo de otros miembros de la misma especie; puede ser beneficiosa, dañina o no tener ninguna influencia en una población (Cap. 12, pág. 338)

velocity / velocidad: Razón de cambio del desplazamiento, la cual incluye tanto rapidez como dirección. (Cap. 6, pág. 150)

vent / chimenea: Abertura por la cual fluye el magma que llega a la superficie terrestre. (Cap. 9, pág. 242)

Venus / Venus: A veces llamado el gemelo de la Tierra, Venus es el segundo planeta a partir del sol. (Cap. 22, pág. 637)

vestigial structure / estructura vestigial: Parte corporal que parece no tener función alguna. (Cap. 12, pág. 350)

volcanic neck / cuello volcánico: Núcleo ígneo sólido que queda después de que el cono de un volcán se erosiona, después de que el volcán deja de hacer erupción. (Cap. 9, pág. 257)

volcano / volcán: Abertura en la superficie terrestre que a menudo forma una montaña, cuando se arrojan y acumulan capas de lava y cenizas volcánicas. (Cap. 9, pág. 240)

waning / octante menguante: Cuando la cantidad de la faz iluminada de la luna, que se puede ver desde la Tierra, comienza a disminuir. (Cap. 21, pág. 614)

water cycle / ciclo del agua: Involucra los procesos de evaporación, condensación y precipitación. (Cap. 17, pág. 500)

waxing / octante creciente: Cuando se hace cada vez más visible la cara iluminada de la luna. (Cap. 21, pág. 613)

white dwarf / enana blanca: Etapa tardía en el ciclo de vida de una estrella, en que su núcleo agota su abastecimiento de helio, se contrae y sus capas externas se escapan hacia el espacio, dejando un núcleo denso y caliente. (Cap. 23, pág. 676)

Index

The index for *Science Voyages* will help you locate major topics in the book quickly and easily. Each entry in the index is followed by the numbers of the pages on which the entry is discussed. A page number given in **boldface type** indicates the page on which that entry is defined. A page number given in *italic type* indicates a page on which the entry is used in an illustration or photograph. The abbreviation *act.* indicates a page on which the entry is used in an activity.

A

Abiotic factors, **483**-484, *483*, 504
Absolute dating, **321**, 321–325, 329
Absolute magnitude, **664**, 692
Acceleration, **152**-155, *153*, 170, *193*
  calculating, 193
  distance and, 152–155
  force and, 183–184, *183*, 186, *186*, 188
Acetic acid, 124, 125, *125*, **406**, *406*
Acid(s)
  amino, 406-**407**, *407*, 411–412, *412*, 421
  carboxylic, 406, *406*, 421
Acid rain, 559, **560**, 567
Actinide series, 68, 87, 88, 93
Action-reaction forces, 192–194, *194*
Activation energy, 132–133, *133*, 141
Adaptation, 338–341
Aerobic respiration, 432–434. *See also* Respiration
Air pollution, 558
Alcohols, 405, *act.* 408, 421
Algae, 484, 492, *496*
Alkali metals, 72, 73, 92

Alkaline earth metals, 74, *74*, 92
Allosaurus, 304
Alloys, **74**, *74*, *act.* 83, 87
Alpha particle, 49, 58, 59, 321
Alternation of generations, **453**
Aluminum, 70, 74, *74*, 75, *75*, 93
Amines, 406, *406*
Amino acids, 406-**407**, *407*, 411–412, *411*, *412*, 421
Amino group, **406**, 421
Ammonia, 77, *77*, 93, 139
  in atmospheres of planets, 642, 644, 645, 646
  on comets, 651
  molecule of, *113*, 117
Amphibians, 376
Angiosperms,
  reproduction of, 460–463, 475
  seed formation, *462*
Angular unconformities, *314*, 315
Animals
  adaptation of, 525, *525*
  endangered and threatened species of, *act.* 514–515
  in forests, *523*
  in grasslands, 524
  in temperate deciduous forests, 521, *521*

  on tundra, *520*
Anticline, 292, *292*
Apatosaurus, 304, 382
Apollo Project, **587**, 617, 618, 620
Apparent magnitude, **664**, 692
Archaeopteryx, 384
Asexual reproduction
  in plants, 451–452, *451*, 474
Asteroid, **653**-654, *653*, *654*, 657
Asteroid belt, *653*
Asthenosphere, **277**-278
Atherosclerosis, 417, *417*
Atmosphere
  of planets, 637, 638, 640, 642, 643–644, 645, *645*, 646–647, 656, 657
  of sun, 667, *667*, 692
Atom(s), 34–61
  models of, 37–45, *37*, *40*, *43*, *44*, 58, 103, *act.* 104–105
  nuclear, 42–43, *43*, *44*, 58
  nucleus of, 43, 44–45, *44*, 47–52, *47*, 58–59
  radioactive decay of, 48–52, 59
  structure of, *act.* 35, 98–103, *98*, *99*, *100*, *101*, *102*, *103*, *act.* 104–105
Atomic number, **47**
Automobiles

Medicine
    alkaline earth metals in, 74, *74*
    isotopes in, 52, 53, *53*, 88
    from nature, 409, *409*
Mendeleev, Dmitri, 64–65, *64*
Mercury (element), 71, 86, 89
Mercury (planet), **636**
    atmosphere of, 637, 638
    core of, 636–637
    size of, *631*
    surface of, 636, *636*, 637, 656
Mercury Project, **586**
Mesosaurus, *268*, 269, *269*, 296
Mesozoic era, 365–*366*, **381**–386
Metal(s), 68, **69**-70, *69*, 92
    alkali, 72, *72*, *73*, 92
    alkaline earth, 74, *74*, 92
    bonding in, 115, *115*
    in boron family, 75, *75*
    coinage, 85, *85*, 93
    heavy, and health, *act.* 90–91
    misch, 87, *87*
    transition elements, 68, 84–88, *84*, *85*, *86*, *87*, 92, 93
Metalloid, **70,** 75, 76, 78, 80, 92
Metamorphic rocks
    and radiocarbon dating, 324
Meteor, 160, **652**
Meteorite, 222, *222*, **652,** *652*, *653*, 657, *657*
Meteoroid, 652, 657
Methane, 399, *399*, 400, 401, 404, *404*, *405*, 406
    in atmospheres of planets, 642, 644, 645, 646
    on comets, 651
    model of, 109
Methyl group, 399

Microwaves, *574*, 575
Mid-ocean ridges, 274, *274*, 275, *275*, *281*, *283*, 296, 297
Milky Way Galaxy, 679, *679*, *680*, 681–682, 693, *693*
Minerals, 108, 544
Mitochondria, 432, 433, *433*, 445
Models
    of atom, 37–45, *37*, *40*, *43*, *44*, 58, 103, *act.* 104–105
    of comet collisions, *act.* 629
    of distances in solar system, *act.* 648–649
    of effects of gravity, 592
    of energy of electrons, *act.* 97
    of freshwater environment, 530
    of invisible things, *act.* 46
    of isomers, 402
    making, 56, 105, 205, 407, 635, *act.* 648–649, *act.* 686, 687
    of methane, 109
    of motion in space, 200
    of motion in two directions, *act.* 190–191
    of periodic pattern, *act.* 63
    of planets, 644
    of rock deformation, *act.* 209
    of universe, *act.* 661
    of volcano, *act.* 239
Moho discontinuity, 220–221
Molds, **307,** 328
Mole, 139
Molecules, **109**-113
    formation of, *109*
    formulas for, 112–113
    nonpolar, 111
    polar, 111, 116
    structure of, 110, *110*

Momentum, **159**-163, *159*, *161*, 170
    changes in, 184, *184*, 185
    conservation of, **161**-163, *161*, *162*, *163*, 169, 171, 199, *199*
    force and, *184*, 185, 199
Moon, 612–623, *612*, *613*, *614*, *615*, *616*, *617*, 624–625, *624*
    comparing sun and, 614
    craters of, 617
    eclipse of, *602*, 616, *616*, *act.* 623, 624
    exploration of, *572*, 586–587, *587*, 595, 620–622, *622*, 625, *625*
    interior of, 617
    of Jupiter, 585, *585*, 643, *643*
    of Mars, 641
    motions of, 612–613, *612*
    of Neptune, 646, *646*
    orbit of, 583, 612, *612*, *614*
    origin of, 618–619, *618–619*
    of other planets, *584*, 585, *585*, 595, 641, 643, *643*, 644, 646, 647, *647*
    poles of, 621, 622, 625
    revolution of, 612–613, *612*
    rotation of, 612–613, *612*
    of Saturn, *584*, 595, *595*, 644
    structure of, 617
    of Uranus, 657
    water on, 595, 622, 625
Moon phases, *600*, **613**-614, *613*, *act.* 623, 624
Moonquakes, 617
Moss life cycle, 453, *453*
Moss, liverwort, fern comparison, *act.* 456
Mosses, *510*
Motion, 146–205, *146*, *act.* 147, *158*, *act.* 175

of moon, 621, 622, 625

Southern hemisphere, 606, 607

Space
measurement of, *act.* 481
measuring distance in, 682
radiation from, 574–579, 596

Space exploration, 572–597, *act.* 573
international cooperation in, 592–595, *592–593*, 597
of moon, *572*, 586–587, *587*, 595, 620–622, *622*, 625, *625*
of planets, *584–585*, 594, 595, *595*, *628*, *act.* 629, 638–640, *639*, *641*, 655, *655*
satellites in, 582–583, *582*, 590–591, 596
telescopes in, 575–580, *576*, *578*, *579*, *act.* 580, 596, *596*

Space probes, *150*, 151, **582-**586, *583*, *584–585*, 586, 594, 595, *595*, 596, 620–621, *620*, *621*, 622, 625, 628, 636, 637, 638–640, 642, 644, 645, 646, 647, 654, 656

Space shuttles, 200–201, *200*, *201*, 577, **590-**591, *590–591*, 592, 594, 597, *597*

Space stations, **591-**592, *592–593*, 593–594, 597, *597*

Spacing, of populations, 488, *488*
endangered and threatened, *act.* 514–515

Species, **334**

Spectrum
electromagnetic, *574–575*, **575,** 596

of stars, 666, *666*, 675, 692

Speed, **148**-149, *148, 149, act.* 156–157, 575

Sphere, **602,** 603

Spiral galaxies, *679*, 680, *680*

Sporophyte,
of a fern, 454, *454, act.* 456
of a moss, 453, *453, act.* 456

Sporophyte stage, **452,** 474

Spring star chart, *691*

Sputnik I, 582, 583, 586

St. Helens, Mount (Washington state), 240, 241, *248–249*, 249, 253, 254

Stamen, **461,** 475

Star(s), 662–677
binary systems of, **670**
black dwarf, *675*
brightness of, 664, 673, 692
cluster of, 670, *670, 681*
constellations of, 662–663, *662, 663*, 688–691, *688, 689, 690, 691*
distance of, 664, 665, *act.* 686–687, 692
evolution of, 674–677, *675, 676, 677, 693, 693*
fusion in, 673–674, *674,* 676
giant, **675,** 693
in main sequence, **672,** *672, 675, 675*
neutron, *673, 675,* **676,** 693
patterns of, 662
protostar, *675*
red giant, 673
relative sizes of, *673*
sighting of, *act.* 588–589
spectrum of, 666, *666,* 675, 692
supergiant, *673, 673,* **676,** 693
supernova, *675, 676, 676, 693, 693*

temperature of, 666, *666,* 672–673, 675, 692
white dwarf, 673, *673, 675,* **676,** 693
See also Sun

Starches, 414, *act.* 418–419

Steel, 84–85, *84*
stainless, 89

Stigma, *462*

Stomata, **426**-427, *426, 427, act.* 435, 444

Streams
as freshwater biomes, 528–529, *528*

Strike-slip faults, **213,** *213,* 284–285, 291, *291*

Strong nuclear force, 48

Subduction zone, 279

Substituted hydrocarbons, 404–407, *404, 405, 406, 407,* 421

Succession. *See* Ecological succession

Sucrose, 414, *414*

Sugar, 413–414, *413, 414*

Sulfur, 78, *79*
isotope of, 54
in tarnish, 112, 117, 126

Sulfuric acid, 78, 93
in atmospheres of planets, 637, 656

Summer, 606, *663, 690*

Sun, 667–671
atmosphere of, 667, *667,* 692
as center of solar system, 631
comparing moon and, 614
distance from Earth, 603, 637, 638
Earth's orbit around, 605, *606, 614*
eclipse of, 614, *614,* 615, *615,* 624
electromagnetic radiation from, 575, 606
energy from, 127

X rays, *74, 575, 575*, 669

Yeast, 432

Zebras, 524
Zinnias, *439*

Art Credits

Photo Credits

Aventurier/Liaison International; 256 (l)Gregg Hade/Tony Stone Images, (r)David Muench; 257 (l)David Hosking/Photo Researchers; (r)Ken M. Johns/Photo Researchers; 259 Greg Vaughn; 260 Doug Martin; 261 Paul Chesley/Tony Stone Images; 262 Tom Bean/DRK Photo; 263 (t)David Muench, (b)Woods Hole Oceanographic Institution.

Chapter 10 - 266-267 Tom Van Sant, The Geosphere Project/Science Photo Library/Photo Researchers; 267 Doug Martin; 270 David M. Dennis; 273 Scripps Institution of Oceanography; 274 (l)Woods Hole Oceanographic Institution, (r)Emory Kristof/National Geographic Image Collection; 279 file photo; 282 Craig Aurness/Corbis Los Angeles; 284 Altitude/Peter Arnold Inc.; 285 CNES/Photo Researchers; 286 NASA; 287 James Balog/Tony Stone Images; 290 Martin G. Miller/Visuals Unlimited; 290-295 (bkgd)A.J. Copely/Visuals Unlimited; 291 E.R. Degginger/Color-Pic; 292 (t)E.R. Degginger/Color-Pic, (b)Bill Beatty/Visuals Unlimited; 293 (t)J. Wengle/DRK Photo, (b)Phil Degginger/Color-Pic; 294 (t)David Matherly/Visuals Unlimited, (b)Martin G. Miller/Visuals Unlimited; 295 (t)Mark Epstein/Visuals Unlimited, (b)Doug Sokell/Visuals Unlimited; 296 (t)file photo, (b)Emory Kristof/National Geographic Image Collection; 297 Bob Kalmbach/University of Michigan.

UNIT 4

300-301 Sisse Brimber/National Geographic Image Collection; 301 Michael Snively/Alaska Stock; Chapter 11 - 302-303 Ken Lucas/Visuals Unlimited; 303 StudiOhio; 304 Louis Psihoyos/Matrix; 305 Phil Degginger/Color-Pic; 306 (tl)Charlie Ott/Photo Researchers, (tr)Francois Gohier/Photo Researchers, (b)Jane Burton/Bruce Coleman Inc.; 307 Dr. E.R.Degginger/Color-Pic.; 308 (t)Vaughan Fleming/Photo Researchers, (bl)Louis Psihoyos/Matrix, (br)Louis Psihoyos/ Matrix; 311 (l)Doug Martin, (r)Fred Bavendam/Peter Arnold, Inc.; 312 Aaron Haupt; 313 John Shelton; 316 Jim Hughes/ PhotoVenture/ Visuals Unlimited; 317 StudiOhio; 320 Kevin Schafer/Allstock/PNI; 321 Aaron Haupt; 324 Jan-Peter Lahall/Peter Arnold, Inc.; 326 Geoff Butler; 328 (t)Dr. E.R.Degginger/Color-Pic., (bl, br)Louis Psihoyos/Matrix, 329 StudiOhio.

Chapter 12 - 332-333 Stan Wayman/Photo Researchers; 333 Aaron Haupt; 334 Tony Ward/FPG; 336 (tl)Christian Grzimek/Okapia/Photo Researchers, (tr)Kevin Schafer/Peter Arnold Inc., (c)Ron Sanford/The Stock Market, (b)Kenneth W. Fink/Photo Researchers; 337 Brian Parker/Tom Stack & Assoc.; 338 (l)John Gerlach/ Visuals Unlimited, (r)Gregory K. Scott/Photo Researchers; 339 (l)Joe McDonald/Tom Stack & Assoc., (r)Mark Boulton/Photo Researchers; 342 Jeremy Woodhouse/DRK Photo; 343 Matt Meadows; 344 Patrick Aventurier/Liaison International; 345 (t)John Cancalosi/Tom Stack & Assoc., (bl)David M. Dennis/Tom Stack & Assoc., (br)Breck P. Kent/Earth Scenes; 347 D. Long/ Visuals Unlimited; 351 Tim Davis/Photo Researchers; 352 (l)Bob Campbell, (r)John Reader; 354 M. Loup/Jacana/Photo Researchers; 355 Frans Lanting/Minden Pictures; 356 (t)Tom McHugh/Photo Researchers, (bl)RIA-Novosti/Sovfoto, (br)E.R. Degginger/Color-Pic; 357 E.R. Degginger/Color-Pic; 358 (t)John Gerlach/Visuals Unlimited, (b)Brian Parker/Tom Stack & Assoc.; 359 (tl)Patrick Aventurier/Liaison International, (tr)John Cancalosi/Tom Stack & Assoc., (bl)Frans Lanting/Minden Pictures, (br)E.R. Degginger/Color-Pic.

Chapter 13 - 362 (l)James L. Amos/Photo Researchers, (r)Gary Retherford/Photo Researchers; 363 (l)Ken Lucas/Visuals Unlimited, (r)David M. Dennis; 366 (l)Breck P. Kent, (c)Sinclair Stammers/Science Photo Library, (r)David M. Dennis; 367 (tl)John Cancalosi/Tom Stack & Assoc., (tr)David M. Dennis, (bl)Sinclair Stammers/Science Photo Library/Photo Researchers, (br)TA Wiewandt/DRK Photo; 368 Ken Lucas/Visuals Unlimited; 369

Larry Lipsky/DRK Photo; 370 Fred Bavendam/Peter Arnold,Inc.; 371 Sinclair Stammers/Sciene Photo Library/Photo Researchers; 372 James W. Collinson, Department of Geology, Ohio State University; 373 Doug Martin; 374 (tl)O. Louis Mazzatenta/National Geographic Image Collection, (tr)O. Louis Mazzatenta/National Geographic Image Collection, (bl)Glenn Oliver/Visuals Unlimited, (br)E.R. Degginger/Photo Researchers; 375 (t)Animals Animals, (b)David J. Books/Visuals Unlimited; 377 Matt Meadows; 378 David Harvey/Woodfin Camp & Assoc.; 382 (t)O. Louis Mazzatenta/National Geographic Image Collection, (bl)O. Louis Mazzatenta/National Geographic Image Collection, (br)Michael Collier; 383 Patti Murray/Animals Animals; 385 Dave Watts/Tom Stack & Assoc.; 386 (t)David M. Dennis, (b)Mark Burnett; 387 David M. Dennis; 388 Fred Bavendam/Peter Arnold,Inc.; 389 (t)Michael Collier, (b)Animals Animals/Patti Murray.

UNIT 5

394-395 Gary Withey/Bruce Coleman Inc./PNI; 395 Philippe Plailly/Eurelios/Science Photo Library/Photo Researchers; Chapter 14 - 396-397 KS Studio; 397 Matt Meadows; 398 (l)Mark Burnett, (r)KS Studio; 400 Mark Burnett; 401 (l, c)Mark Burnett, (r)Will & Deni McIntyre/Photo Researchers; 402 Ted Horowitz/The Stock Market; 404 (l)KS Studio, (c)Michael Kevin Daly/The Stock Market, (r)KS Studio; 406 (t)Roger K. Burnard, (b)John Sims/Tony Stone Images; 408 KS Studio; 409 (l)Ron Spomer/Visuals Unlimited, (r)Jean-Loup Charmet/Science Photo Library/Photo Researchers; 411 412 KS Studio; 413 Mark Burnett; 414 (t)Mark Burnett, (b)KS Studio; 415 Hans Pfletschinger/Peter Arnold,Inc.; 416 (t)Victor Scocozza/FPG International, (b)Tony Craddock/Tony Stone Images; 417 Biophoto Associates/Science Source/Photo Researchers; 418 KS Studio; 420 (t)Mark Burnett, (b)Ted Horowitz/The Stock Market; 421 (t)Roger K. Burnard, (b)KS Studio.

Chapter 15 - 424-425 Tony Stone Images; 425 Doug Martin; 426 Dr. Jeremy Burgess/Science Photo Library/Photo Researchers; 428 Bill Beatty/Visuals Unlimited; 430 Jane Grushow from Grant Heilman; 431 (l)Bill Beatty/Earth Scenes, (r)Joe McDonald/Animals Animals; 433 Biophoto Associates/Photo Researchers; 434 Doug Martin; 435 Matt Meadows; 436 Alan & Linda Detrick/Photo Researchers; 437 Runk/Schoenberger from Grant Heilman; 438 (t)Ralph A. Reinhold/Earth Scenes, (b)Mark Burnett; 439 (l) Patti Murray/Earth Scenes, (r)Dick Keen/Visuals Unlimited, 440 David Cavagnaro/Visuals Unlimited; 441 (t)E. Webber/Visuals Unlimited, (c)David M. Dennis/Tom Stack & Associates, (b)Cabisco/Visuals Unlimited; 442 Matt Meadows; 443 David Newman/Visuals Unlimited; 444 (l)Bill Beatty/Visuals Unlimited, (r)Dr. Jeremy Burgess/Science Photo Library/Photo Researchers; 445 Mark Burnett.

Chapter 16 - 448-449 Uniphoto; 449 Matt Meadows; 450 Mark E. Gibson/Visuals Unlimited; 451 (t)Corbis Media, (b)Jerome Wexler/Photo Researchers; 452 Sylvan Wittwer/Visuals Unlimited; 455 John Trott/Earth Scenes; 456 (l c)Geoff Butler, (r)Amanita Pictures; 457 National Park Service; 458 Jerome Wexler/Photo Researchers; 460 PNI; 461 Earth Scenes/Ken Cole; 463 Aaron Haupt; 464 (l)E.R. Degginger/Photo Researchers, (r)John Sohlden/Visuals Unlimited; 465 (l)Tom Ulrich/Visuals Unlimited, (r)R. Calentine/Visuals Unlimited; 466 David M. Dennis/Tom Stack & Assoc.; 467 David M. Dennis/Tom Stack & Assoc.; 468 Doug Martin; 469 Matt Meadows; 470 through 473 (bkgd)Stephen J. Krasemann/DRK Photo; 471 (t)Earth Scenes, (cl)Tom Bean/DRK Photo, (cr)E.R. Degginger/Color-Pic, (b)Larry Ulrich/DRK Photo; 472 (t)E.R. Degginger/Earth Scenes, (cl)E.R. Degginger, (cr)R. Calentine/Visuals Unlimited, (b)Gerald & Buff Corsi/Visuals Unlimited; 473 (tl)Joseph G. Strauch Jr., (tr)C.C.